MEDITERRANEAN
WILD FLOWERS

MEDITERRANEAN WILD FLOWERS

Colour paintings by
MARJORIE BLAMEY

Text and drawings by
CHRISTOPHER GREY-WILSON

HarperCollins*Publishers*

First published in Great Britain by HarperCollins*Publishers*, 1993

ISBN 0 00 219901 7

Typesetting by Pre-Press, London
Printed by Mandarin Offset, Hong Kong

CONTENTS

5

The Colour Plates between pages 192 and 384

PREFACE

For any lover of wild flowers, the littoral flora of the Mediterranean countries and islands has an indescribable magic, an appeal as old as history. Yet it has lacked a reasonably complete and well-illustrated guide. So when Domino Books asked if we would undertake this task on completion of our *Illustrated Flora of Britain and Northern Europe* (to which the present book is to some extent a southern complement) the idea was irresistible. To say this is in no way to deprecate previous books, notably of course Anthony Huxley and Oleg Polunin's immensely likeable work, more selective (and also more portable!) than this; or the more recent small book of I. and P. Schönfelder, likewise illustrated with a selection of good colour photographs.

There seemed, however, a real need for a book that covered all the important species of the Mediterranean coast – starting actually beyond it with the Portuguese coast, and including the whole coastline eastwards and round to Tangier. So the book is comprehensive with only three limitations:

1 This is the flora of coastal areas and of their hinterland only up to 1000 metres of altitude. Otherwise, mountainous Greece alone would have added hundreds of species, and inland Spain almost as many.

2 We have excluded – except where very conspicuous, or necessary for comparison, or for other good reason – plants that are widespread and well-known throughout northern Europe. Including them would have made the book both longer and more cumbersome.

3 The plants illustrated on the *colour plates* are the prime species in each genus. Others are distinguished in the text, sometimes with marginal line-drawings.

Like all workers in this field, we have benefited from the whole corpus of earlier work by generations of botanists, from the Greek and Roman periods onwards. More personally, we have both been given most generous help in many ways by botanists all over Europe.

Nearer home, we have to thank most warmly the Director of the Royal Botanic Gardens, Kew, Professor Ghillean Prance, and members of his staff for a great deal of kind help and advice: Tom Cope, Phillip Cribb, Tony Hall, Nicholas Hind, Charles Jeffrey, Gwilym Lewis, Gren Ll. Lucas, Brian Mathew, Roger Polhill, Alan Radcliffe-Smith, Mike Sinnott and Jeffrey Wood.

We are also most grateful to Paula and Alex Blamey; Adrian Bloom of Bressingham Gardens, Diss; Desmond Meikle; Mike Nelhams at the Abbey Gardens, Tresco; David Pearman, Frome St. Quentin; Mr Van der Plank of the Greenholm Nursery, Clevedon; Deryck Viney, Curator of the North Cyprus Herbarium, Nicosia; and particularly to Christine Grey-Wilson and Philip Blamey.

Christopher Grey-Wilson
Marjorie Blamey
January 1993

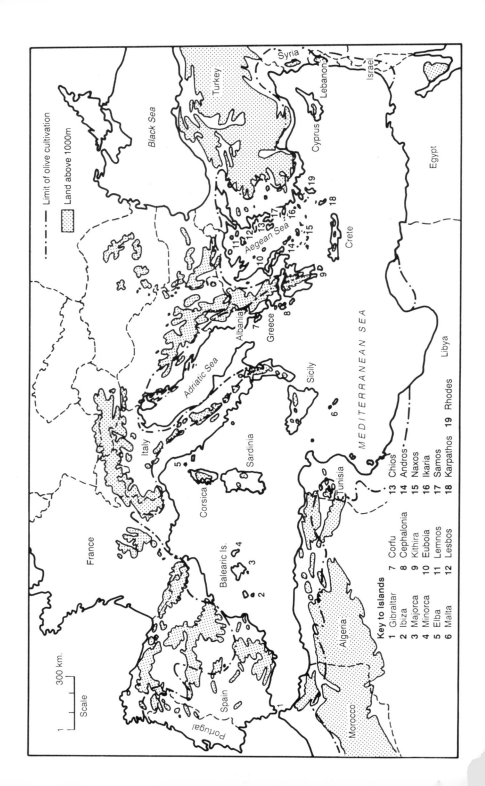

Key to Islands

1	Gibraltar	7	Corfu	13	Chios
2	Ibiza	8	Cephalonia	14	Andros
3	Majorca	9	Kithira	15	Naxos
4	Minorca	10	Euboia	16	Ikaria
5	Elba	11	Lemnos	17	Samos
6	Malta	12	Lesbos	18	Karpathos	19	Rhodes

Scale

300 km.

Limit of olive cultivation
Land above 1000m

INTRODUCTION

The area covered by this book is the Mediterranean basin with the addition of Portugal, where many typically Mediterranean species are to be found, especially in its coastal region with its mild climate. The region thus extends from Portugal and Spain, via southern France, Italy, the Dalmatian coast, Greece and Turkey to Syria in the northern half of the region and from Morocco and Algeria eastwards to Libya, Egypt, Israel and the Lebanon in the southern half. All the Mediterranean islands are covered. The altitudinal limit is from sea level to 1000m. Above this zone the general climate is cooler and often wetter and the flora a montane one with numerous local endemic species on the higher mountains, especially in Spain, Greece and Turkey; they alone would fill another book of this size.

As we go to press, the boundaries of what are now Croatia, Bosnia and Serbia are being fought over. For this first edition we have therefore retained the old 'Yugoslavia' for that beautiful and tragic region, and hope that greater precision will be possible in future editions.

The region is divided into three sections for convenience.

WESTERN MEDITERRANEAN – Iberian Peninsula (Portugal and Spain); Balearic Islands (Minorca, Majorca, Ibiza), S France, Corsica, Sardinia, Italy, Sicily, Crete and the Balkans (the Dalmatian coast, Greece, including Corfu and the islands of the Aegean region).

EASTERN MEDITERRANEAN – Turkey and Rhodes, Cyprus, Syria, Lebanon, W Jordan and Israel.

SOUTHERN MEDITERRANEAN – Morocco, Algeria, Tunisia, Libya and Egypt.

The Mediterranean climate is distinctive in its long hot dry summers with clear skies and cool wet winters. In summer the average temperatures range between 20-24°C and in winter 4-7°C, though within these limits the climate is very variable from one place to another.

Summer thunderstorms occur occasionally, especially over the mountains. Much of the eastern Mediterranean tends to be dominated by a continental high-pressure system throughout the summer, which wards off Atlantic depressions that might otherwise head eastwards.

The winter rains generally begin in the western Mediterranean in late September or early October and continue on through until April, with Atlantic depressions penetrating gradually farther eastwards as the season advances. Few places in the entire region have more than a hundred days with rain in a year. Even in winter, storms and rainy periods can often be interrupted by clear sunny days. Mountain ranges lying close to the Mediterranean shore (those along the Dalmatian coast or the western Pindus Mountains in Greece) receive a far higher rainfall than average, with most of the precipitation falling on the western side.

Frost is rare except in very unusual circumstances, when the results can be clearly seen in total or partial destruction of olive groves and citrus orchards.

A characteristic feature of many parts of the region are the winds. In summer strong winds often blow southwards, sometimes for many days; the

Mistral blows from southern France to the sea; the *Bora* blows from the Karst mountains to the Adriatic, and in the eastern Mediterranean a similar wind is called the *Meltemi*. Hot spring winds, often dusty, may blow northwards from the Sahara; the most famous of these is the *Sirocco* which can carry dust high into the atmosphere over many parts of central and western Europe.

The Mediterranean flora. The climate has favoured the evolution of a correspondingly individual and extremely variable flora, quite different from that of any other part of Europe. It is one of the richest in the numbers of species, but largely dominated by evergreen trees and shrubs, often with tough leathery, dull green leaves. Woodland is variable, ranging from evergreen broad-leaved species to pure pine woodland, particularly at low altitudes. Inland and away from the coast, especially in Europe and Turkey, and on the lower mountain slopes, deciduous species become increasingly important in the composition of the woodland.

Plant growth is restricted primarily to the moist early spring and late autumn periods, with a flush of spring annual flowers, bulbs and orchids, and a less pronounced flush in the autumn. Various plants have been used as indicators of the Mediterranean type of climate; these are plants which thrive in the long hot dry summer and cool wet winters, but which are very susceptible to frost, indeed will not tolerate temperatures below an average of 3°C during the winter months. Typical of these are the Olive, the Holm and Kermes Oaks, various types of citrus such as the Orange, and the Aleppo Pine.

Habitats are variable from place to place, depending on soil types, rainfall and average temperatures. But the greatest influence has been that of man over many centuries, systematically cultivating and modifying much of the region, so that today little remains of the true Mediterranean forest. Instead, in its place there are derived vegetation types, besides large areas of cultivation, habitations, terracing, groves and orchards. Of these derived types, two are particularly important:

Maquis (macchie). A community of dense evergreen small trees and shrubs reaching 1-3m in height, occasionally more. It is often in areas where the true forest has been previously destroyed, sometimes where just the larger trees have been removed. Dense maquis is especially well developed in the western half of the region, especially along coasts facing west or south-west. It usually reaches from sea level up to 600m altitude, but in some areas (Crete for instance) it may occur at heights of up to 1000m or even higher. Maquis can recover from burning, provided the area is not cleared by man or heavily grazed thereafter. Several typical maquis plants such as *Arbutus unedo* and *Erica arborea* have remarkable powers of rejuvenation; if the top is destroyed by fire, new growth will sprout from the base of the plant.

On the higher slopes deciduous shrubs may begin to dominate in what has been termed *Pseudomaquis*. In such places deciduous oaks may predominate instead of evergreen species. Cutting of woodland with evergreen species such as the Kermes Oak and Box, will often result in low communities dominated by deciduous bushes.

Garrigue. A more open community of dwarf evergreen shrubs, seldom more than 0.5m in height. This dwarf shrub community has been given different names in different parts of the region; in Greece it is called *Phrygana*. Garrigue is very widespread in Mediterranean and is characterised by many aromatic small shrubs, colourful in flower. It is more open than maquis, allowing a great variety of smaller herbs to associate with the shrubs, and is richer in annuals, orchids and bulbs.

Maquis and garrigue are general terms used to characterise vegetation types. In reality there are many intermediates between the two types. Bush communities of these types, which are common along the coast and the hills and lower mountains, are maintained by a number of elements. Grazing by livestock, especially sheep and goats, cutting of the large trees and bushes for fuel and charcoal, clearance for cultivation (especially for orchards and olive groves) and fires (both natural and man-induced to produce grazing land), all help to prevent large evergreen trees re-establishing and to promote the dwarf shrub communities. In a few areas where these elements have been eliminated the natural evergreen forest (sometimes called the primary maquis) can reestablish itself quite successfully.

Degeneration of maquis ultimately results in garrigue. At the same time abandoned pastures, orchards, terraces or olive groves will eventually become colonised by dwarf evergreen shrubs and also revert to garrigue. This cycle of degeneration and regeneration is typical of large parts of the Mediterranean region.

However, other influences may work to prevent the cycle functioning. The ground may become too impoverished by overgrazing and erosion to allow recolonisation by even dwarf shrub communities. The result is open bare rocky places, with thin soils, sparse grass and scattered groups of tough, drought-resistant shrubs. Such places, an all too familiar sight in many parts of the Mediterranean, look desperately barren and parched during the summer months, but in the spring and autumn may become a colourful patchwork of herbs and bulbs. Many plants are restricted to such areas, especially where grazing is not too severe. Some plants, like the asphodels, are graze-resistant and often form extensive colonies in severely overgrazed places.

Steppe-like **grasslands** are a feature of some parts of the Mediterranean. These have usually resulted as a result of firing to destroy the scrub communities and are then maintained by grazing, that prevents regeneration.

Drought-resistant and graze-resistant plants are typical adaptations. Plants like the spurges, asphodels and cistuses are generally unpalatable to grazing animals from obnoxious chemicals which they have developed. Centuries of grazing (the Mediterranean basin has been inhabited for at least 8,000 years) has favoured spiny plants which often show adaptations to drought in their tight hummocky habit, and small leathery leaves; many quite unrelated plants reveal this characteristic. Another marked feature of the region as a whole is the great variety of bulbous and tuberous-rooted plants such as crocuses, cyclamen, fritillaries, orchids and tulips. Bulbous plants flower either in the late winter and spring or in the autumn; at these times the weather is cooler and there is plenty of moisture around to promote growth. During the hot summer months the plants have died down and spend the time safely underground as a swollen, fleshy, bulb, rhizome, corm or tuber.

The richness of the flora as a whole is partly explained by the uniqueness of the Mediterranean climate which appears to favour great regional variations in certain groups of plants – many members of the Pea and Daisy Families for instance, and *Campanula*, *Verbascum* and *Ophrys*. During the Ice Ages when much of the flora of northern and central Europe and Turkey was obliterated by the ice sheets and glaciers, the Mediterranean basin escaped unscathed, a haven for plant life and continuing evolution. Many typical Mediterranean plants such as the Carob, Olive and the Judas Tree are relicts from before the Tertiary Ice Ages.

The large number of species in the region and the rapid evolution that has taken, and is still taking place, is reflected in the large numbers of very variable species and in the high rate of endemism in the region. The islands, isolated from the mainland, are rich in endemics, the Aegean Islands, Crete and Cyprus in particular. At the same time the Iberian Peninsula, the Balkan Peninsula and parts of Turkey are also rich in endemic species, though many of these are restricted to the higher mountains and deep gorges.

This book describes the plants growing wild in the coastal regions. Some genera are particularly typical, being centred on the region, such as *Cistus, Convolvulus, Crocus, Cyclamen, Fumana, Halimium, Phlomis, Serapias*, and *Ophrys*. Many commonly naturalised or widely planted exotics are also included, as are common and widely distributed grasses, and typical sedges, rushes, horsetails and ferns.

The scientific order of plants adopted generally follows that in the five volumes of *Flora Europaea*. Two further works have been a major source of reference: P.H. Davis, *Flora of Turkey* and R.D. Meikle, *Flora of Cyprus*. Other regional floras for the eastern Mediterranean region and the north African countries have also been consulted in drawing up the list of species included in this work. All species are numbered in sequence. Subspecies have the same number as the species to which they belong, followed by a letter (e.g. 209a, 209b), and numbers in **bold** type indicate plants illustrated in the colour section.

The illustrations show the features of the plants most important for easy identification. As far as possible they have been painted from living specimens and are at least in part life size. The paintings are captioned with the plants' Latin (scientific) names since these are common to all countries and languages.

Scientific names follow the works outlined above. However, these are constantly in a state of flux, reflecting as they do the latest studies in the complex relationship between and within the different plant categories. As various genera and species are studied and reviewed, their classification and names are often modified. Infuriating though this may sometimes be to the casual reader, it does reflect the advance of scientific knowledge. Important synonyms are included in brackets, thus: *Cistus creticus [C. corsicus, C. incanus]*.

Common English names are another matter. There is no consistency in the use of common names for many Mediterranean plants, and many have none at all. Those in common use, such as Rosy Garlic for *Allium roseum* and Crown Anemone for *Anemone coronaria,* are given here. No attempt has been made to invent common English names for those that have none, nor has there been any attempt to translate common names from those of other countries. Genuine common names of flowers, birds and other animals are a part of the folklore and history of a country and part of its language. To invent new ones solely for a book seems presumptuous and is often confusing.

The text descriptions, although necessarily concise, give the main features of each plant and the characters useful for accurate identification. Important diagnostic characters or those used to compare closely allied species are stressed in *italics*. Closely allied (subsidiary) species generally refer back to the main species and give only points of distinction, for example: 'Like the previous species, but a taller plant with leaves *hairy* beneath; petals 5-7mm long (not 12-17mm)'. Technical terms have been kept to the minimum, although the use of some – such as bract, calyx, ray, flowerhead or lanceolate – has been unavoidable. They are explained in the Glossary on pages 19-26.

Important variations, subspecies and varieties, are described under the main species. However, certain genera have species complexes that are extremely difficult to sort out; in such cases only the principal species or complexes are described – in *Centaurea, Senecio, Crepis* and *Trifolium*, for instance. Many familiar, common and widespread Northern European weeds such as the Dandelion, *Taraxacum officinalis*, and Shepherd's Purse, *Capsella bursa-pastoris*, are not included, except occasionally for purposes of comparison with less familiar allies.

Height. Plants vary greatly both in height and spread from species to species, and sometimes within a species. Height is presented as follows:

Low – plants up to 10cm in height.
Short – plants ranging from 10-30cm in height.
Medium – plants ranging from 30-60cm in height.
Tall – plants ranging from 60-90cm in height.

For trees and shrubs, as well as some herbs, taller than 90cm, the normal maximum height is given: '.....a tall perennial to 1.8m.'

Habit. The general habit of the plant is presented in two parts. First, its nature is stressed – for instance 'annual', 'perennial', 'shrub' or 'large deciduous tree'. Secondly the growth form, for instance 'cushion-forming', 'erect' or 'prostrate'.

Flower colour. This, unless otherwise indicated, refers to the petals (corolla) or, if these are absent or insignificant, to the sepals (calyx). In certain cases, as in many bulbous plants such as crocuses and tulips, where sepals and petals are very similar then the colour is referred to the collective term 'tepal'. Colour range within a species is also stressed and is often shown in the colour plates.

Flower size. Unless otherwise stated this refers to flower or flowerhead diameter. Where the measurement is for length, this is specified: for example '...9-14mm long.' Similarly, the size of fruit is that of its diameter unless otherwise stated.

Roots are not mentioned unless they are of particular interest. In any event, plants can be identified without digging them up to examine underground features. Plants should never be dug up in the wild under any circumstances – apart from this being a criminal offence in many countries. But a few small pieces of leaf or flower, carefully pressed, may be of great value for later accurate determination, especially where this cannot be determined satisfactorily in the field.

Habitat. Identifying the habitat type is often useful, as many plants have a specific habitat requirement – deciduous woodland, scrub, sand-dunes, marshes, meadows and so on. Whereas many have specific habitat requirements, others will tolerate a wide range of conditions, particularly the widespread weed species of lowland regions. For example the Sea Daffodil, *Pancratium maritimum*, is only found in coastal sandy habitats, whereas the

Groundsel, *Senecio vulgaris*, can be found growing in a wide range of habitats from cultivated and waste land, to coastal habitats, light woodland and road-sides. Even within a single habitat different species may prefer different as-pects; in woodland one species may prefer the dense shade, while another could grow only in the lighter more open places, others may prefer acid to neutral soils rather than alkaline ones.

Flowering time. The months given are those when the plant can normally be expected to be found in flower. Flowering times can be greatly affected by seasonal weather conditions, by latitude and by altitude. For instance, some parts of the southern and eastern Mediterranean have an earlier flowering sea-son than some of the northern parts and on many of the islands the same spe-cies will come into flower earlier than on the adjacent mainland because of the warming influence of the surrounding sea.

In any event, throughout the Mediterranean region as a whole the spring comes considerably earlier than in the colder regions to the north and east, except on the higher mountains. Spring can arrive at any time from early Feb-ruary to April. In the autumn the flowering of late-flowering annuals and bulbs is primarily influenced by cooler days and the arrival of the autumn rains. These can vary considerably from one year to the next and are difficult to predict.

Distribution. This is often another critical guide to species' identity, as closely similar species may often grow in quite different regions. Where a species is found only in a few countries, these are stated. However, where the distribu-tion is more widespread a more generalised distribution is given, such as 'Spain eastwards to Greece, including NW Africa, but not the Balearic Is.' Species that occur throughout the region covered by the book are indicated by T (throughout). The word endemic is only used for plants found solely in a single country or on a single island.

Introduced and exotic species. Naturalised and planted species included in the book have their country of origin in brackets, for instance (South Africa). Their distribution within the Mediterranean region is often rather vague be-cause, by their very nature, they could occur almost anywhere. It is also im-portant to remember that some species can be native in one part of the region, while naturalised in another; when this occurs it is stated.

Sometimes it is difficult to tell what is a native and which an introduced species, but many of the latter prefer disturbed and cultivated land, orchards, abandoned cultivation and places close to habitation. Exotic species such as Oleander, Bougainvillea and Hibiscus are often planted along roadsides.

Altitude. The upper altitudinal limit covered by this book is 1000m. Many species range from sea level onto the hills and lower mountains, whereas oth-ers are specific only to the coastal belt or to the hillslopes. Such information is presented when known, although altitudinal ranges are poorly documented in the region as a whole.

Frequency. When useful, the frequency of different species is given. Some species are widespread in varying habitats throughout the region, others are common yet restricted to a particular habitat type, for instance 'coastal sand-dunes'. Some species are widespread yet never common, while others are rare and restricted to very few localities. Populations of some species, especially some bulbs (tulips, fritillarias and crocuses) and orchids have been drastically reduced in recent years through a combination of land modification, especially for agriculture and building, and over-collecting by both commercial and amateur plant-collectors. At the same time some plants, especially some of the orchids, may be frequent in a given locality in one season, but apparently scarce in another. The reasons for this are not clearly understood, but have much to do with climatic conditions – such as lack of winter rainfall, or an especially hot summer the previous year.

General information. At the end of species accounts there may be additional notes on the plant's uses, whether it is poisonous or edible, if it is cultivated in gardens and any other feature that may be of interest.

Family and generic introductions. Characteristics of plant families are presented before the species descriptions. These give the general details, often a unique set of characters, that distinguishes one particular family from another. Generic descriptions are only given for those genera which contain three or more species within the region.

Classification. The modern classification of plants was in the main conceived by the famous Swedish botanist Carl von Linné (Linnaeus) in the eighteenth century, with the publication in 1753 of his *Species Plantarum*. Of the four major groups of plants which include fungi, algae, mosses, liverworts and ferns, the seed-bearing plants are evolutionarily the most advanced and by far the largest group and the one covered by this book. These, technically referred to as the Spermatophyta, are divided into two main groups:

Firstly the **gymnosperms** which contain all the conifers and related plants. These are characterised by their naked female cells (*gumnos* in Greek means naked). In many these are held in cone-like structures which are rarely showy in the fertile stage.

Secondly the true flowering plants, the **angiosperms**, by far the largest group. In these the female cells are hidden and enveloped by a protective ovary wall, the carpel (*angeion* is a vessel). Angiosperms are further subdivided into two main groups:

Dicotyledons are readily distinguished by their two seed-leaves or cotyledons, a diverging system of leaf-veins (often forming a network) and by the flower parts which are generally in multiples of four, five or seven, sometimes more. The majority of flowering plants belong here from the buttercups and catchflies, to the carrots and cow parsleys, deadnettles, bellflowers and the daisies and thistles.

In the *Monocotyledons* there is only a solitary seed-leaf and many of the species have leaves with parallel veins and with flower parts in multiples of three. Here belong the orchids, arums and palms, the daffodil, iris and lily families.

Hybrids. These sometimes occur in the wild, especially where allied species grow close to one another. Hybrids can cause a great deal of confusion when it comes to identification because they often appear to have intermediate characteristics. If a hybrid is suspected then it is wise to search around the area to find possible parents, and establish whether the plant in question is a solitary individual or one in a more complex swarm of hybrids and parents. Many naturally occurring hybrids are sterile or partially sterile, so that there is little likelihood of them continuing in the wild for very long as individual plants.

Identification. We have not included dichotomous keys: they would have made an already long book longer, heavier and more expensive. Moreover, many who are not experienced botanists find them difficult and prefer simply to look for their plant in colour plates and then check in the text for similar species. But for the beginner, on pages 192-3, preceding the colour plates, is an illustrated summary of the 18 most important families, with some distinctive plants or groups in each. The typical characteristics of these families are as follows:

CARYOPHYLLACEAE. Leaves opposite. Sepals 5, separate or fused into a tube. Petals 5, separate, sometimes long-clawed. Fruit a capsule with 6, 8 or 10, teeth.

RANUNCULACEAE. Leaves usually alternate (opposite in *Clematis*), often divided. Sepals present or not, 3 or 5. Petals 5-7, occasionally more, separate. Stamens numerous. Fruit a collection of achenes or follicles.

CRUCIFERAE. Leaves usually opposite. Sepals 4, separate. Petals 4, separate and forming a typical cross. Fruit a 2-parted pod.

PAPAVERACEAE. Leaves usually alternate, often with yellowish juice when cut. Sepals 2, deciduous. Petals 4, separate. Stamens numerous. Fruit a pod with pores or splitting lengthwise.

ROSACEAE. Leaves alternate, often pinnate or palmate; stipules present. Sepals 5, fused together at the base; epicalyx sometimes present. Petals usually 5. Fruit very variable, but including the apple, blackberry, quince, hip and haw.

LEGUMINOSAE. Leaves alternate, often pinnate; stipules present. Calyx 5-toothed, sometimes 2-lipped. Petals 5, the upper a standard, the lateral 2 wings and the lower 2 fused into a keel – the typical pea flower. Stamens 10. Fruit the typical pea pod, often splitting lengthwise into two, sometimes coiled or splitting into short segments.

EUPHORBIACEAE. Plants with a milky latex when cut. Leaves usually alternate. Flowers often without petals, male and female separate, on the same or different plants. Styles 3. Fruit a 3-parted capsule.

MALVACEAE. Leaves alternate usually. Calyx with 5 teeth; epicalyx often present. Petals 5, fused together at the base. Stamens numerous, borne on a column with the style. Fruit a ring of mericarps or a capsule.

UMBELLIFERAE. Leaves alternate, simple or, more often, 2-4-pinnately divided. Flowers borne in characteristic umbels consisting of rays like the spokes of an umbrella, often subtended by conspicuous bracts. Petals 5, those of the outermost flowers often uneven. Stamens 5 usually. Fruit two-parted, each pressed close together, parting when mature.

BORAGINACEAE. Leaves usually alternate, often bristly. Flowers borne in characteristic coiled cymes. Calyx 5-toothed. Petals 5, fused into a short or long tube. Stamens 5. Fruit 5 nutlets, often ornamented.

LABIATAE. Plants often glandular and aromatic, with square stems. Leaves opposite. Flowers borne in whorls (often congested) at the upper nodes. Calyx with 5 teeth, often 2-lipped. Corolla 2- (occasionally 1-) lipped. Stamens 2 or 4. Fruit consisting of 4 nutlets hidden at the base of the calyx.

SCROPHULARIACEAE. Leaves alternate or opposite. Stem square or round. Flowers borne in cymes or spike-like racemes. Sepals 4-5. Petals 4-5, fused near the base or into a distinct tube, sometimes 2-lipped. Stamens 2, 4 or 5. Fruit a 2-parted capsule.

CAMPANULACEAE. Plants often with milky juice when cut. Leaves mostly alternate. Sepals with 5 teeth, fused together at the base. Petals 5, fused into a bell-shape or sometimes 2-lipped. Stamens 5. Fruit a capsule.

COMPOSITAE. Flowers aggregated into distinctive, daisy-like, dandelion-like or thistle-like heads surrounded by a ruff of bracts. Individual flowers (florets) small, tubular, 5-lobed or flattened into strap-like rays. Fruit a single-seeded achene, often with a hairy pappus attached at one end.

LILIACEAE. Leaves often narrow, untoothed and with parallel veins. Tepals 6, petal-like, separate or partly fused together. Stamens 6. Ovary superior. Fruit a 3-parted capsule or berry.

AMARYLLIDACEAE. Leaves basal, slender, with parallel veins, untoothed. Tepals 6, petal-like; corona sometimes present. Stamens 6. Ovary inferior. Fruit a 3-parted capsule.

IRIDACEAE. Leaves narrow with parallel veins, untoothed. Flowers with 6 petal-like tepals, similar in *Crocus*, dissimilar in *Iris*. Stamens 3. Ovary inferior. Fruit a 3-parted capsule.

ORCHIDACEAE. Leaves in a basal rosette, or alternate up the stem, narrow, parallel-veined and untoothed. Flowers in spikes or racemes. Sepals 3, sometimes petal-like. Petals 3, the lateral 2 spreading and wing like or coming together with one or all of the sepals, the lower petal forming a distinctive, often lobed lip. Pollen in sticky masses or pollinia, 2 to a flower. Ovary inferior. Fruit a 3-parted capsule.

A ×10 magnifying lens, preferably of the folding type that can be easily put in a pocket or held on a string round the neck, is a useful tool to enable fine details of the plant to be observed – especially tiny glands or hairs on various parts of the plant.

At first glance there seems to be a bewildering range of flowers to be found in the Mediterranean region as a whole and there is no doubt that familiarisation with the plants will make identification ever easier. It is surprising how, with a little practice, many genera can be told apart in an instant. Further practice allows one to get to know the species. Some genera are easier than others. The medicks, *Medicago*, for instance, have many closely similar looking species, however, a detailed look at the curious fruits will reveal many details useful in diagnosis. Identifying plants can bring endless hours of pleasure and many rewards to those who are willing and patient enough to work out what each species in an area is.

Always try to identify a typical specimen in a population, not the unusual one with darker flowers or a taller habit. These may be local variants or perhaps hybrids. Many species produce occasional white-flowered (albino) forms, which are otherwise identical to the normal plant. Fruits are sometimes essential for accurate identification and these are often scarce at the beginning of the season. Others, especially the crucifers and umbellifers, often obligingly carry both flowers and fruits at the same time – a great help with these difficult and complex families.

When to go. The flowers of the Mediterranean are best enjoyed in the spring and early summer and then again in the autumn. In mid-winter there is little to see, while at the height of summer the landscape is parched and the flowers dried up and withered. The seasons vary from place to place. In southern Portugal, Morocco, Cyprus and Crete there will be much in flower in March and early April at low altitudes.

Mid and late April are better for Italy and the Greek mainland, although spring may not reach the slopes above 500m until rather later. There will still be much to be seen in May and early June when the early displays of bulbs, orchids and small annuals will have been replaced by the coarser herbs of early summer. Autumn bulbs are a feature of some parts of the Mediterranean, especially Crete, the Greek Peloponnese and parts of southern Turkey; the best time for them is from mid-October until the end of November.

GLOSSARY

achene

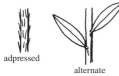

actinomorphic

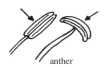

adpressed

alternate

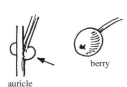

anther

auricle

berry

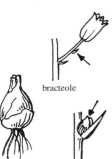

bract

bracteole

bulb   bulbil

Achene. A single-seeded dry fruit, not splitting.

Actinomorphic. A regular flower, radially symmetrical and capable of being cut into two equal halves in various directions.

Adpressed (or appressed). Pressed close to another organ – hairs close to the stem for instance.

Aeriole. Spot on the surface of cacti where clusters of spines or bristles arise.

Alien. A plant which is not native but which has almost certainly been introduced to an area by man and has become naturalised.

Alternate. Leaves alternating along the stem, as opposed to opposite or whorled.

Annual. A plant that completes its life cycle from seed to flowering and fruiting in a single season and then dies.

Anther. The fertile part of the stamen – the upper part which contains the pollen.

Apomixis. The production of seed without fertilisatiion – without sexual fusion.

Aeriole. Spots where spines or spine clusters arise – as on the surface of many cacti.

Ascending. Curving or pointing upwards.

Auricle. Small ear-like projections or appendages, often at the base of leaves.

Awn. A stiff bristle-like projection, sometimes barbed or feathered.

Axil. The angle between the leaf and stem.

Basal. At the base of the plant.

Berry. A succulent (fleshy) fruit containing several seeds, but without a stone layer around the seeds.

Biennial. A plant that takes two seasons to complete its life-cycle, germinating in the first year and flowering, seeding and then dying in the second.

Bisexual. With both stamens and ovary in the same flower – hermaphrodite.

Bract. An organ, often small and scale-like, but sometimes leaf-like, located where the flower-stalk (pedicel) joins the stem.

Bracteole. A bract on the secondary branches of an inflorescence.

Bulb. An underground storage organ developed from the fleshy bases of leaves or scales, with or without an outer skin or tunic.

Bulbil. A small bulb-like organ arising in the leaf-axils of aerial stems.

19

calyx

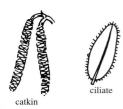

catkin

ciliate

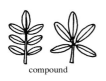

compound

corm

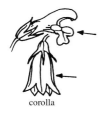

corolla

corymb

cyme

deflexed

disk-floret

Calyx. A collective name for the sepals – the outer whorl of organs in most flowers.

Capitulum. A distinctive head of small flowers all crowded together in a regular arrangement, as in many daisies.

Carpel. One of the compartments or units making up the ovary. Carpels may be free from one another or variously joined together.

Catkin. An erect or pendent tassel of tiny flowers crowded together.

Chlorophyll. The green pigment of plants which harnesses the sun's energy by a complex chemical reaction – photosynthesis.

Ciliate. Fringed with hairs – generally along the margin of a leaf, petal etc.

Cladode. A green, leaf-like organ that is in reality a flattened stem.

Claw. A narrow lower part of a petal or sepal.

Compound. Leaves that are composed of several distinct leaflets, or an inflorescence in which the main axis is branched.

Composite. A member of the daisy family, Compositae.

Corm. A swollen underground organ produced from the swollen stem base, generally annual with the new corm arising on top of the old.

Corolla. A collective name for the petals, the second whorl of organs in most flowers, which are located within the sepals (calyx). Petals are generally large and often brightly coloured.

Corona. A cup- or trumpet-like projection from the centre of a flower.

Corymb. A compound inflorescence with the lower branches longer than the upper so that all end up at the same level.

Cotyledon. The initial leaf or leaves of a seedling plant. They may be below or above the ground. Monocotyledons have a single seed-leaf, while Dicotyledons have two.

Crucifer. A member of the cress family, Cruciferae.

Cyathia. A specialised flower-cluster found in Spurges (*Euphorbia*), consisting of a cup-like organ surrounded by large glistening glands and containing a single ovary and several stamens.

Cyme. An inflorescence in which the main axis and lateral branches are repeated, terminated by a flower. Cymes may be regularly and symmetrically branched or one-sided and asymmetrical.

Deciduous. Losing the leaves in the autumn.

Deflexed. Bent sharply downwards.

Dehiscent. Splitting open to release the seeds.

Digitate. With finger-like lobes; generally refers to a leaf or bract.

Disk-floret. The central florets of a flowerhead which form a distinctive disk, as in the flowerheads of many daisies.

elliptic

epicalyx

filament

follicle

gland

glandular

globose

glume

Drupe. A fleshy fruit with one or sometimes several seeds surrounded by a hard stone.

Elliptic. Forming an ellipse, widest in the middle and pointed at both ends.

Endemic. Confined to one country, island or area.

Entire. See Untoothed.

Epicalyx. A calyx outside the true calyx – the calyx thus appears to be composed of two whorls.

Farina. Powdery or woolly deposits found on the surface of leaves.

Filament. The stalk of a stamen, connecting the receptacle to the anther.

Filiform. Thread-like; slender and parallel-sided.

Flexuous. Wavy.

Flowerhead. Refers to flowers which are aggregated into tight, formal heads, as in members of the daisy and scabious families. The individual flowers of a flowerhead may be all of the same kind or 2-3 distinct types.

Floret. The individual flowers that make up a flowerhead.

Foetid. With a strong and unpleasant smell.

Follicle. A dry, dehiscent fruit developed from a single carpel. Follicles may be solitary or clustered together.

Free. Not joined to one another.

Fruit. The seeds and the structures that contain them, whether dry or fleshy.

Gland. A small rounded or oblong structure on the plant's surface containing oil or some other liquid. When they occur at the tip of a hair they are called glandular hairs – they often make leaves and stems sticky.

Glandular. Covered with glands – often seen as tiny dots.

Glaucous. Covered with a waxy bloom, giving a bluish or greyish colouration.

Globose. Globe-like, rounded.

Glume. Two, occasionally only one, empty bracts at the base of a spikelet – refers to grasses.

Head. Refers to crowded clusters of flowers or fruits, terminating in a common stalk.

Herb. Any vascular plant that does not develop a woody stem. Those used specifically for flavouring food are called culinary herbs.

Herbaceous. Refers to plant organs that are green and with a leaf-like texture. Herbaceous perennials are plants that die to the ground each season.

Hermaphrodite. Having both male and female organs in the same flower.

internode

involucre

keel

lanceolate

lemma

ligule

Heterostylous. Having stamens and styles at different levels in flowers on different plants of the same species.

Hilum. A characteristically shaped scar left on the surface of a seed when it becomes detached from the ovary.

Hyaline. Thin and transparent.

Hybrid. A plant originating from a cross between two distinct species.

Indehiscent. Fruits that do not split open to release their seeds.

Inferior. Refers to flowers in which the ovary appears to lie below the other flower-parts (i.e. with sepals, petals and stamens attached to the top of the ovary).

Inflorescence. The flowering branch or branches, flowers and bracts above the uppermost leaves on a stem. Inflorescences are very variable from one species to another.

Internode. The portion of a stem between two nodes.

Introduced. Not native. Thought on good evidence to have originated elsewhere.

Involucre. Flower-bracts forming a cup or ruff surrounding the base of a flower cluster or head.

Irregular. See zygomorphic.

Keel. A petal which has a sharp keel-like edge – as the keel of a boat. The lower petal in a pea-flower.

Labiate. A member of the mint family, Labiatae.

Lanceolate. Lance-shaped: more or less elliptical but broadest below the middle.

Latex. Milky juice or sap produced by stems, leaves and other organs. It may be white or variously coloured.

Lax. Loose.

Legume. A member of the pea family, Leguminosae.

Lemma. The lower of two bracts enclosing the flower: in grasses.

Ligule. A small flap of tissue, often located at the base of a leaf of petal.

Linear. Narrow and parallel-sided.

Lip. A petal or petals (occasionally the sepals) which form a distinct organ sharply divided from the other petals or sepals and which acts as a landing stage for visiting insects. 2-lipped flowers have both an upper and a lower lip, the upper forming a hood.

Lobed. Divided but not separated entirely. Leaves, for instance, may be shallowly or deeply lobed.

Marginal Along, or on, the margin.

Membranous. Thin and dry, often opaque or transparent – like a membrane.

lip

lobed

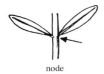

node

ochrea

ovule

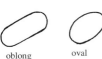

oblong   oval

palmate

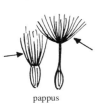

pappus

petal

petiole

Mycorrhiza. An association of roots and fungi, dependent or partially dependent upon one another.

Native. Occurring naturally in a country or region.

Naturalised. A species that has become established in an area outside its native distribution.

Nectary. A nectar producing organ. Nectaries are often located at the base of a petal, in a modified petal, at the base of a stamen or in the tip of a spur or pouch. Nectar is sweet and sugary and much sought by pollinating insects.

Node. Points on the stem where the leaves arise; they are often regularly spaced.

Oblong. Rectangular with rounded ends – used to describe a leaf or petal shape.

Ochrea. A sheath-like structure which is an extension of the leaf-stalk base and surrounding the stem just below the leaf.

Opposite. Two leaves or other organs that arise on opposite sides of the stem and at the same level.

Orbicular. Rounded; as wide as long.

Oval. A broad ellipse, with rounded rather than pointed ends.

Ovary. The female organ containing the ovules.

Ovule. The organ containing the egg, which after fertilisation develops into the seed.

Palate. A projecting area close to the mouth of a flower.

Palea. Upper of two bracts enclosing the flower – in grasses.

Palmate. Hand-like.

Panicle. A branched racemose inflorescence.

Pappus. Thistle-down – tufts of hairs on achenes and fruits.

Parasite. A plant that gains all its sustenance from another plant (the host). True parasitic plants have no chlorophyll.

Pedate. Foot-like, with lobes broadest in the upper half.

Pedicel. The stalk of an individual flower.

Peduncle. The stalk of an inflorescence or partial inflorescence.

Perennial. A plant living for a number of years (often long-lived). Herbaceous perennials die down to ground level each season, producing new shoots each year.

Perianth. A collective word for all the floral leaves – petals and sepals when both are present. Often used when the organs cannot be easily separated.

Petal. The inner perianth segments when they clearly differ from the outer – often brightly coloured.

Petaloid. Brightly coloured and resembling a petal.

Petiole. The leaf-stalk.

Phyllodes. Modified and flattened green leaf-stalks (petioles), which function as leaves.

pinnate

pinnately-lobed

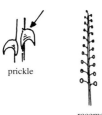

prickle   raceme

ray

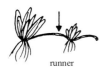

ray-floret

runner

scape

Pinnate. A leaf composed of more than three leaflets arranged in two rows along a common axis, with or without an end leaflet.

Pinnately-lobed. A leaf that is lobed in a pinnate fashion, but not separated into distinct leaflets.

Pod. A fruit formed from a single carpel, dry and splitting – as in a pea pod.

Pollen. Tiny particles produced by the anthers and containing the male gametes – often called pollen grains.

Pollinia. Pollen grains aggregated into regular masses – refers to orchids.

Polyploid. Having a multiple greater than two of the basic chromosome number.

Pouch. A pocket or sac at the base of a corolla or petal, often housing a nectary or several nectaries.

Prickle. A sharp point, often hooked, developed from the outer tissues of stems, or sometimes leaves.

Prostrate. Lying close to and along the ground.

Pseudoterminal. Appearing to be terminal, but actually lateral when closely examined.

Pungent. Sharply aromatic.

Raceme. A spike-like inflorescence in which the individual flowers are stalked.

Radiate. Flowerheads in which the outer flowers are larger than the others, or in which the outer petals are significantly larger.

Ray. A stalk radiating out from an umbel – like the spokes of an umbrella.

Ray-floret. The outer florets of a flowerhead such as a daisy; often elaborated into a distinctive strap-shaped or lobed, partly tubular structure (ligule). They often surround a central disk of dissimilar florets.

Receptacle. The part of the stem from which all the floral organs arise.

Recurved. Turned backwards in a curve.

Regular. See actinomorphic.

Reticulate. Netted.

Revolute. Rolled downwards – generally applies to leaves in which the margins are turned downwards and inwards.

Rhizome. An underground or surface stem, often thick and swollen.

Runner. A form of aerial stolon which often roots down at the nodes to form a new plant.

Saprophyte. A plant without chlorophyll which lives on humus (leaf-mould) – often growing in the darker areas of woodland where there is little competition.

Scape. A leafless stem bearing flowers.

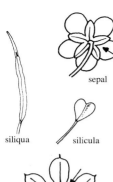

sepal

siliqua   silicula

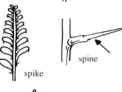

sinus

spine

spike

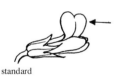

spur

stamen

standard

stigma

stipule

style

Scorpioid. A coiled cyme, as in the inflorescences of many members of the Boraginaceae.

Semi-parasitic. Only partially dependent on a host plant, but unable to survive without it.

Sepal. A member of the outer perianth whorl in most flowers. The sepals collectively make up the calyx.

Sheath. The lower part of a leaf surrounding the stem – as in grasses.

Silicula. A pod-like fruit that is not more than twice as long as broad, being sometimes broader than long.

Siliqua. A slender fruit pod that is many times longer than broad.

Simple. Not compound – unbranched.

Sinus. The gap between two lobes.

Sorus (plural **Sori**). A group of sporangia found in ferns.

Spathe. A large bract-like organ that envelops or partly envelops an inflorescence – as in arums.

Spatulate. Shaped like a paddle.

Speculum. A shiny, shield-like patch, as on the lips of many orchids.

Spike. A simple elongated inflorescence in which the individual flowers are unstalked.

Spikelet. A unit of a grass flower comprising usually two outer bracts (glumes) and one or more flowers each borne between a lemma and a palea.

Spine. A stiff, sharply pointed structure, often a modified shoot or stem.

Sporangium. A tiny structure containing spores.

Spores. Minute and often unicellular body; asexual.

Spur. A hollow cylindrical or pouched structure projecting from the calyx or corolla and generally containing nectar.

Stamen. The male organ of a flower, consisting of the stalk or filament and the anther, which contains the pollen.

Staminode. An infertile, often modified, stamen.

Standard. The upper petal in a pea flower.

Stellate. Shaped like a star – often refers to hairs.

Stigma. The receptive tip of a style to which pollen grains adhere.

Stipule. A leaf-like or scale-like structure located where leaf meets stem – not always present.

Stolon. A creeping stem, below or along the ground; often produced from the base of stems.

Style. The stalk that connects the stigma to the ovary.

Sub. Nearly or not quite: e.g. subacute – not quite acute.

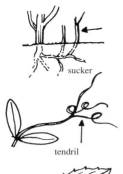

sucker

tendril

toothed

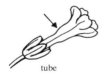

trifoliate

tube

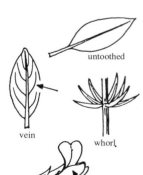

umbel

Subspecies. A subdivision of a species, generally separated from the typical plant by several characters, but also separated geographically or ecologically.

Subtending. Immediately adjacent to; to have another organ in its axil.

Sucker. A shoot arising from the roots.

Superior. Refers to flowers in which the ovary is in the centre and above the other flower parts (i.e. with sepals, petals and stamens attached to the receptacle below the ovary).

Tendril. A climbing organ, often thread-like and coiling around supports, branched or unbranched.

Thorn. A stiff woody structure, generally pointed and formed from a modified stem.

Throat. The opening to a tubular or funnel-shaped flower.

Toothed. Refers to leaf or petal margins that are toothed (serrated).

Trifoliate. With three leaflets.

Tube. A fused, often cylindrical, part of a calyx or corolla.

Tuber. A swollen underground organ, developed from underground stems or sometimes from the roots.

Umbel. An inflorescence in which all the branches (rays) arise from the same point, like the spokes of an umbrella.

Unarmed. Without spines or prickles.

Unisexual. Having only one sex in the flower or plant, either male or female.

Untoothed. Margins of leaves or petals that are not toothed (entire).

Variety. A subdivision of a species or subspecies, often differing in a single character; often growing with or close to the typical plant.

Vein. A strand, strengthening or conducting tissue running through leaves, petals etc.

Verticillater. A condensed cyme produced at the leaf-nodes and often forming distinctive whorls of flowers up the stem – as in many members of the Labiatae.

Vittae. Resin canals.

Wedge-shaped. Narrow at the point of attachment, but gradually widening and with straight sides – as in a wedge.

Whorl. More than two organs arising at the same point on the stem – leaves or flowers.

Wing. The lateral petals in a pea flower, many orchids etc.

Zygomorphic. An irregular flower having only one plane of symmetry.

untoothed

vein

whorl

wing

zygomorphic

CLASS – GYMNOSPERMS

An important group of seed-bearing plants, but unlike the Angiosperms (Dicotelydons, 23-2083, and Monocotyledons, 2084 onwards) the ovules are naked and not enclosed in a protective ovary. The Gymnosperms are trees and shrubs, mostly evergreeen and often with narrow needle-like leaves. The seeds are borne in a woody or fleshy cone. The firs, spruces, pines and cedars all belong here.

PINE FAMILY Pinaceae

Evergreen trees with spirally arranged needle-like leaves, borne in clusters of 2, 3 or 5. Male flowers borne in small cones at the base of young shoots – producing copious pollen. Female cones produced on the same tree, far more substantial, borne initially at or close to the shoot tip, taking one or several years to mature. Seeds often, but not always, winged. A very important family of decorative and timber producing species. Many are cultivated and only native species or those commonly planted are included here.

1 *Pinus halepensis* **ALEPPO PINE.** Medium-sized tree to 20m, occasionally more, with an irregular pyramidal or rounded crown at maturity; bark silver-grey, becoming reddish brown and fissured; branches often rather crooked and twigs pale grey and hairless; buds not sticky. Leaves in pairs, green, 6-13cm long, less than 1mm wide, straight or sometimes twisted. Cones egg-shaped, 5-12cm long, shiny, rich brown, on *recurved stalks*; seeds winged. Hills and rocky ground, plantations, roadsides – extremely drought-resistant. Mar-May. T – most frequent in the W; widely planted. In Greece the trees are tapped for their resin which is used to flavour and preserve the local wine, Retsina. An important timber-producing and fuel tree in some regions.

2 *Pinus brutia [P. halepensis* subsp. *brutia].* Similar, but twigs reddish-yellow or greenish and leaves 11-16cm long. Cones *spreading*, very short-stalked. S Italy, Crete, Cyprus and Syria.

3 *Pinus pinea* **STONE PINE, UMBRELLA PINE.** Large, majestic tree to 30m with a characteristic *umbrella shape* when mature; bark grey-brown flaking to reveal orange-red patches. Leaves 8-20cm long, wider than previous species, 2mm. Cones broadly rounded, shiny, reddish-brown; seeds unwinged or scarcely winged. Coastal habitats and hills, often forming pure stands – frequently planted. Apr-May. T – including Portugal. Probably not native in E Med or N Africa. The seeds are extracted from the cones and eaten all around the Med. They resemble almonds in general flavour and can be eaten raw or used in cakes and sweets.

4 *Pinus nigra* **AUSTRIAN PINE.** Robust tree to 45m, though often less, with a pyramidal crown; bark grey to dark brown, deeply fissured; twigs dark brown or blackish and buds slightly sticky. Leaves in pairs, dark green, 6-18cm long, 1-2mm wide, straight or somewhat twisted. Cones solitary or clustered, long-egg-shaped, 5-8cm long, yellowish-brown or pale brown, shiny, scarcely stalked. Rocky mountain slopes, sometimes planted in the region. May-June. Italy, Sicily, Yugoslavia, Balkan Peninsula, Turkey and Cyprus. The form from Turkey, the Balkans and Cyprus is sometimes assigned to subsp. *pallasiana* (4a), although intermediates between it and typical *P. nigra* do occur. An important, but slow-growing, timber tree. Also found in the higher mountains, to more than 1700m altitude.

5 *Pinus pinaster [P. maritima]* **MARITIME PINE**. Tall pyramidal tree to 40m; bark reddish-brown, becoming deeply fissured; twigs hairless, dark brown, and buds not sticky. Leaves in pairs, *long*, 18-25cm, rigid and spine-tipped. Cones large, long-egg-shaped, 8-22cm long, symmetrical, pale shiny brown. Forest, often extensive, on calcareous or sandy soils – widely planted for timber, turpentine production and for soil conservation, especially stabilising sand-dunes. Mar-Apr. W and C Med from Spain to Yugoslavia and N Africa.

Two further species are occasionally planted. *P. radiata*, the **Monterey Pine** (6) from California, has leaves in threes and markedly asymmetrical cones and *P. canariensis* (7) from the Canary Is. has very long leaves, 25-30cm.

8 *Abies cephalonica* **GRECIAN FIR**. Large evergreen tree to 30m with a pyramidal crown and dark brown bark tinged with orange, becoming darker and fissured with age; twigs hairless and buds very sticky. Leaves needle-like, spreading, thick, 1.5-3.5cm long, 2-3mm wide, usually spine-tipped, eventually falling to leave an oval scar on the twigs. Cones erect, cylindrical, 12-16cm long, with *deflexed bracts*, tongue-like between the scales. Mountain slopes. May-June. S Balkans, where often forms extensive forests; planted in Italy, occasionally elsewhere. Often host to a subspecies of the common mistletoe, *Viscum album* subsp. *abietis*. An important timber tree for the ancient Greeks; today areas of fine forest of this species are carefully preserved and encouraged to re-seed, although some trees are still extracted for timber.

9 *Cedrus atlantica* **ATLAS CEDAR**. Very large evergreen tree to 40m with horizontal branches when mature; bark dark grey and smooth, later shallowly fissured. Leaves blue-green, spirally arranged or in dense clusters on short lateral branchlets, 1-3cm long, needle-like. Cones erect, barrel-shaped, 5-8cm long, ripening pale brown-purple; scales numerous, closely overlapping, deciduous. Mountain slopes – widely planted at lower altitudes. Aug-Oct. Algeria and Morocco. Parks and gardens throughout the Med.

10 *Cedrus libani [Cedrus brevifolia]* **CEDAR OF LEBANON**. Similar, but leaves often deep green and cone slightly pointed at the top, not hollowed. Similar habitats. Also widely planted. E Med from SE Turkey to Syria and Lebanon. The form from Cyprus is generally referred to subsp. *brevifolia* (10a). Wild plants are only found in the mountains; in Cyprus above 1100m.

CYPRESS FAMILY Cupressaceae

Trees or shrubs with resin and leaves opposite or whorled, either scale-like or needle-like. Fruit a woody cone, often rather berry-like.

11 *Cupressus sempervirens* **ITALIAN CYPRESS**. Tall evergreen tree to 30m, but often less, forming a lean *columnar* shape (often called var. *pyramidalis*); bark grey-brown. Leaves very small and scale-like, 0.5-1mm long, paired, dull green. Cones oblong to rounded in outline, 2.5-4cm, shiny, green when young but becoming woody and yellow-grey when ripe. Hillslopes, roadsides, cemeteries, gardens and plantations. Mar-May. T – probably only native in Greece and Crete. The tapered pencil-shape is a characteristic sight in many parts of the Med; often planted along roadsides, in parks and gardens and around churches. The hard wood has long been used in building, although today it is most often planted for ornament.

11a Var. *horizontalis*. Similar, but a tree with spreading horizontal or ascending branches forming a rather irregular shape. Similar distribution. Both are widely planted and naturalised and can frequently be seen growing together.

12 *Cupressus macrocarpa* **MONTEREY CYPRESS**, from California, is often planted as a hedge or specimen tree in maritime areas. It can be distinguished by its bright green foliage which is *lemon-scented* when crushed. Cypress wood is hard and very durable.

Juniperus **JUNIPERS**. Aromatic evergreen shrubs or trees. Leaves awl-shaped and spine-tipped when young, often, but not always transforming to small paired scales as the species reaches maturity. Male cones small, solitary or clustered; female borne on the same or on a different plant, globose, berry-like at first, with 3-8 united scales that become woody at maturity – in 1-3 years.

13 *Juniperus communis* **COMMON JUNIPER**. Dense greyish shrub to 5m tall. Leaves always needle-like, 10-20mm long, *borne in threes*, with a single white band above. Cones egg-shaped to rounded, 5-7mm, green at first but black with a bluish bloom when ripe (in 2-3 years); male cones solitary. Rocky hill and mountain slopes, woodland, generally replacing *Juniperus oxycedrus* at higher altitudes. Mar-May. T – except the extreme E Med, Balearic Is., Crete and Cyprus. The source of oil of juniper, distilled from the green cones; also used in flavouring gin as well as meat and poultry. The cones and branches contain various alkaloids used in some medicines. The common juniper of many parts of Europe and western Asia – native to Britain, where it is very variable in form.

14 *Juniperus drupacea* **SYRIAN JUNIPER**. Similar, but a tree to 15m with leaves 10-25mm long and male cones in clusters; female cones *much larger*, 20-25mm, powder-blue when ripe. S Greece to Turkey and Syria.

15 *Juniperus oxycedrus* **PRICKLY JUNIPER**. Greyish evergreen shrub or small tree to 14m, but usually far less; bark grey or reddish, rough and scurfy. Leaves awl-shaped, borne in threes, spine-tipped, to 25mm long, with *two whitish bands* above. Cones rounded or pear-shaped, 8-10mm, ripening in second year to dark red-brown or purplish, shiny. Garrigue and maquis, rocky mountain slopes, pine forests. Mar-May. T. The commonest juniper in the Med region; often parasitised by *Arceuthobium oxycedri* (16), a small juniper-like parasite related to mistletoe. The very durable wood has been used for statues and furniture, and with other species of juniper is used locally for making charcoal.

15a Subsp. *macrocarpa*. Similar, but often a prostrate shrub; cones with a bluish bloom when young, larger, 12-15mm at maturity. Maritime rocks and sand. T.

17 *Juniperus phoenicea* **PHOENICEAN JUNIPER**. Small evergreen tree to 8m; bark grey-brown, peeling in narrow strips. Leaves awl-like, 5-14mm long, in the juvenile state; adult leaves small and scale-like, 0.7-1mm, blunt, closely pressed to the stem. Cones rounded to egg-shaped, 8-14mm, blackish at first but becoming yellowish-green and finally, in the second year, red-brown. Dry rocky ground, seashores, pine forests, primarily at low altitudes. Feb-Apr. T. Seashore specimens can be wholly prostrate. An important forest tree in dry Med regions such as North Africa, where it is tolerant of a surprising degree of drought.

18 *Juniperus excelsa* **GRECIAN JUNIPER**. Evergreen tree to 20m, forming a pyramidal shape; bark greyish, peeling in long strips. Leaves awl-like, 5-6mm long, sparse and opposite in the juvenile state; adult leaves scale-like, 1-1.5mm, *pointed*, loosely pressed to the stem; with a distinct resin pit above. Cones rounded ripening black or dark violet-purple in the second year, 7-8mm, each with 4-6 seeds. Rocky mountain slopes, especially on igneous rocks. Dec-June. Balkans to Turkey, Syria and Cyprus.

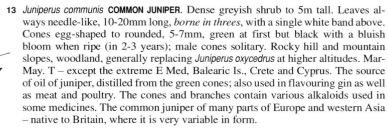

19 *Juniperus foetidissima.* Similar, but generally smaller with *rounded*, not quadrangular twigs; scale leaves usually without a resin pit above; cones with only 1-2 seeds. Similar habitats and distribution.

JOINT PINE FAMILY Ephedraceae

Tough shrubs with green rush-like stems and small opposite or whorled leaves. Flowers borne on short shoots, solitary or clustered, enclosed in 2-4 membranous segments. Fruit berry-like, with fleshy red or yellow scales. The source of the drug ephedrine.

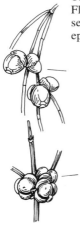

20 *Ephedra fragilis* **JOINT PINE**. Scrambling, weeping or climbing shrub to 5m, with *flexible*, rather fragile stems. Leaves scale-like, to 2mm. Male flowers in clusters of 4-8 pairs, female solitary or paired. Fruit red, 8-9mm. Rocks, garrigue, hedges and bushy places. Jan-July. Portugal to Sicily and N Africa, including the Balearic Is.

20a Subsp. *campylopoda*. Similar, but twigs more flexible, with a white, not yellow or brown, pith. Similar habitats. Balkan Peninsula, Cyprus and E Med.

21 *Ephedra distachya.* Low tough shrub to 0.5m, spreading by underground rhizomes to form a low thicket; stems erect and *rigid*, broom-like. Leaves 1.5-2mm, green on the back. Fruit red, 6-7mm. Rocky places, sandy shores and stream banks. Jan-June. Portugal to Sicily and Yugoslavia.

22 *Ephedra major.* Similar, but often only 10-20cm tall. Leaves mostly completely *membranous*, not green on the back. Usually on rocky slopes. Apr-June. T – not Portugal or most islands except Corsica, Sardinia, Sicily and Cyprus.

CLASS – ANGIOSPERMS

By far the largest grouping of seed-bearing plants, the Angiosperms include trees, shrubs and a vast range of herbs. The flowers are generally hermaphrodite, more rarely unisexual. The ovules are enclosed in a protective ovary. This Class is divided into two major Orders – the Dicotelydons (species 23-2083) and the Monocotyledons (2084 onwards).

Order – Dicotyledons

Dicotyledons ('dicots') have two seed-leaves (cotyledons), rarely one by reduction. The stem vessels are generally arranged in a single ring and the leaves normally have diverging, often netted, veins. The flowers are typically 4- or 5-parted. Many important families belong here, including the Ranunculaceae, Cruciferae, Leguminosae, Boraginaceae, Labiatae, Scrophulariaceae and Compositae.

OAK FAMILY Fagaceae

Trees or shrubs with alternate, undivided leaves. Male flowers borne in long slender catkins; female separate but on the same plant, 1-3 together, surrounded by a cluster of bracts, each flower with 3 or 6 styles.

23 *Castanea sativa* **SWEET CHESTNUT**. Large spreading deciduous tree to 30m; trunk with grey-brown bark, splitting into long ridges, often spiralled. Leaves large, to 25cm long, oblong-lanceolate, pointed, sharply toothed, scaly beneath. Flowers yellowish, in erect or spreading catkins, female at the base, male above. Fruit (chestnut) in groups of 1-3, brown, shiny, in a very spiny, splitting husk. Woods on well-drained acid soils, widely cultivated. June. France, Corsica and Sardinia eastwards to Turkey; absent on smaller islands. Long grown for its edible fruits. The wood is used for furniture and fencing.

Quercus **OAKS**. Trees or shrubs with evergreen or deciduous leaves. Male flowers in slender pendent catkins, female separate, few. Fruit a typical nut (acorn) surrounded at the base by a cupule (cup).

24 *Quercus coccifera* **KERMES OAK**. A variable dense evergreen shrub to 2m, rarely a small tree; bark grey, smooth, scaly when old. Leaves leathery, dark green, 1-4cm long, spiny and *holly-like*, short-stalked, hairless at maturity. Fruit ripening in second year, solitary or paired; cup 1-3cm, covered in small prickly scales; acorn 1.5-3cm long. Maquis and garrigue. Mar-May. European Med and N Africa.

24a Subsp. *calliprinos*. Similar, but more robust. Leaves often 4-5cm long. Turkey, Cyprus and E Med.

The common scrub oak of the Med. A red cloth dye is derived from the dried female scale insects, *Coccus ilicis*, that often infect this species. The bark is rich in tannin from which a black dye is produced, although rarely today. The Kermes Oak is generally small and scrubby, especially in dry exposed or heavily grazed places; when allowed to it occasionally grows into a small tree, to 6m.

25 *Quercus ilex* **HOLM OAK**. Large evergreen tree to 25m, with downy twigs; bark grey, finely fissured. Leaves leathery, oblong to lanceolate, spiny-toothed to untoothed, *downy beneath* at maturity, fruit ripening in first year; cup with scales closely pressed together, downy; acorn bitter tasting, 1.5-2cm long. Maquis and rocky slopes, but often planted. Apr-May. T. The hard and durable wood has been used

31

since early times for construction (it decays very slowly underground) and charcoal. This large and dark evergreen tree is often planted in parks and large gardens, sometimes as a street tree. The hard wood is often used for making charcoal.

26 *Quercus rotundifolia.* Similar, but leaves rounded to broadly oval, bluish-grey. Acorn sweet tasting. France, Spain and Portugal.

27 *Quercus suber* CORK OAK. Evergreen tree to 20m, with downy twigs; bark very thick, very *corky*, deeply ridged. Leaves oblong, 3-7cm long dark green, grey-downy beneath, deeply toothed. Fruit usually ripening in the first year; cup with the outer scales long and spreading, inner closely pressed together; acorn 1.3cm long. Rocky places, especially on hillslopes, frequently planted. Apr-May. Med Europe E to NW Yugoslavia. The bark on the trunk and lower branches is often stripped for cork – this usually follows a strict rotation with the trees being stripped in a regular 10-15 year cycle. Cork is used in particular for bottles and floor tiles and is the basis of an important local industry in parts of the Med.

28 *Quercus aegilops* [*Q. macrolepis*] VALONIA OAK. A semi-evergreen tree to 20m with downy twigs; bark grey and fissured. Leaves large, oblong, 5-14cm long, somewhat shiny, leathery, downy beneath, with 3-7 pairs of pointed lobes, long-stalked. Fruit ripening in the second year; cup large with thick, flattened, *recurved* scales; acorn 2-3cm long. Woodland and scrub. Mar-Apr. S Italy, Balkans, Aegean Is., Crete, Turkey; planted in Cyprus. The 'cups' (the largest of any Med species of oak) are used locally in tanning.

29 *Quercus infectoria.* Similar, but leaves toothed rather than lobed, scarcely downy or hairless beneath and cup with short closely pressed scales. S Turkey, Cyprus and E Med.

30 *Quercus faginea.* Like *Q. infectoria*, but leaves densely downy beneath. Spain, Portugal, Balearic Is. and NW Africa.

31 *Quercus pubescens* DOWNY OAK. Deciduous tree to 25m, occasionally a shrub, with densely downy twigs; bark dark grey, finely cracked into scales. Leaves grey-green, oblong-lanceolate, bluntly lobed, 6-12cm long, densely *downy* beneath, especially when young, short-stalked. Cup with narrow, closely pressed, hairy scales; acorns short-stalked. Woodland and rocky slopes. Apr-May. European and E Med, but absent from most of the smaller islands.

RAFFLESIA FAMILY Rafflesiaceae

A primarily tropical family of parasitic plants, containing the largest flower in the world, *Rafflesia.*

32 *Cytinus hypocistis* CYTINUS. A low parasitic perennial with *no chlorophyll.* Stem short with fleshy overlapping scales, orange or yellow. Flowers yellow or cream, 10-12mm long, with 4 spreading rounded lobes, borne in clusters surrounded by the scales, lower female with 1 style, upper, male with 8 stamens. Fruit a pulpy berry. Maquis and garrigue on white-flowered *Cistus* species. Mar-June. W France E to Sicily, Yugoslavia, Turkey and Cyprus.

32a Subsp. *macranthus.* Similar, but flowers larger, to 20mm long. Parasitic on *Halimium* species Portugal and N Africa.

32b Subsp. *orientalis.* Like the type, but scales usually bright red and flowers 17-18mm long. Parasitic on *Cistus parviflorus.* Crete, Gavdhos and E Med.

Although quite showy in flower, these interesting little plants nestle on the ground beneath shrubs and are often difficult to find.

33 *Cytinus ruber.* Like *C. hypocistis*, but scales always crimson or carmine and flowers *white or pale pink.* Parasitic on pink-flowered *Cistus* species Apr-June. European Med and N Africa.

BALANOPHORA FAMILY Balanophoraceae

A primarily tropical family of parasitic plants, often of rather sombre appearance.

34 *Cynomorium coccineum* **CYNOMORIUM.** Low to short, dark red to purplish-black parasitic herb (no chlorophyll). Stem fleshy, unbranched, with scale-like leaves, mostly below ground. Flowers tiny, massed in clusters, forming a dense *club-shaped*, erect structure, male, female or hermaphrodite. Rocky and sandy ground, saltmarshes, generally close to the coast; parasitic on various plants in saline habitats. Apr-May. Spain, Portugal, S Italy, Sardinia, Sicily, Gozo, N Africa and the E Med. Used in the past to staunch wounds, especially during the Crusades. This rare and local species, with its dark and sombre appearance, cannot be mistaken for anything else in the Med region.

WILLOW FAMILY Salicaceae

A familiar family in temperate regions but poorly represented in the Med region.

35 *Salix pedicellata* **MEDITERRANEAN WILLOW.** Deciduous shrub or tree to 10m; bark with numerous long ridges, flaking; twigs grey-downy. Leaves oblong to lanceolate, toothed to almost untoothed, slightly hairy beneath. Stipules present, large and heart-shaped, but soon falling. Catkins 3-6cm long, male and female borne on separate plants. Streamsides and ravines, often local. Feb-Apr. Spain, Corsica and Sardinia to Italy, Sicily and Greece.

HORNBEAM FAMILY Corylaceae

Deciduous trees or shrubs with alternate leaves. Fruit a nut surrounded by a ruff of bracts.

36 *Carpinus orientalis* **EASTERN HORNBEAM.** Deciduous shrub or small tree to 15m; bark smooth purplish-grey. Leaves oval to elliptic, pointed, finely toothed, hairy between veins beneath. Male catkins pendent; female on the same tree with large *leaf-like* bracts, deep green, Fruit a small winged nut. Woodland and ravines. Mar-May. From Italy and Sicily to Turkey and W Asia – not Cyprus.

37 *Ostrya carpinifolia* **HOP HORNBEAM.** Deciduous tree to 15m; bark grey-brown, fissured. Leaves oval, pointed, finely toothed, hairy when young. Male catkins to 10cm long, female hanging in hop-like clusters, 3-5cm in fruit, with oval whitish bracts. Fruit a nut. Woodland. Apr-May. From SE France to Turkey – only on the larger islands, but not Crete. In classical times it was considered very unlucky to bring any part of this plant into the house.

ELM FAMILY Ulmaceae

Deciduous trees and shrubs with simple, alternate leaves, often with an asymmetrical base. Fruit a winged nut, notched at the apex.

38 *Ulmus canescens* **MEDITERRANEAN ELM.** Deciduous tree to 3om; twigs slender, white downy. Leaves alternate, oval-elliptic, toothed, grey-hairy. Flowers small, borne in 5-6mm clusters on one year old twigs, before the leaves appear, hermaphrodite or male; stamens purplish. Fruit a winged nut, 18-20mm. Moist rocky slopes and ravines, occasionally planted. Feb-Mar. C Med from Italy eastwards to Palestine, including Cyprus.

39 *Celtis australis* SOUTHERN NETTLE TREE. Deciduous tree to 20m with smooth grey bark. Leaves oval to lanceolate, pointed, toothed, *3-veined* at the base, rather rough. Flowers small, generally solitary, with the young leaves, either male or hermaphrodite. Fruit berry-like, 9-12mm, brownish-black when ripe, edible. Hillslopes, roadsides and near old buildings, often planted. Mar-Apr. T, except parts of the W Med. Often planted in parks and along streets, occasionally in gardens.

40 *Celtis tournefortii*. Similar, but often shrubby, to 6m. Leaves blunt-toothed, *hairless beneath*. Dry calcareous hillslopes. Sicily east to Yugoslavia, Greece, Turkey and Cyprus.

MULBERRY FAMILY Moraceae

A large and mainly tropical family of economic importance and containing, besides the fig and mulberry, the bread-fruit.

41 *Morus alba* WHITE MULBERRY. Deciduous tree to 15m, with white juice (latex); branches slender and smooth. Leaves oval with a heart-shaped base, blunt-toothed. Flowers in dense spikes, 1-2cm long, often, but not always, male or female. Fruit berry-like, 1-2.5cm long, insipid tasting, white becoming pink or purplish. Roadsides and cultivated land, widely planted. Apr-May. Naturalised in Crete, Albania, Greece, Turkey and Cyprus. (China). Formerly widely cultivated; the leaves are collected to feed silkworms for making silk locally – in Greece and Turkey particularly. In Asia the fruit is dried for winter use.

42 *Ficus carica* FIG. Deciduous spreading tree to 10m with stout greyish stems and white juice (latex). Leaves large and rough, palmately lobed. Flowers tiny, borne inside a small green structure (syncarp). Fruit the familiar fig, fleshy, pear-shaped, 3-7cm, green or brownish-violet when ripe. Rocky places, by streams, often near habitation, widely planted. Mar-Apr. T, but only native in the E Med. An important source of food since biblical times, the fruit being eaten both fresh and dried, and today also canned. The cultivated form has no male flowers and the fruit ripen parthenocarpically (without fertilisation). In contrast the wild species bears both male and female flowers. The young fruits appear on the branches in the summer and overwinter, ripening late the following summer. A number of different varieties are grown in orchards and gardens; Spain, Italy and Turkey are the largest producers. Some varieties produce a single crop in summer; others bear two crops a year, in early summer and in early autumn.

43 *Ficus sycomorus*. Leaves oblong, untoothed. Flowers 2cm, roundish, borne in clusters from the trunk and older branches. Long cultivated in E. Med. (Ethiopia and E Africa).

SANDALWOOD FAMILY Santalaceae

A small family of herbs and shrubs with entire leaves and small flowers with a 4-5-parted calyx, but no petals. Fruit 1-seeded.

44 *Osyris alba* OSYRIS. Broom-like shrub to 1.2m. Leaves alternate, leathery, linear-lanceolate, untoothed. Flowers sweetly scented, yellowish, *3-parted*, 3-4mm, male in small clusters, female solitary, borne on separate plants. Fruit a red berry, 5-7mm. Dry shrubby places, often forming thickets. Apr-July. T.

45 *Osyris quadripartita*. Similar, but to 2.4m, the leaves with pronounced lateral veins. Flowers 3-4-parted. Berry 7-10mm. Similar habitats. Spain, Portugal and Balearic Is.

NETTLE FAMILY Urticaceae

Herbs with opposite or alternate, simple leaves; no stipules. Flowers usually either male or female, on the same or separate plants, 4-5-parted; no petals. Fruit a small achene.

Urtica **NETTLES**. Annual or perennial herbs with stinging hairs. Leaves opposite, toothed; stipules present. Flowers small, unisexual, borne in clusters or spikes, male and female on separate plants or on the same plant, 4-parted. Fruit an achene.

46 *Urtica atrovirens*. Medium-tall hairy perennial. Leaves dull green, lanceolate to oval, with a heart- or wedge-shaped base; stipules 4 at each node. Racemes 1-6cm long, longer than subtending leafstalk, *with both* male and female flowers, spreading to horizontal. Waste and disturbed ground. Feb-Apr. Balearic Is., Corsica, Sardinia and Italy.

47 *Urtica dioica* **STINGING NETTLE**. Similar, but more robust, to 1.5m, and racemes to 10cm long, male and female flowers borne on separate plants. Woods, waste places and cultivated land, often near habitation. Mar-June. T. The common nettle of N Europe, often colonising nitrogen-rich places such as pastures.

48 *Urtica pilulifera* **ROMAN NETTLE**. Medium-tall hairy annual. Leaves oval-heart-shaped, toothed or not. Male and female flowers on same plant; male in interrupted racemes, female in *globose heads*. Fruit in globose clusters, 9-11mm diam. Waste and disturbed ground, roadsides and terraces, near buildings. Feb-May. T. Various medicinal uses.

49 *Urtica membranacea [U. caudata, U. dubia]* **MEMBRANOUS NETTLE**. Short to tall annual. Leaves oval-heart-shaped; stipules *only 2* at each node. Male and female racemes on the same plant; male longer, often coiling, generally on the upper part of the plant, female on the lower part. Waste and disturbed ground, by habitations; often local. Mar-June. T.

Parietaria **WALL PELLITORIES**. Annual or perennial herbs with alternate, untoothed leaves. Flowers small, greenish, 4-lobed, in lateral clusters, hermaphrodite or unisexual.

50 *Parietaria judaica [P. diffusa]* **PELLITORY OF THE WALL**. Short-medium, tufted, sprawling hairy perennial; stems reddish, *much-branched*. Leaves oval, pointed, 1-7cm. Flowers either male or female, borne on the same plant. Damp rocks, walls and banks, occasionally in caves. Jan-Oct. T.

51 *Parietaria officinalis* **COMMON PELLITORY**. Similar, but taller, with erect simple or scarcely-branched stems. Leaves to 12cm. Dry open places. T – except extreme W

52 *Parietaria cretica* **CRETAN PELLITORY**. Short-medium spreading, hairy annual. Leaves *small*, 0.3-1.5cm, oval to elliptical. Bracts small, becoming brown and fused around the flowers. Dry rocky places and sandy ground near the sea, local. Feb-Apr. S Greece, Crete, Aegean Is., islands near Sicily, Cyprus and Libya.

53 *Parietaria mauritanica*. Similar, but often lower. Leaves often larger, to 5cm, oval, *long-pointed*. Similar habitats. Spain and Portugal, NW Africa.

54 *Parietaria lusitanica*. Like *P. cretica*, but with inconspicuous bracts. Walls and rock crevices; local. Mar-May. T.

CANNABIS FAMILY Cannabaceae

Herbs with opposite or alternate leaves. Male and female flowers distinct and borne on separate plants.

55 *Cannabis sativa* **CANNABIS**. Tall, erect, strong-smelling annual. Leaves alternate, with *3-9* lanceolate, toothed leaflets. Flowers greenish, small; male in branched racemes, female in spikes, borne on separate plants. Fruit a smooth nutlet enclosed in a persistent perianth. Casual on waste and cultivated land, rubbish dumps. May-Sept. T. (E Europe and W Asia). The source of hemp and the narcotic drug marijuana. Often included in seed mixtures for cage birds. Sometimes a common wayside weed.

56 *Humulus lupulus* **HOP**. Climbing perennial to 6m; stems rough, square, twining. Leaves opposite, 3-5-lobed, coarsely toothed. Male flowers 4-5mm, in much-branched racemes; female on separate plants, pale green, in *cone-like* clusters, 15-20mm, with overlapping bracts – enlarging in fruit to 30mm. Hedges and woodland margins. June-Sept. T – except Crete. Cultivated for brewing beer; the female fruit heads are used in brewing. A form with decorative yellow leaves is grown in gardens.

BIRTHWORT FAMILY Aristolochiaceae

A small family of climbing shrubs and herbs primarily from tropical and Med regions.

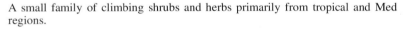

Aristolochia **BIRTHWORTS**. Perennial herbs, sometimes climbers, often with a tuberous rootstock. Leaves alternate, untoothed. Flowers lateral, with a straight or curved tube, swollen at the base and extended into a unilateral limb at the apex (often likened to a Dutchman's pipe), with the ovary situated below; stamens 6, fused to the style into a column. Fruit a capsule.

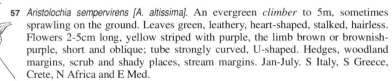

57 *Aristolochia sempervirens [A. altissima]*. An evergreen *climber* to 5m, sometimes sprawling on the ground. Leaves green, leathery, heart-shaped, stalked, hairless. Flowers 2-5cm long, yellow striped with purple, the limb brown or brownish-purple, short and oblique; tube strongly curved, U-shaped. Hedges, woodland margins, scrub and shady places, stream margins. Jan-July. S Italy, S Greece, Crete, N Africa and E Med.

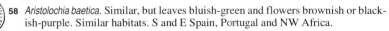

58 *Aristolochia baetica*. Similar, but leaves bluish-green and flowers brownish or blackish-purple. Similar habitats. S and E Spain, Portugal and NW Africa.

59 *Aristolochia cretica*. Short to medium hairy perennial with erect or spreading stems. Leaves kidney-shaped to triangular-oval, stalked. Flowers 5-12cm long, dull purple with numerous pale bristles in the mouth and a *thick curved tube*, the limb thick and expanding widely, with two broad 'ears' at the base. Rocky habitats and open scrub. Mar-Apr. Crete and Karpathos.

60 *Aristolochia guichardii*. Similar, but a short plant with rather smaller flowers. Similar habitats. SW Turkey and Rhodes.

61 *Aristolochia hirta.* Like *A. cretica*, but the upper leaves pointed and the flowers dark maroon-brown with an oval limb. Similar habitats. E Aegean Is. and Turkey.

62 *Aristolochia pistolochia.* Short to medium hairy perennial. Leaves oval-triangular, short-stalked, the margin and lower surface minutely *horny*. Flowers 2-5cm long, brown with a dark purple, oval, broad limb; tube narrow and straight, longer than the limb. Dry rocky and scrubby places. Apr-June. W Med – W France, Spain, Portugal, Corsica, Sardinia and Morocco.

63 *Aristolochia rotunda.* Short to medium, generally hairless perennial; stems erect, simple or slightly branched. Leaves oval-heart-shaped, scarcely stalked, *clasping the stem*. Flowers 3-5cm long, yellow with a long dark brown limb bent over the opening of the straight tube. Hedges, dry fields, rocky and stony places. Apr-June. T – except Morocco.

64 *Aristolochia pallida.* Short to medium perennial, hairy at first; stems simple or slightly branched. Leaves kidney-shaped, short-stalked. Flowers 3-6cm long, greenish-yellow or pale brown with brown or purplish stripes, the limb often darker, *short and slightly curved*; tube straight. Similar habitats and flowering time. Mar-June. T.

65 *Aristolochia longa.* Similar, but taller, the leaves more triangular and the flowers greenish-brown with a brownish-purple limb. Similar habitats. European Med and NW Africa.

66 *Aristolochia parvifolia.* Like *A. pallida*, but leaves more heart-shaped. Flowers greenish-brown, often blotched with chocolate. Calcareous rocks and wall crevices. Dec-June. E Aegean Is., Turkey, Cyprus and E Med.

67 *Aristolochia clematitis* **BIRTHWORT**. Medium to tall stinking, hairless perennial; stems erect, unbranched. Leaves heart-shaped, blunt, stalked. Flowers 2-3cm long, yellow with a short brown limb, borne in *small clusters* at the base of the upper leaves; tube straight. Scrub and waste places, often close to water. June-Sept. T. Long cultivated as a medicinal herb, used to aid births, as well as a relief for wounds and snakebites.

68 *Aristolochia microstoma.* Short to medium hairy perennial with simple unbranched stems. Leaves heart-shaped, blunt, short-stalked. Flowers 1.5-3cm long, club-shaped, brownish, with an apical pore, the limb very small or absent. Scrub and rocky places. Apr-June. S Greece and Cyclades.

69 *Aristolochia bianorii.* Short hairless perennial with branched stems. Leaves deeply and narrowly heart-shaped, very short-stalked. Flowers 1-3cm long, brownish-yellow with brown stripes and a *reddish limb*. Rocky places and scrub. Apr-May. Balearic Is. – Mallorca.

DOCK FAMILY Polygonaceae

A large, primarily temperate family of herbs, shrubs or climbers. Leaves alternate with stipule-like ochrea sheathing the stem above each leaf. Flowers 3-6-parted, sometimes unisexual, the perianth often enlarging in fruit; stamens 6-9. Fruit an elliptical or triangular nut.

Polygonum **KNOTGRASSES**. Herbs, usually with narrow leaves. Flowers in small clusters or spikes; perianth 5-parted; stamens often 8; styles 2-3. Nut not winged.

70 *Polygonum maritimum* **SEA KNOTGRASS**. Low, prostrate or sprawling perennial with a woody stock. Leaves narrow-elliptical, bluish-green, with down-rolled margins;

ochrea reddish-brown at base but silvery and transparent above, generally longer than the internodes, with 8-12 strong veins. Flowers white or pink, solitary or in small clusters – these making up a *leafy spike*. Maritime sands and shingle, sand-dunes. Mar-Aug. T.

71 *Polygonum equisetiforme*. Similar, but with long wiry branches and ochrea mostly *shorter* than the internodes. Flowers in lax spikes; bracts small and not leafy. Waste places and roadsides, field margins. Apr-Oct. NW Africa and Spain eastwards to Turkey – not France, Yugoslavia or Cyprus.

72 *Polygonum romanum*. Like *P. maritimum*, but ochrea with *fewer*, fainter veins leaves linear to linear-lanceolate. Flowers whitish, in short leafy spikes. W Med; Spain, Italy, Balearic Is. and Sardinia.

73 *P. salicifolium*. Like *P. equiseteforme*, but ochrea all brown and with a *ciliate* margin. Wet places and ditches. Widespread in Med.

Rumex **DOCKS**. Perennials with tubular ochrea. Flowers in whorls making up simple or branched racemes, with 6 segments. Fruit a nut, usually winged.

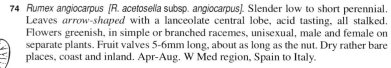

74 *Rumex angiocarpus [R. acetosella* subsp. *angiocarpus]*. Slender low to short perennial. Leaves *arrow-shaped* with a lanceolate central lobe, acid tasting, all stalked. Flowers greenish, in simple or branched racemes, unisexual, male and female on separate plants. Fruit valves 5-6mm long, about as long as the nut. Dry rather bare places, coast and inland. Apr-Aug. W Med region, Spain to Italy.

75 *Rumex tingitanus*. Similar, but a rhizomatous perennial with oval to lanceolate, often somewhat lobed, leaves. Fruit-valves several times longer than the nut. Maritime sands. W Med from Spain to Italy, including Portugal.

76 *Rumex intermedius*. Like *R. angiocarpus*, but leaves linear with narrow diverging basal lobes and an undulate margin. Fruit valves longer than the nut. Spain, France and Balearic Is.

77 *Rumex cyprius*. Like *R. angiocarpus*, but annual with all leaves long-stalked and fruit *large*, the valves 10-20mm long. Dry stony slopes, walls and cultivated fields. Mar-May. Cyprus and E Med.

78 *Rumex bucephalophorus*. Very variable low to medium annual, with one or several wiry stems. Leaves very small, lanceolate to elliptical or spatular shaped. Flowers greenish, very small, in racemes or spike-like; flower-stalks either slender and short or long and flat. Fruit on *recurved* stalks. Sandy and rocky coastal habitats, moist fields and river shingles. Mar-May. Med region E to W Turkey, including Portugal, not in Cyprus.

79 *Emex spinosa* **EMEX**. Hairless low to short annual, rather fleshy; stems erect to somewhat sprawling. Leaves oval, often with a heart-shaped base, stalked. Flowers with 6 segments, male or female, borne on the same plant; female flowers unstalked at base of the raceme, male at top, stalked. Fruit a spiny nut. Sandy shores, disturbed and cultivated land. Jan-Apr. W and C Med region east as far as Greece, including Portugal.

FATHEN FAMILY Chenopodiaceae

A large and complex family of herbs and shrubs, mostly with alternate, rather suc-culent, leaves. Flowers small and greenish, with a 3-5-lobed perianth, often en-larging in the one-seeded fruit.

80 *Beta vulgaris* subsp. *maritima* **SEA BEET**. A very variable low to medium, rather fleshy, hairless annual or perennial; stems sprawling to erect, often reddish. leaves oval to lanceolate, sometimes with a heart-shaped base, leathery, untoothed. Flowers small, green to purplish, in dense leafy clusters forming long spikes. Fruit with swollen flower segments which become corky and fuse together in small clusters. Rocky coastal habitats, cliffs, salt marshes or a weed of cultivated fields. Feb-May. T – not Cyprus. The ancestor of the cultivated beet and mangold.

81 *Beta macrocarpa*. Similar, but spikes with bracts to the top, not just at the base or absent altogether. N Africa, Portugal, Spain, Italy, Sardinia and Greece – always very local.

82 *Arthrocnemum perenne [Salicornia perennis, S. radicans]* **PERENNIAL GLASSWORT**. Dwarf hairless subshrub, creeping to form mats 1m. across; stems jointed, short and erect, becoming reddish or orange and woody with age, fleshy when young. Leaves opposite, *scale-like*. Flowers tiny, borne in threes, each with two yellow stamens; flowers falling to leave 3 holes in a segment. Coastal habitats, particularly salt marshes and gravelly ground. Aug-Oct. W and C Med east as far as Greece.

83 *Arthrocnemum fruticosum [Salicornia fruticosa]*. Similar, but stouter, to 1m; stems not rooting down, *bluish-green*. Similar habitats. T – not Cyprus or parts of the E Med.

84 *Arthrocnemum macrostachya [A. glaucum, Salicornia glauca, S. macrostachya]*. Like *A. fruticosum*, but to 50cm tall, stems becoming yellowish-green or reddish; clusters of three flowers falling to leave a single crater. Similar habitats. May-July. T.

85 *Salicornia europaea* **GLASSWORT, SEA SAMPHIRE**. Very variable, low to medium, hairless annual. Stems translucent, erect, occasionally prostrate, with ascending branches, green or bluish-green but flushed with pink or red at flowering time. Leaves opposite, scale-like. Flowers tiny, in threes, forming spikes 10-50mm long. Coastal habitats, muddy marshes, sandy shores, often low on the seashore, occasionally inland. May-Oct. T. The young stems can be eaten as a vegetable, and taste rather like asparagus.

86 *Halopeplis amplexicaulis [Holostachys perfoliata, Salicornia amplexicaulis]* **HALOPEPLIS**. An erect, fleshy, low to short annual, green, bluish green or pinkish, hairless; stems swollen at the nodes. Leaves alternate, distant, subglobose, 1.5-5mm, *clasping* the stem. Flowers tiny, in threes but aggregated to form cylindrical spikes, 5-20mm. long; perianth segments 3. Coastal habitats, particularly margins of salt lakes. July-Sept. T – except France, Greece and Yugoslavia.

87 *Halocnemum strobilaceum [Salicornia strobilacea]* **HALOCNEMUM**. A short to medium fleshy subshrub, much-branched. Leaves opposite, scale-like, *papery*, fused together around the stem. Flowers tiny, in groups of three borne in rounded or oblong spikes, opposite or whorled; perianth segments membranous. Salt marshes and margins of salt lakes. Aug-Oct. T – except Portugal, France, Italy and Yugoslavia.

88 *Chenopodium botrys* **STICKY GOOSEFOOT**. Short to medium, *sticky*, aromatic annual, glandular-hairy. Leaves alternate, oblong, pinnately divided, usually with 4 lobes on each side. Flowers small, greenish, in narrow spike-like clusters – these forming a leafy inflorescence. Cultivated and fallow fields, roadsides and vineyards. May-July. T.

89 *Chenopodium murale* **NETTLE-LEAVED GOOSEFOOT**. Similar, but taller, slightly mealy, but not hairy. Leaves diamond-shaped, coarsely toothed. Similar habitats as well as sandy seashores. Feb-Sept. T.

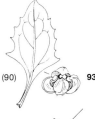

Other weedy species in region are *C. botyrodes* (90) (leaves green or reddish, scarcely toothed), W Med; *C. ficifolium* (91) (leaves narrow, with divergent basal lobes), T, scattered; *C. glaucum* (92) (leaves narrow, toothed, bluish-green and mealy beneath), T – scattered.

(90)

93 *Suaeda maritima* **ANNUAL SEABLITE.** Very variable short to medium branched annual, bluish-green but becoming purple then reddish often. Leaves alternate, fleshy, *semi-cylindrical*, pointed, untoothed. Flowers small, greenish, 1-3 in axils of the upper leaves. Coastal habitats, especially muddy salt marshes. July-Sept. T.

94 *Suaeda vera* **SHRUBBY SEABLITE.** Rather similar, but a *shrub* to 1.2m with similar but smaller and more crowded leaves, 5-18mm long (not 10-50mm). Coastal habitats and rocky hillslopes close to the coast. Oct-May. T.

95 *Suaeda splendens.* Like *S. maritima* but leaves *semi-transparent* with a deciduous apex and perianth inflating in Fruit. T – not Balearic Is., Cyprus or Sicily.

96 *Atriplex halimus* **SHRUBBY ORACHE.** Stout erect shrub to 2.5m, with grey peeling bark. Leaves alternate, *silvery-white*, oval to diamond-shaped, leathery and untoothed to lobed. Flowers yellowish, small, in more or less leafless terminal branched spikes. Sandy and rocky seashores, occasionally dry places inland. July-Oct. T.

97 *Atriplex prostrata [A. hastata, A. triangularis]* **SPEAR-LEAVED ORACHE.** Variable, medium to tall, hairless annual, much-branched, mealy when young. Leaves opposite or the upper alternate, green or grey-mealy, triangular with *spreading* basal lobes, toothed or untoothed. Flowers borne in leafy panicles. Sandy seashores and arable land. July-Oct. T.

98 *Atriplex littoralis* **GRASS-LEAVED ORACHE.** Similar, but leaves *narrow*, linear to linear-oblong, the lower short-stalked. Flowers in slender, spikes, leafy at least below. Coastal habitats and saline places inland. W Med from Spain to Yugoslavia.

99 *Atriplex rosea.* Like *A. prostrata,* but leaves grey- or white-mealy. Cultivated and waste ground, roadsides. June-Oct. T.

100 *Halimione portulacoides [A. portulacoides]* **SEA PURSLANE.** A short to medium shrub, spreading and often rooting down. Leaves silvery-mealy, mostly opposite, thick and fleshy, oblong, *untoothed.* Flowers small, greenish-yellow, in small practically leafless panicles. Salt marshes, especially edges of pools and channels. July-Oct. T.

101 *Noaea mucronata [Salsola echinus, S. mucronata]* **NOAEA.** A short to medium *thorny* shrub; young twigs hairless, ending in a sharp spine. Leaves alternate, deciduous, linear, pointed. Flowers small in spikes with bracts; perianth becoming pink in fruit, papery and with spreading wings 5-6mm long. Coastal garrigue, sand-dunes and rocky hillslopes. July-Oct. E Med, including Cyprus.

102 *Salsola kali* **PRICKLY SALTWORT.** Very variable erect to sprawling, short to medium succulent annual. Leaves cylindrical with a short *spine-tip*, untoothed. Flowers small, green or sometimes pink-tinged, solitary in the axils of spine-tipped bracts; perianth segments 5, membranous. Sandy or rocky seashores, dunes and sandy fields. May-Sept. T.

103 *Salsola soda* **SALTWORT.** Similar, but often taller with non-pungent leaves which are pointed but without a spine tip. Sandy seashores. T.

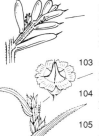

104 *Salsola vermiculata.* Like *S. soda,* but a *hairy* shrub to 1m. Leaves with a broadened half-clasping base. Coastal habitats. W Med and NW Africa, from Spain to Sicily.

105 *Salsola inermis.* Like *S. soda,* but a slender wiry *grey-hairy* plant. Sandy seashores, occasionally saline habitats inland. Sept-Nov. E Med, including Cyprus.

AMARANTH FAMILY Amaranthaceae

Herbs, generally with alternate leaves. Flowers mostly hermaphrodite, borne in dense heads or spikes; perianth dry and membranous, 4-5-parted; styles 2-3. Fruit dry, with a membranous wall. A primarily tropical and subtropical family.

106 *Amaranthus retroflexus* **PIGWEED**. Short to tall annual with erect or ascending, stout stems, hairy above. Leaves oval to diamond-shaped, pale green, stalked, white-hairy on veins beneath. Flowers greenish-white, small, 2-3mm, numerous, borne in branched spikes; flowers unisexual. Fruit capsule dehiscent. Naturalised on cultivated and waste ground, roadsides. June-Oct. Widespread in the Med region, but local. (North America).

107 *Amaranthus hybridus*. Similar, but plant often reddish-tinged, and flowers often yellowish, reddish or purplish. Similar habitats, occasionally on seashores. T. (North America).

108 *Amaranthus albus*. Like *A. retroflexus,* but inflorescence leafy to the top, not just at the base. Similar habitats. July-December. T, but local. (North America).

109 *Amaranthus viridis [A. gracilis]*. A short to tall annual; stem *slender*, usually hairy towards the top. Leaves oval to diamond-shaped, long-stalked, the margin untoothed or somewhat lobed. Flowers green, usually in branched spikes. Fruit-capsule indehiscent. Cultivated ground and waste places. July-Nov. Widely naturalised, but local, in the Med. (Probably from the Americas).

BOUGAINVILLEA FAMILY Nyctaginaceae

A family of trees and herbs from tropical and warm temperate regions of the world. Leaves usually opposite and flowers often with a large and colourful involucre of bracts subtending the flowers.

110 *Bougainvillea glabra* **BOUGAINVILLEA**. Vigorous spiny climber or shrub, to 10m, though often less. Leaves opposite or in whorls, dark green, oval, blunt, untoothed, hairless or slightly hairy. Flowers in threes, rather insignificant, whitish or yellowish, funnel-shaped, but surrounded by large leaf-like, purple *bracts*, one to each flower; corolla covered in short curved hairs. Widely planted, not or rarely naturalised. Feb-Oct. T. Often seen in parks and gardens and planted along roads; sometimes grown as a house plant.

111 *Bougainvillea spectabilis*. Very similar, but leaves softly hairy and corollas with straight hairs; flower-bracts red-purple. Similar distribution and flowering time. Hybrids with white, orange and violet flower-bracts also exist.

POKEWEED FAMILY Phytolaccaceae

A small family of trees, shrubs, lianas and herbs from tropical and warm temperate regions of the world, particularly America.

112 *Phytolacca acinos [P. americana, P. decandra]* **AMERICAN POKEWEED**. Robust, tall, hairless perennial to 2m; stems often red. Leaves large, oval to lanceolate, untoothed. Flowers greenish-white, 5-6mm, in erect spike-like racemes. Fruit *berry-like*, ribbed and fleshy, 9-10mm, purplish black when ripe (poisonous). Cultivated ground and waste places, sometimes casual. July-Oct. T – local (North America).

113 *Phytolacca dioica [P. arborea]* **OMBU**. An evergreen tree to 15m, with a pale buttressed trunk. Leaves alternate, *ace-of-spades* shaped, stalked, untoothed. Flowers

greenish, in drooping racemes, male and female on separate trees, the female shorter stalked than the male. Fruit a juicy berry, roundish, 9-10mm, black and shiny when ripe. A commonly planted shade tree in the Med. June-Sept. T – but scattered. (South America).

AIZOON FAMILY Aizoaceae

A large family of primarily succulent herbs, mainly from Southern Africa, but also Australia. Leaves opposite, sometimes alternate. Flowers often large and showy, brightly coloured; sepals 5 often but petals numerous; stamens few to many. Fruit a capsule, often rather fleshy. Many species are cultivated for their showy flowers.

114 *Aizoon hispanicum* **AIZOON**. Low to short, slightly succulent annual, erect to spreading. Leaves opposite below, alternate above, oblong-lanceolate, blunt, minutely hairy. Flowers solitary, mostly in stem forks, *unstalked*, 9-10mm, with 5 greenish sepals and yellow stamens. Bare places, clayey or sandy soils. Mar-May. S Spain, N Africa, Cyprus and Palestine.

115 *Carpobrotus edulis* **HOTTENTOT FIG**. Low trailing and mat-forming perennial with a woody stem. Leaves opposite, united together at the base, narrow and tapered, *3-angled*, upwardly curving. Flowers large, 8-9cm, with numerous yellow, yellowish-pink or pale purple linear 'petals'; stamens yellow. Fruit fleshy and slightly fig-like, edible. Rocks, cliffs and sandy places, often planted near coasts and sometimes forming extensive naturalised colonies, often with both colours together. Apr-July. T, scattered, but commoner in the W. (South Africa).

116 *Carpobrotus acinaciformis* **RED HOTTENTOT FIG**. Robust low perennial with trailing and mat-forming stems, woody at the base. Leaves like *C. edulis*, but bluish-green and broadest in the middle. Flowers spectacular, 11-12cm, bright purple or purple-magenta, with numerous 'petals'; stamens purple. Habitats and flowering times as for *C. edulis*. (South Africa).

117 *Carpobrotus chilensis*. Similar, but *smaller*, the flowers only 2.5-5cm. Spain, possibly elsewhere. (W America).

118 *Mesembryanthemum crystallinum [Cryophytum crystallinum]* **ICE PLANT**. Low, sprawling annual covered in *glistening* crystalline hairs. Leaves spatula-shaped to oval, mostly alternate, untoothed, only the lower stalked. Flowers solitary, terminal, yellowish or whitish, 20-30mm, 'petals' longer than the sepals. Sandy or gravelly ground, salt marshes, usually close to the sea. May-Aug. T – not Turkey.

119 *Mesembryanthemum nodiflorum [Gasoul nodiflorum]*. Similar, but less crystalline, the leaves *linear*; 'petals' shorter than the sepals (not longer). Coastal habitats, sandy and rocky, sandy fields. Apr-July. T.

120 *Lampranthus glaucus* **LAMPRANTHUS**. Short erect shrub to 25cm; branches tortuous. Leaves opposite, linear-oblong, *3-angled*, somewhat crystalline, untoothed. Flowers terminal, bright yellow, 24-30mm, with numerous narrow 'petals'. Widely planted and occasionally naturalised in sandy and rocky coastal habitats. Apr-Aug. Only truly naturalised in Portugal. (South Africa).

121 *Lampranthus roseus* is similar, but with rather longer leaves and pink flowers 30-40mm. Widely planted in the Med region and occasionally naturalised on coastal rocks. (South Africa).

fruit

leaf

leaf

MOLLUGO FAMILY Molluginaceae

A small family of mostly herbs from tropical and warm temperate regions, especially Africa.

122 *Glinus lotoides* **GLINUS**. Low, sprawling, much-branched annual, covered in starry white hairs. Leaves in *whorls* of 3-4, unequal, oblong to spatula-shaped, dull green, stalked. Flowers 10-12mm, with greenish-yellow sepals and numerous shorter, white, linear 'petals'. Waste places, ditches, alluvial ground, muddy areas. July-Nov. T – but local.

123 *Telephium imperati* **TELEPHIUM**. Low to short hairless sub-shrub with a stout woody base. Leaves *alternate*, oblong, rather fleshy, grey-green, with membranous, fringed stipules at the base. Flowers white, 4-5mm, 5-parted, in dense, branched heads; petals longer than sepals. Rocky and stony places, not coastal. May-Aug. Scattered localities from Spain and France eastwards to Palestine.

124 *Mollugo cerviana* **MOLLUGO**. Low to short, sprawling or ascending, hairless annual. Leaves whorled in groups of 3-10, linear, with papery margins. Flowers greenish, in *flat-topped* clusters, without 'petals'. Sandy and gravelly places. Mar-June. Spain, Portugal, NW Africa, Italy and Greece.

PINK FAMILY Caryophyllaceae

Herbs with opposite leaves, rarely alternate, each pair at right angles to those above and below; occasionally with membranous stipules. Flowers regular, generally hermaphrodite; sepals 4-5, free or fused together; petals 4-5, free, clawed or not, sometimes absent; stamens often 8-10, sometimes fewer; stigmas 2-5. Fruit a capsule, splitting with as many or twice as many teeth as styles. A large family, primarily from temperate regions of the world.

125 *Arenaria bertolonii* **BERTOLONI'S SANDWORT**. Low, laxly tufted perennial, with slender stems. Leaves lanceolate, pointed, hairy. Flowers solitary or 2-3 together, white, *large*, 20-32mm, petals notched. Rocky habitats. Mar-June. Corsica, Sardinia, Italy and Sicily.

126 *Arenaria balearica* **BALEARIC SANDWORT**. Creeping, bright green *mat-forming* perennial. Leaves tiny, oval to rounded. Flowers white, 5-7mm, solitary on long slender stalks above the foliage; petals not notched. Damp, shaded and generally rocky places. Apr-July. Balearic Is., Corsica, Sardinia and Sicily. Grown in gardens, in damp places and on old walls.

127 *Moehringia pentandra* **MOEHRINGIA**. Delicate spreading, low to short annual, occasionally a short-lived perennial. Leaves oval, with 3-5 main veins, with a ciliate stalk. Flowers greenish, 4-8mm, with 5 sepals, but *no petals*. Dry scrubby places. Apr-June. W and C Med from NW Africa and Portugal to Greece.

128 *Cerastium ligusticum* **CERASTIUM**. Low to short annual; stem finely glandular. Lower leaves spatula-shaped, middle and upper oblong, all hairy. Flowers white, 10-16mm, long stalked, the petals *deeply notched*, longer than the sepals. Rocky places and scrub. Mar-June. C Med from Corsica and Sardinia to Crete and Yugoslavia.

129 *Cerastium siculum*. Similar, but with clustered flowers; petals *shorter* than the sepals. W Med from Portugal to Italy and Sicily.

130 *Cerastium tomentosum* **SNOW-IN-SUMMER, DUSTY MILLER**. Low to short mat-forming perennial, covered in white or greyish *wool*. Leaves linear-lanceolate, the margins

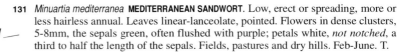

slightly rolled under. Flowers in branched cymes, white, 20-28mm, petals deeply notched. Rocky habitats, but widely grown and naturalised. Apr-June. Italy and Sicily, but widely naturalised elsewhere. Commonly grown in gardens, where it may become an invasive weed.

131 *Minuartia mediterranea* **MEDITERRANEAN SANDWORT.** Low, erect or spreading, more or less hairless annual. Leaves linear-lanceolate, pointed. Flowers in dense clusters, 5-8mm, the sepals green, often flushed with purple; petals white, *not notched*, a third to half the length of the sepals. Fields, pastures and dry hills. Feb-June. T.

132 *Minuartia geniculata [Rhodalsine geniculata].* Similar, but a more robust perennial, *glandular-hairy*; flowers somewhat larger and less congested, petals white or occasionally pink, as long as the sepals. Dry rocky and sandy places, usually coastal. Mar-July. T – not France, Yugoslavia or Crete.

133 *Minuartia hybrida.* Like *M. mediterranea*, but inflorescences laxer and flower-stalks longer (not shorter) than the sepals. Cultivated and fallow ground, rocky places and vineyards. Feb-June. T.

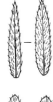

Paronychia **PARONYCHIAS.** Perennial herbs with small opposite leaves; stipules conspicuous and silvery. Flowers small, in dense clusters surrounded by silvery bracts; calyx 5-lobed; petals absent or tiny; stamens 5. Fruit an achene with a membranous wall.

134 *Paronychia capitata [P. euboea, P. nivea].* Low matted perennial, much-branched. Leaves grey-green, narrow oblong to linear-lanceolate, pointed, hairy. Flowerclusters *globular*, 8-10mm, concealed by the silvery bracts; bracts longer than the flowers; calyx all green. Dry rocky and stony places, sand-dunes. Mar-June. W and C Med from Spain to Greece, Crete, as well as N Africa.

135 *Paronychia macrosepala.* Very similar, but leaves oval to oblong and *bracts* 5-6mm long (not 6-10mm). C and E Med from Greece to Palestine.

136 *Paronychia argentea.* Similar to *P. capitata*, but leaves awned, almost hairless and calyx-lobes with *transparent margins*. Dry and waste ground, sand-dunes, roadsides. Dec-July. T.

137 *Paronychia echinulata.* Differs in being annual, spreading to erect. Flower-clusters 3-8mm; bracts inconspicuous, shorter than the flowers. Dry sandy and stony places. Mar-May. T.

138 *Herniaria cinerea* **HERNIARIA.** Low prostrate annual, hairy. Leaves grey-green, opposite, but alternate towards the shoot tips, oblong, untoothed. Flowers small, *grey-green*, in dense lateral and terminal clusters, 5-parted, no petals; stamens 2. Dry sandy and stony places, fields and waste places. Feb-May. T.

139 *Herniaria hirsuta.* Similar, but plants bright pale green; stamens 2-5. T.

140 *Pteranthus dichotomous* **PTERANTHUS.** Low sprawling hairless annual. Leaves *linear*, opposite or in whorls. Flowers small, greenish, 6mm long, 4-parted, in groups of 3, no petals; sepals awned. Fallow fields, bare and waste places. Mar-June. N Africa, Cyprus and E Med.

141 *Polycarpon tetraphyllum [P. alsinifolium]* **FOUR-LEAVED ALSEED.** Low, hairless, much-branched annual. Leaves apparently mostly in *whorls of four*, oval, green or purplish. Flowers in branched clusters, white, tiny, 2-3mm; petals notched, narrow, shorter than sepals. Dry places, fields, banks, sand-dunes, coastal and inland. Feb-Aug. T.

142 *Polycarpon polycarpoides [P. peploides]*. Similar, but a perennial with a woody base; leaves *rounded*; petals not notched. Coastal rocks. Mar-July. W Med from Spain to Italy and Sicily.

143 *Loeflingia hispanica* **LOEFLINGIA**. Low glandular-hairy annual, much-branched. Leaves linear, *long-pointed*, fused by their bases in pairs. Flowers greenish, small, 3-4mm, in branched spikes; sepals and petals 5, the latter very small; stamens 3. Dry sandy habitats. Mar-June. W Med; France, Spain, Portugal and Sicily.

Spergularia **SEA SPURREYS**. Annual or perennial herbs; stems thickened at the joints. Leaves linear, opposite, united round the base by membranous stipules, often with leaf-tufts borne on one side at each joint. Flowers in branched 'racemes', 5-parted; sepals free; petals not notched; stamens 10. A difficult group widespread in Europe and Asia, often growing close to the coast. Sometimes several species may be found growing together.

144 *Spergularia media [S. marginata]* **GREATER SEA-SPURREY**. Low to short, almost hairless perennial. Leaves *fleshy*; stipules half-fused on young stems. Flowers bluish-pink or white, 9-12mm; petals equal to or exceeding sepals. Salt marshes, coastal and inland, seashores. T.

fruit

145 *Spergularia nicaeensis*. Similar, but biennial with a stout woody base; fruit-capsule less (not more) than 6mm long. Waste places and saline soils. Mar-July. W Med from Spain to Italy.

146 *Spergularia rubra* **SAND-SPURREY**. Low to short sticky-hairy annual or perennial with spreading stems. Leaves not fleshy, *strongly whorled*; stipules silvery, lanceolate. Flowers pink, 3-6mm. Sandy, not saline, soils. Apr-Aug. T.

uit

147 *Spergularia marina* **LESSER SAND-SPURREY**. Similar, but leaves fleshy; inflorescence *little-branched* and petals white or pink with a white base. Saline places, coastal and inland. Apr-Sept. T.

148 *Spergularia purpurea* **PURPLE SAND-SPURREY**. Low to short, rather slender annual or biennial. Leaves not fleshy; stipules silvery, lanceolate. Flowers *rose-purple*, 7-9mm; petals longer than sepals. Sandy, non-saline habitats and waste places. Feb-July. Spain and Portugal.

149 *Spergularia fimbriata*. Similar, but perennial with leaves *long-awned*; stipules very long, 6-10mm; flowers lilac, 8-12mm. Coastal habitats. Iberian Peninsula and NW Africa.

150 *Spergularia heldreichii*. Like *S. purpurea*, but *stipules* heart-shaped, petals pink to lilac, shorter or equalling sepals; seeds black and smooth (not brown and warted). Coastal sands. France, Spain, Italy, Yugoslavia and Greece.

fruit

151 *Spergularia bocconii*. Like *S. heldreichii*, but petals pink with a white base or white and seeds pale brown (not black). Coastal habitats, occasionally fields inland. Probably T.

152 *Spergularia diandra*. Similar to *S. purpurea*, but inflorescence without bracts in the upper half and *petals* narrow-elliptical (not oval). Saline and sandy habitats, waste places. T.

fruit

153 *Agrostemma githago* **CORNCOCKLE**. Medium to tall erect, hairy annual. Leaves linear-lanceolate. Flowers deep, rather dull, purple, 30-50mm, solitary, with 5 long leaf-like sepals, *much longer* than the un-notched petals, borne on slender hairy stalks. Arable land, especially wheat fields. Apr-June. T – often local. Far less widespread now because of modern farming practices and herbicides. It is

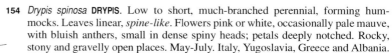

probably only native in the E Med, although widely naturalised throughout, but rarely in large numbers today. The seeds are poisonous.

154 *Drypis spinosa* **DRYPIS.** Low to short, much-branched perennial, forming hummocks. Leaves linear, *spine-like*. Flowers pink or white, occasionally pale mauve, with bluish anthers, small in dense spiny heads; petals deeply notched. Rocky, stony and gravelly open places. May-July. Italy, Yugoslavia, Greece and Albania.

155 *Saponaria calabrica* **CALABRIAN SOAPWORT.** Short to medium stiff, erect perennial, glandular-hairy above. Lower leaves spoon-shaped, upper oval. Flowers pale purple, 7-10mm, borne in lax, flat-topped clusters; petals *not notched*; calyx long-tubed. Rocky places and open scrub. Apr-June. C and E Med from Italy to Turkey – not Cyprus.

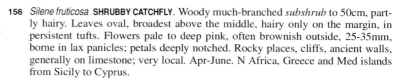

Silene **CATCHFLIES and CAMPIONS.** Annual or perennial herbs. Flowers usually in branched inflorescences. Sepals joined into a tube, with 5 teeth. Petals separate, long-clawed, often with scales at the base of the limb. Styles 3 or 5, protruding. Fruit capsule with twice as many teeth as styles. There are many species in the region, especially in the Balkans – only the commoner and more widespread ones are included here.

156 *Silene fruticosa* **SHRUBBY CATCHFLY.** Woody much-branched *subshrub* to 50cm, partly hairy. Leaves oval, broadest above the middle, hairy only on the margin, in persistent tufts. Flowers pale to deep pink, often brownish outside, 25-35mm, borne in lax panicles; petals deeply notched. Rocky places, cliffs, ancient walls, generally on limestone; very local. Apr-June. N Africa, Greece and Med islands from Sicily to Cyprus.

157 *Silene vulgaris* **BLADDER CAMPION.** Very variable short to medium, greyish, usually hairless perennial. Leaves rather fleshy, linear-lanceolate to oval. Flowers white, 12-16mm, in lax, branched clusters; petals deeply notched; calyx-tube *inflated*, bladder-like; styles 3. Cultivated and fallow fields, roadsides, waste places and coastal rocks. Mar-July. T. Widespread in Europe and Asia.

158 *Silene latifolia [S. alba, Melandrium album]* **WHITE CAMPION.** Densely *stickily-hairy* medium-tall perennial, occasionally annual. Leaves oval to lanceolate, the lowermost stalked. Flowers white, 18-30mm, the calyx *not* inflated; petals deeply notched; styles 5. Separate male and female flowers are borne on different plants. A weed of disturbed and cultivated land. T.

159 *Silene succulenta.* Low to short stickily hairy perennial, often with numerous attached *sand-grains*; stems numerous, spreading or ascending. Leaves rather fleshy, oval, widest above the middle. Flowers white, 16-18mm, in small leafy clusters; petals notched; calyx with greyish or reddish veins. Coastal sands. Apr-June. Corsica, Sardinia, Crete, N Africa, Turkey to Palestine – not Cyprus.

160 *Silene armeria* **SWEET WILLIAM CATCHFLY.** Short, hairless, greyish annual or biennial; stems unbranched. Leaves lanceolate to oval, the upper clasping the stem, lower stalked. Flowers bright pink, 10-12mm, borne in lax rather *flat-topped* clusters; petals slightly notched. Dry open or shaded places. May-July. T – often local, not in Cyprus.

161 *Silene italica* **ITALIAN CATCHFLY.** Medium greyish perennial, sticky above. Leaves oval to elliptical, pointed, hairy, the basal ones in tufts and stalked. Flowers *erect*, white (occasionally with greenish veins), greenish or reddish beneath, in lax pyramidal panicles; petals deeply bilobed, inrolled during the day but opening fully in the evening, lobes rounded; calyx often purplish. Rocky slopes, crevices

and dry cultivated land. Apr-July. T. Widespread in many parts of central and southern Europe and Asia; naturalised in Britain.

162 *Silene longipetala*. Similar, but flowers *nodding*, greenish-white, the petal-lobes strap-shaped; calyx hairless and pale. Stony ground, especially in pine woodland. Mar-July. E Med from Greece eastwards, including Cyprus.

163 *Silene sedoides*. Low to short tufted, *densely hairy* annual with slender stems, sticky above. Leaves rather fleshy, those of the stems less than 10mm long; bracts green. Flowers pink or whitish, borne on raceme-like branches in a much-branched inflorescence; petals small, often slightly notched; calyx often purplish, abruptly contracted at the base, 6-8mm long. Rocky coastal habitats. Mar-June. T – particularly on the islands, often local.

164 *Silene fuscata*. Similar, but calyx 11-16mm long, *tapered* towards the base; flowers larger, rose-pink. Cultivated ground and fields. Feb-May. T, except parts of N Africa, Yugoslavia and the Balkans.

165 *Silene rubella*. Like *S. fuscata*, but calyx *less than* 11mm long, whitish with a reddish tinge. Arable land, often by irrigation channels. Feb-May. T, except the Balkans.

166 *Silene aegyptiaca*. Like *S. fuscata*, but bracts *membranous* and whitish (not green); calyx 14-18mm long. Moist places, cultivated ground, vineyards and groves; often abundant. Feb-July. Turkey and E Med.

167 *Silene cretica* **CRETAN CATCHFLY**. Medium annual; stems erect and branched, hairy at base but more or less hairless and sticky above. Basal leaves oval, broadest above the middle, stalked; upper leaves, smaller, pointed, unstalked. Flowers pink, in lax, branched clusters; calyx 10-13mm long *hairless*; petals notched. Cultivated fields, fallow ground. Apr-June. C and E Med, N Africa, but widely introduced to other parts.

168 *Silene behen*. Similar, but a smaller short annual, *hairless*, the leaves rather bluish-green. Similar habitats. Feb-May. C and E Med from Italy and Sicily eastwards.

169 *Silene littorea*. Low to short annual, glandular-hairy, *sticky*, often covered in sand grains. Leaves mostly oblong to spoon-shaped. Flowers pink, few borne in raceme-like inflorescences, usually leafy; calyx 10-19mm long, not inflated; petals notched. Coastal sands. Mar-June. Spain, Portugal, Balearic Is. and N Africa.

170 *Silene pendula*. Similar, but calyx inflated and widest in the middle; flowers pink but occasionally white. Coastal and rocky habitats. Italy, Sicily and Crete; casual elsewhere.

171 *Silene psammitis [S. agrostemma]*. Like *S. pendula*, but stem leaves linear to linear-lanceolate (not oval). Spain and Portugal.

172 *Silene dichotoma* **FORKED CATCHFLY**. Medium to tall, erect, hairy annual; stems branched above, not sticky. Leaves lanceolate, lower stalked, upper narrower and unstalked. Flowers white, rarely pale pink, 15-18mm, in one sided *spike-like* branched inflorescences, opening in the evening or during dull weather; calyx 12-15mm, green or purplish; petals deeply notched. Cultivated ground, rocky and waste places. Mar-June. C and E Med from Crete and Greece eastwards; casual elsewhere.

173 *Silene nicaeensis*. Short to medium hairy annual; stems stout, much-branched, sticky. Lower leaves narrow spatula-shaped, upper linear-lanceolate, often curved. Flowers white or reddish-pink, erect, mostly in *clusters* of 2-8 borne on simple or branched inflorescences; calyx 10-13mm; petals deeply notched. Coastal sands. Mar-June. W and C Med east to Greece.

174 *Silene discolor*. Similar, but a low to short annual; flowers pale-pink, borne singly on inflorescence, *not clustered*. Coastal sands and sandy hills. T, eastwards as far as Cyprus and S Turkey.

175 *Silene nocturna*. Like *S. discolor*, but a short annual; flowers white or mauve-pink; calyx usually greenish, without purplish veins, 6-15mm long. Cultivated and fallow ground, waste places and roadsides. T.

176 *Silene gallica* [*S. anglica*] **SMALL-FLOWERED CATCHFLY**. Very variable short to medium stickily-hairy annual; stems erect, branched. Leaves lanceolate to linear, only the lower stalked. Flowers white or pink (crimson spot at petal base in var. *quinquevulnera*) (**176a**), 6-10mm, erect, in one-sided spike-like racemes; calyx 7-10mm long, constricted at apex in fruit; petals notched or unnotched. Cultivated, fallow and waste ground, sandy seashores. Mar-May. T. Native in southern Britain.

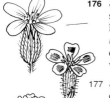

177 *Silene bellidifolia*. Similar, but often taller, to 60cm; calyx 14-17mm long; petals deeply notched. Rocky and sandy habitats. W and C Med east as far as W Turkey.

(176a)   178 *Silene tridentata*. Like *S. gallica*, but calyx 10-13mm long with *slender teeth* one third of the length; petals inconspicuous. Sandy ground and dry hillsides. S and E Med from Morocco to Palestine and Cyprus, also in S Spain.

179 *Silene cerastoides*. Like *S. gallica*, but whole plant rather *bristly*; flowers pink; calyx 8-11mm long. Spain, Portugal, Balearic Is., Yugoslavia and Greece.

(177)

180 *Silene colorata*. Very variable erect or spreading, short to medium annual. Leaves linear to oval-spatular shaped, the lower stalked. Flowers pink, occasionally white, *showy*, 12-18mm, in lax clusters of 1-4 usually; calyx club-shaped, 10-15mm long; petals deeply notched. Cultivated and waste or fallow ground, roadsides, on dry sandy or stony ground; often abundant. Feb-May. T. A very characteristic plant of the early spring in many parts of the Med.

181 *Silene apetala*. Similar, but calyx *turban-shaped*, 6-8mm long; petals inconspicuous or absent (present and longer than calyx in var. *grandiflora* 181a). Coastal habitats or cultivated land close to the sea. T.

182 *Silene conica* **SAND CATCHFLY**. Short to medium stickily-hairy annual, rather greyish, often covered in sand grains. Leaves lanceolate, the lowest stalked. Flowers rose-pink or whitish, 4-5mm, solitary or few to a cluster; calyx *30-veined*, 8-18mm long, flask-shaped but broadening considerably in fruit; petals slightly notched. Sandy and waste places, often near the sea. Mar-June. T, except some of the smaller islands and Portugal.

183 *Silene conoidea*. Similar, but often taller and less hairy and flowers *larger*, 12-18mm; calyx 15-25mm, long in fruit (not 10-15mm). Arable land, fallow fields, vineyards and olive groves. T – often casual.

184 *Silene macrodonta*. Similar to *S. conica*, but the flowers are rather smaller and the calyx has 60 *veins* crowded close together. Similar habitats to *S. conoidea*. Feb-May. E Med and Crete.

calyx
in
fruit

185 *Vaccaria hispanica* [*Vaccaria pyramidata*] **COW BASIL**. Erect, medium, hairless annual; stems usually branched above. Leaves bluish-green, oval to lanceolate, untoothed. Flowers pink to dark purple, 8-16mm, long-stalked, borne in a laxly branched inflorescence; calyx green, with 5 broad *wings*; petals notched or unnotched. Cultivated, waste and fallow land, waste places. Feb-July. T.

186 *Petrorhagia illyrica* [*Tunica gallica*] **PETRORHAGIA**. Short to medium perennial, hairless or glandular-hairy. Leaves linear, 3-veined. Flowers white or occasionally pale yellow, often veined or spotted with pink or purple in the middle, 5-10mm, borne in a spreading to erect panicle; calyx with membranous bands but no bracts;

petals oblong, *not notched*. Rocky habitats and hillslopes. Apr-July. Italy and Sicily to Greece and Crete.

187 *Kohlrauschia velutina [Petrorhagia velutina, Tunica velutina]* **KOHLRAUSCHIA**. Short annual or biennial, usually glandular-hairy. Leaves oblong-linear to linear. Flowers pink, veined with red in centre, 7-8mm, borne in heads surrounded by pointed dry *bracts*, one flower opening at a time; petals lobed. Grassy and rocky hillslopes, sandy places, garrigue. Feb-May. T.

188 *Kohlrauschia glumacea [Petrorhagia glumacea]*. Similar, but stems not glandular-hairy and calyx-bracts not pointed, flowers larger and usually purple, sometimes pink; petals *usually toothed*. Similar habitats. Apr-June. Yugoslavia, Greece and Crete.

189 *Kohlrauschia prolifera [Dianthus prolifera, Petrorhagia prolifera]*. Like *K. velutina*, but stems *not* glandular-hairy; petals lobed. Similar habitats and flowering time. T – not Balearic Is., Sardinia or Cyprus.

190 *Gypsophila pilosa* **GYPSOPHILA**. Short to tall erect annual, hairless below but hairy in the upper part. Leaves oblong to lanceolate, 3-5-veined, the uppermost leaves linear. Flowers white or pale pink, 6-8mm, borne in lax, branched, inflorescences; calyx shortly tubular with 5 short teeth; petals notched. Cultivated and waste ground. Apr-Aug. E Med from Turkey and Cyprus eastwards.

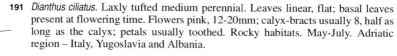

Dianthus **PINKS**. Tufted, often cushion-forming perennials, usually greyish or bluish-green. Leaves linear to lanceolate. Flowers solitary or clustered. Calyx tubular, with 2-4 pairs of scale-like bracts in the lower half. Petals long-clawed, fringed or toothed. A large and complicated genus with many localised species in the Med region.

191 *Dianthus ciliatus*. Laxly tufted medium perennial. Leaves linear, flat; basal leaves present at flowering time. Flowers pink, 12-20mm; calyx-bracts usually 8, half as long as the calyx; petals usually toothed. Rocky habitats. May-July. Adriatic region – Italy, Yugoslavia and Albania.

calyx

192 *Dianthus haematocalyx*. Low to short tufted, hairless perennial. Leaves linear to linear-lanceolate, pointed or blunt. Flowers bright pinkish-purple, yellowish beneath, 16-20mm, solitary or up to 5; calyx-bracts 4 or 6; petals toothed. Rocky slopes, mostly in the mountains. June-Aug. The Balkans.

193 *Dianthus strictus*. Similar, but a taller plant to 50cm, the basal leaves withered by flowering time; flowers pink with purple spots, 12-20mm; calyx-bracts usually 4. Rocky and waste places, fallow land and roadsides, coastal and in the mountains. May-July. C and E Med from Crete and the Aegean eastwards – the commonest *Dianthus* in the E Med region.

yx

194 *Dianthus tripunctatus*. Short to medium annual with linear-lanceolate leaves. Flowers pink marked with 3 dark lines in the centre; calyx-bracts 4. Dry exposed coastal habitats, occasionally inland. May-July. Scattered localities from Portugal and Algeria, Crete and Greece, but more common in the E Med, including Cyprus.

calyx

195 *Velezia rigida* **VELEZIA**. Low to short, rather rigid, usually glandular-hairy annual; stems much-branched, wiry. Leaves linear, pointed. Flowers *unstalked*, pink, 5-7mm; calyx with a long slender tube, but without overlapping bracts at the base; petals with a long claw and deeply notched limb. Garrigue, dry rocky and grassy places. Apr-July. T – except some of the smaller islands.

196 *Velezia quadridentata*. Similar, but calyx slightly swollen in the middle and the *petals* four-toothed. Similar habitats. Greece, Aegean Is. and Turkey.

BARBERRY FAMILY Berberidaceae

Shrubs, or in our area, herbs with alternate leaves. Flowers hermaphrodite, generally 3-4-parted, the inner segments petal-like and often in several series; stamens usually 4-6, opposite the petals. Fruit a capsule. A medium-sized and widespread family found in many temperate and subtropical regions of the world – the largest genus, *Berberis*, has more than 400 species in Europe, Asia, Africa and the Americas.

197 *Bongardia chrysogonum [Leontice chrysogonum]* **BONGARDIA**. A short to medium tuberous-rooted, hairless perennial. Leaves all basal, more or less horizontal, *pinnately-lobed*, the leaflets wedge-shaped, toothed, greyish-green, often with a reddish zone towards the base. Flowers yellow, 9-20mm, with 6 'petals', borne in a slender panicle. Fruit egg-shaped, 14-16mm, inflated, papery when ripe. Arable and ploughed fields, occasionally on fallow land. Feb-Apr. Aegean Is. and Turkey eastwards, including Cyprus.

198 *Leontice leontopetalum* **LEONTICE**. Short to medium tuberous-rooted, hairless perennial. Leaves 2-3-ternate, bluish or greyish-green, the lobes broad and untoothed. Flowers yellow, 10-15mm, with 6-8 petals, borne in a broad pyramidal raceme; bracts conspicuous. Fruit inflated and bladder-like, 25-40mm. Arable and ploughed fields, waste places. Feb-Apr. N Africa, Crete and SE Balkans eastwards, including Cyprus.

LAUREL FAMILY Lauraceae

A large and predominantly tropical family of trees and shrubs, many aromatic. Here belong the cinnamon, camphor and avocado pear.

199 *Laurus nobilis* **LAUREL, SWEET BAY**. Much-branched evergreen shrub or small tree, to 10m; bark black; twigs hairless. Leaves alternate, oblong-lanceolate, untoothed, *dotted* with oil glands. Flowers greenish-yellow, borne in small clusters in the leaf-axils, 4-petalled; male and female separate but on the same plant. Fruit an oval berry, black when ripe. Rocky places, ravines, scrub; frequently planted. Mar-Apr. T. Grown throughout the Med as a culinary herb; the leaves are used for seasoning food and are often dried. The leaves and wood burn explosively from their high oil content: Oil of Bay is produced from this species. Greatly esteemed since classical times – Laurel provided the wreaths bestowed on heroes and scholars.

BUTTERCUP FAMILY Ranunculaceae

A large, mainly temperate, family of herbaceous plants – except *Clematis*, which is woody. Leaves usually alternate, often dissected. Flowers often large and showy with 5, sometimes more, sepals or petals or both; nectaries or nectariferous 'petals' often present; stamens numerous. Fruit a collection of achenes or follicles. Many of the species contain alkaloids and can be extremely poisonous both to humans and animals.

Helleborus **HELLEBORES**. Robust herbaceous perennials with digitately lobed leaves. Flowers in branched clusters, with 5 large sepals, no petals but a ring of conspicuous green nectaries outside the stamens. Fruit a cluster of follicles. All the species are grown in gardens. Poisonous.

typical fruit

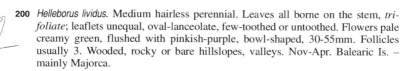

200 *Helleborus lividus.* Medium hairless perennial. Leaves all borne on the stem, *trifoliate*; leaflets unequal, oval-lanceolate, few-toothed or untoothed. Flowers pale creamy green, flushed with pinkish-purple, bowl-shaped, 30-55mm. Follicles usually 3. Wooded, rocky or bare hillslopes, valleys. Nov-Apr. Balearic Is. – mainly Majorca.

201 *Helleborus argutifolius [H. corsicus].* Similar, but more robust, to 1.2m or more. Leaflets with *spiny* margins. Flowers pale green, 25-50mm. Rocky scrub in maquis or garrigue, open hillslopes and ravines. Jan-May. Corsica and Sardinia. The most robust of all hellebores.

202 *Helleborus foetidus* **STINKING HELLEBORE.** Similar, but the leaves with 7-10 narrow, deep green leaflets and the nodding bell-shaped flowers, green with a purplish-brown rim, 15-20mm long. Woods and scrub. Jan-May. Balearic Is., Corsica, Sardinia and Sicily. More common in Europe away from the Med; a British native. The flowers are visited by various bees.

203 *Helleborus cyclophyllus.* Medium tufted, stemless perennial. Leaves mostly basal, *not* overwintering, with 5-9, toothed, leaflets, hairy beneath; leaves on flowering scapes smaller, with 3-5 leaflets. Flowers few, pale yellowish-green, bowl-shaped, 40-60mm; sepals broad. Woods and thickets and hillslopes, on rather dry soils. Feb-May. C and S Yugoslavia and the Balkans – not on the islands. The common hellebore of the Balkans.

204 *Helleborus multifidus [H. odorus* subsp. *multifidus].* A short to medium tufted perennial, stemless. Leaves mostly basal with *numerous,* 20-45, linear to linear-lanceolate, toothed leaflets, hairy beneath; leaves on flowering scapes with fewer divisions. Flowers clear green, bowl-shaped, 35-45mm; sepals rather narrow. Scrub and rocky slopes. Feb-May. W and SW Yugoslavia and Albania.

    204a Subsp. *hercegovinus.* Like the type, but leaves with 45-70 linear leaflets. Woodland and rocky hillslopes. SW Yugoslavia and probably Albania.

    204b Subsp. *istriacus.* Like the type, but with fewer, 10-14, broader leaflets. Woodland and grassy scrub. NE Italy and NW Yugoslavia.

    204c Subsp. *bocconei.* Differs from the type in its leaves which have only 5-7 rather broad, usually hairless, leaflets; flowers 45-60mm. Similar habitats. S Italy and Sicily.

Clematis **CLEMATIS.** Woody climbers (except *C. recta*) with opposite pinnate leaves; leaf-stalks often twinning. Flowers in branched clusters, rarely solitary, 4-'petalled'. Fruit a bunch of achenes, each achene usually with a persistent feathery style.

205 *Clematis flammula* **FRAGRANT CLEMATIS.** Deciduous climber to 5m. Leaves *2-pinnate*; leaflets oblong to rounded, untoothed, sometimes 3-lobed. Flowers white, 15-30mm, fragrant; 'petals' hairy outside. Scrub, hedges, old walls and waste places. May-Aug. T – not Cyprus. Grown in gardens.

(206)

206 *Clematis vitalba* **TRAVELLER'S JOY.** Similar, but much more robust, to 30m and leaves 1-pinnate; leaflets often *toothed*. Flowers greenish-white; 'petals' hairy on both surfaces. Woodland and hedges, old buildings. June-Sept. T – not most of N Africa. A British native.

achene

207 *Clematis recta.* Rather like *C. flammula,* but a herbaceous perennial to 1.5m with 1-pinnate leaves; 'petals' white, hairless. Scrub and rocky ground. May-June. Spain, France, Corsica, Italy and Yugoslavia.

208 *Clematis cirrhosa* **VIRGIN'S BOWER.** An evergreen climber to 4m. Leaves shiny green, 1-2-ternate, or 3-lobed or simple and toothed. Flowers cream, often red-spotted

achene

inside, nodding *bell-shaped*, 18-30mm long, silky outside, honey-scented. Woods, maquis and scrub. Dec-Apr. T. Grown in gardens – some forms have heavily spotted flowers while others are more or less plain.

209 *Clematis viticella*. Deciduous climber to 4m. Leaves pinnate, with oval untoothed leaflets. Flowers *blue or purple*, 30-60mm, opening widely into a broad bowl shape, fragrant; styles not feathered. Scrub, hedgerows and open woodland. May-July. C Med from Italy eastwards, including most of the islands. Widely grown in gardens and a parent of a range of garden hybrids.

210 *Clematis campaniflora*. Similar, but a slenderer plant with *smaller* pale violet flowers, 20-30mm, broadly bell-shaped; styles feathered in the lower part. Portugal and S Spain.

Anemone **ANEMONES**. Perennial herbs. Leaves basal and in a whorl of 3 below the flower. Flowers cup-shaped with 5 or more 'petals' and apparently no sepals. Fruit a cluster of achenes, smooth or woolly. Most species are poisonous.

stem leaves

211 *Anemone coronaria* **CROWN ANEMONE**. Short to medium hairy perennial. Basal leaves 2-ternate, the divisions narrow, toothed; stem leaves *similar* but short-stalked. Flowers pink, red, blue, lavendar or purple, often with a pale zone in the centre, bowl-shaped, 35-75mm; 'petals' 5-8, oval; anthers blue. Hillslopes, grassy fields, waysides, olive groves and vineyards. Jan-Apr. T. Grown in gardens and as a cut flower – cultivated forms include those with single, semi-double or double flowers. The common anemone of most parts of the Med.

stem leaves

212 *Anemone pavonina* **PEACOCK ANEMONE**. Short to medium, hairy perennial. Basal leaves palmately-lobed, the lobes oval to lanceolate, toothed; stem leaves *bract-like*, unlobed or 3-lobed at apex. Flowers scarlet, pink or purple, often with a white or yellowish central zone, 30 – 60mm, opening widely; 'petals' 7-12, oval; anthers bluish-black. Fields, cultivated ground, waste places and olive groves. Feb-Apr. SE France eastwards to Turkey, including Corsica and Crete. Sometimes grows in colonies together with *A. coronaria*; these two species are often confused, but the former is easily recognised by its bract-like stem leaves and narrower, more numerous, petals. Grown in gardens.

213 *Anemone hortensis*. Similar, but the basal leaves less divided and 'petals' 12-19, *narrow-elliptical*, pink to pale purple; double-flowered forms are sometimes encountered. W and C Med from France to Yugoslavia, including Sicily. Cultivated in gardens – more frequently so than *A. pavonina*.

214 *Anemone* × *fulgens [A. hortensis* × *A. pavonina]*. Intermediate between the parent species and sometimes found where both grow together.

215 *Anemone heldreichii*. Like *A. hortensis,* but flowers rather smaller, whitish flushed with pink and with a bluish or pinkish reverse. Crete, Karpathos and Ionian Is. Sometimes considered a form of *A. hortensis*.

fruit

216 *Anemone blanda*. Low, somewhat hairy perennial. Basal leaves 2-ternate, the broad lobes deeply toothed, hairless beneath; stem leaves similar, short-stalked. Flowers blue, purple, pink, violet or white, occasionally bicolored, 20-40mm; 'petals' 11-15, narrow; anthers white or cream. Heads of achenes *pendent*. Rocky places, scrub and open woodland, mainly in the mountains. Mar-May. Albania and Greece eastwards to the Lebanon, including Cyprus. Colonies with many colour forms can be found, especially in Greece. Sold as dried tubers by the bulb trade and widely grown in gardens.

fruit

217 *Anemone apennina* **BLUE ANEMONE**. Similar, but leaves hairy beneath. Flowers blue, occasionally white, rather smaller, 'petals' 8-14. Heads of achenes *erect*. Corsica and Italy eastwards to Yugoslavia, including Sicily. Occasionally grown in gardens.

218 *Anemone palmata* **YELLOW ANEMONE.** Low to short hairy perennial. Basal leaves suborbicular, with 3-5 shallow, toothed lobes. Flowers bright *yellow*, 25-35mm, with 10-15 oblong 'petals'. Head of achenes erect. Rocky habitats and grassy slopes. Mar-May. Spain, Portugal, S France, Sardinia and Sicily.

Adonis **PHEASANT'S EYES.** Erect hairless annuals with feathery 2-3-pinnate leaves. Flowers buttercup-like with both sepals and petals. Fruit an erect head of achenes.

achene

219 *Adonis annua* **PHEASANT'S-EYE.** Short to medium annual with pale green leaves. Flowers bright scarlet with a black centre, cup-shaped 10-25mm, with 5-8 oblong suberect petals; sepal hairless, *spreading away* from the petals. Achenes, up to 30 borne in an egg-shaped head, with a straight inner margin. Fields, cultivated and waste ground, damp meadows, vineyards and olive groves. Feb-July. T.

220 *Adonis flammea.* Similar, but flowers 20-30mm, occasionally yellow; sepals slightly hairy, *pressed* close to the petals; achenes with a rounded projection below the beak. Similar habitats. T – except Cyprus and parts of E Med.

achene

221 *Adonis aestivalis.* Like *A. annua,* but flowers larger, 25-40mm, opening almost flat; inner margin of achene with *two* small projections. Similar habitats and distribution.

222 *Adonis microcarpa [A. cupananiana]* **YELLOW PHEASANT'S-EYE.** Short to medium annual rather like *A. annua.* Flowers yellow to orange or reddish-violet, 15-28mm. Achenes 30 or more borne in an *elongated* head, each with a transverse ridge. Fields, cultivated and fallow ground, grassy places and vineyards. Feb-May. T.

223 *Adonis dentata.* Similar, but plants seldom more than 12cm. Flowers yellow, each petal with a black *blotch* at the base. N Africa, E Med, including Turkey.

224 *Ceratocephalus falcatus [Ranunculus falcatus]* **CERATOCEPHALUS.** A low hairy annual. Leaves trifoliate with narrow, forked, segments. Flowers solitary, yellow, 10-15mm. Fruit a head of achenes each with a long *sickle-shaped* end. Cultivated fields and fallow and waste ground. Mar-May. Scattered localities in Spain, Italy, Yugoslavia, Greece, Turkey, Cyprus and N Africa.

achene

Nigella **LOVE-IN-A-MISTS.** Annual herbs with 2-3-pinnately divided leaves. Flowers with 5 'petals', but no sepals apparently; nectaries present as a ring outside the stamens, often 2-lobed. Stamens numerous. Fruit generally 5 partly or wholly fused follicles with long styles. This small genus has its centre of distribution in the Med basin.

225 *Nigella arvensis.* Short hairless annual. Leaves *all* alternate, with linear segments. Flowers pale blue or whitish, often veined green, 20-28mm. Follicles 3-8, fused a half their length, each 3-veined; styles coiled when young. Cultivated land, waste places and hillslopes. Apr-Aug. T. Becoming scarcer with modern farming practices but still the most widespread species.

226 *Nigella degenii.* Similar, but leaf-segments *short*, narrow-oblong; follicles separated almost to the base. Crete, Greece, Cyclades and Karpathos.

227 *Nigella cretica.* Like *N. arvensis,* but stems generally branched from the base and stem leaves with a few oval segments or unlobed. Crete.

228 *Nigella doerfleri.* Like *N. cretica,* but plant with few branches; flowers small, greenish-blue; follicles fused for most of their length. Crete.

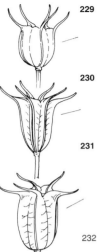

229 *Nigella sativa* **EDIBLE LOVE-IN-A-MIST**. Short to medium erect *hairy* annual. Leaves with narrow-lanceolate divisions. Flowers whitish or pale blue, tinged with green, 20-34mm. Follicles 4-8, fused almost to the top; seeds edible, used as a condiment. Cultivated and waste ground, waysides. Apr-Aug. E Med, including Cyprus; casual elsewhere.

230 *Nigella hispanica* **SPANISH LOVE-IN-A-MIST, FENNEL FLOWER**. Short-medium erect annual; lateral, branches rather upright. Leaves with narrow-lanceolate segments. Flowers bright blue, 35-70mm, with reddish-purple anthers. Follicles fused for most of their length, minutely *glandular*. Fields and waste places, waysides. June-July. Spain, Portugal and NW Africa.

231 *Nigella damascena* **LOVE-IN-A-MIST**. Short to medium annual, generally branched above. Leaves with slender linear divisions; uppermost leaves in a *whorl* just beneath the flower. Flowers pale to bright blue, rarely whitish, 20-32mm, with yellow or greenish anthers. Fruit inflated and bladder like, the 5-6 follicles united for their entire length; seeds edible. Fields, rocky and waste places, waysides; commonly grown in gardens, where white, pink, purple and blue forms occur. Apr-July. T.

232 *Nigella fumariifolia*. Similar, but flowers smaller, 15-20mm, greenish or bluish; anthers crimson-purple; fruit *star-shaped*, the 5 follicles fused only towards the base. Grassy hillslopes and fallow ground. Apr-June. Cyprus, Rhodes, Karpathos and neighbouring islands.

233 *Nigella nigellastrum*. Short to medium, slender, erect perennial; stem hairless. Leaves all alternate, with linear segments; upper leaves small and stalkless. Flowers greenish, purplish or blue, with whitish nectaries, 11-13mm; nectaries slightly *longer* than the 'petals'; anthers purplish. Fruit small of 2 fused follicles; styles short. Cultivated, waste and fallow ground, open garrigue. Mar-June. Scattered localities T, except N Africa.

234 *Nigella ciliaris*. Short to medium, slightly hairy annual. Leaves all alternate with slender linear segments. Flowers yellow or yellowish, 20-30mm; anthers yellow. Fruit with 5-13 follicles united in the lower third and spreading out almost flat. Cultivated and fallow fields, waste ground. Apr-June. Cyprus and Palestine.

Ranunculus **BUTTERCUPS**. Terrestrial or semi-aquatic annual or perennial herbs. Leaves entire to pinnately-lobed or trifoliate, often toothed. Flowers solitary or in spreading cymes; sepals and petals generally 5, occasionally more; petals frequently shiny, often yellow or white, occasionally pink or red, with basal nectaries; stamens numerous. Fruit a head of single-seeded achenes. A large and complex genus distributed almost throughout the world.

235 *Ranunculus velutinus*. Medium to tall perennial, silkily hairy especially in the lower half. Basal leaves *broadly oval*, with 3 wedge-shaped toothed or lobed divisions; stem leaves smaller. Flowers yellow, 15-25mm, borne on slender stalks; sepals reflexed. Fruit-head globular, hairless. Damp meadows and waysides. Mar-June. C and E Med from France and Corsica eastwards – not Cyprus.

236 *Ranunculus cornutus*. Short to medium erect or spreading annual, hairless or slightly hairy. Leaves with 3-5 bluntly toothed lobes, stalked; upper leaves with a few narrow lanceolate divisions. Flowers yellow, 14-20mm, *leaf-opposed*; sepals reflexed. Fruit-head globular; achenes winged. Damp places, wet fields and ditches. Feb-May. E Med from Turkey eastwards.

237 *Ranunculus macrophyllus*. Medium, rather robust, hairy perennial. Leaves mostly basal, pentagonal to heart-shaped in outline with 3-5, wide, toothed divisions;

Flowers yellow, 25-30mm; sepals at first spreading then a stout beak, usually hairy. Rocky and damp places. Apr-⌐pain to Sicily – not Italy.

⌐politanus. Similar, but flower-stems *furrowed* and sepals reflexing ⌐nt the flowers open. Damp places, hillslopes. C and E Med from Italy ⌐ards – not Sicily.

Ranunculus sardous **HAIRY BUTTERCUP**. Short to medium, hairy annual; stem scarcely swollen at the base. Basal leaves trilobed, the lobes toothed, *often* shiny, the middle lobe larger and often itself trilobed; upper leaves unlobed or with three simple untoothed divisions. Flowers pale yellow, 12-25mm; sepals reflexed. Grassy meadows, arable land, damp places, waysides. Apr-Aug. T – not Cyprus. A British native.

240 *Ranunculus bulbosus* subsp. *aleae* **BULBOUS BUTTERCUP**. Similar, but a robust perennial with the central leaflet of the basal leaves clearly *stalked*; most stem leaves like the basal, but smaller; flowers bright yellow, 20-30mm. Meadows, grassy slopes, waysides, road verges. Med Europe and N Africa. A British native (subsp. *bulbosus*); widespread in Europe and western Asia.

241 *Ranunculus marginatus.* Like *R. sardous,* but the basal leaves rounded-heart-shaped, toothed, with the stalks broadly winged at the base; flowers smaller, *deep golden yellow*, 8-11mm. Damp ground, often by streams and ditches. Apr-July. From Corsica and Sardinia and Greece eastwards, including Cyprus, but not Italy.

242 *Ranunculus monspeliacus.* Short to medium *white-woolly or silvery* perennial. Basal leaves variable, oval-heart-shaped in outline, with three oblong, shallowly to deeply toothed, segments. Flowers yellow, 23-26mm; sepals reflexed. Fruit-head oblong, usually slightly hairy. Rocky and grassy places. Apr-June. W and C Med from Spain to Italy and Sicily – not Sardinia or the Balearic Is.

243 *Ranunculus muricatus.* Short to medium, usually hairless annual; stems usually numerous and branched from the base. Basal leaves *kidney-shaped*, 3-7-lobed; upper leaves 3-5-lobed, very occasionally unlobed. Flowers yellow, 12-16mm, the oblong petals about as long as the semi-reflexed sepals. Fruit-head rounded; achenes with a broad wing, with short spines on both surfaces. Damp places, fields, roadsides and ditches. Mar-May. T – often casual. One of the commonest buttercups in the Med region.

244 *Ranunculus arvensis* **CORN CROWFOOT**. Short to medium, often hairless annual. Basal leaves spatula-shaped, simple or 3-lobed, toothed; upper leaves often with three narrow segments. Flowers pale greenish-yellow, 4-12mm, borne in branched clusters; sepals erect or spreading. Achenes few, relatively large, covered with long rigid spines. Cultivated, waste and disturbed land. Mar-June. T. A British native.

245 *Ranunculus parviflorus* **SMALL-FLOWERED BUTTERCUP**. Short spreading hairy annual. Lower leaves with 3-5 toothed lobes; upper leaves simple or with oblong lobes. Flowers *small*, 3-6mm, with reflexed sepals; achenes smaller than *R. arvensis*, only 3mm (not 6-8mm), covered with shorter, hooked, spines. Dry grassy places, roadsides, occasionally on cultivated land. Mar-June. W and C Med, including N Africa, east to Greece.

246 *Ranunculus chius.* Similar, but leaves 3-lobed and flower-stalks greatly *thickening* in fruit. Moist fields, stream and ditch sides, woodland. Feb-May. C and E Med from Corsica and Sardinia eastwards.

247 *Ranunculus gracilis.* Low to medium, rather delicate, slightly hairy or hairless perennial; stems unbranched or few-branched. Basal leaves sub-rounded with 3 shallow

lobes; upper leaves deeply cut into 3 wedge-shaped, toothed, segments. Flowers yellow, 14-22mm, often solitary, or 2-3; sepals reflexed. Fruit-head cylindrical; achenes with a short, curved beak. Stony and grassy places, hillslopes and waste places. Mar-June. Italy and the Balkans.

248 *Ranunculus isthmicus.* Similar, but a *dwarf* plant only 2-4cm high, hairy. Flowers on leafless stalks, yellow. occasionally flushed with bronze. Rocky and grassy places. Jan-Apr. Sicily, Greece, Turkey and Cyprus.

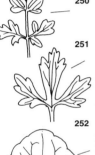

249 *Ranunculus paludosus [R. flabellatus]* **JERSEY BUTTERCUP.** Very variable short to medium, hairy perennial. Basal leaves shallowly 3-lobed; upper leaves with 3 linear segments. Flowers yellow, 20-32mm; sepals *not* reflexed. Fruit-head dense, cylindrical, slightly hairy. Seasonally waterlogged ground in maquis, open woodland, grassy and stony places. Feb-May. T – except the smaller islands, often local. (In Britain confined to Jersey.)

250 *Ranunculus cupreus.* Similar, but a smaller plant to 20cm with the basal leaves divided to the base. Flowers 14-16mm, *copper* on the outside. Rocky and grassy places. Mar-Apr. Crete.

251 *Ranunculus sceleratus* **CELERY-LEAVED CROWFOOT.** Medium, rather stout, mostly hairless annual. Leaves rather *shiny green*, the basal leaves 3-lobed, the lobes further lobed and toothed; upper leaves 3-lobed, unstalked. Flowers yellow, 5-10mm, numerous in branched clusters; petals equalling the reflexed sepals. Fruit-head cylindrical. Wet and marshy places, particularly by pools, streams and ditches. T – not Cyprus. A British native.

252 *Ranunculus ficaria [Ficaria verna]* **LESSER CELANDINE.** Variable low tufted hairless perennial. Leaves *heart-shaped*, rather fleshy, dark green, sometimes with deeper markings. Flowers glistening yellow, turning white on ageing, 20-40mm, with 8-12 narrow petals; sepals 3. Damp meadows and woodland, ditches and pathsides, roadsides. Feb-May. W and C Med, including N Africa, eastwards to Sicily. A British native – often becomes a weed in gardens.

252a Subsp. *ficariiformis.* Similar, but more robust with flowers 30-60mm, yellowish-white. The commoner plant in the Med region occurring T, except for parts of the extreme eastern Med.

253 *Ranunculus ficarioides.* Like *R. ficaria,* but seldom more than 7cm high with coarsely toothed or shallowly lobed leaves; sepals yellowish, not green. Achenes hairless or at least not hairy. Greece.

254 *Ranunculus millefoliatus.* Short, hairy perennial; stems unbranched or few-branched. Leaves *2-3-pinnate*, with linear segments, mostly basal; upper leaves short-stalked or unstalked. Flowers golden-yellow, 15-30mm; sepals spreading, often bronze-tinged. Fruit-head cylindrical. Grassy hillslopes, meadows and rocky places. Feb-May. Sicily and Italy to the Balkans and Cyprus, where it is subsp. *leptaleus* (254a).

255 *Ranunculus millefolius.* Similar, but stems far more leafy and plant *white-hairy*; flowers yellow, 15-25mm, with the flowerstalk rather swollen near the top; sepals with long white hairs. Rocky and stony places. Cyprus and eastern Med, not Europe.

256 *Ranunculus bullatus.* Low to short hairy perennial. Leaves all basal, stalked, oval to rounded, toothed but not lobed. Flowers solitary on leafless stalks, yellow, 18-26mm, *violet-scented*; petals 5-12. Rocky and stony places. Nov-Mar. W and C Med from Portugal to Greece, including N Africa.

256a Subsp. *cytheraeus*. Like the type, but smaller and less hairy; flowers on spreading stalks, 10-15mm. Crete, Kythera, Cyprus, Turkey, Rhodes and Cyrenaica.

257 *Ranunculus asiaticus [Cyprianthe asiaticus]* **TURBAN BUTTERCUP**. Low to medium hairy annual, tuberous-rooted; stems simple or branched above. Leaves mostly basal, 3-lobed, the lobes further lobed or toothed; upper leaves smaller with deeper, narrower, segments. Flowers large, white, yellow, pink, scarlet or purple, occasionally bicoloured, 25-70mm, with a central boss of *purple-black stamens*. Fruit-head cylindrical. Grassy and rocky hillslopes, garrigue, borders of cultivated land, roadsides; colonies usually one-coloured, rarely mixed. Mar-May. Crete, S Greece, Karpathos and much of the E Med, including Cyprus. Widely cultivated, especially in the double-flowered or turban buttercup varieties, which are grown primarily as a cut flower.

Delphinium **DELPHINIUMS**. Annuals or perennials with palmately-divided leaves, generally with rather broad segments. Flowers in erect racemes, with 5 petals, the upper one spurred at the back; nectariferous 'petals' 4, the upper two with a spur. Fruit a collection of 3-5 follicles.

fruit

258 *Delphinium peregrinum* **VIOLET LARKSPUR**. Medium to tall, hairy annual or biennial; stems erect with a whitish *bloom* and spreading hairs. Lower leaves palmate with narrow-lanceolate segments; upper leaves unlobed. Flowers dirty violet or bluish-violet, 12-18mm; spur upturned longer than the petals; nectariferous 'petals' hairless. Fruit usually hairy. Cultivated places, waysides, grassy and rocky hillslopes. Apr-Sept. C and E Med from Italy and Sicily eastwards, including Cyprus. Often occurring in large numbers.

259 *Delphinium halteratum*. Similar, but stems without a bloom and hairs not spreading – pressed close to the stem, and flowers bluer. S France, Sardinia, Italy and Sicily.

260 *Delphinium hirschfeldianum*. Like *D. peregrinum*, but flowers deep blue and spur the same length as the petals. Aegean Is.

261 *Delphinium staphisagria*. Medium to tall hairy annual or biennial. Leaves large, with 5-7, oblong or lanceolate, 3-lobed segments. Flowers deep blue, large, 24-40mm, borne in long racemes; spur *short*, blunt and downturned, shorter than the petals – not more than one third the length. Fruit with inflated follicles, slightly hairy. Rocky slopes, screes, rarely coastal. May-July. T. The commonest *Delphinium* in the Med region.

262 *Delphinium pictum*. Medium to tall hairy annual or biennial. Leaves with lanceolate, somewhat lobed segments. Flowers pale blue, 22-26mm, borne in long racemes; spur about two-fifths the length of the petals. Fruit with inflated follicles. Rocky habitats. May-July. Balearic Is., Corsica, Sardinia and Italy.

263 *Delphinium requienii*. Similar, but plant with longer, more silky, hairs and bracts in *middle* (not at the base) of the flower-stalks. S France and Corsica.

Consolida **LARKSPURS**. Like *Delphinium*, but leaves usually with many thread-like segments and fruit consisting of only a single follicle.

fruit

264 *Consolida regalis [Delphinium consolida]* **FORKING LARKSPUR**. A medium, downy annual, widely branching. Leaves with linear lobes. Flowers violet-blue to dark blue, 20-28mm, borne in lax-branched *panicles*; all bracts linear; spur 12-25mm long. Seeds black. Arable fields, waste and disturbed land, waysides. May-July. T

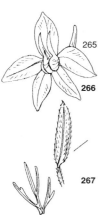

– except Balearic Is., Corsica, Sardinia, Crete and Cyprus. Widely grown in gardens.

265 *Consolida pubescens [Delphinium pubescens]*. Similar, but a hairier plant, with the lower bracts usually *dissected*. Flowers violet, pale blue or whitish. Seeds grey or reddish. France, Spain, Italy and Sicily.

266 *Consolida orientalis* **EASTERN LARKSPUR.** Medium to tall, stickily-hairy annual; stems simple or branched. Leaves with narrow-oblong or linear lobes. Flowers purplish-violet, 18-26mm, borne in a fairly dense *raceme*; flower-stalks shorter than the lower dissected bracts; spur 10-12mm long. Fruit hairy; seeds reddish-brown. Arable fields and other cultivated ground, waste places and waysides. May-July. Scattered localities from Portugal and Spain to Greece and Turkey – avoiding all the islands. Grown in gardens.

267 *Consolida ambigua [Delphinium ambiguum]*. Similar, but flowers deep blue, usually borne in branched racemes, and *spur* 13-18mm long. Seeds black. T – absent from most of the smaller islands.

PEONY FAMILY Paeoniaceae

fruit

Herbs with alternate 1-2-ternately divided leaves. Flowers large and showy, solitary, with usually 5 sepals and 5-13 satiny petals, all separate; stamens numerous. Fruit consisting of 2-5, rather fleshy follicles set upon a fleshy disk; seeds large black or reddish.

268 *Paeonia officinalis* **COMMON PEONY.** Medium, tufted, almost hairless perennial. Leaves with 17-30 leaflets, green above, bluish-green beneath. Flowers red, not cup-shaped, 7-13cm; stamens with red stalks (filaments) and yellow anthers. Follicles 2-3, hairy. Meadows and bushy places; widely cultivated. May-June. France, Italy, Yugoslavia and Albania.

269 *Paeonia humilis [Paeonia officinalis* subsp. *humilis]*. Similar, but leaflets cut for only a third of their distance (not to the base); follicles hairless. Spain and Portugal.

270 *Paeonia peregrina*. Similar to *P. officinalis*, but leaflets with tiny bristles along the main veins above and flowers cup-shaped. Italy, Balkans and Yugoslavia.

271 *Paeonia clusii* **CLUSIUS'S PEONY.** A tufted medium perennial, hairy in part. Leaves with 30 or more narrow-oblong or elliptical leaflets, sometimes hairy beneath. Flowers white, white flushed with pink, or occasionally pink, 7-12cm, cupped at first, but soon opening widely. Follicles 2-4, hairy. Field margins, rocky slopes, beneath trees, banks, in the hills and mountains. Late Mar-early June. Crete and Karpathos – endemic.

272 *Paeonia rhodia*. Similar, but flowers always white. Rhodes – endemic.

273 *Paeonia mascula [P. corallina]*. A medium to tall tufted perennial, sometimes hairy. Leaves 2-ternate, the leaflets *not* divided, hairless beneath. Flowers red, opening widely, 8-14cm; stamens with red stalks (filaments) and yellow anthers. Follicles 3-5, usually hairy. Bushy places, hillslopes, generally away from the coast. May-June. C Med from France to Greece – not Crete or the Aegean Is.

274 *Paeonia arietina [P. officinalis* subsp. *arietina]*. Similar, but leaves with narrow elliptical leaflets, *hairy* beneath. N Italy to Turkey, but absent from the islands.

275 *Paeonia russii [P. officinalis* subsp. *russii]*. Like *P. arietina*, but leaves with only 9-10 (not 12-15) broad-oval leaflets. Corsica, Sardinia and Sicily.

276 *Paeonia broteroi.* Like *P. mascula,* but lower leaves generally with 17 or more (not 9-16) leaflets, bluish-green beneath. Flowers carmine to purplish-red, 8-10cm. Follicles densely hairy. Rocky places and scrub. Spain and Portugal.

277 *Paeonia coriacea.* Medium tufted perennial, usually hairless. Leaves 2-ternate, dull green and rather leathery, with 9-14 broad-elliptical leaflets. Flowers rose-pink, 10-15cm. Follicles usually only 2, hairless, with the top tapering into the stigma. Rocky and bushy places. Late Apr-June. S Spain, possibly also Corsica and Sardinia.

278 *Paeonia cambessedesii.* Short to medium tufted perennial, hairless. Leaves 2-ternate, green, but usually flushed with purple or red and with a rather metallic look; leaflets lanceolate to oval. Flowers rose-red or purplish red, 6-10cm, opening widely. Follicles 5-8, hairless, purplish. Shrubby and rocky places. Mar-May. Balearic Is. – endemic.

CAPER FAMILY Capparaceae

A primarily tropical and subtropical family related to Cruciferae. Flowers with 4 sepals and 4 petals, numerous stamens and the ovary on the end of a stalk (gynophore), so that it is often held among the stamens.

279 *Capparis spinosa* **CAPER.** Straggling greyish shrub, with pairs of spines at each leaf-base. Leaves alternate, rounded to oval, untoothed, thick, not spine-tipped. Flowers white, occasionally flushed with pink, 50-70mm; sepals purplish. Fruit large and berry-like, to 50mm long, green or yellowish, splitting eventually into two. Rocky habitats, cliffs and walls. May-July. T. The flower-buds are the edible capers; locally cultivated for this purpose. In some regions the young shoots and fruits are also pickled. It is grown commercially in France, Spain, Italy and elsewhere. A coastal variant with fleshy leaves and no spines is often referred to var. *inermis* (279a).

280 *Capparis ovata.* Similar, but leaves oblong to elliptical, *spine-tipped*; flowers smaller, 40-50mm, more irregular. Cliffs and dry hillslopes. Probably T – but distribution unclear because of confusion with the previous species.

POPPY FAMILY Papaveraceae

Annuals or perennials, often with milky or coloured juice. Leaves 1-2-pinnate. Flowers solitary or in lax clusters; sepals 2, falling as the flowers open; petals 4, separate, often crumpled-looking. Stamens usually numerous but only 4 in *Hypecoum.* Fruit a capsule with pores at the top, or splitting lengthwise into 2-4 valves.

Papaver **POPPIES.** Fruit-capsule with a star-shaped stigmatic disk at the top, opening by apical pores.

281 *Papaver somniferum* **OPIUM POPPY.** Medium to tall, almost hairless, greyish, rather fleshy annual. Leaves oval, large, wavy, pinnately-lobed, the upper clasping the stem. Flowers large, 40-90mm, purple or lilac with a dark centre, or white; anthers pale yellow. Capsule globose, 20-30mm long, hairless. Arable land, waste places, hillsides, vineyards and waysides. Apr-July. T. Cultivated since ancient times as a drug plant and food plant – the seeds used in cooking. Gummy latex collected from the young fruit-capsule is the source of opium and heroin, and from them morphine, codeine etc. The seeds are not toxic.

282 *Papaver setiferum*. Very similar, but each leaf-lobe ending in a *bristle*. T.

283 *Papaver rhoeas* **COMMON POPPY**. Variable medium to tall, rather bristly annual. Leaves 1-2-pinnate, deep green. Flowers scarlet or crimson, with or without a dark centre, the dark centre sometimes edged with white; anthers bluish; flower-stalks with spreading hairs. Capsule almost *round, hairless*. Cultivated ground, waysides and waste places, roadsides, occasionally along seashores. Mar-June. T. The common wheatfield poppy throughout most of Europe but less common now from modern farming and herbicides.

284 *Papaver dubium* **LONG-HEADED POPPY**. Variable medium annual, bristly. Leaves 1-2-pinnate; segments linear-lanceolate. Flowers pale scarlet, usually without a dark centre, 35-60mm; anthers violet; flower-stalks with hairs pressed close to the stem. Capsule *oblong, hairless*. Cultivated ground, waste places and roadsides. Mar-June. T.

285 *Papaver pinnatifidum*. Similar, but leaf-segments oval-triangular and *anthers* yellow (not violet). European Med.

286 *Papaver stipitatum*. Like *P. dubium*, but a shorter plant with *smaller* flowers, 28-32mm. Capsule *stalked* above point of petal attachment, with 5 (not 7-9) rays. Aegean – Skopelos and Turkey.

287 *Papaver argemone* **PRICKLY POPPY**. Short to medium bristly annual; hairs pressed close to the stem. Leaves 1-2-pinnate. Flowers pale scarlet, occasionally with a dark centre, 35-45mm; anthers bluish. Capsule oblong, ribbed, *bristly*. Cultivated land and waste places, waysides, especially on sandy soils, occasionally along the coast. Mar-June. T – except Cyprus and E Med.

288 *Papaver minus*. Similar, but stems spreading outwards close to the ground at first and flowers crimson or purplish with *erect* petals; anthers yellowish. Generally in the mountains. Apr-May. E Med, including Cyprus.

289 *Papaver nigrotinctum*. Like *P. argemone*, but a short plant with a basal leaf-rosette. Flowers with a large dark *centre*. Capsule 10-15mm (not 15-25mm) long. S Greece and Aegean region.

290 *Papaver hybridum [P. hispidum]* **ROUGH POPPY**. Short to medium bristly annual. Leaves 1-2-pinnate, the lower stalked. Flowers crimson or purplish red, with a dark centre, 20-40mm; anthers bluish-violet; flower-buds hairy; flower-stalks with hairs pressed close to the stem. Capsule *globose*, ribbed and with pale bristles. Cultivated ground, waste places, waysides. Feb-June. T. Like *P. dubium*, and *P. rhoeas*, widespread in Europe and western Asia.

291 *Papaver apulum*. Rather like *P. hybridum*, but a less bristly, slightly hairy annual. Leaves 2-pinnate. Flowers red with a dark centre, 40-50mm; flower-buds *hairless*; flower-stalks with hairs pressed close to the stem. Capsule bristly, but usually not ribbed. Cultivated ground and waste places, olive groves, occasionally in garrigue. Mar-June. S Italy, Sicily, Crete, Balkan Peninsula and the Aegean region.

292 *Roemeria hybrida [R. violacea]* **ROEMERIA**. A short, slightly hairy annual with yellow juice. Leaves 3-pinnate; segments linear. Flowers poppy-like, solitary, violet or purplish, with a dark centre; anthers yellow. Capsule *linear*, usually bristly, 4-valved. Cultivated ground and waste places. Mar-June. T. The flowers last for a few hours only, the petals falling by mid-morning.

Glaucium **HORNED-POPPIES**. Poppy-like plants, often rather fleshy. Flowers solitary. Fruit capsules long, slender and usually curved, splitting lengthwise into 2 valves.

293 *Glaucium flavum* **YELLOW HORNED-POPPY**. Medium to tall grey-green biennial or perennial, somewhat hairy. Leaves oblong, wavy, pinnately-lobed, the upper clasping the branched stem. Flowers yellow, 55-75mm, the petals sometimes with an orange blotch at the base. Capsule *very long*, 15-30cm, hairless. Coastal habitats, in sandy or gravelly places. Apr-Aug. T. Widespread along the coast of Europe and the Med. A British native. The plant exudes a yellow juice when cut. Poisonous. Grown in gardens.

294 *Glaucium leiocarpum [G. flavum var. leiocarpum]*. Similar, but a more slender plant with deep yellow or tawny-coloured flowers. Capsule rarely exceeding 15cm. C and E Med from Crete and Yugoslavia eastwards.

295 *Glaucium corniculatum* **RED HORNED-POPPY**. Short, hairy or bristly annual or biennial. Leaves rough, grey-green, pinnately-lobed, the upper clasping the stem. Flowers orange or red, occasionally yellow, 30-50mm, often with a dark blackish centre. Capsule 11-15cm, covered with hairs pressed closely to the side. Coastal habitats, cultivated and waste ground. Apr-June. T. Grown in gardens.

Hypecoum **HYPECOUM**. Annual herbs with watery juice. Flowers small, borne in clusters; petals often 3-lobed. Fruit-capsule a jointed pod, splitting into one-seeded portions.

296 *Hypecoum procumbens*. Low to short, delicate, spreading, blue-grey annual. Leaves 2-pinnately-lobed; segments linear to lanceolate; bracts leaf-like. Flowers yellow, 5-15mm; petals *all 3-lobed*, the outer two petals with a large central lobe. Capsule erect, curved, well jointed. Sandy habitats, especially close to the sea. Feb-May. T. Often forming scattered colonies.

297 *Hypecoum imberbe [H. grandiflorum]*. Similar, but a more erect plant; *bracts* linear or with a few slender divisions. Flowers usually orange-yellow, 10-15mm, the outer two petals evenly lobed. Cultivated ground and waste places, generally inland. Jan-May. T.

298 *Hypecoum pendulum*. Like *H. procumbens*, but the outer two petals unlobed or scarcely lobed. Capsule *pendent*, straight, scarcely jointed. Cultivated ground, fallow and waste places, field margins, roadsides, sandy shores, coastal and inland. Feb-May. T.

FUMITORY FAMILY Fumariaceae

Sometimes included in the Poppy Family, Papaveraceae. Annuals or perennials with colourless juice and thin stems, hairless. Leaves pinnately-divided. Flowers borne in short spike-like racemes, 2-lipped; sepals 2, small; petals 4, the upper one spurred. Fruit rounded, not splitting, or a capsule splitting into two lengthwise.

299 *Fumaria agraria*. Short annual. Leaf-segments flat, oval to, oblong. Flowers pinkish-white, 12-14mm long, inner petals with *dark purple tips*; racemes longer than their stalks (peduncle), with 15-22 flowers. Fruit keeled, notched at the top. Cultivated land and waste places. Mar-June. W Med east to Yugoslavia.

300 *Fumaria bella*. Similar, but flowers pink with the upper lip and inner petals purple. Fruit *not* notched, often slightly pointed. W Med east to Italy and Sicily – not Balearic Is. or Sardinia.

301 *Fumaria gaillardotii*. Like *F. bella*, but flowers 10-12mm (not 12-14mm) and fruit slightly square. C and E Med from Italy and Sicily eastwards.

fruit

fruit

302 *Fumaria macrocarpa.* Like *F. agraria,* but flowers pale pink *overall,* 9-11mm. Fruit 3-4mm diam. (not 2.5-3mm), not notched. Cultivated and waste ground, rocky places. Yugoslavia and Greece eastwards.

303 *Fumaria capreolata* **RAMPING FUMITORY.** Short to tall spreading and scrambling annual. Leaf-segments pale or greyish green, flat, wedge-shaped with blunt lobes. Flowers creamy-white or pale pink, *tipped* with reddish-black, 10-14mm long; racemes shorter than their stalks, to 20-flowered. Fruit scarcely keeled, with a rounded apex, 2.5mm diam. Walls and hedgerows, rocky places and cultivated ground. Mar-June. T. One of the commonest fumitories in the Med region.

304 *Fumaria bicolor.* Medium annual. Leaf-segments flat, oblong, lobed. Flowers white, gradually *turning* pink, tipped with dark purple, 10-13mm long; raceme shorter than the stalk, 8-12-flowered. Fruit with a blunt tip, 2-2.25mm diam. Cultivated ground, waste and rocky places. Mar-June. W Med from France and the Balearic Is. to Sicily.

305 *Fumaria judaica.* Similar, but sepals smaller, 2mm at most, and fruit larger, 3mm diam. E Med from Italy and Sicily eastwards.

306 *Fumaria officinalis* **COMMON FUMITORY.** Weak, bluish-green, scrambling or spreading annual. leaf-segments flattened, narrow-oblong to lanceolate. Flowers pinkish-purple, tipped reddish-black, 7-9mm long; raceme longer than the *short* stalk. Fruit kidney-shaped, 2-2.5mm diam. Cultivated, fallow and waste ground. Mar-June. T. A widespread weed of cultivation.

307 *Fumaria parviflora.* Similar, but leaf-segments channelled. Flowers *small,* 5-6mm long, white flushed with pink. Jan-July. T.

308 *Fumaria vaillantii.* Like *F. parviflora* but leaf-segments *not* channelled. Flowers pale pink; bracts shorter (not longer) than flower-stalks. W and C Med eastwards to Albania.

309 *Fumaria schleicheri.* Like *F. vaillantii,* but flower-stalks longer, 4mm (not 2.5mm). W Med eastwards to Yugoslavia – no islands except Sardinia.

CRESS FAMILY Cruciferae

siliculas

siliquas

Annual or perennial herbs. Leaves usually alternate. Flowers usually in racemes, very distinctive with 4 separate sepals and 4 separate petals, arranged crosswise; stamens 6. Fruit a 2-parted capsule, either long and thin (siliqua) or broad and short, variously shaped (silicula). Fruit shape is very important in identification.

310 *Isatis tinctoria* [*I. canescens, I. littoralis, I. taurica*] **WOAD.** Medium to tall, mostly hairless, greyish biennial. Leaves forming a basal rosette in the first year; stem leaves arrow-shaped, clasping the stem. Flowers yellow, 3-4mm, in much-branched racemes. Fruit an oblong, flattened, *pendent* silicula, 11-27mm long, dark brown when ripe. Dry habitats, rocky waste and fallow ground, roadsides, cliffs. Apr-July. T – not Balearic Is., Crete, Cyprus or much of the E Med. Used by the Greeks and Romans as a medicinal plant. During the Middle Ages it was widely cultivated for the production of a blue dye, Indigotine, produced by crushing the stems and leaves.

311 *Bunias erucago* **BUNIAS.** Medium, rough-hairy annual or biennial, branched. Leaves pinnately-lobed, wavy-margined; upper leaves unlobed, toothed or not. Flowers yellow, 10-14mm, petals notched. Silicula 10-12mm long, square in section with *toothed wings* on angles. Cultivated land and waste places. May-July. T. Edible –

the young leaves can be eaten as salad, and the plant is sometimes grown as such in the Med region.

312 *Hesperis laciniatus* CUT-LEAVED DAME'S VIOLET. Medium to tall hairy biennial or perennial. Leaves pinnately-lobed to deeply toothed, often wavy-margined; stem leaves unstalked. Flowers purple or yellow suffused with purple, 15-25mm, borne in long racemes. Siliqua linear, *very long*, 50-150mm, hairy or not. Cliffs and rocky places. Apr-July. W and C Med eastwards to Greece and the Aegean Is., excluding most of the islands.

Malcolmia MALCOLMIAS. Annual or perennial herbs. Flowers usually pink or violet, occasionally white. Fruit a siliqua, linear-cylindrical.

313 *Malcolmia littorea* SAND STOCK. Short to medium perennial, woody at base, with *many* non-flowering stems, *white-downy*. Leaves elliptical, deeply toothed or untoothed, mostly unstalked. Flowers purple, 15-20mm. Siliqua 30-65mm long, not beaded. Coastal sandy and rocky places. Mar-June. W Med eastwards to Italy, including NW Africa.

314 *Malcolmia lacera*. Similar, but basal leaves short-stalked. Siliqua 20-40mm long, *beaded*. Spain and Portugal.

315 *Malcolmia ramosissima* [*M. parviflora*]. Low to short grey-hairy annual. Leaves oblong, deeply wavy-toothed to untoothed. Flowers violet or pink, 4-8mm. Siliqua 15-35mm long, *beaded, hairy*. Coastal sandy and rocky places, sometimes inland. Mar-June. W and C Med eastwards to Greece, including N Africa. Often confused with *Maresia* (below) whose fruit has an opaque, not transparent, septum (central membrane).

316 *Malcolmia maritima* VIRGINIA STOCK. Short, hairy annual. Leaves oblong, toothed or untoothed. Flowers pink to purple, with a white or orange 'eye', relatively large, 13-20mm; petals notched. Siliqua 35-80mm long, spreading, hairy. Coastal rocks and sandy places, occasionally inland. Mar-June. Greece and Albania; naturalised widely in the W Med and N Africa. Widely grown in gardens.

317 *Malcolmia flexuosa*. Similar, but petals 12-17mm long (not 12-25mm); siliqua 2-3mm diam, as wide as the stalk (not 1-2mm diam. and wider than the stalk). Coastal rocks and cliffs, walls, occasionally in maquis or inland. Feb-May. C and E Med from Greece to Turkey and Cyprus; naturalised in parts of the W Med.

318 *Malcolmia chia*. Low to short, hairy annual, usually erect and much-branched; stems often purplish. Leaves thin, oblong, toothed or not. Flowers pale pink to violet, occasionally whitish, *small*, 6-9mm. Siliqua 25-70mm long, ascending to almost erect. Rocky and stony places, cliffs, coastal and inland, roadsides. Feb-June. C and E Med from Yugoslavia eastwards. Very common in the early spring in much of the E Med.

319 *Ricotia cretica* RICOTIA. Low to short, somewhat hairy annual, rather like *Malcolmia maritima* in general appearance. Leaves alternate, pinnately-lobed, greyish-green, the lobes oval, usually toothed. Flowers pink or lilac, 10-20mm, often with a paler centre, borne in lax racemes. Siliqua flat, *oblong*, 30-50mm long, 8-9mm wide. Cliffs, screes and rocky places. Mar-May. Crete – endemic.

320 *Maresia nana* [*Malcolmia confusa, M. nana*] MARESIA. A low to short hairy annual; hairs stellate. Leaves oblong, wavy-toothed to untoothed. Flowers violet to pink, 4-5mm, borne in flat-topped clusters overtopped by the developing fruits. Siliqua 10-28mm long, *beaded*, with a distinct, but short, style. Sandy coastal habitats – dunes and on the shoreline. Feb-June. T.

321 *Cheiranthus cheiri* **WALLFLOWER**. Variable short to tall perennial; hairs pressed close to stem and leaves. Leaves narrow-lanceolate to oblong, untoothed. Flowers yellow, or orange-brown, *very fragrant*, 20-25mm, borne in elongating racemes. Siliqua 25-75mm long, erect, somewhat flattened. Cliffs, walls and rocky places. Mar-May. S Greece and Aegean; widely cultivated and naturalised in the Med.

322 *Arabis verna* **SPRING ROCKCRESS**. Low to short thinly hairy annual; stems arising from a basal leaf-rosette. Leaves oblong to oval, toothed; stem leaves few, heart-shaped. Flowers purple to pale violet or whitish, *small*, 4-7mm, few in a lax raceme; petals narrow with a rounded apex. Siliqua linear, 45-60mm long, ascending. Shaded places, rocks and walls, roadsides. Feb-May. T. A very common early spring flower in many parts of the Med.

323 *Arabis cypria*. Similar, but a perennial, white- or grey-hairy; flowers larger, 10-16mm, white or lilac-pink. In the hills, not coastal. Cyprus – endemic.

324 *Aubrieta deltoidea* **AUBRIETA**. Low to short hairy, cushion-forming or straggling perennial. Leaves spoon-shaped to rhombic, slightly toothed or untoothed. Flowers purplish-red to violet, or white, 11-18mm, few in short racemes; petals slightly notched. Siliqua linear-oblong, 6-16mm long, downy. Rocky places and walls. Mar-May. S Greece, Aegean Is. and Sicily; naturalised in France, Spain, Italy and Yugoslavia, widely cultivated.

325 *Aubrieta columnae*. Similar, but flowers smaller and siliqua with only star-shaped hairs (not star-shaped and simple hairs) – seen under a ×10 hand-lens. S Italy and Sicily, W Yugoslavia and Albania.

Matthiola **STOCKS**. Annual to perennial herbs, often with lobed and rather hoary leaves. Flowers often sweetly scented, borne in lax racemes. Fruit a siliqua, with a distinctive 2-lobed stigma.

326 *Matthiola sinuata* **SEA STOCK**. Low to medium, rather stout, white-hairy biennial, occasionally perennial or annual, usually becoming rather woody at the base. Leaves oblong, deeply toothed or pinnately-lobed, lobes blunt; upper stem leaves generally unlobed. Flowers pale purple or pinkish, 18-30mm. Siliqua linear, erect to spreading, 50-150mm long, *sticky* with large yellow or black glands; fruit terminating in a 2-lobed stigma. Sandy coastal habitats. Feb-May. T – but rarer in the E Med and in parts of N Africa.

327 *Matthiola incana* **HOARY STOCK**. Similar, but *all leaves* usually untoothed or only slightly toothed. Flowers purple, pink or white, slightly larger, the petals 20-30mm long (not 17-25mm). Siliqua 45-160mm long, hairy but not glandular. Coastal habitats, sandy and rocky, cliffs; often cultivated. Feb-May. T – east to W Turkey and Cyprus.

328 *Matthiola fruticulosa* [*M. tristis, Cheiranthus fruticulosus*]. Short to medium perennial, becoming woody at the base, sparsely hairy to densely white-hairy. Leaves mostly *linear or narrow-lanceolate*, untoothed or slightly toothed or lobed; some leaves in non-flowering basal rosettes. Flowers yellowish or brownish tinged with brown or purplish-red, 15-28mm; petals strap-like, 12-25mm long. Siliqua linear, 25-120mm long, terminating in 2 inconspicuous horns. Dry rocky ground, coastal and inland. Feb-May. T – but rare in Turkey, Cyprus and much of the E Med.

329 *Matthiola tricuspidata* **THREE-HORNED STOCK**. Low to medium annual, to 40cm tall, covered in loose, rather woolly hairs. Leaves oblong in outline, shallowly lobed to pinnately-lobed; lobes blunt. Flowers mauve to purple, 18-25mm, the petals star-shaped, 15-22mm long. Siliqua 25-100mm long, spreading to deflexed, with a distinctive *3-horned* apex. Sandy coastal habitats. Feb-May. T.

(324)

leaf

leaf

(329)

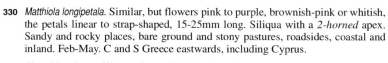

330 *Matthiola longipetala.* Similar, but flowers pink to purple, brownish-pink or whitish, the petals linear to strap-shaped, 15-25mm long. Siliqua with a *2-horned* apex. Sandy and rocky places, bare ground and stony pastures, roadsides, coastal and inland. Feb-May. C and S Greece eastwards, including Cyprus.

331 *Alyssoides sinuata [Alyssum innata, Vesicaria sinuata]* **ALYSSOIDES.** A short to medium, grey-hairy perennial. Leaves lanceolate to oblong, the lower usually deeply lobed or toothed. Flowers yellow, 6-10mm, with erect sepals and notched petals. Silicula distinctly inflated, globose to elliptical, 7-12mm. Rocky habitats. Mar-June. Adriatic coastal region – Italy, Yugoslavia and Albania.

332 *Alyssoides cretica.* Similar, but silicula *hairy*; flowers larger with sepals 7-11mm long (not 3-4mm). Crete and Karpathos – endemic.

333 *Alyssum saxatile* **GOLDEN** or **YELLOW ALYSSUM.** Densely tufted, short to medium, rather variable perennial. Leaves *grey*, oblong pinnately-lobed or unlobed. Flowers borne in broad, branched, rather flat-topped clusters, bright yellow, occasionally pale yellow, 4-7mm, the petals notched, 3-6mm long. Silicula hairless, flattened, 4-9mm, with a rounded or slightly notched apex. Rocky habitats, cliffs, generally inland. Mar-June, occasionally later. Italy to W Turkey – not Cyprus.

334 *Alyssum corymbosum.* Similar, but a taller and more erect plant, greener, with smaller flowers, the petals only 2mm long. Silicula somewhat inflated, 4.5-6mm, with 8 or more seeds (not 2-4). Stony and rocky habitats. Apr-June. W and S Balkans – Yugoslavia, Albania and Greece.

335 *Fibigia clypeata* (incl. *F. eriocarpa*) **FIBIGIA.** A short to medium, densely tufted, grey-felted, erect perennial. Leaves grey or green, the lower oblong, often broadest above the middle. Flowers yellow, 6-9mm, borne in racemes, often branched. Silicula bat-shaped, elliptical in outline, 14-28mm long, *grey-felted.* Rocky and grassy places. Apr-July. Italy, the Balkans, to Turkey and Syria; perhaps in Cyprus.

336 *Lobularia maritima* **SWEET ALISON.** Low to short, much-branched, greyish or whitish annual, occasionally a short-lived perennial, usually hairy. Leaves linear-lanceolate, usually pointed, untoothed. Flowers in dense racemes, elongating in fruit, white, 3-4mm, *sweetly scented*; petals not notched, 2.5-3mm long. Silicula rather flattened, oval or rounded, usually hairy, 2- 3.5mm, generally with only 2 seeds. Dry sandy and rocky places, hillsides and waste ground. Feb-June, occasionally later. T. Widely grown in gardens, where pink-and purple-flowered forms exist.

337 *Lobularia libyca.* Similar, but a more straggly plant with smaller flowers, the petals only 2mm long. Silicula oval, *larger*, 4-5mm, with 6-10 seeds. Dry sandy places. Feb-May. S Spain, N Africa, Aegean Is. and E Med, including Cyprus.

338 *Clypeola jonthlaspi* **CLYPEOLA.** Slender erect, low to short, grey-hairy annual, rarely more than 20cm tall, often branched from the base. Leaves linear to oblong, usually broadest above the middle, untoothed. Flowers *tiny*, 2-3mm, yellow, borne in short racemes which elongate in fruit; petals blunt or slightly notched. Silicula rounded to elliptical, winged, usually hairy. Stony hillslopes, waste ground and roadsides. Feb-May. T. A tiny plant, easily overlooked.

339 *Hymenolobus procumbens [Hornungia procumbens]* **HYMENOLOBUS.** Slender, low to short, erect or spreading annual or biennial, usually hairless. Lower leaves lyre-shaped to unlobed; upper leaves all unlobed. Flowers tiny, 2-3mm, white, many borne in lax racemes; sepals *as long as* the petals. Saline or brackish marshes, generally on the coast. Feb-Apr. T.

340 *Aethionema saxatile [A. graecum]* **BURNT CANDYTUFT.** Low to short annual or perennial, with erect stems, branched near the base or unbranched. Leaves oval to oblong, untoothed, the upper narrower. Flowers white, purplish or lilac, 3-6mm, the petals notched, 2-5mm long. Silicula flattened, subrounded and broadly winged, 5- 9mm, notched. Rocky and stony habitats in hills and mountains. W and C Med from Spain to Greece, including Crete, Sardinia and Sicily.

341 *Biscutella didyma* **BISCUTELLA**. Very variable, erect, short to medium, hair annual; stems simple or branched. Leaves green, often in a flat basal rosette at first, elliptical to oblong, usually broadest above the middle, finely toothed; upper leaves linear and untoothed. Flowers pale yellow, occasionally tinged with lilac, 3-5mm, borne in dense, elongating, racemes; petals not notched, 2-4mm long. Silicula consisting of *paired* disks, each lobe 4.5-7mm long. Dry rocky and stony slopes, arable and waste land. Feb-May. T. Widespread in Europe and western Asia.

342 *Biscutella auriculata*. Similar, but a more or less hairless plant with deeply toothed leaves, the upper *clasping* the stem. Flowers much larger with petals up to 15mm long. Silicula less distinctly 2-lobed. W Med, from Portugal to Italy, including the Balearic Is.

Iberis **CANDYTUFTS**. Annual or perennials herbs, sometimes subshrubby with simple or lobed leaves. Flowers in racemes or panicles, often forming flat-topped clusters; petals unequal, 2 long and 2 short, the long petals pointing outwards in the inflorescence. Fruit a silicula, winged and usually notched, compressed.

343 *Iberis sempervirens* **EVERGREEN CANDYTUFT**. Small evergreen subshrub, hairless, stems branched and spreading, up to 25cm tall. Leaves oblong to spatula-shaped, blunt, untoothed, thick. Flowers white, in broad, *flat-topped* clusters, elongating in fruit, borne on lateral stems. Silicula oval, broadly winged and deeply notched, 6-7mm long, longer than wide. Rocky mountain slopes. Apr-June. W and C Med from Spain to Greece and Albania – on no islands except Crete. Common in gardens.

344 *Iberis semperflorens* **SHRUBBY CANDYTUFT**. Similar, but a shrub to 80cm tall with larger leaves, 30-70mm long (not 10-25mm). Silicula narrowly winged, 5-8mm long, *wider than long*, scarcely notched. Maritime cliffs. Nov-Mar. W Italy and Sicily.

345 *Iberis pruitii*. Very variable, low to short, tufted annual or perennial, not more than 15cm tall; stems spreading to ascending. Leaves rather *fleshy*, spatula-shaped, untoothed or with a few teeth near the apex. Flowers white to lilac, borne in dense flat-topped clusters, staying fairly dense in fruit and scarcely elongating. Silicula broadly winged, 6-8mm long, deeply notched, with erect, pointed lobes. Rocky places in hills and mountains. Apr-July. W and C Med from Spain to Greece; absent from most islands except Sardinia and Sicily.

346 *Iberis linifolia*. Very similar, but a larger plant, to 30cm, and with *linear* leaves. SW Spain and Portugal.

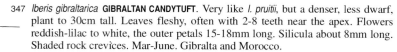

347 *Iberis gibraltarica* **GIBRALTAN CANDYTUFT**. Very like *I. pruitii*, but a denser, less dwarf, plant to 30cm tall. Leaves fleshy, often with 2-8 teeth near the apex. Flowers reddish-lilac to white, the outer petals 15-18mm long. Silicula about 8mm long. Shaded rock crevices. Mar-June. Gibralta and Morocco.

348 *Iberis pinnata* **ANNUAL CANDYTUFT**. An erect short annual, almost hairless; upper branches long, straight and leafless. Leaves oblong, *pinnately-lobed*, with 2-6 linear segments. Flowers white to lilac, fragrant, borne in dense, round-topped clusters. Silicula almost square, 5-6mm long, shallowly notched, hairless. Arable fields and stony ground. Apr-July. From Spain and the Balearic Is. east to Turkey, but absent from most islands. Widely cultivated as a summer annual in gardens.

349 *Iberis umbellata* **CANDYTUFT**. Similar, but more robust, to 70cm tall. Leaves linear, *unlobed*. Flowers pink or purplish. Silicula 6-10mm long, deeply notched. Bushy and rocky places on calcareous soils or serpentine, occasionally cultivated. Apr-July. C Med from France to Greece, absent from the islands; naturalised in Spain and Portugal.

Lepidium **PEPPERWORTS**. Annual or perennial herbs, usually with unbranched hairs. Flowers small, borne in terminal, often lax racemes; petals usually white, occasionally yellow. Fruit a flattened silicula, the valves keeled or winged, notched.

350 *Lepidium spinosum*. Short to medium, hairless annual, to 40cm tall. Basal and lower leaves pinnately-lobed, with slender segments; upper leaves linear and unlobed. Flowers white, 2-3mm, borne in an elongated cylindrical inflorescence, terminal or lateral. Silicula heart-shaped, 5-6mm long, *deeply* notched. Fallow fields and waste places, usually on rather moist ground. Mar-June. C and E Med from Crete and Greece eastwards, including Cyprus; naturalised in Spain and the Balearic Is.

351 *Lepidium perfoliatum* **PERFOLIATE PEPPERWORT**. Short to medium erect annual with a single stem. Leaves of two distinct kinds, the lower 2-3-pinnately-lobed, with slender segments, but the upper leaves simple and oval, untoothed and clasping the stem. Flowers pale yellow, tiny, 1-1.5mm, the petals slightly longer than the sepals. Cultivated land, waste and disturbed places. Apr-June. C and E Med from Crete and Albania eastwards, including Cyprus; naturalised in Spain, France and Italy.

352 *Lepidium latifolium* **DITTANDER**. Tall, hairless, *stoloniferous* perennial; stems much-branched above. Leaves leathery, oval, toothed, occasionally pinnately-lobed, the lower long-stalked; upper leaves narrower, untoothed and unstalked. Flowers white, small, 2-3mm, borne in large branched panicles. Silicula oval, small, 2mm long, not notched or winged. Damp, often shaded habitats, marshy ground, stream and ditch margins, occasionally on sandy seashores. Apr-June. T. Used for flavouring food before the discovery of pepper.

353 *Cardaria draba [Lepidium draba]* **HOARY CRESS**. Short to tall, hairless or somewhat hairy, variable greyish perennial. Leaves oblong. Basal leaves oblong, pointed, deeply toothed, long-stalked; stem leaves similar but *clasping* the stem. Flowers white, 5-6mm, borne in dense, branched, umbel-like clusters. Silicula kidney-shaped, 3-4.5mm long, inflated, not splitting. Cultivated and waste ground, roadsides, field boundaries, on calcareous and neutral soils. Mar-June, occasionally later. T. A common weed in many parts of Europe.

354 *Moricandia arvensis* **MORICANDIA**. Short to medium short-lived, hairless perennial; stems branched. Leaves mostly towards the base, fleshy and rather *cabbage-like*, oval, blunt-toothed; upper leaves smaller, heart-shaped and clasping the stem, untoothed. Flowers violet-purple, showy, 18-22mm, borne in rather lax, branched racemes. Siliqua linear, 30-80mm long, slightly squarish in cross-section. Rocky places, old walls, fields and uncultivated ground, on calcareous soils. Mar-June. W and C Med from Spain to Greece and N Africa – not on Sardinia or Crete.

355 *Brassica oleracea* subsp. *robertiana* **WILD CABBAGE**. Coarse hairless, medium to tall, grey perennial; stems becoming woody below. Leaves fleshy, the basal large, pinnately-lobed, undulate, blunt-toothed, stalked; upper leaves unlobed and clasping the stem. Flowers yellow, 20-30mm, borne in large, branched racemes; petals not notched, 15-20mm long. Siliqua 50-70mm long, with a short conical *beak* 4-8mm long. Coastal habitats, especially maritime cliffs. Apr-July. From Spain to S Italy – not on the islands. The ancestor of modern cultivated cabbages, including Brussel sprouts and the cauliflower. A British native.

356 *Brassica fruticulosa*. Medium, erect, hairy annual or perennial, becoming rather woody at the base. Leaves lyre-shaped to pinnately-lobed, long-stalked, the uppermost similar but smaller, or unlobed. Flowers yellow, 8-12mm, borne in lax racemes, without bracts. Siliqua 15-40mm long, *constricted* at intervals and with a short, 2-7mm long, beak. W and C Med from Spain to Greece and NW Africa – not Balearic Is., Corsica or Crete.

357 *Brassica tournefortii*. Similar, but with smaller, pale yellow flowers; petals only 5-7mm (not 9-10mm) long and often violet at the base, narrow and rather inconspicuous. Siliqua 35-65mm long; beak 10-20mm long. Rocky, sandy and waste places. W and C Med from Portugal eastwards to Italy and Greece, including N Africa.

358 *Brassica balearica* **BALEARIC CABBAGE**. Small evergreen subshrub to 40cm, hairless; stems becoming bare and woody below. Leaves fleshy, shiny green, borne in rosettes, lyre-shaped or deeply lobed and *resembling* an oak leaf, long-stalked. Flowers yellow, 12-20mm, borne in short racemes. Siliqua linear, 20-60mm long, with a few constrictions and a very short, 1.5-2mm beak. Limestone; cliffs and sloping rocks. Mar-June. Majorca; endemic. Occasionally seen in cultivation as an ornamental species.

359 *Sinapis arvensis* **CHARLOCK**. Tall rather bristly annual, occasionally hairless. Leaves mostly lyre-shaped or pinnately-lobed with a large, coarsely toothed terminal lobe; upper leaves unstalked, lanceolate, toothed but not lobed. Flowers bright yellow or lemon yellow, 15-20mm, borne in long racemes; sepals spreading, petals 8-12mm long, long-clawed. Siliqua ascending, 25-45mm long, beaked; beak *shorter* than the 3-7-veined valves, 10-15mm long, conical. Cultivated, waste and disturbed ground – a widespread weed. Mar-Sept. T.

360 *Sinapis alba* **WHITE MUSTARD**. Similar, but *all leaves* stalked and pinnately-lobed. Flowers pale yellow. Siliqua 20-40mm long, the beak flattened and sword-like, as long or longer than the valves. Similar habitats. Feb-July. T. The seeds are the source of white mustard.

361 *Eruca sativa* (incl. *E. vesicaria*) **ERUCA**. A short to tall bristly annual, to 1m tall. Leaves mostly stalked, pinnately-lobed, with a large terminal leaflet, toothed or untoothed. Flowers white or pale yellow, the petals with *violet veins*, 18-30mm, borne in long racemes; sepals erect, often purple-stained, petals 15-20mm long. Siliqua ascending to erect, 12-25mm long, beaked; beak flattened and sword-shaped, shorter than the 1-veined valves. Cultivated, waste and disturbed ground. Feb-June. T. Cultivated in the Med region as a salad crop – the young leaves and inflorescences are succulent.

362 *Succowia balearica* **SUCCOWIA**. Short to tall hairless or somewhat rough-bristly annual. Leaves oval in outline, 1-2-pinnately-lobed, usually toothed. Flowers yellow, 8-14mm; petals 7-10mm long, short-clawed. Silicula 3-6mm, covered in long conical spines. Coastal rocks and stony places, often in partial shade. Mar-June. Spain eastwards to Italy and Sicily, including N Africa and most of the islands.

363 *Cakile maritima* **SEA ROCKET**. Variable, low to short, rather succulent, spreading, hairless annual. Leaves grey-green, irregularly pinnately-lobed, the lobes narrow and untoothed. Flowers violet, pink or white, 6-13mm, borne in dense congested racemes which elongate considerably in fruit; petals 5-14mm long. Siliqua pale brown and rather spongy, 10-25mm long, 2-parted; lower segment with an *arrow-shaped* base, the upper oval with 4 angles, both indehiscent but the upper eventually falling off and containing a single seed. Sandy coastal habitats. Feb-July. T. The Med plant is often referred to subsp. *aegyptiaca* (363a).

364 *Crambe hispanica* **SPANISH SEAKALE.** Slender, erect, short to tall, bristly annual, to 1m tall. Lower leaves large, kidney-shaped or rounded, toothed, usually with 1-2 pairs of small lateral lobes below. Flowers white, 3-4mm, the petals sometimes tinged with purple at the base, borne in a large, *much-branched* panicle. Siliqua 2-4mm, with a short sterile lower part and a globose, smooth, pale brown upper part containing a single seed, indehiscent. Arable land, rocky pastures and garrigue, coastal or inland. Mar-June. T – but often rather local.

365 *Crambe filiformis.* Similar, but leaves with 3 or more pairs of lateral lobes and lower, sterile segment of fruit longer than the upper, fertile, segment. S Spain and N Africa.

366 *Morisia monanthos* **MORISIA.** Low, somewhat hairy, stemless perennial. Leaves in tight, neat *rosettes*, rather leathery, deep green, narrow and pinnately-divided. Flowers solitary, long-stalked, golden-yellow, 11-14mm, erect at first but as the fruit develops the stalk curves downwards to bury the fruit. Silicula 2-parted, the lower segment egg-shaped and the upper conical, both fertile and indehiscent. Sandy coastal habitats and dry rocky hillslopes. Mar-June. Corsica and Sardinia.

367 *Enarthrocarpus arcuatus* **ENARTHROCARPUS.** Low to medium, bristly annual; branches spreading to ascending. Leaves stalked, pinnately-lobed, the lower usually in a rosette, the upper alternate; lobes alternate, oblong, scarcely toothed. Flowers yellow or whitish with violet veins, 12-20mm, borne in racemes with bracts only at the base of the lowermost flowers; petals 10-15mm long. Siliqua recurved, 40-90mm long, cylindrical, beaked, somewhat beaded and covered with short bristles; lower segment much shorter than the upper segment. Rocky coastal pastures, occasionally on sandy ground or on sea cliffs. Mar-May. E Med from Turkey and Cyprus eastwards.

368 *Enarthrocarpus lyratus.* Similar, but inflorescence with bracts almost to the top and flowers *smaller*, the petals 6-7mm long, yellow stained with purple at the base. Disturbed and waste ground, roadsides. Mar-May. Cyprus and the E Med – not Turkey.

369 *Raphanus raphanistrum* **WILD RADISH.** Very variable short to tall, bristly annual, to 1.5m tall; stems erect, branched. Flowers white or yellow, often with lilac or violet veins, 15-30mm, borne in branched racemes; petals 12-20mm long. Siliqua 30-90mm, *jointed and beaded*, with a prominent beak, breaking easily at the 2 joints. Arable land, fields and waste places, roadsides and sandy shores. Apr-Sept. T.

    369a Subsp. *maritimus* **SEA RADISH**, common along the coast of NW Europe, is restricted in the Med to the west. It can be distinguished by having the basal leaves in a rosette, by the yellow, scarcely veined, flowers (petals 15-25mm long) and by the thicker siliqua, 5-8mm wide (not 2-4mm).

370 *Raphanus sativus* **GARDEN RADISH.** Similar, but distinguished by its thickened, carrot-like root, by the purple or mauve flowers and by the thick, 6-20mm wide, siliqua which is scarcely beaded. Cultivated land, occasionally casual or naturalised on waste ground. T. Feb-May. Long cultivated for its edible roots (radishes); the young fruits can also be eaten in salads.

371 *Calepina irregularis* **WHITE BALL MUSTARD.** Slender short to tall, erect or spreading, hairless annual or biennial; stems usually branched near the base. Leaves oval, unlobed or pinnately-lobed with a large terminal leaflet, toothed or untoothed, the basal leaves in a rosette, the upper leaves similar but smaller and clasping the stem with pointed lobes. Flowers white, occasionally pink-tinged, small, 2-4mm, with *unequal* petals, outer two long and inner two short, borne in branched racemes. Silicula egg-shaped with a short point, 2.5-4mm, rough when dry. Cultivated and waste ground, roadsides. Mar-May. T.

372 *Didesmus aegypticus [Myagrum aegyptium]* **DIDESMUS.** A short to medium, hairless or slightly bristly, spreading annual; stems much-branched. Leaves 1-2-pinnately-lobed or deeply cut, toothed or untoothed. Flowers white, 8-12mm, borne in dense, round-topped clusters (corymbs) with narrow oval petals, 6-10mm long; sepals often violet-tinged; flower-stalks *thickening* in fruit. Silicula erect, 2-parted, 6-10mm long; lower segment fertile, with 4-6 ribs, upper segment sterile (seedless), egg-shaped. Rocky habitats and garrigue, usually on limestone, coastal and inland. Mar-June. N Africa and the E Med from Crete and Greece eastwards.

373 *Erucaria hispanica [Sinapis hispanica]* **SPANISH MUSTARD.** A short to medium, hairless or somewhat bristly annual, erect or spreading, to 40cm tall. Leaves stalked, pinnately-lobed with linear lobes, or unlobed and linear to oblong. Flowers mauve or pale purple, rarely white, 12-17mm, borne in congested racemes which elongate in fruit; petals 10-15mm long. Siliqua erect, often *pressed* close to the stem, 10-15mm long, longitudinally veined, 2-parted; lower segment cylindrical, upper abruptly narrowing into the style, both fertile. Cultivated and waste ground, occasionally on sandy ground close to the sea. Jan-June. E Med and N Africa from Crete and Greece eastwards.

374 *Coronopus squamatus* **SWINECRESS.** Low to short, prostrate or spreading, usually hairless annual or biennial. Leaves at first in a rosette, petiolate, deeply pinnately-lobed with narrow acute segments; leaves on secondary shoots smaller. Flowers white, occasionally violet-tinged, tiny, 1.5-2mm, borne in a short raceme; anthers yellow or dirty violet. Silicula *kidney-shaped*, 3-4mm, indehiscent, rough with transverse ridges. Moist, often brackish, ground, bare places, coastal and inland. Mar-June. T. A widespread weed.

MIGNONETTE FAMILY Resedaceae

Annual or perennial herbs. Leaves simple or variously lobed. Flowers borne in terminal racemes or spikes; bracts present; sepals and petals 4-8, the petals separate, often deeply cut; stamens 7-25. Fruit with 3-7-carpels, capsular.

375 *Reseda alba* **WHITE MIGNONETTE.** Medium to tall, erect perennial, occasionally annual; stems branched above. Leaves pinnately-lobed, with 10 or more narrow lobes, untoothed. Flowers white, 8-9mm, sepals and petals 5-6, the petals all lobed to a third or more of their length. Fruit-capsule erect, elliptical in outline, 8-15mm long, constricted at the apex into 4 short lobes, with *persistent* stamen filaments. Dry rocky ground, disturbed and waste places, roadsides. Jan-May. T – rarer in the E Med.

376 *Reseda lutea* **WILD MIGNONETTE.** Short to tall leafy perennial, or occasionally biennial, bushy and often becoming rather woody at the base; stems leafy and slightly rough. Leaves stalked, mostly with 3-5 narrow, untoothed lobes. Flowers yellow, 4-5mm, with 6 sepals and petals, the upper two 3-lobed, lower two unlobed. Fruit-capsule erect, oblong in outline, 7-12mm long, 3-parted. Cultivated, disturbed and waste ground, field margins, roadsides, generally on calcareous soils. Feb-Sept. T.

377 *Reseda luteola* **WELD, DYER'S ROCKET.** Medium to tall erect biennial, to 1.3m tall. All leaves *unlobed*, lanceolate, with a wavy margin. Flowers yellow, or greenish yellow, 4-5mm; sepals and petals 4, the uppermost 4-8-lobed, the others 4-lobed or unlobed. Fruit-capsule erect, globular, 3-4mm long. Stony and sandy places,

waste ground, road and path sides, field margins. Apr-July. T. Grown in the past for a yellow dye.

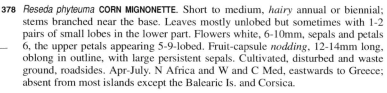

378 *Reseda phyteuma* **CORN MIGNONETTE**. Short to medium, *hairy* annual or biennial; stems branched near the base. Leaves mostly unlobed but sometimes with 1-2 pairs of small lobes in the lower part. Flowers white, 6-10mm, sepals and petals 6, the upper petals appearing 5-9-lobed. Fruit-capsule *nodding*, 12-14mm long, oblong in outline, with large persistent sepals. Cultivated, disturbed and waste ground, roadsides. Apr-July. N Africa and W and C Med, eastwards to Greece; absent from most islands except the Balearic Is. and Corsica.

379 *Reseda orientalis* **ORIENTAL MIGNONETTE**. Similar, but stem leaves mostly lobed and with rather smaller scented flowers; sepals *longer* than the petals (not the same length); upper petals appearing 9-19-lobed. Fruit-capsule nodding, 7-13mm long, oval in outline. Cultivated and waste ground, stony hillsides. Feb-May. Crete, Greece and E Med, including Cyprus.

380 *Reseda odorata* **MIGNONETTE**. Similar, but stem leaves mostly unlobed and fruit-capsule *subglobose*, 9-11mm long. Arable land, especially cornfields. Feb-May. N Africa and E Med. Long cultivated for its sweetly scented flowers and sometimes found as a casual throughout the region.

SUNDEW FAMILY Droseraceae

A small family of insect-trapping plants, cosmopolitan in distribution, but favouring nitrogen-poor habitats. Only one species is found in the Med region.

381 *Drosophyllum lusitanicum* **DROSOPHYLLUM**. Short glandular perennial; stem ascending, occasionally branched. Leaves in a large crowded rosette, linear and tapering, covered on the upper surface with red-tipped *glandular hairs*. Flowers yellow, 20-40mm, 5-petalled, borne in a lax cluster (cyme) on a distinct scape up to 30cm long. Dry rocky places near the coast or in garrigue or maquis, on acid soils. Apr-June. Portugal, S Spain and NW Africa. Related to the sundews, *Drosera*, and like them catches small insects on its sticky, glandular leaves. The soft parts of the insect bodies are then absorbed by digestive enzymes produced by the plant and assimilated into the leaves. Unlike *Drosera*, the glandular hairs are rigid and non-mobile.

leaf

STONECROP FAMILY Crassulaceae

Succulent annual or perennial herbs. Leaves alternate, opposite or whorled. Flowers regular, star- or bell-shaped; petals 3-20, stamens equal in number to, or twice as many as, the petals. Fruit a cluster of carpels, usually the same number as the petals.

Sedum **STONECROPS**. Leaves not in rosettes but alternate or opposite. Flowers usually 5-parted; stamens twice as many as the petals. A large genus with over 600 species in northern temperate regions of the world but also on the mountains in Africa and South America.

382 *Sedum sediforme* [*S. altissimum, S. nicaeensis*]. Robust, short to medium perennial, with both flowering and sterile shoots, becoming woody at the base. Leaves greyish-green, thick, oblong, borne in close spiralled rows, with a short spur at the base of each leaf. Flowers greenish-white or yellowish, 8-14mm, borne in a dense, erect inflorescence with recurved branches, becoming concave in fruit;

leaves

sepals and petals 5-8; stamens 10-16. Rocky places, cliffs, old walls, coastal and inland. Apr-July. T.

383 *Sedum ochroleucon [S. anopetalum].* Similar, but rarely as tall, with linear-cylindrical leaves. Flowers pale yellow, *larger*, 14-20mm; inflorescence flat-topped (not rounded) in bud. Rocky habitats. Apr-July. Spain eastwards to Crete and Greece, but absent from the other islands.

384 *Sedum tenuifolium [S. amplexicaule].* Short slender perennial with ascending stems. Leaves grey-green, closely overlapping, narrow-cylindrical, pointed, 3-lobed and *clasping* the stem at the base. Flowers yellow, 12-16mm, the petals 5-8, usually with a red mid-vein, borne in lax clusters; stamens 10-16. Rocky and sandy habitats, scrub. May-July. T, except Cyprus, the extreme east and most of the smaller islands.

385 *Sedum acre* **WALLPEPPER.** Variable, low tufted, bright green, hairless perennial. Leaves small, 3-6mm long, alternate, egg-shaped, blunt, closely overlapping. Flowers *bright yellow*, 10-12mm, borne in small clusters; petals 5; stamens 10. Rocky habitats, walls, old roofs and sandy places. May-July. T – except E Med, Balearic Is., Corsica and Sardinia.

386 *Sedum album* **WHITE STONECROP.** Low to short, hairless, laxly tufted perennial, with creeping, rather woody stems. Leaves alternate, linear-cylindrical to almost egg-shaped, 4-12mm long, blunt, often flushed with red. Flowers *white*, rarely pale pink, with pink follicles, 6-9mm, borne in flat-topped, much-branched clusters; petals 5; stamens 10. Rocky places, roadsides and old walls. May-July. T – not Cyprus.

387 *Sedum dasyphyllum* **THICK-LEAVED STONECROP.** Low tufted, stickily hairy perennial, tinged with greyish pink. Leaves *mostly opposite*, egg-shaped, blunt. Flowers white streaked with pink, 5-6mm, borne in lax clusters; petals 5 or 6; stamens 10 or 12. Generally growing on acid rocks, occasionally on old walls. May-Aug. European Med and NW Africa.

388 *Sedum stellatum* **STARRY STONECROP.** Low to short hairless annual, to 15cm high, with stout, erect to ascending stems. Leaves *flat*, rounded, 10-15mm long, blunt-toothed, the lower opposite but the upper alternate. Flowers pink, 8-10mm, borne in lax, rather flat-topped leafy clusters; petals usually 5, occasionally 4; stamens 8-10. Rocky habitats and walls. Apr-June. W and C Med, from Spain to Crete and the Greek islands.

389 *Sedum rubens [Crassula rubens]* **REDDISH STONECROP.** Low erect annual, hairy and often sticky with glands above. Leaves *linear*, alternate, 10-20mm long, greyish but often flushed with red. Flowers white or pink, 8-11mm, borne in small clusters, the 5 petals often with a purplish keel; stamens usually 5. Rocky and stony places, old walls. Apr-June. T.

390 *Sedum caespitosum.* Similar, but *hairless* and the leaves egg-shaped, 3-6mm long. Flowers white tinged with pink, 6mm. Dry hillsides and rocky ground. Feb-Apr. T – but absent from the Balearic Is., Portugal and parts of N Africa.

391 *Sedum porphyreum.* Like *S. rubens*, but flowers smaller, 6-9mm, borne in a lax cluster and follicles erect (not spreading); stamens usually 7-8. Rock crevices and screes, dry rocky ground. Mar-May. Cyprus.

392 *Sedum litoreum.* Like *S. rubens*, but leaves oblong to spatula-shaped and flowers *yellow*, 5-8mm. Rocks and cliffs. Apr-May. From France to Cyprus, Turkey and Palestine.

393 *Sedum caeruleum.* Low to short, rather bushy, erect annual, often hairy above, tinged with red. Leaves alternate, linear-oblong. Flowers *sky blue* with a whitish centre, 6-7mm, borne in a lax panicle; petals usually 7; stamens usually 14. Rocky and sandy habitats. Mar-June. NW Africa, Corsica, Sardinia and Sicily.

394 *Crassula vaillantii [Tilaea vaillantii]* **CRASSULA.** A low, hairless annual, erect or ascending. Leaves fleshy, opposite, *fused in pairs*, linear-oblong, reddish. Flowers pink, tiny, 1-2mm, on slender stalks, borne in irregular leafy clusters; sepals and petals 4. Moist muddy places and rock pools, generally wet in winter but dry in the summer. Feb-Apr. T, east as far as Cyprus and Libya.

395 *Crassula alata.* Similar, but generally a taller plant with the leaves and sepals *pointed*, not blunt and flowers borne in denser clusters. Moist sandy fields and depressions. Feb-Apr. Aegean Is. and Libya eastwards.

Umbilicus **NAVELWORTS.** Tuberous perennial herbs. Basal leaves orbicular with the stalk (petiole) coming from the centre of the blade; stem leaves smaller. Flowers borne in spike-like racemes or in panicles, with bracts; sepals and petals 5, the corolla tubular or bell-shaped; stamens 10.

396 *Umbilicus rupestris [U. pendulina, Cotyledon pendulina]* **NAVELWORT.** A very variable, medium erect perennial. Basal leaves orbicular with a central 'navel' and a long stalk, the margin somewhat scalloped; stem leaves becoming progressively and gradually smaller upwards. Flowers whitish-green to straw-coloured, occasionally tinged with pink, tubular, 7-10mm long, *pendent*, borne in long tapered racemes that are more than half the length of the stem. Rocks, cliffs and old walls, coastal and on mountains. Mar-June. T – in Africa only in the NW.

397 *Umbilicus parviflorus [Cotyledon parviflora]* **SMALL-FLOWERED NAVELWORT.** Similar, but flowers erect or horizontal, *smaller*, 4-6mm long, yellow, with corolla-lobes longer (not shorter) than the tube. Rocks and cliffs. Mar-May. Crete and S Greece.

398 *Umbilicus horizontalis [Cotyledon horizontalis].* Like *U. rupestris,* but upper stem leaves small and bract-like and racemes *less than* half the length of the stem; flowers horizontal, 7mm long. Limestone rocks and cliff crevices, old walls, coastal and in the mountains. Apr-May. W and C Med from Spain to Crete and Greece and in NW Africa; absent from Corsica and Sardinia.

399 *Aeonium arboreum* **AEONIUM.** An erect medium to tall subshrub with branched, thickened, somewhat woody stems. Leaves aggregated at stem tips into large *disk-like*, flat rosettes with numerous spirally arranged, fleshy leaves; leaves spatula-shaped with a rounded apex, bright shiny green, occasionally bronze or reddish-purple; margin bristly. Flowers bright yellow, 12-14mm, borne in large panicles; petals separate, 9-11. Rocky places, mostly cultivated. Jan-Mar. Morocco, but widely naturalised or grown in most Med countries. Cultivated since classical times.

PLANE TREE FAMILY Platanaceae

A small family with only 6-7 species, confined to the northern hemisphere.

400 *Platanus orientalis* **PLANE TREE.** Large deciduous tree to 30m, with a broad, rather irregular crown; bark dark brown, peeling away in irregular scales to reveal paler patches beneath. Leaves alternate, palmate with 5-7 lobes, coarsely toothed, long-stalked. Flowers borne in *globose clusters*, 3-6 on a pendent stalk, male and female separate but on the same tree; perianth 4-6-parted. Seeds with a tuft of long hairs at the base. In valleys bottoms, along streams and rivers, but widely planted in towns and as a roadside tree, or in parks and gardens. Apr-May. From Crete and Yugoslavia eastwards.

401 *Platanus* × *hybrida* [*P. occidentalis* × *P. orientalis*] **LONDON PLANE**. Similar, but bark peeling away in large pieces to give a distinctive patchwork appearance and leaves lobed less than halfway (not more) and with a *heart-shaped* base. Female flower clusters paired. Commonly planted along roadsides, in parks and town squares. Apr-May. T.

PITTOSPORUM FAMILY Pittosporaceae

A fairly small family of mainly trees and shrubs from the Old World, particularly Australasia. Flowers usually 5-parted, with both sepals and petals. Fruit a capsule or berry.

402 *Pittosporum tobira*. Dense evergreen shrub or small tree to 5m. Leaves alternate, deep green and leathery, paler beneath, oblong, the margins untoothed and *rolled under*. Flowers white, becoming cream, 18-22mm, very fragrant, borne in dense, flat-topped, terminal clusters; petal-lobes 5, blunt. Widely cultivated, sometimes as a hedge or street tree. May-Sept. Widely planted in the Med region (E China and Japan). A form with variegated leaves is sometimes encountered.

403 *Pittosporum undulatum*. Similar, but a larger more robust tree to 10m, occasionally more. Leaves laurel-like, leathery, deep green and shiny, with *wavy* margins. Flowers creamy-white, smaller, 12-18mm, in dense clusters. Occasionally planted in the Med, especially in Europe. May-July. (Australia).

ROSE FAMILY Rosaceae

A large and diverse family of trees, shrubs and herbs, with a worldwide distribution. Leaves alternate, simple or compound; stipules present. Flowers terminal, solitary or in racemes, cymes or panicles, often 5-parted, but generally with numerous stamens and few to many carpels; receptacle generally hollowed, but very variable, often with all the flower organs (except the carpels) attached to the rim. Fruit extremely variable from a capsule, to a collection of achenes, a drupe (plum and cherry) or a pome (apple and pear).

Rosa **ROSES, BRIARS**. Prickly shrubs, mostly deciduous. Leaves pinnate with toothed leaflets; stipules present. Flowers terminal, solitary or clustered. Sepals and petals usually 5. Stamens numerous, clustered with the sepals and petals on the rim of a deep cup- or urn-shaped hypanthium. Styles separate or fused into a column. Fruit a globose or pear-shaped hip.

404 *Rosa sempervirens*. Large trailing or scrambling evergreen shrub to 5m; stems with sparse curved prickles. Leaves leathery, hairless and shiny; leaflets usually 5-7, oval to lanceolate, sharply toothed. Flowers white, 22-40mm, borne in clusters of 3-7; sepals unlobed, recurved and soon falling; styles united into a *column*. Hip globose or egg-shaped, 10mm, red when ripe. Scrubby and bushy places, open woodland. May-July. T – except much of N Africa and the E Med.

405 *Rosa pimpinellifolia* **BURNET ROSE**. Suckering and patch-forming deciduous shrub to 1m; stems with numerous narrow prickles mixed with bristles. Leaves green and hairless; leaflets 5-11, oval to elliptical, sharply toothed. Flowers white, rarely pink, 20-40mm, solitary; styles short, not fused. Hip globose, 6-10mm, *black*

when ripe. Rocky and sandy places and scrub. Apr-June. France to Italy and the Balkans. Sometimes cultivated.

406 *Rosa glutinosa* **MEDITERRANEAN SWEET BRIAR.** Densely branched deciduous shrub to 1m; stems with stout prickles, mixed with bristles. Leaves yellowish green, *hairy*, with tiny glands on the upper surface; leaflets 5-7, oval, doubly serrate. Flowers pink, 20-30mm, borne in small cluster; styles hairy, not fused. Hip globose, 9-10mm, red, with stalked glands; sepals persistent and erect. Rocky habitats, occasionally in sandy places. Apr-June. C Med from Italy and Sicily to the Balkans, including Crete.

407 *Rosa sicula.* Similar, but the stems with narrower prickles and no bristles. Leaves hairless but glandular above. Similar habitats and flowering time. France to the Balkans, but not Crete.

408 *Rosa serafinii.* Like *R. sicula,* but prickles distinctly hooked and leaflets *shiny* and hairless above. Sepals reflexed and soon deciduous. Hip without glandular hairs. Similar habitats and flowering time. Corsica, Sardinia, Italy and Sicily.

409 *Neurada procumbens* **NEURADA.** Prostrate, white-hairy annual, not more than 14cm tall, with numerous radiating branches. Leaves oval, irregularly lobed, stalked. Flowers greenish, 4-5mm, solitary and axillary, with 5 oblong petals; stamens and styles 10. Fruit *disk-like*, 10-18mm, tough and woody, smooth below, but covered in spines above, 10-valved. Sandy coastal habitats. Mar-June. N Africa, E Med, including Cyprus.

410 *Poterium verrucosum [Sanguisorba minor* subsp. *magnolii]* **MEDITERRANEAN SALAD BURNET.** Variable, greyish, short to tall shrub; stems usually densely hairy. Leaves mostly in a basal rosette, pinnate, with 3-12 pairs of rounded or elliptical leaflets, toothed. Flowers in egg-shaped or globose heads with the upper flowers female and with reddish styles, the lower male with yellow anthers; sepals bright green, petals absent. Grassy and scrubby places, garrigue, field margins. Mar-May. C and E Med from Greece and Crete eastwards, including Cyprus.

411 *Sarcopoterium spinosum [Poterium spinosum, Sanguisorba spinosa]* **THORNY BURNET.** A dense, much-branched *spiny shrub* to 60cm; shoots densely hairy when young, branches interwoven, the lateral ones leafless and terminating in a spine. Leaves small, pinnate, with 9-15 ovate leaflets. Flowers greenish, in globose or oblong heads to 30mm, female flowers with purple feathery styles, above the male in each cluster. Fruit fleshy, bright red. Dry stony and rocky places, garrigue, embankments and open woodland. Feb-Apr. C and E Med from Sardinia eastwards.

412 *Potentilla hirta.* Short to tall, hairy perennial, to 70cm; stems and leaves with long hairs. Leaves *digitate*, with 5-7 green or grey linear to oblong leaflets, each with 3-7 blunt teeth or small lobes at the apex. Flowers bright yellow, 12-24mm, borne in lax clusters (cymes), with 5 sepals and petals; epicalyx present. Grassy, rocky and sandy places. Apr-June. W Med; Spain, France, Corsica and Italy.

413 *Aphanes arvensis [Alchemilla arvensis]* **PARSLEY-PIERT.** A low to short, slender, hairy annual; stems much-branched from the base, spreading to ascending. Leaves grey-green, 3-lobed, the lobes oblong and toothed, all stalked; stipules lobed and *fused together* in pairs. Flowers greenish, tiny, in stalkless clusters opposite the leaves; sepals 4 but petals absent. Cultivated ground and open habitats, woodland clearings, rarely at sea-level. Apr-June. T – but absent from most of N Africa. A British native.

414 *Aphanes microcarpa.* Similar, but lobes of stipules oblong (not triangular) and flowers less (not more) than 2mm. Open sandy, generally acid, habitats. NW

Africa and European Med except for the Balearic Is., Crete and much of the Balkans.

415 *Aphanes floribunda*. More robust than the two previous species, with *erect*, rather leafy stems, the upper leaves unstalked. Fruit 3.5mm long. Dry acid soils. Scattered localities from the Balearic Is. eastwards to Turkey and the E Med.

416 *Pyrus amygdaliformis [P. parviflora]* **ALMOND-LEAVED PEAR**. Deciduous shrub or small tree to 6m, often densely branched and sometimes spiny; branches grey, hairy when young. Leaves green and shiny at maturity, narrow-lanceolate to elliptical, usually untoothed but occasionally 3-lobed, stalked. Flowers white, 15-20mm, borne in dense clusters on short lateral branches (spurs); petals 5, usually notched at the apex. Fruit globose, 15-30mm, dull yellow-brown when ripe, with persistent sepals. Dry rocky, often open habitats, mountainsides. Mar-Apr. T – except parts of N Africa, the E Med, Balearic Is., Crete and Cyprus. The small hard fruits are inedible.

417 *Pyracantha coccinea [Cotoneaster pyracantha]* **FIRE THORN**. Densely branched evergreen shrub to 3m; branches *spiny*. Leaves elliptical, deep green, blunt-toothed, short-stalked, hairless or slightly hairy beneath. Flowers creamy-white, 7-8mm, borne in dense rounded clusters on short lateral shoots (spurs). Berry bright red, occasionally orange, 5-7mm, with small persistent sepals. Rocky slopes, scrub and woodland margins. May-June. From Spain to Turkey – absent from the islands. Widely cultivated as an ornamental plant or for hedging and naturalised in some Med countries outside its native distribution, particularly Portugal.

418 *Crataegus azarolus* **MEDITERRANEAN MEDLAR**. Deciduous tree or shrub to 10m forming a dense crown; young twigs white-cottony, later becoming blackish and smooth, generally with a few spines. Leaves oval with 3, sometimes 5, blunt, untoothed lobes. Flowers white, 15-20mm, borne in dense clusters on short lateral spurs; styles generally 2-3. Fruit (haw) sub-globose, 15-25mm, orange-red or yellow when ripe. Dry hillsides, lowland and in the mountains, rocky places, roadsides, field boundaries and woodland. Mar-Apr. Scattered localities from France to the E Med, including Cyprus – also in Algeria. Widely cultivated for its edible fruits (which have a pleasant, though somewhat acid, taste) and extensively naturalised in some places. The wild plant, which is referable to var. *aronia* (418a), is probably only truly native to Crete.

419 *Crataegus laciniata*. Similar, but the leaves with 3-7 acute, toothed lobes. *Styles* 3-5. Fruit 15-20mm. Rocky slopes and mountain thickets. Apr-May. Spain, Sicily, Crete and the Balkans.

420 *Crataegus monogyna* **HAWTHORN**. Widespread and variable species distributed throughout much of Europe is a more thorny plant than the preceding species, with *smaller* flowers, 8-15mm; styles 1. Fruit dark or bright red, 6-10mm, with deflexed sepals. Rocky places, hedges and thickets. Apr-May. T. A British native. Widely used as a hedging plant, especially in Europe.

421 *Prunus dulcis [Amygdalus communis, A. dulcis, Prunus communis]* **ALMOND**. A deciduous shrub or tree, to 8m, spiny, intricately branched. Leaves oblong-lanceolate, hairless, toothed, with glands on the short stalk. Flowers appearing *before* the leaves, bright pink in bud but fading to pale pink or white, 40-50mm, mostly in pairs. Fruit egg-shaped but somewhat compressed, 35-60mm, grey-green and velvety, the fleshy outer husk eventually splitting to reveal the hard pitted shell of the almond. Rocky places, roadsides, field boundaries and orchards – extensively cultivated. T – but only truly native in N Africa and W Asia. The cultivated form is generally taller with straighter, spineless branches. The fruits of the wild tree

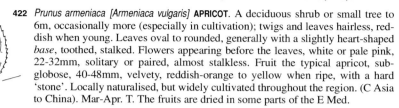

are generally bitter and contain poisonous prussic acid. In contrast, the edible almond, which contains a sweet edible oil, is known as var. *dulcis* (421a).

422 *Prunus armeniaca [Armeniaca vulgaris]* **APRICOT**. A deciduous shrub or small tree to 6m, occasionally more (especially in cultivation); twigs and leaves hairless, reddish when young. Leaves oval to rounded, generally with a slightly heart-shaped *base*, toothed, stalked. Flowers appearing before the leaves, white or pale pink, 22-32mm, solitary or paired, almost stalkless. Fruit the typical apricot, subglobose, 40-48mm, velvety, reddish-orange to yellow when ripe, with a hard 'stone'. Locally naturalised, but widely cultivated throughout the region. (C Asia to China). Mar-Apr. T. The fruits are dried in some parts of the E Med.

423 *Prunus persica* **PEACH**. Deciduous tree to 6m; twigs straight, reddish and hairless. Leaves oblong-lanceolate, rather *willow-like*, pointed, finely toothed, short-stalked. Flowers appearing before the leaves, deep pink, 22-30mm, mostly solitary. Fruit the familiar peach, 40-80mm, globose, velvety, yellow or pale green, with a reddish blush, and succulent when ripe. Extensively cultivated in orchards and gardens throughout the region, occasionally along roadsides, in hedges and on rocky slopes. Mar-Apr. T. (Probably China). Many forms are grown, including var. *nucipersica* (423a), the **NECTARINE**, which has smooth-skinned fruits.

424 *Prunus spinosa* **SLOE, BLACKTHORN**. Dense, twiggy, deciduous shrub to 4m, *suckering* to form thickets; branches spiny, with blackish bark, the young twigs usually hairy. Leaves oval, generally broadest above the middle, finely toothed, short-stalked. Flowers white, 10-15mm, mostly solitary, appearing before the leaves. Fruit (sloe) globose, 10-15mm, plum-like, black with a bluish bloom when ripe, very astringent. Woods, thickets, hedgerows and rocky places. Mar-May. T. Sloe Gin is made by steeping the ripe fruits in gin with sugar for some months. A British native.

425 *Prunus prostrata* **PROSTRATE CHERRY**. Low spreading, densely twiggy, deciduous shrub, growing flat on the ground or making hummocks; young twigs finely hairy. Leaves linear-oblong to elliptical, sharply toothed, grey-hairy beneath. Flowers bright pink, 12-15mm, mostly solitary. Fruit a small cherry, 8mm, red when ripe. Rocky, generally exposed habitats in hills and mountains. May-June. Spain and N Africa to Turkey and the Near East – absent from Portugal, France, Italy and Sicily, Balearic Is. and Cyprus.

426 *Prunus domestica* **WILD PLUM**. Very variable, often suckering, deciduous shrub or small tree, to 10m; branches often spiny in the wild form; bark dull dark brown. Leaves oval to elliptical, toothed, dull green and hairless above, but paler and hairy beneath. Flowers white, often tinged with green, 15-25mm, in small clusters with the emerging leaves. Fruit (plum) globose to egg-shaped, 20-75mm, red, purple, yellow or green when ripe, sweet- or acid-tasting, with a hard 'stone'. Widely cultivated and naturalised. Mar-May. T – not Crete. (Caucasus). The cultivated plant, which is spineless, is generally referred to subsp. *insititia* (426a).

427 *Prunus lusitanica* **PORTUGAL LAUREL**. Rather dense evergreen shrub or tree to 17m, occasionally more; young twigs and leaf-stalks red, hairless. Leaves elliptical to oblong, pointed, toothed, dark shiny green above. Flowers whitish, 10-15mm, borne in *long racemes*, suberect, longer than the leaves. Fruit egg-shaped to globose, 8-13mm, purplish-black when ripe. Rocky habitats, occasionally planted, rarely at sea level. May-June. Spain and Portugal. Planted elsewhere for ornament but seldom becoming naturalised.

428 *Rubus sanctus* Agg. *[R. ulmifolius]* **BRAMBLE, BLACKBERRY**. Very variable, thicket-forming, semi-evergreen shrub with arching or scrambling stems, armed with stout prickles, hairy or not. Leaves *pedate* (hand-like) with 3-5 elliptical to ovate, toothed leaflets, dark green above but whitish hairy beneath. Flowers pink or white, 20-32mm, borne in large prickly panicles. Fruit (blackberry) red at first, purplish-black when ripe, edible. Woodland, thickets, hedgerows, fields, banks and rocky places. June-Oct. T.

429 *Eriobotrya japonica* **JAPANESE LOQUAT.** Robust evergreen bush or small tree to 10m; young stems covered in reddish-brown felted hairs. Leaves *large*, to 30cm long, elliptical, toothed, ribbed, reddish-brown felted beneath. Flowers white, 10-12mm, borne in large terminal panicles; stamens 20. Fruit pear- or egg-shaped, 30-60mm, yellow when ripe and containing 1-3 hard seeds. Widely cultivated in the region as an ornamental and for its edible fruits – loquats. Aug-Sept. T. (C China). It has been cultivated in the Med region since the early nineteenth century.

PEA FAMILY Leguminosae

A large family in the region and generally very distinctive. Trees or herbs with trifoliate or pinnate leaves; occasionally with spines or tendrils. Flowers 5-petalled, most pea-shaped; upper petal (standard) often broad and erect, overlapping the lateral two (wings) which lie on each side of the lower two united petals (keel), which conceal the 10 stamens and style; sepal tube with 5 short or long teeth. Fruit a pod, often splitting when ripe, very variable.

430 *Cercis siliquastrum* **JUDAS TREE.** Deciduous tree to 10m with ascending branches; branches hairless. Leaves rounded with a heart-shaped base and a rounded or notched apex, untoothed, stalked, hairless. Flowers pea-shaped, borne in clusters directly on the *branches and trunk*, before or with the young leaves, pink-purple, rarely white, 15-20mm long; calyx bell-shaped. Pod linear-oblong, flattened, 60-100mm, with a narrow wing along one edge, pointed, pendent. Rocky and stony hillsides, thickets, but widely cultivated and naturalised. Mar-May, occasionally in the autumn. T. Traditionally said to be the tree upon which Judas Iscariot hanged himself and whose flowers blush with shame. Often planted.

431 *Ceratonia siliqua* **CAROB, LOCUST TREE.** An evergreen tree or shrub to 10m with stout trunk and branches. Leaves deep green and leathery, pinnate, but without an end leaflet; leaflets 2-5 pairs, heart-shaped to rounded, untoothed. Flowers green or reddish, either male or hermaphrodite, small, borne in short lateral racemes, each flower with 5 short sepals but no petals. Pod large, to 20cm, linear-oblong, flattened, brownish-violet, pendent. Dry rocky places, garrigue, maquis, woodland margins, scrub and field boundaries, often cultivated. July-Nov. T. The pods are an important source of fodder for livestock. The sweet, rather sickly, pods are also used for carob chocolate. The large, rather even-sized seeds were the original 'carats' used by jewellers.

Acacia **ACACIAS or WATTLES.** A large genus distributed from Africa and India to Australia, where there are many species. Shrubs or trees. Leaves variously pinnate or reduced to leaf-like phyllodes. Flowers borne in dense oblong or rounded, sometimes branched, heads; calyx and corolla 4-5-parted; stamens many and conspicuous, giving the inflorescences their fluffy 'mimosa-like' appearance. Pod linear to strap-shaped, usually splitting when ripe. Many species are grown in Med gardens.

432 *Acacia dealbata* **SILVER WATTLE.** Tree to 30m, with smooth grey bark; twigs and young leaves silvery-hairy. Leaves *2-pinnate*, bluish-green, with 8-10 pairs of

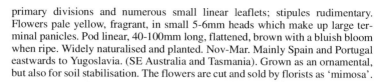

primary divisions and numerous small linear leaflets; stipules rudimentary. Flowers pale yellow, fragrant, in small 5-6mm heads which make up large terminal panicles. Pod linear, 40-100mm long, flattened, brown with a bluish bloom when ripe. Widely naturalised and planted. Nov-Mar. Mainly Spain and Portugal eastwards to Yugoslavia. (SE Australia and Tasmania). Grown as an ornamental, but also for soil stabilisation. The flowers are cut and sold by florists as 'mimosa'.

433 *Acacia farnesiana* CASSIE, POPINAC. Similar, but smaller, often only 3-4m, and deciduous; branches *spiny*; spines up to 25mm long. Leaves with 2-8 pairs of primary divisions. Flower-heads 10-12mm. Pod cylindrical, 50-90mm long. Widely cultivated as an ornamental species or for perfumery. Feb-Mar. Mainly Spain, France, Italy and Sardinia. (Dominican Republic). The flowers yield a violet-scented oil, cassie, used in perfumery.

434 *Acacia karroo.* Like *A. farnesiana,* but spines stouter, to 100mm long, and flower-heads in clusters of 4-6. Pod *flattened.* Grown in gardens and parks, occasionally as a hedge, locally naturalised. Mainly Spain, Portugal, Corsica and Sicily. (South Africa).

435 *Acacia pubescens* HAIRY WATTLE. Like *A. dealbata*, but generally a shrub to only 2-5m, with *velvety-white* leaves and young branches. Leaves with 3-10 pairs of primary divisions. Locally cultivated in the western Med. Mar. (Australia).

In the following evergreen species of *Acacia* the leaves of mature plants are reduced to flattened leafstems or phyllodes which are green and serve the function of leaves.

436 *Acacia longifolia* WHITE SALLOW, SYDNEY GOLDEN WATTLE. Shrub or small tree to 8m, with smooth grey bark; twigs stiff and hairless. 'Leaves' oblong-lanceolate, straight, pale green, with 2-4 main veins. Flowers bright yellow, strongly scented, borne in lateral *spikes*. Pod linear-cylindrical, 70-150mm long, straight and constricted between the seeds. Widely planted in the south-western Med for sand-dune stabilisation. Feb-Mar. Mainly Spain, Portugal, France and Italy. The bark is used in the tanning industry.

437 *Acacia melanoxylon* BLACKWOOD ACACIA. Large tree to 40m, often making a broad pyramidal shape; bark dark brown and furrowed; young twigs hairy. 'Leaves' lanceolate to elliptical, slightly curved, dull dark green, 60-130mm long, 3-5-veined; the phyllodes are occasionally mixed with immature 2-pinnate leaves or transitional forms. Flowers *creamy-white*, in heads 10mm diam. Pod 70-120mm long, twisted, reddish-brown when ripe. Widely planted, especially for timber and shade, but locally naturalised. Mar-Apr. Mainly Spain, Portugal, France and Italy. (SE Australia and Tasmania).

438 *Acacia retinoides.* Bush or tree to 10m with smooth brown twigs. 'Leaves' ascending, linear-lanceolate, 60-150mm long, straight, pale green, *1-veined.* Flowers pale yellow in 4-6mm heads, 5-10 of these to a raceme. Pod 60-120mm long, not or only slightly constricted between the seeds. Widely planted in parks and gardens, roadsides, occasionally naturalised. Feb-Mar. Mainly Spain, Portugal, France, Italy, Yugoslavia and Cyprus. (S Australia).

439 *Acacia cyanophylla* BLUE-LEAVED WATTLE. Similar, but twigs *pendent*, grey or greyish-brown and 'leaves' bluish-green, generally wider, 4-30mm (not 4-13mm). Flower-heads larger, 10-15mm. Pod constricted between the seeds. Widely grown in parks, gardens and along roads, but also used for sand-dune stabilisation. Similar distribution but also Corsica, Sardinia, Sicily and Greece. (W Australia).

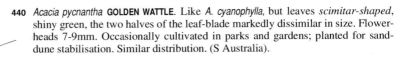

440 *Acacia pycnantha* **GOLDEN WATTLE**. Like *A. cyanophylla*, but leaves *scimitar-shaped*, shiny green, the two halves of the leaf-blade markedly dissimilar in size. Flower-heads 7-9mm. Occasionally cultivated in parks and gardens; planted for sand-dune stabilisation. Similar distribution. (S Australia).

441 *Acacia cultriformis*. Similar to *A. pycnantha*, but 'leaves' only 15-37mm long (not 40mm or more). Flower-heads 10-12mm. Pod linear, somewhat constricted between the seeds. Cutivated in parks, gardens and along roadsides. Mar-Apr. E Med, including Cyprus, occasionally elsewhere.

442 *Acacia armata* **KANGAROO THORN**. Spreading *spiny* shrub to 3-4m. Leaves simple, ending in a sharp spine, vertical with one edge pressed against the stem and the other curved and wavy; stipules spine-like, to 6mm long. Flower-heads yellow, 8-9mm, solitary on a short stalk. Pod linear, 30-50mm long, silky. Cultivated in parks and gardens, rarely naturalised. (Australia). Mar-Apr. Locally naturalised in the Med particularly in Europe.

443 *Albizia julibrissin* **ALBIZIA**. Deciduous tree to 15m forming a broad crown at maturity; stems hairless. Leaves large, 2-pinnate, with numerous oblong leaflets that are slightly hairy beneath. Flowers 10-50 in large spherical heads, long-stalked; corolla tubular, with 5 even teeth, greenish-white, 7-8mm; stamens with conspicuous silky, rose-pink filaments, 25-30mm long. Pod narrow-oblong, stalked, flattened, 130-160mm long. Widely planted in parks, gardens and streets; rarely naturalised. June-August. T. (Iran to China).

444 *Prosopis farcta* [*Mimosa farcta*, *Prosopis stephaniana*] **MEDITERRANEAN MESQUITE**. A spreading to erect, suckering, spiny shrub, to 50cm. tall; spines solitary or paired, slightly hooked. Leaves *2-pinnate*; leaflets small, oblong, hairy. Flowers greenish-yellow, borne in spike-like racemes; racemes 30-50mm long, flowers 3.5mm long; petals all separate. Pod thick, globose to oblong, 15-40mm long, dark brown when ripe. Cultivated and fallow fields, waste ground, scrub. June-July. Turkey and Cyprus eastwards.

445 *Prosopis juliflora* **HONEY MESQUITE**. Larger than the previous species, a tree to 15m, with larger leaves and cream flowers borne in spikes up to 60mm long. Pod linear, somewhat beaded, 150-250mm long. Occasionally planted in the hotter regions of the Med. (W Indies). A valuable tree in arid areas. The flowers produce a great deal of nectar for honey bees and the pods are useful cattle fodder.

446 *Anagyris foetida* **BEAN TREFOIL**. A spreading evil-smelling shrub, to 4m, rather laxly branched. Leaves trifoliate, the leaflets elliptical; stipules fused together at base of leaf-stalk. Flowers yellow, 18-25mm, the standard petal with a dark, blackish, blotch at the base, borne in short lateral racemes, opposite a leaf (leaf-opposed); standard petal *much shorter* than the other petals. Pod stalked, pendent, linear-oblong, 100-200mm long, hairless, somewhat constricted between the seeds. Rocky places, field boundaries, roadsides, scrub, generally on dry calcareous soils. Jan-Apr. T.

447 *Argyrolobium zanonii* **ARGYROLOBIUM** [*A. argenteum*. *Cytisus argenteus*, *C. zanonii*]. A small subshrub to 25cm tall, woody only at the base; stems and lower leaf-surfaces *silvery-hairy*. Leaves trifoliate, stalked; leaflets elliptical to lanceolate, hairless above or almost so. Flowers yellow, terminal, solitary or in groups of 2-3, 9-12mm long. Pod flat, slightly curved, 15-35mm long, silvery-hairy. Dry open habitats, stony and grassy places, open woodland, especially over limestone. Apr-July. From Spain and Portugal and NW Africa to Sicily and Yugoslavia.

448 *Argyrolobium uniflora* [*Cytisus uniflorus*]. Similar, but flowers always solitary and opposite the leaves, not terminal, 4-6mm long. Pod grey-brown, less hairy, 15-

25mm long. Limestone rocks, scrub, especially close to the coast. N Africa, Turkey, Cyprus and the E Med.

449 *Colutea arborescens* **BLADDER SENNA.** Much-branched deciduous shrub to 3m tall; young shoots often slightly hairy. Leaves pinnate with 4-6 pairs of elliptical to oval leaflets. Flowers yellow, 16-20mm, borne in few-flowered lateral racemes. Pod *inflated and bladder-like*, 50-70mm, brown and papery when ripe and often persisting well into the winter. Dry rocky and and grassy slopes, open woodland, on calcareous soils. May-Aug. T – absent from the Balearic Is., Crete, Cyprus and most of the Aegean Is. Widely cultivated as an ornamental shrub.

450 *Colutea orientalis.* Similar, but the flowers are orange-red and the pod split at one end. Occasionally cultivated in the Med region. (Caucasus). Hybrids between these two species are called *C.* × *media.*

451 *Podocytisus caramanicus* **PODOCYTISUS.** An erect, non-spiny shrub to 2m, with slender grey-green branches. Leaves trifoliate, with oval leaflets broadest above the middle. Flowers yellow, 12-15mm, borne in *erect* pyramidal, generally branched, racemes up to 15cm long. Pod oblong, flattened, 50-70mm long, with thin papery valves and a broad wing along one margin. Rocky habitats and scrub. Apr-June. Balkans – not most of the islands.

452 *Calycotome infesta [C. spinosa]* **THORNY BROOM.** Much-branched, *densely spiny* shrub to 3m, with alternate branches; spines stout, straight and lateral; young twigs slightly hairy. Leaves trifoliate, the leaflets oval, broadest above the middle, silvery-hairy beneath, but hairless above. Flowers mostly solitary, yellow, 12-18mm long. Pod narrow-oblong, 26-30mm long, usually hairless. Maquis, garrigue, scrub, cleared woodland and dry rocky ground. Jan-May. W Med from Spain to Italy and Sicily.

453 *Calycotome villosa* **HAIRY THORNY BROOM.** Very similar, but flowers mostly in clusters or short racemes of 2-15 and pod usually hairy. Similar habitats. Dec-Apr. T – absent from some of the smaller islands.

Cytisus **BROOMS.** Shrubs, without spines. Leaves with one or three leaflets, alternate. Flowers lateral but forming leafy racemes; calyx 2-lipped; corolla yellow or sometimes white. Pod linear to oblong, splitting when ripe, often explosively.

454 *Cytisus villosus [C. triflorus, C. lanigerus, Spartium villosum].* An erect shrub to 2m, with ascending branches, rigid and 5-angled. Leaves trifoliate, stalked; leaflets oblong-elliptical, hairy beneath. Flowers yellow, 15-18mm long, borne in groups of 2-3 or solitary, the standard petal lined with dark red at the base; calyx teeth dropping away to leave a cup like base. Pod narrow-oblong, 15-18mm long, hairy. Maquis, woods, scrub and rocky fields, generally on dry acid soils. Dec-Apr. From Spain and NW Africa to Greece – not Crete.

455 *Cytisus sessilifolius.* Similar, but leaves *stalkless* or almost so and leaflets broad-oval. Flowers in clusters or short racemes of 3-12, 10-13mm long. Deciduous woodland, scrub and rocky places. Mar-May. E Spain, S France and Italy.

456 *Cytisus scoparius [Sarothamnus scoparius]* **BROOM.** A very variable, much-branched shrub to 2m, occasionally more; stems slender, green and usually 5-angled, hairy or not. Leaves small, usually trifoliate but with single leaflets on young twigs; leaflets elliptical to oval. Flowers relatively large, 16-20mm long, golden-yellow, solitary or paired. Pod oblong, compressed, 25-40mm long, hairy along the margins only, black when ripe. Woods, heaths, rocky places, occasionally on sand-dunes, usually on acid soils. Apr-July. From Spain and Portugal eastwards to Sicily and Yugoslavia – not the Balearics. Occasionally planted in the region.

Introduced to many parts of the world; in some it has become naturalised and a nuisance.

457 *Chamaecytisus hirsutus [Cytisus hirsutus, C. pumilus, C. leucotrichus]* **HAIRY BROOM**. An extremely variable shrub, 20-100cm tall, with erect or spreading branches, sometimes spreading close to the ground; branches hairy. Leaves trifoliate, oval to elliptical, hairy beneath, hairy or not above. Flowers yellow, large, 20-25mm long, with a hairy calyx, the standard petal *often* with brown blotches. Pod linear, 25-40mm long, hairy at least on the margins. Woods, rocky and bushy places, mainly in the mountains. May-June. From France to Turkey, but absent from the islands.

458 *Chronanthus biflorus [Cytisus fontanesii, Spartium biflorum]* **CHRONANTHUS**. An erect to somewhat spreading, densely branched, unarmed shrub, to 50cm tall, though often less; branches 5-10-angled, hairy and producing flowers in their first year (on the current years' growth). Leaves trifoliate; leaflets linear to lanceolate, hairy. Flowers yellow, 8-12mm long, in groups of 2-4, occasionally solitary. Pod 10-15mm long, with translucent valves, hairless, *enclosed within* the persistent corolla. Scrub and woodland. Apr-May. Spain and the Balearic Is.

459 *Teline monspessulana [Cytisus monspessulanus]* **TELINE**. An erect, unarmed shrub, to 3m, though often less; *stems leafy*. Leaves trifoliate, stalked, the leaflets oval, broadest above the middle, somewhat hairy. Flowers deep yellow, 10-12mm, borne in lateral clusters; calyx silvery. Pod narrow-oblong, flattened, 18-20mm long, white-woolly, not splitting. Scrub and open woodland, rocky places. Apr-May. From Spain and Portugal to Greece – absent from the Balearic Is. and Crete.

460 *Teline linifolia [Cytisus linifolius, Genista linifolia]*. Similar, but rarely more than 1.5m tall, with narrower leaflets that are silkily-hairy and noticeably paler beneath. Flowers larger, in leafy clusters. Similar habitats and flowering time. Spain, France and the Balearic Is.

Genista **GREENWEEDS**. Spiny or non-spiny shrubs with simple leaves. Flowers yellow, borne in heads or racemes, with a 2-lipped calyx. Pod usually splitting open.

461 *Genista tinctoria* **DYER'S GREENWEED**. Very variable, suckering, rather erect shrub to 2m tall but often far less, unarmed. Leaves *simple*, oval to linear-lanceolate, hairy or not. Flowers yellow, 8-15mm, borne in leafy, stalked spikes, sometimes branched. Pod narrow-oblong, hairless. Grassy and rocky places, roadsides, heaths and open woodland. Apr-June. T – but absent from most of the smaller islands. Long used as a dye plant – yielding both green and yellow dyes; the seeds have purgative properties.

462 *Genista sphacelata [G. fasselata]*. Densely branched shrub to 1.5m tall, the branches with numerous recurved spines; branches opposite and alternate. Leaves trifoliate or simple; leaflets elliptical, broadest above the middle, silvery-hairy. Flowers yellow, 6-7mm, borne singly or in clusters, often *directly* on the spines. Pod egg-shaped, generally one-seeded. Dry rocky places and fields, maquis and garrigue. Mar-July. Crete, S Aegean Is. and the E Med, including Cyprus.

463 *Genista scorpius*. An erect or spreading, intricately branched shrub with stout lateral, spreading spines. Leaves inconspicuous, *simple*, elliptical, slightly hairy beneath. Flowers orange-yellow, 7-12mm long, borne in clusters directly on the spines. Pod narrow-oblong, 15-40mm long, constricted between the seeds. Exposed rocky and bushy slopes, lowland and in the mountains. Apr-June. Spain and France.

464 *Genista corsica.* Very similar, but flowers never borne directly on the spines and pod 12-20mm long. Garrigue and maquis. Corsica and Sardinia.

465 *Genista hispanica* **SPANISH GORSE.** Low, intricately branches spiny, gorse-like shrub to 50cm tall; young stems (current year) spineless and leafy but older stems leafless dark green and with numerous *branched* lateral spines. Leaves simple, lanceolate to elliptical, hairy beneath. Flowers yellow, 6-8mm long, borne in terminal clusters; bracts tiny. Rocky habitats and scrub, lowland and in the mountains. Apr-June. E Spain and France.

466 *Genista hirsuta.* Similar, but the spines are usually unbranched and the flowers are borne in distinctive *silvery-hairy* spikes; bracts leaf-like. Scrub and open woodland, lowland and in the mountains. Mar-May. S and W Spain, Portugal and NW Africa.

467 *Genista acanthoclada.* Low densely branched, very spiny shrub to 50cm tall; branches opposite, terminating in a spine; older branches with prominent *swellings* to the base of the leafstalks (where the stipules should be). Leaves trifoliate; leaflets narrow elliptical, broadest above the middle; bracts leaf-like. Flowers yellow, 6-10mm long, borne in clusters on the spines. Pod egg-shaped, 8-9mm long, silky-hairy, 1-seeded. Maquis and garrigue, pine woodland. June-July. Greece, Crete and the E Med – not Cyprus.

468 *Genista cinerea.* Large bush to 2m tall; stems densely branched, erect and arching, unarmed, ribbed and *greyish-white* with hairs. Leaves simple, elliptical, rather inconspicuous, silver-hairy beneath but hairless above. Flowers yellow, 10-12mm, mostly in pairs along the stems. Pod 15-18mm long. Woods and scrub, rocky open places, generally on calcareous soils. Mar-June. W Med, including NW Africa, from Portugal to Italy. The branches are used for making brooms.

469 *Genista aetnensis* **MT. ETNA BROOM.** Large shrub or small tree to 5m forming a substantial trunk in time, to 30cm diameter, sometimes more; young stems slender, green and much-branched. Leaves simple, small, elliptical, soon falling. Flowers yellow, 9-13mm, borne in lax racemes. Pod oval, flattened, 6-10mm long, hairless. Rocky places and scrub. Apr-June, occasionally later. Sardinia and Sicily. A frequently planted ornamental tree that can reach 9-10m in cultivation. Sometimes mistaken for *Spartium junceum* in the young state.

470 *Genista ephedroides.* Similar, but smaller, to only 1m tall with trifoliate leaves. Similar habitats and flowering time. Sardinia, Sicily and S Italy.

471 *Genista spartioides [G. retamoides].* Similar, but leaves simple and silvery-hairy on both surfaces. Flowers in small clusters which make up an interrupted raceme. Similar habitats and flowering time. S Spain and NW Africa.

472 *Genista umbellata [G. equisetiformis].* Densely tufted shrub to 60cm tall; branches mostly opposite; stems erect, green and rush-like, ribbed. Leaves simple, narrow-elliptical, silvery-hairy. Flowers yellow, borne in *heads* of 4-6; bracts leaf-like. Pod narrow-oblong, containing 2-5 seeds. Hot dry, generally rocky places. Mar-May. S Spain and NW Africa.

473 *Ulex parviflorus* **SMALL-FLOWERED GORSE.** A densely spiny shrub to 1.5m tall, though often less; long shoots hairy or almost hairless; spines straight or recurved, the terminal ones up to 30mm long. Leaves small and scale-like, alternate. Proper trifoliate leaves, as in all species of *Ulex*, are only produced in the seedling stage. Flowers yellow, 6.5-9mm long, the wings shorter than the keel petal, borne in lateral clusters or solitary; calyx yellowish, *2-lipped*, hairy at first. Pod egg-shaped, hairy, mostly held within the persistent calyx. Rocky and stony places, scrub. Mar-July. Spain, Portugal, France and the Balearic Is.

473a Subsp. *funkii* has larger flowers, 9-11mm long. S Spain and NW Africa.

474 *Ulex argenteus*. Similar, but young twigs and spines *covered* by short white hairs. Similar habitats and flowering time. S Portugal and Spain.

475 *Ulex europaeus* **GORSE**. Stouter bush than the preceding, to 2.5m, the calyx and fruit with spreading (not appressed) hairs and the flowers larger, 16-20mm long. Rocky places, cliffs, hedgerows, roadsides and woodland margins. Mar-Sept. Spain, Portugal, France and Corsica. Widely planted inside and outside the area as a hedging or fodder plant; sometimes naturalised. When ripe the seed pods explode to expel the seeds, especially during hot dry weather.

476 *Stauracanthus boivinii [Ulex boivinii]* **STAURACANTHUS**. A densely and intricately branched, spiny shrub to 50cm tall; stems and spines hairless or hairy; spines straight, the terminal ones 3-4mm long. Leaves small and scale-like, generally opposite. Flowers yellow, 9-12mm long, the petals much longer than the 2-lipped calyx; calyx brown-hairy, tubular in the lower half. Pod oblong, 8-12mm long, *greatly exceeding* the calyx. Rocky, sandy and gravelly habitats. Apr-June. Spain and Portugal.

477 *Stauracanthus genistoides*. Very similar, but standard petal the same length as the calyx (not longer) and the pod 15-25mm long. Similar habitats and distribution.

478 *Lygos sphaerocarpa [Retama sphaerocarpa]* **LYGOS**. A spineless shrub to 2m, much-branched, the branches erect to spreading, hairless, ribbed, with a *silvery sheen*. Leaves small, linear to linear-lanceolate, silvery-hairy, soon falling. Flowers yellow, small, 5-8mm long, borne in erect, lateral clusters; calyx persistent in fruit. Pod egg-shaped, 7-9mm long, smooth. Dry habitats, especially on sandy soils, coastal or in the hills. Mar-May. Portugal and S Spain.

479 *Lygos raetam [Retama raetam]* **WHITE BROOM**. Erect, much-branched shrub to 2m; lateral branches pendent, silvery when young. Leaves sparse, linear, silvery-hairy, soon falling. Flowers *white*, becoming cream on ageing, 15-17mm long, borne in masses in dense racemes, sweetly scented; calyx falling after the flowers open. Pod club-shaped, 10-20mm long, beaked. Maritime sands. Feb-Apr. Sicily and N Africa, occasionally in the E Med.

480 *Lygos monosperma [Retama monosperma]*. Similar, but a taller shrub to 3m with smaller flowers, 10-12mm long. Pod rough when mature. Similar habitats and flowering time. SW Spain and S Portugal.

481 *Spartium junceum* **SPANISH BROOM**. Large, spineless shrub to 3m, occasionally more, with numerous cylindrical, bluish-green, *rush-like* stems. Leaves sparse, linear-oblong, soon falling. Flowers large, bright yellow, 20-25mm long, generally solitary but borne in profusion, sweetly scented. Pod flattened, 50-80mm long. Dry slopes, maquis, open woodland, roadsides, generally on calcareous soils. May-Aug. T – not Cyprus and parts of the E Med, but widely planted. The flexible branches are sometimes used for making baskets and weaving.

482 *Adenocarpus complicatus [A. intermedius]* **ADENOCARPUS**. A very variable, generally erect, spineless shrub, to 4m; twigs and leaves sparsely to densely hairy, sometimes glandular. Leaves trifoliate, the leaflets elliptical, broadest above the middle. Flowers *orange-yellow*, 10-15mm long, borne in terminal racemes or clusters. Pod narrow-oblong, 15-45mm long, usually covered in glandular warts. Rocky and shrubby habitats, garrigue, occasionally in open woodland. Mar-June. From Spain and Portugal to E Greece and Turkey, but absent from the islands, except Sicily.

Lupinus **LUPINS**. Annual or perennial herbs with long-stalked digitate leaves, with the 5-11 leaflets all arising from a single point. Flowers borne in terminal or lateral spike-like racemes, the individual flowers alternate or whorled.

483 *Lupinus luteus* **YELLOW LUPIN**. Medium-tall hairy annual. Leaflets oblong, sparsely hairy. Flowers *bright yellow*, 13-16mm long, borne in whorls along the raceme, scented. Pod 40-50mm long, densely hairy, black when ripe. Generally on light acid soils, sandy places. roadsides; widely cultivated for fodder and as a green manure. Mar-July. From Spain and Portugal to Italy and Sicily.

484 *Lupinus micranthus [L. hirsutus]* **HAIRY LUPIN**. Short to medium, brown-hairy annual. leaflets oblong, often broadest above the middle, sparsely hairy. Flowers blue, 10-14mm long, the standard petal with a whitish central zone and the keel tipped with blackish-violet, borne in irregular whorls along the raceme. Pod 30-50mm long, *hairy*, reddish-brown when ripe. Acid soils, waste ground, waysides, road verges, open woodland. Mar-May. T – absent from the islands.

485 *Lupinus albus* **WHITE LUPIN**. Similar, but flowers larger, white to pale blue, all alternate in the raceme. Pod 60-100mm long, almost hairless, yellow when ripe. Cultivated, waste and disturbed ground. From Crete and Yugoslavia eastwards, but widely cultivated in the western Med. The seeds are edible; widely grown for fodder.

486 *Lupinus angustifolius* **NARROW-LEAVED LUPIN**. Short to tall, hairy annual. Leaflets *narrow*, linear to spatula-shaped, slightly hairy beneath, not more than 5mm wide. Flowers dark blue, 11-13mm long, borne alternately in the raceme. Pod with short hairs, yellow to black when ripe. Cultivated land, vineyards, field margins, garrigue, mainly on acid sandy soils. Mar-May. T.

487 *Lupinus varius*. Short to medium softly-hairy annual. Leaflets oblong. Flowers blue, *larger* than the previous species, 15-17mm long, the standard petal with a pale purple blotch or with a white and yellow patch; flowers borne in irregular whorls in the raceme. Pod 40-50mm long, 13-20mm wide (up to 12mm wide in other species), softly hairy, dark reddish-brown when ripe. On light sandy, acid soils, cultivated and waste land. Mar-June. From NW Africa and Portugal eastwards to Crete and Greece.

488 *Robinia pseudacacia* **FALSE ACACIA**. A deciduous tree to 25m, often suckering; bark pale greyish-brown, irregularly fissured; young branches usually with spine-like stipules. Leaves pinnate; leaflets elliptical to oval, usually hairless. Flowers white, 15-20mm, scented, the standard petal yellowish at the base, borne in *pendent* racemes. Pod linear-oblong, 50-100mm long, flattened. Commonly planted for ornamental purposes or for stabilising light or sandy soils. May-June. Widely planted and naturalised. (C and E North America). The wood, hard and long-lasting, is used for fencing. Sometimes parasitised by Mistletoe.

489 *Robinia viscosa*. Similar, but twigs and leafstalks sticky with glands and racemes of *purple* flowers shorter. Pod bristly-glandular. Occasionally planted in the region, especially in Europe. (SE North America).

490 *Galega officinalis* **GOAT'S-RUE**. Medium to tall, hairless or somewhat hairy perennial to 1.5m; stems erect. Leaves pinnate with 4-8 pairs of oblong to lanceolate leaflets; stipules green. Flowers white to pale purplish-lilac, 10-15mm long, borne in lateral racemes. Pod cylindrical, *constricted* between the seeds, 20-50mm long, erect to spreading. Woodland margins, scrub, waysides and cultivated land. June-Aug. From Spain to Turkey but widely cultivated for ornament and frequently naturalised.

Astragalus **MILK-VETCHES**. Annual or perennial herbs or small shrubs. Leaves pinnate, ending in a leaflet or a spine. Flowers borne in lateral racemes or clusters; calyx tubular or bell-shaped, 5-toothed. Pod very variable.

491 *Astragalus boeticus.* Hairy short to medium annual, with erect stems; hairs simple. Leaves with 10-15 pairs of oblong leaflets, notched at the apex, hairless above but sparsely hairy beneath. Flowers yellow, 12-14mm long, borne in dense racemes on stalks half as long as the leaves; wing petals longer than the keel. Pod oblong, triangular in cross-section, 20-40mm long, grooved beneath, with a hooked beak covered in short hairs. Cultivated land. Feb-May. From NW Africa and Portugal eastwards to Greece.

492 *Astragalus hamosus.* Similar, but leaflets 9-11 pairs and flowers smaller, 7-8mm long; hairs mostly T-shaped (medifixed). Pod linear, *sickle-shaped*, linear-cylindrical, 20-50mm long. Cultivated and waste land, roadsides and rocky places. Feb-Apr. T.

493 *Astragalus stella.* Low to short annual, rarely more than 20cm tall, with spreading to ascending stems. Leaves with 9-11 pairs of oblong leaflets, often broadest above the middle, usually densely hairy on both surfaces. Flowers yellowish, 9-11mm long, borne in dense racemes on stalks a half to the same length as the leaves. Pod lanceolate, straight, 10-15mm long, pointed, borne in distinctive *star-shaped* clusters, hairy. Cultivated and waste ground, waysides. Mar-May. NW Africa, Spain, Portugal and France; rare in Greece.

494 *Astragalus sesameus.* Similar, but taller and more robust with less hairy leaflets and racemes scarcely stalked. Pods generally erect. Similar habitats and flowering time. From NW Africa and Portugal eastwards to Sicily and Greece – not Crete.

495 *Astragalus epiglottis.* Somewhat similar to *A. stella*, but leaflets usually only 5-7 pairs and flowers small, only 3-4mm long and with 5, not 10, stamens. Pod *heart-shaped*, hairy, not erect. Dry places on open hillslopes, waste ground and roadsides. Mar-Apr. T – but often local.

496 *Astragalus massiliensis [A. tragacantha]* **TRAGACANTH**. A laxly tufted, *extremely spiny* perennial to 30cm tall, woody at the base. Leaves with 6-12 pairs of oblong or elliptical leaflets, ending in a stiff spine, densely hairy beneath. Flowers white, 13-17mm long, borne in short racemes. Pod oblong, pointed, 9-10mm long, covered with short hairs. Sunny, usually rocky places. Apr-June. NW Africa and Portugal eastwards to Corsica and Sardinia – not Balearic Is.

497 *Astragalus sirinicus.* Similar, but more densely tufted and leaflets often pointed. Flowers yellowish tinged with violet, 14-19mm long. Pod 10-13mm long. C Med from France and Corsica to Italy and Greece.

498 *Astragalus balearicus.* Like *A. massiliensis*, but only 3-5 pairs of leaflets, less hairy. Flowers 11-12mm long. Pod 7-9mm long. Balearic Is.

499 *Astragalus spruneri. Stemless*, non-spiny, prostrate perennial. Leaves with 5-10 pairs of oval leaflets, grey-white-hairy. Flowers pale purple or violet, 20-30mm long, borne in racemes with stalks longer than the leaves. Pod oblong, 12-20mm long, curved and wrinkled. Dry hillslopes, rocky places, scrub. Mar-May. Balkans, Rhodes and Turkey.

500 *Astragalus cyprius.* Very similar, but pods long, narrow and tapered. Flowers dirty-pink or yellowish. Dry hillslopes on sandy or calcareous soils – not at sea level. Feb-May. Cyprus, endemic.

501 *Astragalus echinatus [A. pentaglottis]*. Short to medium, somewhat hairy annual. Leaflets 6-9 pairs, oblong, notched or truncated at the apex, slightly hairy beneath but hairless above. Flowers purplish, 8-9mm long, borne in dense racemes with stalks equalling or longer than the leaves. Pod oval-triangular, flattened, 12-15mm long, *covered* in bristles and contorted scales, with a hooked beak. Cultivated and waste ground, hillslopes. Mar-May. NW Africa and Portugal to Crete and Greece, but absent from most of the islands.

502 *Astragalus graecus.* Stout medium perennial, to 40cm tall; stems erect and hairy. Leaves with 20-35 pairs of oval to heart-shaped leaflets, woolly beneath but hairless above. Flowers yellow, *large*, 30-40mm long, borne in short-stalked racemes. Pod oblong, scarcely flattened, 25-30mm long, hairy. Fields, meadows, waste ground and waysides. Apr-June. C and S Greece, Rhodes and Samos.

503 *Astragalus drupaceus.* Similar, but smaller and leaves with 8-25 pairs of leaflets. Racemes only 3-5-flowered (not 5-10). Pod 10-17mm long, hairless. S Greece. (Peloponnese).

504 *Astragalus lusitanicus.* An erect, occasionally spreading, greyish-hairy, medium to tall perennial, to 1m. Leaves with 8-12 pairs of oblong to elliptical leaflets, hairless above. Flowers creamy or greenish-white, 20-35mm long, borne in long-stalked lateral, dense, oblong racemes. Pod oblong, 50-70mm long, inflated, pendulous, greyish-hairy, brown or black eventually. Dry rocky places, garrigue, beneath pine trees – not at sea level. Mar-June. Spain, Portugal and NW Africa.

504a Subsp. *orientalis* differs in having the leaflets hairy above and a densely hairy calyx. Feb-May. Greek Peloponnese, Aegean Is., Turkey and the E Med, including Cyprus.

505 *Bisserula pelecinus [Astragalus pelecinus]* **BISSERULA.** A short to medium hairy, erect to sprawling annual. Leaves pinnate with 7-15 pairs of linear-oblong to rounded, notched leaflets. Flowers blue, or pale yellow with a blue tip, 4-6mm long, borne in lateral racemes. Pod 10-40mm long, flat, with coarsely toothed margins, like a *two-edged sword*, hairy or not. Bare and arid places, generally on sandy ground, fallow fields. Mar-June. T.

506 *Glycyrrhiza glabra [G. glandulifera]* **LIQUORICE.** A medium to tall, robust perennial. Leaflets with 4-8 pairs of elliptical to oblong leaflets, usually *sticky* with glands. Flowers pale purple or violet, 8-12mm long, borne in racemes shorter than the leaves. Pod linear-oblong, flattened and straight, 15-30mm long, often glandular, sometimes bristly. Sandy or marshy habitats, scrub and by ditches. Apr-June. T – absent from some of the smaller islands. Cultivated as a source of liquorice (which comes from the roots) and often naturalised.

507 *Glycyrrhiza echinata* **SPINY-FRUITED LIQUORICE.** Similar, but often taller and with 2-6 pairs of leaflets. Pods borne in distinctive heads, each pod 12-16mm long and with glandular reddish-brown *spines*. Marshy places, particularly by streams and rivers. Italy, the Balkans, Crete and Turkey.

508 *Psoralea bituminosa* **PITCH TREFOIL.** Short to tall, rather dull grey-green perennial, sparsely to densely hairy, *smelling of bitumen*. Leaves trifoliate, long-stalked; leaflets narrow-lanceolate to oval or rounded, untoothed, with transparent glands (dots seen against the light). Flowers violet-blue or lilac, 15-20mm long, borne in lateral long-stalked heads. Pod oval, 5-15mm long, with a curved beak. Dry, arid and rocky places, roadsides, fallow and cultivated ground. Apr-July. T.

509 *Psoralea americana [P. dentata].* Similar, but leaflets *toothed* and flowers smaller, whitish-violet, borne in distinct racemes. Similar habitats. W Med from Portugal to Italy and Sicily, but not the other islands.

Vicia **VETCHES**. Annual or perennial herbs, often climbing with the aid of leaf tendrils; stems often ridged, but not winged. Leaves pinnate, terminating in a tendril or sometimes a point, but not a leaflet; stipules small and green. Flowers solitary, clustered or in racemes; calyx even or 2-lipped. Pod oblong, often rather flattened, curved and pointed.

510 *Vicia villosa* **FODDER VETCH**. Short to tall clambering, hairy annual, to 2m, though often less; stems with long hairs. Leaves with 4-12 pairs of linear to elliptical leaflets; tendrils branched; stipules *unlobed*. Flowers violet, purple or blue, rarely with whitish or yellowish wings, 10-20mm long, 10-30 borne in racemes whose stalk is shorter than the subtending leaf. Pod 20-40mm long, brown, hairless stalked. Cultivated and waste places, waysides, garrigue. Mar-June. T – except for some of the smaller islands. Widely cultivated as a fodder crop.

510a Subsp. *varia [Vicia dasycarpa]*. Similar, but stems hairless or with short (appressed) hairs and racemes generally longer than the leaves. Similar habitats as well as hedgerows and stony ground. T – widely naturalised.

510b Subsp. *microphylla*. Similar to the previous subspecies, but racemes with only 2-10 flowers and pod hairy or hairless. S Greece and the Aegean Is.

511 *Vicia cretica* **CRETAN VETCH**. Similar to *V. villosa*, but a short plant with only 3-4 pairs of leaflets to each leaf and tendrils branched or unbranched. Flowers white or yellowish with a purple tip; racemes 1-6-flowered. Pod brown, hairy or not. Rocky and bushy places. Mar-May. From Crete and Greece eastwards, including Cyprus. Often grows in association with *Sarcopoterium spinosum*.

512 *Vicia monantha*. Similar to *V. cretica*, but almost hairless and leaves with 4-7 pairs of leaflets. Flowers pale purple. Pod yellowish, hairless. Rocky and waste ground. Mar-May. T – except Portugal, Yugoslavia and some of the smaller islands.

513 *Vicia benghalensis [V. atropurpurea]*. Short to tall hairy annual, or short-lived perennial. Leaves with 5-9 pairs of linear to elliptical leaflets; tendrils branched; stipules toothed or untoothed. Flowers reddish-purple, usually *black* at the tip, 10-18mm long, 2-12 borne in racemes longer than the leaves. Pod brown, 25-40mm long, hairy at least in part. Cultivated and waste places, waysides, occasionally on stony ground. Apr-June. W and C Med from Portugal and NW Africa to Greece.

514 *Vicia altissima*. Similar to *V. benghalensis*, but a larger plant, often reaching 1.5m or more. Leaflets oblong, sometimes finely toothed; stipules distinctly toothed. Flowers white with bluish veins on the standard, 15-19mm long. Pod brown, 40-50mm long, usually hairless. Bushy and waste places, roadsides. Apr-June. W Med from France to Italy and Sicily.

515 *Vicia onobrychioides* **FALSE SAINFOIN**. Similar to *V. altissima*, but leaflets narrower, only 1-4mm (not 4-9mm) wide. Flowers violet or blue with a paler keel, 17-24mm long. Similar habitats and flowering time. Portugal to Turkey and NW Africa.

516 *Vicia ervilia*. Low to medium hairy or hairless annual, without tendrils. Leaves ending in a short awn, with 8-15 pairs of linear to oblong leaflets; stipules lobed or unlobed. Flowers white tinged with red or purple, 6-9mm long; racemes 1-4-flowered. Pod yellow, 10-30mm long, hairless, *constricted* between the seeds. Waste and cultivated land, roadsides and stony slopes. Feb-June. T.

517 *Vicia leucantha*. Similar to *V. ervilia*, but upper leaves generally with tendrils and leaflets 5-10 pairs. Flowers pale purple. Pod pale brown, usually *hairy*, not constricted between the seeds. Similar habitats and flowering time. C Med from Balearic Is. and NW Africa to Yugoslavia – not France.

518 *Vicia viciodes*. Similar to *V. leucantha*, but flowers smaller, 4-8mm long (not 6-10mm) and pod yellowish with a *long stalk* (between the pod and the calyx). Spain, Portugal and NW Africa.

519 *Vicia hirsuta* **HAIRY TARE**. Short to medium, rather delicate, hairy annual. Leaves with 4-10 pairs of linear to oblong leaflets, often notched at the tip; tendrils branched; stipules slightly toothed or untoothed. Flowers dirty-white with a purple tinge, *small*, 2-4mm long; racemes 1-8-flowered. Pod black, 6-14mm long, generally hairy. Cultivated and waste ground, roadsides. Mar-July. T.

520 *Vicia palaestina*. Like *V. hirsuta*, but a sparsely hairy or almost hairless plant with milky-blue flowers. Pods *larger*, 18-25mm long, hairless, pale brown. Garrigue, rocky and bushy places. Feb-Apr. Cyprus, Turkey and the E Med.

521 *Vicia laxiflora [V. tenuissima]* **SLENDER TARE**. Short to medium, almost hairless annual. Leaves with 2-5 pairs of linear leaflets; stipules untoothed. Flowers pale blue to pale purple, 6-9mm long; racemes 2-5-flowered, long-stalked. Pod brown, 12-17mm long, hairy or not. Scrub, hedgerows, open pine forest, roadsides, garrigue. Feb-May. T.

522 *Vicia pubescens*. Like *V. laxiflora*, but leaflets wider, 3-5mm (not 0.5-3mm). Pod usually hairy. Similar habitats and flowering time. T. Often grows in association with *V. laxiflora*.

523 *Vicia tetrasperma* **SMOOTH TARE**. Like *V. laxiflora*, but racemes 1-2-flowered, *equalling*, not longer, than the leaves. Pod 9-16mm long. Similar habitats, often in grassy or bushy places and along roadsides. Feb-July. T – except Crete and Corsica.

524 *Vicia sepium* **BUSH VETCH**. Medium to tall, usually hairy, clambering perennial to 1m. Leaves with 3-9 pairs of oval to oblong leaflets, rounded or notched at the tip; tendrils branched; stipules lobed, with a *dark spot* near the base. Flowers purplish-blue, 12-15mm long, in clusters of 2-6, with a very short common stalk. Pod black, 20-35mm long, hairless. Rocky, bushy and grassy places, garrigue, hedgerows, woodland margins and roadsides. Mar-Sept. T – except the Balearics Is., Corsica and Crete and much of the E Med.

525 *Vicia lutea* **YELLOW VETCH**. Low to medium, prostrate or clambering, hairy annual. Leaves with 3-10 pairs of linear to oblong leaflets; tendrils branched; stipules toothed or untoothed. Flowers pale *sulphur yellow*, sometimes flushed with purple, 20-35mm long, solitary or 2-3 together; standard petal hairless on the back. Pod yellowish-brown to black, 20-40mm long, hairy. Cultivated ground, tracksides, grassy coastal habitats, stabilised shingle and sand-dunes. Apr-Aug. T, except Cyprus and parts of the E Med.

526 *Vicia pannonica*. Short to medium hairy annual, generally much-branched from the base. Leaves with 4-10 pairs of oblong leaflets; tendrils branched; stipules untoothed, with a spot at the base. Flowers dirty-purple or pale yellow, 14-22mm long, in very short-stalked clusters of 2-4; standard petal *hairy* on the back. Pod yellow, 20-35mm long, hairy. Cultivated fields and waste ground, often close to sea level. Apr-June. Spain eastwards to Turkey and Cyprus.

527 *Vicia hybrida* **HAIRY YELLOW VETCHLING**. Similar, but leaflets 3-8 pairs and flowers *solitary*, 18-30mm long. Pod brown, 25-40mm long, hairy. Cultivated ground, fields, tracks, forest margins, sand-dunes, often in moist shaded places. Mar-June. T.

528 *Vicia melanops*. Short to tall, sprawling to clambering, hairy annual. Leaves with 5-10 pairs of oblong leaflets, rounded or notched at the end. Flowers greenish-yellow, the wings tipped with black and the keel purple, 15-22mm long, solitary or in clusters of 2-4. Pod brown, 20-50mm long, hairy, warted along the margins.

Garrigue, bushy and grassy places, olive groves, roadsides. Mar-June. From France to Turkey, but absent from most of the islands, except Sicily.

529 *Vicia grandiflora* **LARGE YELLOW VETCH**. Like *V. melanops*, but flowers larger 23-35mm long, yellow, sometimes tinged with purple, the wings occasionally black-tipped. Pod black, 30-50mm long, hairy. Similar habitats and flowering time. C and E Med from Italy and Sicily to Crete, the Balkans and Turkey.

530 *Vicia barbazitae*. Like *V. grandiflora*, but flowers smaller, 18-22mm long, yellow with *blue* wings. Pod brown, glandular, hairless at both ends. Similar habitats and flowering time. C Med from France and Corsica to the Balkans – not Crete.

531 *Vicia sativa* **COMMON VETCH**. Very variable, short to medium, sprawling to clambering, hairy annual. Leaves with 3-8 pairs of linear to heart-shaped leaflets; tendrils branched; stipules toothed, usually with a dark spot. Flowers purple, 10-30mm long, solitary or paired. Pod yellowish-brown to black, 25-70mm long, breaking the calyx when mature. Cultivated and waste ground, roadsides and grassy habitats. Jan-Apr. T. Widely grown for fodder and often escaping.

532 *Vicia lathyroides* **SPRING VETCH**. Similar to *V. sativa*, but always low and spreading and with simple unbranched tendrils and unspotted stipules. Flowers small, 5-8mm long. Pod black, 15-30mm, hairless, with a short, curved beak. Garrigue and dry mountainsides, often on acid soils. Mar-Apr. T.

533 *Vicia peregrina* [*V. megalosperma*]. Similar to *V. sativa*, but stipules *untoothed* and flowers not more than 16mm long, with a deeply notched standard petal. Similar habitats as well as rocky hillsides, garrigue and pastures. Feb-June. T.

534 *Vicia narbonensis*. Short to medium, hairy annual; stems rather robust, ascending to erect, not climbing. Leaves with 2-3 pairs of oblong to elliptical leaflets, toothed or not, the lower leaves *without tendrils*; stipules toothed or not. Flowers white veined purple or all purple, 20-30mm long, solitary or paired, the wings often with a deep purple blotch near the apex. Pod black or brown, 30-70mm long, hairless, with a somewhat toothed margin. Cultivated and waste places, roadsides, garrigue and bushy areas. Feb-June. T – except for the smaller islands. Closely related to the Broad Bean, *Vicia faba* (535) which is often cultivated in the region and sometimes naturalised.

Lathyrus **PEAS**. Annual or perennial herbs, often with leaf tendrils. Like *Vicia* but usually with winged stems and fewer leaflets. Leaves sometimes reduced to grass-like phyllodes. Flowers borne in axillary racemes, sometimes solitary. Pod usually narrow-oblong and compressed.

536 *Lathyrus tingitanus* **TANGIER PEA**. Medium to tall, clambering, hairless annual, to 1.2m; stem winged. Leaves with 1 pair of linear-lanceolate to oval leaflets; tendrils branched; stipules lanceolate to oval with an arrow-shaped base. Flowers bright rosy-purple, 20-30mm, borne in 1-3-flowered racemes. Pod brown, 60-100mm long, hairless, shiny at maturity. Bushy, grassy and rocky places, open woodland, garrigue. Apr-July. Spain, Portugal and Sardinia, NW Africa. Cultivated and sometimes naturalised in the region.

537 *Lathyrus latifolius* **BROAD-LEAVED EVERLASTING PEA**. Very variable, tall, robust, clambering or sprawling perennial to 3m, with a wide-winged stem, hairy or hairless. Leaves with 1 pair of linear to elliptical leaflets, mostly with 5 prominent *parallel* veins; tendrils branched. Flowers magenta-purple, pink or rarely white, 20-30mm, borne in 5-10-flowered, long-stalked racemes. Pod brown, 50-110mm long, hairless. Bushy and grassy places, roadsides and embankments. June-Aug.

W and C Med eastwards to Greece, including NW Africa. Widely cultivated and often naturalised.

538 *Lathyrus sylvestris* **NARROW-LEAVED EVERLASTING PEA**. Very similar, but stipules less (not more) than *half the width* of the winged stem and leaves generally narrower, 3-veined. Flowers purplish-pink, smaller 13-20mm. Pod brown, 40-70mm long, hairless. Bushy places, woodland, hedgerows and roadsides. June-Aug. T – except for parts of the E Med, including Cyprus.

539 *Lathyrus odoratus* **SWEET PEA**. Medium to tall clambering annual, to 2m, usually slightly hairy. Leaves with 1 pair of oval to elliptical, somewhat undulate leaflets; tendrils branched; stipules arrowhead-shaped. Flowers bicolored, pink or purple with a deep purple-magenta standard petal, 20-35mm, *sweetly scented*, 1-3 borne in long-stalked racemes. Pod brown, 50-70mm long, hairy. Bushy places, woodland margins. May-July. S Italy and Sicily. Widely cultivated for ornament; many colour forms exist from white to pink, red, lavender, purple or blue, sometimes bicolored and these may occasionally become naturalised in the region.

540 *Lathyrus saxatilis [L. ciliatus, Vicia saxatilis]*. Short hairy annual; stems not winged. Leaves mostly with 1-3 pairs leaflets but no tendril; leaflets of lower leaves heart-shaped with 3 teeth at the top, those of upper leaves linear. Flowers whitish veined with pale blue, or yellowish, solitary and small, 6-9mm. Pod brown, 15-30mm long, hairless. Rocky places, screes, open pine woodland. Feb-Apr. T – rarer in the E Med.

541 *Lathyrus sphaericus*. Short to medium, hairy or hairless annual; stems not winged. Leaves mostly with 1 pair of linear to lanceolate leaflets; tendrils branched. Flowers *red or orange-red*, 6-13mm, solitary, long-stalked. Pod brown, narrow-linear, 30-70mm long, hairless and with prominent longitudinal veins. Rocky and stony hill and mountain slopes, pine forest, bushy places. Feb-May. T – rarer in the E Med.

542 *Lathyrus inconspicuus*. Similar, but always hairless (except the pod) and flowers pale purple, 4-9mm, *short-stalked* – 2-5mm. Pod hairy when young. Bushy and rocky habitats. Mar-June. T – scattered, but absent from most of the islands.

543 *Lathyrus angulatus*. Similar to *L. sphaericus*, but peduncles longer, 20-70mm (not 5-20mm) and flowers pale blue or purple. Sandy and rocky habitats. Mar-June. W and C Med from Portugal and NW Africa to Greece and Crete.

544 *Lathyrus setifolius*. Like *L. sphaericus*, but stems *narrowly winged* and flowers orange-red and peduncle up to 40mm long. Pod broader, 15-30mm long, hairy along the edge and without prominent veins. Grassy and waste places, garrigue. Feb-May. T – rarer in the E Med.

545 *Lathyrus cicera*. Short to tall hairless annual, to 1m; stems winged. Leaves with 1, occasionally 2, pairs of linear to lanceolate leaflets; tendrils branched. Flowers crimson, orange or brick red, 8-16mm, solitary, on long stalks. Pod brown, 20-40mm long, hairless, with *two keels* on the upper edge. Grassy and bushy habitats, garrigue, waste ground, cultivated fields. Feb-May. T.

546 *Lathyrus gorgonei*. Similar, but flowers rather larger and pale orange or reddish-yellow; sepals usually spreading and not pressed close to the petals. Similar habitats and flowering time. Sardinia, Sicily, Turkey, Cyprus and the E Med.

547 *Lathyrus hirsutus* **HAIRY VETCHLING**. Like *L. cicera*, but plant *sparsely hairy* and flowers red with pale blue wings. Pod hairy and warted. Similar habitats and flowering time. T – but absent from most of the islands.

548 *Lathyrus blepharicarpus.* Like *L. cicera,* but tendrils usually simple and pod with two distinct *wings* on the upper edge. Flowers reddish-pink or terra-cotta. Similar habitats as well as stony hillslopes and open pine woods. Feb-Apr. E Med, including Cyprus.

549 *Lathyrus annuus.* Medium to tall, clambering, hairless annual, to 1.5m; stems winged. Leaves with 1 pair of linear-lanceolate leaflets. Flowers yellow or orange-yellow, *often red-veined,* 12-18mm, 1-3 borne in a long-stalked raceme. Pod pale brown, 30-80mm long, glandular when young. Cultivated and waste ground, waysides. Mar-June. T. Occasionally grown as a fodder crop.

550 *Lathyrus clymenum.* Medium to tall hairless annual, to 1m; stems winged. Leaves with broad *leaf-like stalks,* the lower linear-lanceolate and without leaflets, the upper with 2-4 pairs of linear to elliptical leaflets. Flowers crimson or purple-red, with violet or lilac wings, rarely pale yellow, 16-20mm, borne in 1-5-flowered racemes. Pod brown, 30-70mm long, hairless, with a groove on the upper side. Cultivated and waste ground, hedgerows, roadsides. Mar-June. T – not Cyprus and rarer in the E Med. Formerly grown as a fodder crop.

551 *Lathyrus articulatus.* Very similar, but leaflets narrower, only 0.5-5mm wide (not 6-11mm) and flowers with white or pink wings. Pod *not* grooved on the upper side. Similar habitats and flowering time. T – not Cyprus and rarer in the E Med.

552 *Lathyrus ochrus.* Like *L. clymenum,* but lower 'leaves' (without leaflets) broader, oval or oblong, the upper leaves with 1-2 pairs of leaflets. Flowers *pale yellow.* Pod 40-60mm long, with two wings along the upper edge. Similar habitats and flowering time. T.

553 *Lathyrus aphaca* **YELLOW VETCHLING.** Medium to tall, clambering, hairless annual, to 1m; stems angled, not winged. Leaves reduced to a simple, unbranched tendril but *stipules* large and leaf-like, oval with a heart-shaped base. Flowers yellow, 6-18mm, solitary or occasionally paired, long-stalked. Pod brown, 20-35mm long, hairless. Cultivated, fallow and waste ground, roadsides and hedgerows, rocky slopes or open pine woodland. Jan-May. T.

554 *Lathyrus nissolia* **GRASS VETCHLING.** Short to tall, slightly hairy or hairless annual, not clambering; stem not winged. Leaves *without* leaflets or tendrils, reduced to a simple linear, grasslike blade. Flowers crimson, 8-18mm, solitary or paired. Pod pale brown, 30-60mm long, hairy or not. Grassy and bushy places. Feb-June. T – absent from Cyprus and most of the smaller islands.

555 *Pisum sativum* **WILD PEA.** A very variable medium to tall, clambering, hairless annual, to 2m; stems not winged. Leaves with 1-3 pairs of rounded to elliptical leaflets, often rather heart-shaped at the base; tendrils branched. Flowers white to purple, 15-35mm, borne in 1-3-flowered lateral racemes; wing petals *fused* to the keel. Pod yellow or brown, 30-120mm long, hairless, net-veined. Bushy places, garrigue, cultivated, fallow and waste ground. Apr- July. T. Widely cultivated since prehistoric times for fodder and for its edible seeds.

    555a Subsp. *elatius [Pisum elatius]* can be distinguished by its longer racemes (longer than the leaves) and by the darker flowers which are usually pink or purple with blackish purple wings. Mainly in open woodland and bushy places, garrigue. T.

Ononis **REST-HARROWS.** Stickily-hairy shrubs or annual to perennial herbs. Leaves trifoliate, often with neatly toothed leaflets. Flowers in clusters or racemes, occasionally solitary or paired, usually yellow or pink. Pod oblong to oval, often glandular-hairy.

556 *Ononis natrix* **LARGE YELLOW REST-HARROW.** Very variable, much-branched dwarf subshrub, to 60cm tall; stems becoming woody below. Leaves trifoliate, densely glandular-hairy (sticky); leaflets oval to linear, usually toothed; lower leaves occasionally pinnate. Flowers yellow, the standard petal *veined* with violet or red on the outside, 6-20mm, borne in leafy panicles. Pod 10-25mm long. Sandy, rocky and bushy places. Apr-July. T.

557 *Ononis viscosa.* Similar, but an annual to 80cm tall and leaves bright green with 1-5 leaflets. Flowers 7-12mm, occasionally with a pink standard petal. Cultivated and fallow fields, waste places, roadsides and rocky slopes. Mar-June. T.

558 *Ononis sicula [O. viscosa* subsp. *sicula].* Very like *O. viscosa,* but a smaller plant to only 15cm tall with the flower-stalks glandular-hairy (without long spreading hairs). Flowers 6-8mm. Dry grassy and rocky places. Mar-May. T.

559 *Ononis ornithopodioides* **BIRD'S-FOOT REST-HARROW.** Low to short, erect, much-branched annual; stems glandular-hairy. Leaves trifoliate, with oval leaflets, broadest above the middle. Flowers yellow, occasionally with pink veins, 6-7mm, borne in a sparse leafy panicle which elongates in fruit. Pod brownish, linear, 12-20mm long, *constricted* between the seeds. Rocky and bushy places, garrigue, waste ground, open pine woodland, pathsides, rarely at sea level. Mar-May. T.

560 *Ononis biflora [O. geminiflora].* Similar, but leaves rather fleshy and flowers frequently *paired,* 12-16mm. Pod 17-20mm, not constricted between the seeds. Cultivated and waste ground. Mar-Apr. N Africa, Cyprus and the E Med.

561 *Ononis pubescens.* Like *O. ornithopodioides,* but a hairier plant with only the middle leaves trifoliate, the others with a *single* leaflet. Flowers 14-15mm in a dense inflorescence. Pod small, 8-13mm, pointed. Similar habitats and flowering time. T – absent from most of the smaller islands as well as Corsica, Sardinia and Sicily.

562 *Ononis pusilla [O. columnae].* Short hairy perennial, the stems sometimes becoming woody below. Leaves trifoliate with elliptical to rounded leaflets, sometimes notched at the top. Flowers yellow, 5-12mm, borne in lax *spikes* with leaf-like bracts; corolla the same length as the calyx. Pod small, 6-8mm. Dry rocky and stony slopes, pine forest, generally on calcareous soils, but rarely at sea level. Mar-July. T – not the Balearic Is. or Crete.

563 *Ononis minutissima.* Similar, but a dwarf shrub; stems often spreading and *rooting,* hairless. Flowers borne in dense racemes. Similar habitats and flowering time. W and C Med from Spain to Yugoslavia.

564 *Ononis campestris [O. spinosa]* **SPINY REST-HARROW.** Very variable, patch-forming, *spiny,* hairy shrub, to 80cm, but often less. Leaves trifoliate with linear to oval leaflets, toothed. Flowers pink or purple, 10-20mm, borne in lax racemes; calyx glandular-hairy. Pod 6-10mm, 2-4-seeded. Dry bushy and rocky places, waste ground, roadsides, occasionally on sandy seashores. Apr-July, occasionally later. Mainly W and C Med.

564a Subsp. *antiquorum* has *smaller* flowers, 6-10mm. Pod 1-seeded. European Med; the commonest subspecies in the region.

564b Subsp. *leiospermum.* Like subsp. *antiquorum,* but leaflets larger, 10-20mm long (not 6-10mm). E Med from the Aegean eastwards.

565 *Ononis diffusa.* Short to medium, sticky, glandular-hairy annual; stems spreading to ascending, much-branched. Leaves trifoliate, the basal occasionally pinnate; leaflets rounded to elliptical, often broadest above the middle, toothed. Flowers pink with a whitish keel, 9-11mm, borne in a dense oblong spike; lower bracts

with 3 leaflets, upper with 1. Pod 5-8mm. Sand-dunes and sandy seashores. Mar-June. T – not the Balearic Is. or France.

566 *Ononis alopecuroides.* Similar, but taller and less branched with large leaves with a *single* leaflet and a winged stalk. Flowers larger, 16-19mm; all bracts with 1 leaflet. Pod 8-10mm. Olive groves, field boundaries, hillslopes, occasionally in marshy places. Apr-June. W Med from Spain to Italy and Sicily – not the Balearic Is.

567 *Ononis mitissima.* Like *O. alopecuroides,* but upper leaves and lower bracts trifoliate; stipules of bracts *white* and conspicuous. Flowers 10-12mm. Similar habitats and flowering time. T.

568 *Ononis serrata.* Like *O. diffusa,* but plant lower and with a more spreading habit, often less than 20cm tall. Leaflets with 4-6 (not 10-16) teeth. Flowers white to pale pink, 7-8mm. Similar habitats and flowering time. N Africa, Crete, Karpathos and E Med, including Cyprus.

569 *Ononis variegata.* Low, small, spreading, densely hairy annual, branched from close to the base, the lower part of the plant often buried in the sand. Leaves with a single, narrow-oval leaflet, *bluish-green*, with conspicuous veins, toothed. Flowers yellow, 8-10mm, borne in a lax terminal, occasionally branched, raceme. Pod oblong, 8-9mm, somewhat hairy. Sandy seashores and sand-dunes. Mar-May. T – not the Balearic Is., France or Yugoslavia.

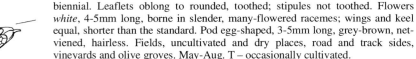

Melilotus **MELILOTS.** Annuals or short-lived perennials with trifoliate leaves; leaflets generally toothed. Flowers small, borne in lateral racemes. Fruit pod usually with only 1-2 seeds.

570 *Melilotus albus* **WHITE MELILOT.** Medium to tall, erect, branched, hairless annual or biennial. Leaflets oblong to rounded, toothed; stipules not toothed. Flowers *white*, 4-5mm long, borne in slender, many-flowered racemes; wings and keel equal, shorter than the standard. Pod egg-shaped, 3-5mm long, grey-brown, net-viened, hairless. Fields, uncultivated and dry places, road and track sides, vineyards and olive groves. May-Aug. T – occasionally cultivated.

571 *Melilotus officinalis [M. arvensis]* **RIBBED MELILOT.** Medium to tall, erect to spreading, hairless biennial, to 2.5m; stems branched. Leaflets oval to lanceolate, all toothed. Flowers yellow, 4-7mm long, borne in lax, slender racemes; wings and standard equal, *longer* than the keel. Pod oval, 3-5mm long, rough with transverse veins, brown. Cultivated and waste ground, often on clay or saline soils. May-July. From Spain and NW Africa to Turkey, but absent from most of the islands and rather rare in the Med region as a whole.

572 *Melilotus indicus* **SMALL MELILOT.** Similar, but an annual to only 50cm tall. Flowers *small*, pale yellow, 2-3mm long. Pod globose, 1.5-3mm, pendent, net-veined, greyish-white when young, pale brown when ripe. Cultivated and waste places, irrigation ditches, damp sandy places. Mar-June. T. The commonest melilot in the Med region.

573 *Melilotus italicus.* Like *M. indicus,* but flowers 6-9mm long and pod yellow or grey-brown when ripe. Dry open habitats. Apr-June. T – except parts of the E Med, including Cyprus.

574 *Melilotus elegans.* Like *M. officinalis,* but annual, the standard and wing petals *shorter* than the keel. Pod brownish-yellow when ripe. Grassy habitats, often close to the sea. W and C Med from Portugal and NW Africa to Italy and Yugoslavia.

575 *Melilotus infestus*. Like *M. elegans*, but stipules *toothed* and the standard and keel petals shorter than the wings. Pod egg-shaped, concentrically ridged, blackish-brown when ripe. Balearic Is., Corsica, Italy and Sicily.

576 *Melilotus segetalis*. Like *M. infestus*, but standard petal shorter than the keel. Pod egg-shaped, *yellow* when ripe. Damp habitats. W and C Med eastwards to Greece.

577 *Melilotus messanensis*. Like *M. infestus*, but racemes shorter (not longer) than the subtending leaf and standard petal longer than the keel. Pod pointed, pale brown when ripe. Marshy and brackish ground and areas subjected to seasonal inundations. Mar-Apr. T – absent from some of the smaller islands.

578 *Melilotus sulcatus* **FURROWED MELILOT**. Like *M. segetalis*, but flowers smaller, 3-4mm long (not 4-8mm) and pod almost globose, not stalked. Cultivated and fallow land, roadsides, open woodland. Feb-June. T.

579 *Melilotus altissimus* **TALL MELILOT**. Medium to tall, hairless biennial or short-lived perennial, to 1.5m; stems erect and branched. Leaflets oblong, sharply toothed. Flowers yellow, 5-7mm long, borne in rather dense, many-flowered racemes. Pod oval, 5-6mm long, flattened, net-veined, *hairy*, black eventually. Damp and saline soils, roadsides, woodland margins. Apr-July. Scattered localities throughout the W and C Med east to Greece, but absent from most of the islands.

580 *Melilotus neapolitanus*. Similar, but annual to only 50cm; stem hairy above. Racemes rather short, with up to 20 only flowers. Pod globose, not flattened, 3-3.5mm long. Dry open habitats. May-July. T – not Cyprus.

Trigonella **TRIGONELLAS**. Annual herbs with trifoliate, toothed leaves. Flowers solitary, in clusters or stalked racemes. Pod linear to oblong, straight or curved, indehiscent or splitting along only one edge.

581 *Trigonella corniculata* **SICKLE-FRUITED FENUGREEK**. Spreading to erect, short to medium, usually hairless annual. Leaflets linear-lanceolate to oval, occasionally notched at the tip. Flowers yellow, 6-7mm long, borne in *long-stalked* cylindrical racemes, with 8-15 flowers; wing petals shorter than the keel; calyx teeth unequal. Pod linear, 10-16mm long, pendent, slightly curved, with thin transverse veins. Grassy places, cultivated and fallow fields. Mar-June. From Spain and NW Africa to Greece, not Crete. Sometimes cultivated for fodder in the Med.

582 *Trigonella balansae*. Similar, but the racemes *globose* and the wing petals equal in length to the keel. Pod 13-23mm long, curved. Cultivated ground and sandy places. Mar-June. S Greece, Aegean Is., Crete, Turkey and Cyprus.

583 *Trigonella maritima*. Like *T. corniculata*, but racemes subumbellate, 5-10-flowered; calyx teeth equal. Pod sometimes slightly hairy, with *thickened* oblique veins. Dry habitats. Feb-May. NW Africa, Sardinia, Italy, Sicily and Turkey.

584 *Trigonella sprunerana*. Like *T. corniculata*, but a prostrate, more sprawling plant with *hairy*, curved pods, 15-25mm long. Coastal garrigue, on rocks and sand-dunes. Feb-May. Crete, Aegean Is. and E Med, including Cyprus.

585 *Trigonella graeca*. Like *T. corniculata*, but leaves somewhat fleshy; flowers larger, 7-10mm long, and pods *flat and papery*, disk-like, 12-20mm, with a broad wing and widely spaced veins. Rocky habitats. Mar-May. S and W Greece and the adjacent islands.

586 *Trigonella spicata*. Like *T. corniculata*, but racemes globose and pod *small*, oval, 3-5mm long, somewhat hairy, net-viened. Dry hillsides, sand-dunes, olive groves, garrigue. Mar-June. Greece and the Aegean and E Med, including Cyprus.

587 *Trigonella caerulea* **BLUE FENUGREEK**. Short to medium, erect, clover-like, plant, slightly hairy. Leaflets oval to oblong, notched at the tip. Flowers *blue*, occasionally white, 5-6mm long, borne in globose heads on long stalks equalling the leaves; calyx bell-shaped. Pod rounded, 4-5mm, erect or spreading, inflated, with a short beak. Cultivated and waste places, widely naturalised. Mar-June. T – but probably not indigenous.

588 *Trigonella coerulescens*. Like *T. coerulea*, but flowers *larger*, 11-13mm, always blue, not more than 15 in a short-stalked raceme and the calyx tubular. Pod not inflated, 10-15mm long, hairy. Dry hillslopes. Mar-Apr. Yugoslavia eastwards to Syria.

589 *Trigonella monspeliaca* **STAR-FRUITED FENUGREEK**. Short hairy annual. Leaflets oval, toothed or not. Flowers yellow, 4mm long, borne in short-stalked umbel-like clusters. Pod linear, 7-15mm long, upcurved, forming *star-like* clusters among the leaves, usually hairy. Cultivated and waste ground, bare patches, pathsides. Mar-June. T.

590 *Trigonella foenum-graecum* **CLASSICAL FENUGREEK**. Short to medium, erect, slightly hairy annual. Leaflets oblong, toothed near the apex. Flowers *cream*, flushed with purple at the base, 10-18mm long, solitary or paired in the axils of the upper leaves. Pod linear, erect, 70-100mm long, with a long beak, hairless, with longitudinal veins. Cultivated for fodder and widely naturalised. Feb-June. T – of unknown origin, but probably from Asia.

591 *Trigonella gladiata*. Similar, but leaflets smaller, only 5-12mm (not 20-25mm) long and flowers pale yellow, sometimes tinged with purple, 8-10mm long. Pod *smaller*, 15-40mm long, sickle-shaped. Dry grassy and stony places. Mar-May. From NW Africa and Spain to Turkey – not W Med islands.

592 *Trigonella cariensis*. Like *T. gladiata*, but often taller and with larger flowers, 15-18mm long. Pod *hairy*, with a long 30-40mm beak (not 10-20mm). Sandy coastal habitats. Mar-May. SE Greece, Aegean Is., Turkey and Cyprus.

593 *Trigonella spinosa*. Short, prostrate or ascending, slightly hairy annual. Leaflets oval, broadest above the middle, usually finely toothed. Flowers yellow, 3-4mm long, borne in small stalkless clusters. Pod pendent, linear, *strongly curved*, often into a circle, hairless. Cultivated and waste ground, open ground, roadsides. Mar-May. Crete, S Aegean Is. and E Med, including Cyprus.

Medicago **MEDICKS**. Annual or perennial herbs, occasionally small shrubs. Leaves trifoliate. Flowers usually yellow, in small lateral clusters or racemes. Pod longer than the calyx, usually dehiscent, straight or curved, but often spiralled, armed with spines or spineless, 1-few seeded. A large genus in the Med region – many of the species look similar in flower, but the fruits vary greatly from one species to another and are very important in identification. Medicks form an important element in the waysides and meadows of the entire region and several species may often be found growing near each other.

594 *Medicago lupulina* **BLACK MEDICK**. Spreading to ascending hairy annual or short-lived perennial. Leaflets rounded to oblong or rhombic, sometimes notched at the tip; stipules oval, toothed or not. Flowers yellow, 2-3mm long, in 10-50-flowered racemes. Pod coiled into a circle, 1.5-3mm, *black* when ripe, net-veined. Cultivated and waste places, stream, ditches and track sides. May-Sept. T. Occasionally cultivated for fodder. A British native.

595 *Medicago secundiflora*. Similar, but a lower *white-hairy* annual with one-sided, 3-10-flowered, racemes. Pod 3.5-4mm. NE Spain, Balearic Is. and S France.

596 *Medicago sativa* **LUCERNE.** Very variable medium to tall, usually hairy perennial. Leaflets oval to linear, generally widest above the middle, toothed at the apex; stipules linear to lanceolate, often toothed at the base. Flowers *blue or violet*, in 5-40-flowered racemes. Pod spiralled, with one and a half or more turns, 4-6mm. Cultivated and waste ground, roadsides. May-July. T. Often grown as a forage crop; important in many parts of Europe in particular, as well as the Med basin. A British native.

    596a Subsp. *falcata [M. falcata]*. Similar, but flowers yellow and pod *sickle-shaped*, not spiralled. Similar habitats and flowering time. T – absent from some of the smaller islands. Sometimes treated as a distinct species; hybrids between the two are called *M.* × *varia*.

597 *Medicago suffruticosa.* Like *M. sativa*, but a lower plant, generally less than 35cm tall; stipules toothed. Racemes only 3-8-flowered; flowers 3-6mm long and pod 4-6mm, spiralled 2-4 times leaving a small hole in the centre. Rocky places. Apr-June. E Spain and S France.

598 *Medicago arborea* **TREE MEDICK.** Silvery-grey, leafy *shrub* to 4m, though often less; young stems white-silky. Leaflets oval, widest above the middle, narrowed at the base, sometimes slightly toothed at the apex; stipules lanceolate, untoothed. Flowers in globose 4-8-flowered racemes, yellow, 12-15mm long. Pod thin, coiled for usually one turn, 12-15mm, with a hole in the centre, hairless, net-veined. Rocky habitats, particularly cliffs, roadsides. From Spain and the Balearic Is. to Greece, Crete and W Turkey. Grown in gardens and sometimes naturalised, especially in Portugal and France. The only shrubby species in the area.

599 *Medicago orbicularis* **LARGE DISK MEDICK.** Low to short, sprawling, hairless or slightly hairy annual. Leaflets oval-wedge-shaped, toothed at the apex; stipules deeply toothed. Flowers yellow, 2-5mm long, in clusters of 1-5. Pod *large*, disk-like, 10-17mm, smooth, spiralled anticlockwise into 4-6 turns, somewhat convex, without a central hole. Cultivated and waste places, fallow land, waysides, rocky ground and olive groves. Feb-June. T.

600 *Medicago scutellata.* Similar, but a glandular-hairy plant with larger, 6-7mm long, flowers in clusters of 1-3. Pod 9-18mm, with 4-8 spirals, *glandular-hairy*, not spiny. Similar habitats and flowering time. T.

601 *Medicago rugosa.* Like *M. scutellata*, but flowers *small*, only 2-4mm long and pod 6-10mm, snail-shaped, with 2-3 spirals, with thickened radial veins, hairless. Similar habitats and flowering time. T.

602 *Medicago intertexta.* An almost hairless, low to short annual, with spreading to ascending stems. Leaflets oval, broadest above the middle, sometimes with a dark blotch, finely toothed; stipules oval, toothed. Flowers mustard-yellow, 6-9mm long, in clusters of 1-7. Pod spherical, 12-15mm, with *6-10 spiny*, anticlockwise spirals, hairless; spines 3-4mm long, curved, closely pressed to the pod. Cultivated and waste ground, often rather marshy. Mar-May. W and C Med from Portugal to Greece; absent from the islands except for Sardinia and Sicily. A form with blotched leaves, the so-called Calvary Clover, is sometimes grown in gardens – *M. echinus* (603) of nurserymen.

604 *Medicago ciliaris [M. intertexta var. ciliaris]*. Like *M. intertexta*, but with *hairy* and glandular pods. T.

605 *Medicago marina* **SEA MEDICK.** Low creeping, prostrate, *white-downy* perennial. Leaflets oval, broadest above the middle, toothed at the apex; stipules oval, toothed or not. Flowers bright yellow, 6-8mm, in short-stalked clusters of 5-12. Pod 5-7mm, with 2-3 anticlockwise spirals leaving a small hole in the centre, white-downy and with two rows of short spines. Maritime sands and dunes. Feb-

June. T. This and the next species is almost exclusively associated with coastal habitats.

606 *Medicago littoralis.* Low to short spreading or prostrate, hairy annual; stems often purplish. Leaflets heart-shaped to oval, broadest above the middle, toothed at the apex, hairy on *both* surfaces; stipules lanceolate, sharply toothed. Flowers yellow or orange, 5-6mm long, in clusters of 1-6. Pod 4-6mm, disk-like to cylindrical, with 3-6, generally clockwise, spiny spirals, hairless; margin with a single keel. Sandy coastal habitats, dunes, dry rocky places, occasionally inland. Feb-May. T. A form without spines on the pods is called var. *inermis* (606a) and is found throughout the Med, often mixed with spiny forms.

607 *Medicago truncatula [M. tribuloides].* Similar, but more robust with 1-3 flowers in a cluster and pods with a *3-keeled* margin; spines more slender and slightly curved. Dry rocky pastures, field margins, roadsides; mostly inland. Feb-May. T.

608 *Medicago tornata.* Like *M. truncatula,* but flowers generally 3 or more in a cluster and pod with up to 8 spirals, often without spines; spines, when present, short and straight. W Med from Portugal and NW Africa to Italy and Sicily.

609 *Medicago aculeata.* Like *M. littoralis,* but more densely hairy and pod larger, 7-10mm, with 5-7 spirals, with dense *short hairs,* with or without spines. Rocky, grassy and sandy places. From Portugal and NW Africa to Crete and Greece.

610 *Medicago rigidula.* Like *M. aculeata,* but pod nearly always spiny and densely *glandular-hairy*; spirals anticlockwise. Fallow fields, grassy places, road and track sides. Apr-June. T.

611 *Medicago blancheana.* Like *M. littoralis,* but a more vigorous plant with more deeply toothed leaflets and flowers 6-7mm long. Pod 8-12mm with 4-6 lax, anticlockwise spirals, not spiny nor hairy. Cultivated and fallow fields. Mar-May. E Med from Turkey eastwards, including Cyprus; naturalised in Portugal and Italy.

612 *Medicago turbinata.* Rather robust, low to short, prostrate or ascending, hairy annual; stems often purplish or reddish. Leaflets oval to lanceolate, toothed. Flowers golden or orange-yellow, 5-6mm long, in clusters of 3-8. Pod *barrel-shaped*, 5-7mm, with 5-6 (clockwise or anticlockwise) spirals, with short, broad spines. Cultivated and fallow ground, waste places, roadsides, marshy places. Jan-Apr. T.

613 *Medicago murex.* Similar, but pod with 5-9, usually anticlockwise spirals, the margin with 3 (not 1) keels; spines long and pointed. Similar habitats and flowering time. T, not Cyprus and parts of the E Med.

614 *Medicago constricta.* Like *M. turbinata,* but a small prostrate plant with solitary or paired flowers, only 3-4mm long, and pod almost globose, with 6-8 anticlockwise spirals. Dry hillsides, fallow fields, waste ground, sand-dunes and roadsides. Feb-May. From Greece and Crete eastwards, including Cyprus.

615 *Medicago disciformis.* Low to short, prostrate or ascending, softly hairy annual; stems much-branched, especially near the base. Leaflets oval, broadest above the middle, toothed at the apex; stipules lanceolate, toothed near the base. Flowers yellow, 4-5mm long, in clusters of 1-4. Pod disc-like, 5-6mm, with 5-7 anticlockwise spirals, with slender erect spines, hairless, the uppermost spiral usually *smaller and not spiny*. Dry rocky and grassy habitats, often in coastal garrigue, sometimes in open pine forest. Mar-May. N Med from Spain to Turkey and Cyprus – absent from most of the islands.

616 *Medicago rotata.* Similar, but *spines* at right angles to the lateral surface of the pod, not erect; leaflets sometimes distinctly lobed. Cultivated and fallow fields. Mar-May. E Med from Turkey eastwards, including Cyprus.

617 *Medicago tenoreana.* Like *M. disciformis,* but pod 5mm with straight spines in *2 rows,* one upward, the other downward, pointing, the upper spiral spiny and equal in size to the others. W Med from Spain to Italy and Sicily – not Balearic Is.

618 *Medicago polymorpha [M. denticulata, M. hispida, M. polycarpa]* **TOOTHED MEDICK.** Low prostrate to spreading, hairy or hairless annual. Leaflets oval, broadest above the middle, toothed at the apex; stipules lanceolate, *deeply toothed* with slender teeth. Flowers yellow, 3-4.5mm long, in clusters of 1-5. Pod disc-like or cylindrical, 4-8mm, with 1-6 anti-clockwise spirals, usually spiny but sometimes only warted; margin with 3 keels. Cultivated and fallow land, grassy and rocky places, road and track sides. Feb-June. T.

619 *Medicago coronata.* Similar, but a smaller plant, always hairy with 3-8-flowered racemes. Pod only 2-4mm with 2-3 spirals; spines 2 rows, one pointing upwards, the other downwards. Dry stony and waste places. Mar-May. T eastwards to Turkey and Cyprus, but absent from most of the smaller islands.

620 *Medicago laciniata.* Like *M. polymorpha,* but leaflets often deeply toothed to lobed and flowers solitary or paired. Pod 2.5-5mm, with 3-7 spirals; spines straight. Rocky, waste and grassy places. N Africa and Turkey; naturalised in Spain, France, Corsica and Italy.

621 *Medicago praecox.* Like *M. laciniata,* but leaflets often only toothed at the apex and flowers only 2-3mm, with somewhat curved spines. Grassy places, roadsides and open pine woodland, rarely at sea level. Mar-May. T – often local.

622 *Medicago minima* **BUR or SMALL MEDICK.** Like *M. polymorpha,* but a smaller densely hairy plant with bright yellow flowers. Pods 3-5mm, somewhat hairy and glandular, with 3-5 spirals; spines slender, *often hooked* at the apex. Similar habitats and flowering time. T – except some of the smaller islands.

623 *Medicago arabica [M. maculata]* **SPOTTED MEDICK.** Low to short prostrate or spreading, slightly hairy or hairless annual. Leaflets oval, broadest above the middle and often notched at the apex, toothed, often with a *conspicuous dark blotch.* Flowers yellow, 5-7mm, in clusters of 1-4. Pod subglobose to cylindrical, 5-6mm, with 4-7 anticlockwise spirals, with spreading spines, hairless; margin with 3 grooves. Cultivated, waste and fallow land, fields, rocky places, road and track sides, open pine woodland. Mar-July. T.

624 *Factorovskya aschersoniana [Trigonella aschersoniana]* **FACTOROVSKYA.** A low, greenish or purplish annual, forming dense mats; stems hairless. Leaves trifoliate, stalked; leaflets wedge-shaped, with a few large teeth, hairy beneath. Flowers yellow, small, 3.5-4mm, solitary; ovary *with a stalk* which elongates rapidly in fruit to 30-60mm long, burying the fruit in the soil. Fruit 2-lobed, 7-9mm, densely hairy. Dry pastures, rocky and waste places, threshing areas. Jan-Apr. N Africa, Turkey, Cyprus and the E Med. A rather insignificant plant and easily overlooked.

Lotus **BIRD'S-FOOT TREFOILS.** Annual or perennial herbs with pinnate leaves; leaflets usually 5, the lower pair resembling stipules; true stipules minute. Flowers solitary or in long-stalked heads. Pod cylindrical, sometimes flattened, dehiscing and many-seeded.

625 *Lotus corniculatus* **COMMON BIRD'S-FOOT TREFOIL.** Very variable, low to short, prostrate to spreading, hairy or hairless perennial with a stout woody stock; stem solid. Leaflets lanceolate to suborbicular, sometimes broadest above the middle.

Flowers yellow or orange-yellow, 10-16mm, borne in heads of 2-7; calyx bell-shaped, the teeth as long as the tube. Pod 15-30mm long. Grassy habitats, field boundaries, roadsides. Apr-July. T. Formerly widely grown for fodder. A widespread and common species in Europe and Asia.

626 *Lotus tenuis [L. tenuifolius]* **NARROW-LEAVED BIRD'S-FOOT TREFOIL.** Similar, but leaflets of upper leaves linear or linear-lanceolate and flowers 6-12mm, in clusters of up to 4. Fresh and saline marshes, irrigation ditches, streamsides. Mar-Sept. T.

627 *Lotus palustris.* Like *L. corniculatus,* but a larger and more robust, hairy plant. Flowers yellow or whitish, smaller, 6-10mm, in clusters of 2-4; calyx teeth noticeably longer than the tube. Wet habitats, especially by springs and streams. May-Sept. S Albania and Greece eastwards, including Cyprus and most of the E Med.

628 *Lotus preslii.* Like *L. palustris,* but flowers larger, 10-15mm long, in heads of 1-6. Wet habitats. Apr-July. W and C Med from Spain to Greece – not Corsica or Sardinia.

629 *Lotus uliginosus* **GREATER BIRD'S-FOOT TREFOIL.** Like *L. corniculatus,* but a short to medium perennial with *hollow* stems, ascending to erect. Leaflets bluish-green beneath. Flowers 10-18mm long in heads of 5-12. Wet habitats, marshes, stream margins. May-July. T.

630 *Lotus tetraphyllus.* Like a small *L. corniculatus,* but leaves with only 4 leaflets and flowers solitary, 6-10mm, yellow lined with red or purple. Limestone crevices. Balearic Is.

631 *Lotus edulis* **EDIBLE LOTUS.** Low to short, spreading, slightly hairy annual. Leaflets oblong, often broadest above the middle. Flowers yellow, 10-16mm long, solitary or paired on stalks longer than the leaves; calyx bell-shaped. Pod oblong, curved, *very inflated,* 20-40mm long, grooved on the back. Fields, stony places, garrigue and roadsides. Feb-May. T.

632 *Lotus creticus* **SOUTHERN BIRD'S-FOOT TREFOIL.** Low to short spreading *silvery-hairy* perennial. leaflets oblong, broadest above the middle. Flowers yellow with a purple tip to the straight keel, 12-18mm long, 2-6 borne in a head; calyx distinctly 2-lipped. Pod straight or slightly curved, 20-50mm long. Maritime habitats, sandy and rocky. Mar-May. NW Africa and Portugal to Greece – absent from the islands.

633 *Lotus cytisoides [L. creticus var. cytisoides].* Similar, but flowers smaller, 8-14mm long, with a short, *curved* keel; standard petal notched. Sandy coastal habitats. Mar-May. T – including most of the islands.

634 *Lotus collinus [L. creticus var. collinus].* Like *L. creticus,* but greener and less hairy, not silvery. Flowers with the keel tipped yellowish or brownish. Rocky habitats, garrigue, sometimes in open pine woodland. Feb-May. NW Africa, Spain, S France, Greece and the E Med, including Cyprus.

635 *Lotus ornithopodioides.* Low to short spreading, hairy annual. Leaves stalked; leaflets oval to rhombic, the lower two often with a heart- or wedge-shaped base. Flowers yellow, 7-10mm long, in heads of 2-5 borne on a stalk generally slightly longer than the leaves; calyx 2-lipped. Pod 20-50mm long, curved, *constricted* between the seeds. Moist habitats, often by springs and streams. Feb-May. T.

636 *Lotus halophilus.* Similar, but a smaller plant with unstalked or scarcely stalked leaves. Flowers 5-8mm long, in heads of 1-9. Pod 20-30mm long, only slightly constricted between the seeds, with a curved tip. Maritime sands and garrigue. Feb-May. S Italy and Crete eastwards, including Cyprus.

637 *Lotus peregrinus.* Like *L. ornithopodioides,* but flower-clusters on a stalk often shorter than the leaves and *pod* not or scarcely constricted between the seeds. Dry rocky places, garrigue, sand-dunes, roadsides. Dec-June. Sicily and Crete eastwards, including the Aegean Is. and Cyprus. Sometimes confused with the preceding species but generally distinguished by its larger leaflets, 10-15mm long (not 2-10mm).

638 *Lotus conimbricensis [L. coimbrensis].* Low to short spreading, hairy or hairless annual. Leaflets oval to rhombic, generally broadest above the middle. Flowers *pale pink* with a violet keel, 5-8mm, solitary on a stalk shorter than the leaves. Pod linear, 20-60mm long, curved upwards. Mar-June. NW Africa and Portugal eastwards to Greece – not Balearic Is.

639 *Ornithopus compressus* **COMPRESSED BIRD'S-FOOT.** Low spreading or prostrate hairy annual. Leaves *pinnate,* with 7-18 pairs of oblong to lanceolate leaflets. Flowers yellow, 5-8mm, in 3-5-flowered heads, subtended by a pinnate, leafy bract. Pod linear, 20-50mm long, somewhat flattened, jointed and constricted between the seeds, with a curved beak. Garrigue, rocky slopes, grassy places, roadsides, open pine forest. Nov-Apr. T.

640 *Ornithopus pinnatus [O. ebracteatus]* **ORANGE BIRD'S-FOOT.** Similar, but leaflets 3-7 pairs and flower-heads *without* a leafy bract. Flowers orange-yellow. Grassy and open stony habitats, garrigue. Feb-May. W Med eastwards to Greece.

641 *Ornithopus sativus* **CULTIVATED BIRD'S-FOOT.** Readily distinguished from the preceding species by its white or pink flowers and pod constricted between the seeds. Occasionally grown for fodder in the region.

Trifolium **CLOVERS.** Annual or perennial herbs with trifoliate leaves; leaflets usually finely toothed. Flowers in heads or spikes, rarely solitary; petals sometimes persistent. Pod small and generally hidden within the persistent calyx, splitting only along one edge. The shape of the calyx (especially in fruit) can be important in identification.

642 *Trifolium repens* **WHITE CLOVER.** Very variable, low to short, creeping perennial; *stems rooting* at the nodes, usually hairless. Leaves bright green, often paler or darker along the veins; leaflets oval to elliptic. Flowers white or pale pink, rarely red, 7-10mm long, borne in dense, long-stalked, globose heads, scented. Pod linear, compressed between the 3-4 seeds. Cultivated and fallow ground, grassy and rocky places, paths and roadsides. Apr-July. T. Widely cultivated for fodder – many cultivars are known.

642a Subsp. *orphanideum.* Similar, but a smaller more tufted plant, not more than 5cm tall and scarcely creeping. Flowers pale pink, only 8-12 in a head. Greece and Crete.

642b Subsp. *prostratum [T. biasolettii].* Distinguished by its *densely hairy* leaf-stalks; flowers pale pink. S France to Corsica and Albania.

643 *Trifolium hybridum* subsp. *elegans* **ALSIKE CLOVER.** A tufted to prostrate, generally hairless, perennial. Leaflets oval, broadest above the middle and often notched at the apex; stipules oval to lanceolate, partly green. Flowers purple, or white turning pink, becoming brown, 7-10mm long, borne in globose pseudoterminal heads. Meadows and pastures. Apr-July. Spain to Turkey, but absent from the islands except for Crete. The typical form, subsp. *hybridum* (643a), which is widely grown for fodder in many parts of Europe, is rare in the Med region.

Other widespread European clovers sometimes seen in the Med are *T. arvense* **HARE'S FOOT** (644), *T. pratense* **RED CLOVER** (645) and *T. dubium* **SUCKLING CLOVER** (646).

(643a)

(645)

647 *Trifolium nigrescens.* Low to short, usually hairless, erect or sprawling annual. Leaflets oval to heart-shaped, often notched at the apex; stipules triangular, pointed. Flowers white, cream or pink, becoming brown, 6-9mm long, in globose heads, the stalk longer than the leaves. Pod often 4-seeded, slightly constricted between the seeds. Moist habitats, meadows, streamsides, sand-dunes and olive groves. T. The eastern Med plants are generally referable to subsp. *petrisarii* (647a).

648 *Trifolium isthmocarpum.* Low to medium hairless annual, branching from the base, spreading to ascending. Leaflets oval to elliptical or almost triangular; stipules membranous, pointed. Flowers pink, occasionally white, 9-12mm long, in globose heads with stalks longer than the leaves. Pod oblong, constricted between the seeds. Moist grassland and sandy soils. Mar-June. W Med, including NW Africa, eastwards to Sicily.

649 *Trifolium spumosum.* Similar, but leaflets wedge-shaped, thin and weakly veined; bracts concave and lined. Pod becoming *much inflated* and papery in Fruit Dry grassy places and disturbed ground, borders of cultivation, olive groves. Mar-Apr. T.

650 *Trifolium vesiculosum.* Like *T. spumosum,* but leaflets oblong to lanceolate and flowers white, becoming pink, the corolla *much longer* than the calyx (not equalling). Similar habitats and flowering time. Corsica eastwards to Turkey.

651 *Trifolium uniflorum.* Variable low, tufted or mat-forming perennial with a long taproot. Leaflets rounded to rhombic, strongly veined, somewhat hairy beneath; stipules broadly triangular. Flowers white, cream, purple or bicolored, 15-22mm long, in clusters of 1-3 in the leaf-axils; standard petal strongly recurved. Pod linear, pointed, hairy in part. Dry pastures, rocky places and pathways. Mar-June. Italy, Sicily, Greece, Crete and Turkey.

652 *Trifolium fragiferum* **STRAWBERRY CLOVER**. A low, prostrate and creeping, somewhat hairy perennial; stems often rooting at the nodes. Leaflets oval to elliptical, sometimes notched at the apex; stipules lanceolate, membranous. Flowers pale pink, 6-7mm long, borne in dense stalked heads which expand in fruit to 10-20mm as the upper lip of the calyx becomes much *inflated* – giving the heads a strawberry-like appearance; calyx 8-10mm long in fruit. Grassy and marshy ground, streamsides, water channels, occasionally by roads. May-Oct. T.

652a Subsp. *bonannii* is similar, but the heads are cylindrical and the corolla is noticeably longer than the calyx; calyx 4-6mm long in fruit. T – the commoner subspecies in the Med region.

653 *Trifolium physodes.* Similar, but stems not rooting at the nodes and bracts tiny, only 0.5-1mm (not 3-4mm). Flowers *larger* 8-14mm long. Garrigue, roadsides, open pine forest. Apr-June. Sicily, Turkey, Cyprus and much of the E Med.

654 *Trifolium speciosum [T. violaceum].* More or less hairy, short annual. Leaflets oblong-elliptical, hairy or not, the terminal leaflet with a short stalk; stipules oval to oblong. Flowers *violet*, 8-10mm long, borne in egg-shaped heads, up to 30mm in fruit; corolla darkening and presisting in fruit. Pod slightly exceeding the calyx. Dry rocky and grassy places, generally in the hills. Apr-June. Sicily and the Balkans eastwards to Turkey, including Crete.

655 *Trifolium boissieri.* Low to short, hairy annual, erect or spreading, generally much-branched. Leaflets oblong, often broadest above the middle; stipules narrow-oblong. Flowers pale or bright *yellow*, browning with age, 7-10mm long, borne in globose heads on stalks equalling or shorter than the leaves. Rocky mountain-sides, waste ground, pine forest, olive groves. Mar-May. Greece eastwards, including Cyprus.

656 *Trifolium campestre* **HOP TREFOIL**. Similar, but flowers only 3.5-5mm long. Cultivated and waste ground, roadsides. Feb-June. T.

657 *Trifolium resupinatum* **REVERSED CLOVER**. Very variable, low to short, prostrate or sprawling, generally hairless annual. Leaflets wedge-shaped. Flowers *reversed* (upside down), pink, red or purple, 4.5-8mm long, born in small, rather starry, short-stalked heads; calyx becoming conspicuously inflated and papery in fruit, sometimes slightly hairy. Moist grassy places, road and stream sides, marshes, garrigue. Mar-July. T.

658 *Trifolium tomentosum* **WOOLLY TREFOIL**. Similar, but a more tufted plant with flowers only 3.5-4mm long and fruit-heads white with hairs, like small 7-11mm *balls of cotton*. Grassy pastures, fallow fields and waste ground, road and track sides. Mar-June. T.

659 *Trifolium pilulare* **BALL COTTON CLOVER**. Low prostrate, much-branched, hairy annual. Leaflets broad-oval, narrowed at the base, bright green with a pale central spot. Flowers whitish, pinking on ageing, 3-3.5mm long, borne in small globose heads. Fruit-heads 9-10mm like white balls of cotton, the pods *concealed* under a dense head of sterile flowers; calyx not inflated. Dry grassy and stony hillsides, roadsides and open pine forest. Mar-June. Aegean Is. eastwards, including Cyprus. Perhaps sometimes confused with the previous species, but the flowers are not reversed nor is the calyx inflated.

660 *Trifolium globosum*. Similar, but flower-heads terminal, not lateral, *larger*, 18-25mm in fruit. Similar habitats as well as coastal sands. Mar-May. Greece, Turkey and Cyprus.

661 *Trifolium incarnatum* **CRIMSON CLOVER**. Robust, short to medium, hairy annual; stems branched from the base, erect to ascending. Leaflets oval to rounded, toothed towards the apex; stipules oval, usually green and sometimes flushed with red. Flowers blood red, rarely white, 10-12mm long, borne in dense *cylindrical heads*. Grassy, cultivated and waste places, roadsides, occasionally coastal. Apr-July. T – except for some of the islands, including the Balearic Is. and Cyprus. Widely cultivated for fodder and often naturalised.

661a Subsp. *molinerii* **LONG-HEADED CLOVER**. Similar, but less robust, hairier and with yellowish-white, occasionally pink, flowers. European Med.

662 *Trifolium stellatum* **STAR CLOVER**. Low to short, erect, hairy annual; stems simple or branched from the base. Leaflets oval, notched, slightly toothed at the apex; stipules oval, toothed, the margins and veins bright green. Flowers pink, occasionally purple or yellowish, 8-12mm, borne in solitary globose heads, up to 15-25mm in fruit; calyx as long as the corolla, densely white-hairy, with slender spreading lobes, *star-like*, often reddish. Cultivated and waste places, fields, stony and rocky ground, roadsides. Mar-July. T. Plants on thin poor soils may be very small.

663 *Trifolium dasyurum* **EASTERN STAR CLOVER**. Similar, but more robust with the stems branching above and leaflets oblong to lanceolate. Flower-heads 20-35mm, *often paired*; flowers 16mm. Similar habitats. Feb-Apr. Crete and Greece eastwards, including Cyprus.

664 *Trifolium hirtum* **HAIRY TREFOIL**. Short, erect to spreading, hairy annual. Leaflets wedge-shaped, finely toothed at the apex; stipules lanceolate, with a long hairy tip. Flowers rose-pink or purple, 12-15mm long, borne in *densely hairy* heads, 15-20mm wide, with a pair of leaves immediately below; corolla longer than the calyx. Dry grassy and stony habitats. Apr-June. NW Africa and Portugal eastwards to Turkey.

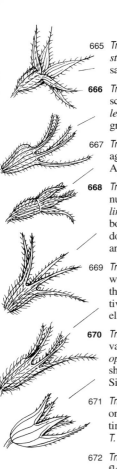

665 *Trifolium lappaceum.* Similar, but calyx-tube hairless and flower-heads *short-stalked*; flowers pink, 7-8mm long. Cultivated and fallow land, dry hills and sandy ground by streams. Apr-June. T.

666 *Trifolium cherleri.* Like *T. hirtum,* but a less robust plant with heart-shaped leaflets, scarcely toothed. Flowers pinkish-white, 8-10mm long, the corolla *equal in length* to the calyx. Grassy and stony habitats, pastures, sand-dunes, fallow ground, garrigue. Mar-June. T.

667 *Trifolium scabrum.* Like *T. hirtum,* but flowers *creamy-white*, becoming pink with age, 7-8mm long. Stony and sandy pastures, fallow land and rocky places. Mar-Apr. T.

668 *Trifolium angustifolium* **NARROW-LEAVED CRIMSON CLOVER.** Short to medium erect annual, somewhat hairy; stems rather stiff, with shorter lateral branches. Leaflets *linear-lanceolate*, pointed; stipules lanceolate. Flowers pink, 10-12mm long, borne in egg-shaped or cylindrical heads, stalked; flowers opening from the top downwards. Garrigue, cultivated and waste ground, dry open woodland, fields and vineyards, on non-calcareous soils. Apr-July. T.

669 *Trifolium purpureum* **PURPLE CLOVER.** Similar, but more robust, often branched above with larger reddish-purple or red flowers, 16-25mm long; flowers opening from the base of the head *upwards*. Fields, disturbed land, sandy places, often cultivated for fodder. Mar-July. S France, Sicily, the Balkans and Turkey, perhaps elsewhere.

670 *Trifolium echinatum [T. supinum].* Low to short, erect or sprawling, hairy annual, very variable. Leaflets oval to oblong, broadest above the middle; uppermost leaves *opposite*. Flowers pink or cream, 8-12mm long, borne in stalked globose or egg-shaped heads. Grassy habitats, roadsides, often on damp soils. Apr-July. Italy and Sicily eastwards to include the whole of the E Med.

671 *Trifolium latinum.* Similar, but leaflets linear-lanceolate, pointed and flower-heads on longer stalks, 60-80mm long (not 20-50mm). Similar habitats and flowering time. Italy, Greece and Turkey. Sometimes regarded as a natural hybrid between *T. echinatum* and *T. leucanthum.*

672 *Trifolium leucanthum.* Like *T. echinatum,* but the leaflets more wedge-shaped and the flowers white or pink, 5-8mm long, the calyx *as long as* the corolla (not shorter). Dry rocky and stony habitats, coniferous woodland. Mar-May. T.

673 *Trifolium squamosum [T. maritimum]* **SEA CLOVER.** Like *T. leucanthum,* but calyx teeth *unequal* (not equal) and flowers pale pink, the corolla longer than the calyx. Damp grassy places, particularly close to the sea. T – not Cyprus.

674 *Trifolium clypeatum* **SHIELD CLOVER.** Rather robust, low to short, hairy, prostrate to sprawling annual. Leaflets broadly wedge-shaped; stipules oval, pointed. Flowers creamy white, but soon turning to pale pink, 20-25mm long, borne in solitary, stalked heads; calyx with conspicuous green sepals which enlarge in fruit and spread outwards to form a *shield*. Moist, shaded and grassy places, often in maquis. Feb-Apr. Crete, S Greece eastwards, including Cyprus.

675 *Trifolium scutatus [T. clypeatum* susbp. *scutatum].* Similar, but flowers *smaller*, 10-12mm long, white or pink tinged. Cultivated and fallow fields, roadsides. Jan-Apr. Turkey, Cyprus and Palestine.

676 *Dorycnium hirsutum [Bonjeanea hirsuta, Lotus hirsutus]* **DORYCNIUM.** A small shrub or perennial to 50cm, usually densely hairy. Leaves pinnate; leaflets 5 oblong separated by a short rachis (stalk), broadest above the middle, the lowest pair stipule-like; stipules minute. Flowers white or pink with a dark red or black *keel*,

10-20mm long, 4-10 borne in a stalked head. Pod oblong, 6-12mm long, the valves remaining straight after dehiscence. Garrigue, maquis and open woodland. Apr-July. T – not Cyprus.

677 *Dorycnium pentaphyllum.* Very like the previous species, but to 80cm, though often smaller. Leaflets all arising from *one point*, without a rachis, linear to oblong. Flowers white with a red-black keel, 3-6mm long, 5-25 in a head. Pod eggshaped, 3-5mm long. Similar habitats and flowering time. Probably T, but not Crete or Cyprus.

678 *Dorycnium rectum [Bonjeania recta].* Like *D. hirsutum,* but less hairy, to 1.5m and flowers only 5-6mm long, white stained purple, the keel tipped with purple. Pod linear-oblong, 10-12mm, the valves twisting spirally on dehiscence. Damp ground by streams and springs. May-July. T – rare in N Africa.

679 *Dorycnium graecum [Lotus graecus].* Like *D. pentaphyllum,* but calyx teeth equal (not unequal), flowers whitish with a purple-tipped keel, 6-7mm long, and pod oblong, 4.5-7mm long. Maquis and woodland. Apr-July. Greece, Turkey and Cyprus, including the Aegean Is.

Tetragonolobus **ASPARAGUS PEAS.** Like *Lotus,* but leaves trifoliate and stipules leaf-like. Flowers solitary or paired. Pod square in section with a keel or wing on the angles.

680 *Tetragonolobus maritimus [Lotus siliquosus]* **DRAGON'S TEETH.** Low, spreading to prostrate, hairy or hairless perennial. Leaflets oval, broadest above the middle; stipules like the leaflets, pointed. Flowers pale yellow, 25-30mm long, solitary on long stalks, with a bract-like leaf just below the flower. Pod 30-60mm long, usually hairless, *winged on the angles.* Dry grassy habitats, waste ground, field margins, banks, generally on calcareous soils. Apr- July. Local and rather rare in Spain, France, Corsica and Sardinia, Italy and Yugoslavia.

681 *Tetragonolobus biflorus [Lotus biflorus].* Similar, but an annual with flowers in clusters of 1-4, deep *bright orange,* 17-25mm long. Pod 20-40mm long, hairy. S Italy, Sicily and NW Greece.

682 *Tetragonolobus purpureus [Lotus tetragonolobus]* **WINGED PEA, ASPARAGUS PEA.** Low to short, ascending to sprawling, hairy annual. Leaflets oval to rhombic, usually broadest above the middle. Flowers *crimson,* rarely copper-coloured, 15-22m long, solitary or paired on stalks shorter than or equalling the leaves. Pod 30-90mm long, hairless, with broad wings on the angles. Disturbed, cultivated and waste land, fields, roadsides, occasionally in garrigue. Feb-May. T – absent from Portugal and Corsica. Widely cultivated for its edible pods, sometimes for fodder.

683 *Tetragonolobus requienii.* Like *T. purpureus,* but flowers bright red, 13-15mm long. Pod 25-65mm long, with narrow wings only on the upper two angles. W Med from Portugal to Italy – not Corsica or Sardinia.

684 *Scorpiurus muricatus* **SCORPIURUS.** Low, hairy to hairless, sprawling or prostrate annual with *simple* leaves. Leaves elliptical, broadest above the middle, often with 3 prominent parallel veins, untoothed, the upper short-stalked or unstalked. Flowers yellow, sometimes stained with red or purple, 5-10mm long, in long-stalked clusters of 2-5. Pod 30-50mm long but coiled and twisted, ribbed, the ribs covered in short spines or warts, rarely smooth. Fields and waste ground, roadsides, sand-dunes. Feb-July. T.

685 *Scorpiurus vermiculatus.* Similar, but flowers generally solitary, 10-20mm long. Pod with warts on the outer ridges. W Med from Portugal and NW Africa, eastwards to Italy – not Balearic Is.

Anthyllis **KIDNEY VETCHES**. Shrubs or herbs. Leaves pinnate, occasionally simple. Flowers usually in dense lateral heads or clusters, rarely terminal. Pod hidden in the persistent calyx, often indehiscent.

686 *Anthyllis barba-jovis* **JUPITER'S BEARD**. Rather straggly shrub to 90cm tall, with woody branches. Leaves with 13-19 pairs of narrow elliptical leaflets, silvery-hairy beneath, greenish above. Flowers yellow, 9-11mm long, 10 or more in long-stalked, terminal heads subtended by digitate bracts. Pod 1-seeded. Rocky coastal habitats. Apr-June. From E Spain to Greece, Crete and NW Africa.

687 *Anthyllis aegaea*. Similar, but leaflets very narrow and flowers only 5-9 in a head; calyx 6.5-9mm long (not 4-6mm). Crete and the Cyclades.

688 *Anthyllis cytisoides*. Like *A. barba-jovis,* but flowers solitary or in lateral clusters and the uppermost leaves *trifoliate;* lower leaves often with a single leaflet. A shrub to 60cm with white or greyish branches. S and E Spain, Balearic Is. and S France.

689 *Anthyllis hermanniae*. Similar, but a denser shrub with contorted branches, *spine-tipped,* and flowers in leafy clusters. From the Balearic Is. and Corsica to Crete, Greece and Turkey.

690 *Anthyllis vulneraria* subsp. *praepropera [A. praepropera, A. spruneri]* **MEDITERRANEAN KID-NEY VETCH**. A low tufted, hairy perennial; stems ascending to erect. Lowest leaves with a single leaflet but the upper ones with 7-13, elliptical. Flowers *red or purple,* 12-15mm long in long-stalked heads with a pair of *leaflike bracts* immediately beneath; calyx shiny with silky hairs, purplish tipped. Grassy, stony and rocky places, garrigue. Mar-July. From the Balearic Is. and Corsica eastwards to Turkey – not Sicily or Cyprus.
    690a Subsp. *reuteri [A. hispida]* is similar, but with red flowers, the calyx with spreading hairs, *not* shiny. Spain.
    690b Subsp. *maura*. Like subsp. *praepropera,* but with larger flowers, the calyx 14-17mm long (not 12-14mm). Spain, Portugal, NW Africa, Italy and Sicily.

691 *Anthyllis tetraphylla [Physanthyllis tetraphylla]* **BLADDER VETCH**. Low hairy annual, usually spreading. Leaves generally with 5 leaflets, the terminal one much larger and oval. Flowers pale yellow, often with darker wings, 8-12mm long, in dense lateral clusters of 1-7; keel often tipped with red; calyx silvery-haired, becoming greatly *inflated* and bladder-like in fruit, pale green, often tipped with red or purple. Cultivated and fallow land, road and track sides, garrigue. Mar-June. From Portugal and NW Africa eastwards to Greece and Crete – not Balearic Is.

692 *Hymenocarpus circinnatus [Medicago circinnata]* **DISK TREFOIL**. A low prostrate or sprawling annual, much-branched and hairy. Leaves variable, the lower simple, the upper pinnate with 5-7 leaflets, the terminal one much the largest. Flowers yellow or orange, 5-7mm long, in long-stalked heads of 2-5. Pod flattened, twisted into a *kidney-shape and disk-like,* 10-15mm, the outer edge membranous and usually finely toothed. Fields, fallow and waste ground, dry hillslopes, occasionally on sandy seashores. Feb-June. T – not Spain, Portugal or the Balearic Is.

Coronilla **SCORPION VETCHES**. Annuals, perennials or dwarf shrubs with pinnate, occasionally simple, leaves. Flowers in lateral heads; calyx bell-shaped. Pod jointed but not constricted between the seeds, often with longitudinal ridges.

693 *Coronilla emerus* **SCORPION VETCH or FALSE SENNA**. Rather dense shrub to 1m with green branches. Leaflets 2-4 pairs, glossy dark green, oval, broadest above the middle, the end leaflet often larger. Flowers pale yellow, 14-20mm long, the standard with a long claw, borne in stalked clusters of 1-5. Pod pendent, straight,

50-110mm long, with 3-12 segments. Garrigue, scrub, woodland margins, open woodland and shaded cliffs. Mar-June. W and C Med eastwards to Italy.

693a Subsp. *emeroides [C. emeroides]*. Similar, but flowers in clusters of 4-8 on stalks longer than (not equal to) the leaves and pod without obvious joints. C and E Med from Italy eastwards, including Cyprus.

The bitter-tasting leaves were added to various purgatives, particularly the true Senna, *Cassia acutifolia* (694).

695 *Coronilla valentina*. Like *C. emerus*, but leaves bluish-green, with 3-6 pairs of notched leaflets. Flowers in clusters of 4-12, 7-12mm long; claw of standard *short*, as long as the calyx (not 2-3 times longer). Pod 10-50mm long with 3-7 rather bulging segments. Scrub and cliffs. Mar-June, occasionally earlier. SE France to Albania. Widely grown in gardens.

695a Subsp. *glauca [C. glauca]*. Similar, but leaflets only 2-3 pairs and pod with only 1-4 segments; stipules membranous, not green. NW Africa and Portugal to Greece.

696 *Coronilla juncea* **RUSH-LIKE SCORPION VETCH**. Like *C. valentina*, but stems green and *rush-like* with few leaves. Leaves with 2-3 pairs of elliptical or rounded leaflets, soon falling. Dry, rather open habitats, coastal garrigue and cliffs. Apr-June. From Portugal and NW Africa to Yugoslavia – not Corsica or Sardinia.

697 *Coronilla varia* **CROWN VETCH**. Short to tall, sprawling to ascending perennial, much-branched. Leaves pinnate, with 7-12 pairs of oblong or elliptical leaflets, each with a narrow membranous margin. Flowers *white, pink or purple*, often bicolored, 10-15mm long, borne in long-stalked heads of 10-20. Pod 20-20mm long, 4-angled, with 3-8 oblong segments. Rocky and grassy habitats, scrub, garrigue and roadsides. May-July. T – but absent from most of the islands with the exception of Crete. Often cultivated for fodder, sometimes also in gardens.

698 *Coronilla cretica*. Similar, but leaves with only 3-8 pairs of leaflets and flowers smaller, 4-7mm long, white or pink, in heads of 3-6. Pod 30-80mm long, with a curved beak. Grassy and waste places. Greece, Crete and Albania.

699 *Coronilla globosa*. Like *C. varia*, but flower-heads with 15-40, generally white, flowers. Pod with 2-5 segments. Cliffs. Crete only.

700 *Coronilla rostrata*. Like *C. cretica*, but leaflets *notched*. Flowers white, pink or pale yellow, 7-11mm long. Pod strongly curved. Pastures, waste ground, garrigue, field boundaries. Feb-May. From Crete and Albania eastwards, including Cyprus.

701 *Coronilla scorpioides* **ANNUAL SCORPION VETCH**. Prostrate to almost erect, low to short, hairless, bluish-green annual. Leaves simple or trifoliate, the terminal leaflets elliptical to rounded, *much larger* than the others. Flowers yellow, 4-8mm long, in stalked heads of 2-5; standard petal sometimes veined with brown. Pod 20-60mm long, curved, with 2-11 clearly jointed segments, ridged. Garrigue, dry open habitats, cultivated and fallow fields. Jan-June. T.

702 *Coronilla repanda*. Similar, but upper leaves *pinnate*, with 2-4 pairs of leaflets. Flowers becoming red on drying. Pod with curved (not straight) segments. Coastal rocks and sands. Feb-Apr. N Africa, Portugal, Spain, Balearic Is., Sicily, Cyprus and Palestine.

703 *Coronilla securidaca [Bonavenia securidaca, Securigera securidaca]*. Low to short sprawling to ascending annual, hairless. Leaves pinnate, with 4-7 pairs of oblong, sometimes notched, leaflets. Flowers yellow, 4-8mm long, borne in long-stalked heads of 4-8; keel beaked. Pod linear, 50-100mm long, with a recurved, pointed, tip, ascending to erect, with thickened margins and *no obvious* segments. Cultivated

and fallow fields, waste places, along irrigation ditches and streams. Mar-May. S France eastwards, including Cyprus – not N Africa.

Hippocrepis **HORSESHOE VETCHES.** Annual or perennial herbs with pinnate leaves. Flowers in lateral, long-stalked clusters. Fruit a jointed pod, the segments characteristically moon- or horseshoe-shaped, or rectangular with a semicircular bite out of one side.

704 *Hippocrepis glauca.* Hairy low to short, spreading to ascending perennial, woody at the base. Leaflets 4-7 pairs, linear to oval, often broadest above the middle, *densely white-downy* beneath. Flowers yellow, 6-12mm long, in heads of 4-8 on stalks twice as long as the leaves or more. Pod 30-40mm long, with moon-shaped segments, white-bearded. Dry sunny habitats. Apr-June. From Spain to Greece, but absent from the islands except for Sicily.

705 *Hippocrepis squamata.* Similar, but a more densely tufted, *silvery-hairy* plant. Pods smaller, 10-25mm long, more prominently bearded. Similar habitats and flowering time. C and S Spain.

706 *Hippocrepis unisiliquosa.* Very variable, low to short, prostrate to ascending, slender annual, generally much-branched from the base. Leaflets 3-7 pairs, linear to oval. Flowers yellow, 4-7mm long, *generally solitary*, occasionally paired, very short-stalked. Pod 15-40mm long, straight or curved, with 7 or more horseshoe-shaped segments, hairless, sometimes slightly bearded. Fields, hillslopes, waste ground, cultivated land, garrigue, sometimes by streams. Mar- June. T, but rare in the E Med.

706a Subsp. *bisiliqua.* Similar, but distinguished by its slighter habit, thinly hairy stems, paired flowers and generally *bearded* pods. Greece eastwards – the predominant subspecies in the E Med.

707 *Hippocrepis ciliata.* Like *H. unisiliquosa,* but flowers smaller, 3-5mm long, borne in clusters of 2-6 on stalks *equalling* the leaves. Pod flattened, often curled upwards into almost a complete circle, more prominently bearded. Garrigue, rocky slopes, open pine forest, coastal sands. Mar-May. T.

708 *Hippocrepis multisiliquosa.* Like *H. ciliata,* but flowers larger, 5-8mm long. Pod often curled *downwards* into an almost complete circle, hairless or somewhat bearded. Similar habitats and flowering time to *H. unisiliquosa.* T.

709 *Hippocrepis salzmanii.* Similar, but flower-heads with stalks longer than the leaves and flowers *larger*, 12-15mm long. Maritime sands. S Spain and Morocco.

Hedysarum **HEDYSARUM.** Annual or perennial herbs with pinnate leaves. Flowers in lateral racemes. Pod flattened, jointed, each segment 1-seeded.

710 *Hedysarum coronarium* **ITALIAN SAINFOIN, FRENCH HONEYSUCKLE.** Robust, short to tall, somewhat hairy perennial. Leaves with 3-5 pairs of elliptical to rounded leaflets, hairy beneath, untoothed. Flowers *bright reddish-purple*, 12-15mm long, borne in dense, long-stalked, racemes. Pod with 2-4 spiny segments, hairless. Cultivated and fallow land, roadsides, occasionally in garrigue. Apr-June. Spain to Italy and Sicily, but widely naturalised in the Med region. Cultivated for fodder.

711 *Hedysarum flexuosum.* Similar, but leaflets generally 1-3 pairs, hairy and flowers purple, crimson or pink, smaller, 8-12mm long. Pod with 2-8 segments. Rocky and sandy coastal habitats. Mar-June. S Spain, S Portugal and N Africa.

712 *Hedysarum humile.* Like *H. coronarium*, but a hairier, shorter, plant with *6-16 pairs* of linear to oblong leaflets. Flowers violet-purple, 9-14mm long. Pod with 2-3 segments, spiny and hairy. France and Spain.

713 *Hedysarum spinosissimum* **SPINY SAINFOIN**. Low to short, sprawling to suberect, somewhat hairy annual. Leaves with 4-8 pairs of elliptical to oblong leaflets. Flowers white to pale pinkish-purple, 8-11mm long, 2-10 borne in small racemes. Pod with 2-4 segments, hairy and with *hooked* purplish spines. Garrigue, sand-dunes, rocky places, open pine forest. Feb-May. T – not Portugal, Italy or Yugoslavia.

714 *Hedysarum glomeratum [H. capitatum].* Similar, but leaflets often oval and broadest above the middle. Flowers *larger*, 14-20mm long, pinkish-purple. Portugal and NW Africa eastwards to Greece – not Crete.

715 *Alhagi graecorum* **ALHAGI**. *Spiny* shrub to 60cm, much-branched; stems hairless. Leaves alternate, simple, oblong to lanceolate, densely hairy, especially beneath. Flowers purple or crimson, 7-10mm long, solitary or paired, borne on short, slender, lateral spines. Pod 20-40mm long, irregularly and shallowly constricted between the seeds, hairy when young, pale brown. Waste and cultivated ground, sand-dunes, generally close to sea level. SE Greece. (Cyclades) and E Med including Cyprus.

716 *Alhagi maurorum.* Slenderer plant than *A. graecorum* with 3-8 flowers in *short* racemes. Pod hairless, markedly constricted between the seeds. Similar habitats and flowering time. Turkey, Rhodes, Cyprus and Palestine.

Onobrychis **SAINFOINS**. Annual or perennial herbs with pinnate leaves. Flowers in lateral racemes, often white or purple. Pod not jointed, indehiscent, rounded and compressed, with net veins and a toothed margin and 1-3 seeds.

717 *Onobrychis saxatilis [Hedysarum saxatile]* **ROCK SAINFOIN**. Low to short tufted, white-hairy perennial, stemless or with a short stem. Leaves with 6-15 pairs of linear leaflets, hairless above. Flowers pale pink or pale yellow with pink veins, 9-14mm long, in slender spikes. Pod 5-8mm long, *without* marginal spines, but with sunken hairy pits on the sides. Rocky and stony habitats, mainly on limestone. Apr-June. France, Spain and Italy.

718 *Onobrychis caput-galli [Hedysarum caput-galli]* **COCKSCOMB SAINFOIN**. A short to tall, hairless or somewhat hairy, erect to sprawling annual. Leaves with 4-7 pairs of oblong to linear leaflets. Flowers reddish-purple, 7-8mm long, borne in few-flowered racemes, the stalk generally shorter than the leaves; calyx-tube hairless. Pod 6-10mm, with a crest of *slender spines*, the sides also spiny. Garrigue, limestone rocks, cultivated and waste ground, pathsides, occasionally in open pine forest or on sand-dunes. Feb-July. T – not Balearic Is., Corsica or Sardinia.

719 *Onobrychis crista-galli [Hedysarum crista-galli].* Similar, but flowers pale to dark pink with a hairy calyx-tube. Pod larger, 8-14mm, with a crest of flattened oblong or triangular, spiny, *lobes.* Similar habitats, but on non-calcareous soils. N Africa, Aegean Is., E Med, including Cyprus.

720 *Onobrychis aequidentata [Hedysarum aequidentata].* Like *O. caput-galli,* but a hairier plant with flowers 10-14mm long, borne in racemes whose stalks greatly exceed the leaves. Pod 6-12mm, with a cockscomb-like crest, non-spiny or with a few small spines. Similar habitats and flowering time. N Med from S France to Turkey and Cyprus.

721 *Onobrychis venosa [Hedysarum venosum]* **CYPRIOT SAINFOIN**. Low to short, tufted, somewhat hairy perennial, with a very short stem or no stem. Leaves with 3-4 pairs of oblong to oval leaflets, green with conspicuous purple or bronze veins, hairy beneath. Flowers creamy-yellow veined with purple or red, 9-10mm long, borne in long-stalked racemes. Pod flattened, *orbicular*, curved upwards, 10-15mm, papery and finely hairy. Dry rocky places in garrigue, sometimes on coastal sands. Feb-May. Cyprus – endemic.

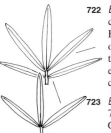

722 *Ebenus creticus* **SHRUBBY SAINFOIN.** Spreading to rather upright shrub to 50cm, occasionally taller, grey-hairy. Leaves with 3-5 elliptic-oblong leaflets, silkily hairy. Flowers bright pink with deeper veins, 10-15mm, borne in dense *silky-silver* oblong or cylindrical racemes; calyx with silvery-haired teeth. Pod hidden within the calyx, 1-2-seeded. Rocky habitats, cliffs and dry slopes. Apr-June. Crete – endemic. A very beautiful plant that has proved over the years very difficult to cultivate in gardens.

723 *Ebenus sibthorpii.* Similar, but herbaceous, only woody at the base and leaves with 7-9 leaflets. Flowers in *globose heads*, reddish-purple. Cliffs and rocks. SE Greece and Rhodes.

The following decorative legumes are exotic species widely grown in parks and gardens in parts of the Med region.

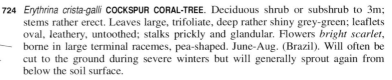

724 *Erythrina crista-galli* **COCKSPUR CORAL-TREE.** Deciduous shrub or subshrub to 3m; stems rather erect. Leaves large, trifoliate, deep rather shiny grey-green; leaflets oval, leathery, untoothed; stalks prickly and glandular. Flowers *bright scarlet*, borne in large terminal racemes, pea-shaped. June-Aug. (Brazil). Will often be cut to the ground during severe winters but will generally sprout again from below the soil surface.

725 *Wisteria sinensis* **CHINESE WISTERIA.** Vigorous deciduous climber to 15m, with slender twining stems that become greatly thickened and woody eventually. Leaves pinnate, alternate; leaflets often 11, oval, untoothed. Flowers violet and pale lilac, pea-shaped, borne in blunt *drooping* racemes, 20-30cm long, fragrant. Pod oblong, velvety. May-June. (China). Various cultivars are grown in gardens including those with white, bluish-mauve, pink or mauve flowers.

726 *Wisteria floribunda* **JAPANESE WISTERIA.** Similar, but leaves with up to 19 leaflets and racemes long and *tapered*, to 120cm long, lilac or white. May-June. (Japan).

727 *Sophora japonica* **PAGODA TREE.** Spreading deciduous tree to 20m eventually. Leaves alternate, pinnate; leaflets 9-15, oval, dark green. Flowers *creamy-white*, pea-shaped, borne in long clusters, up to 26cm long. Aug-Sept. (China and Korea). A form 'Pendula', with weeping branches, is also cultivated.

(727)

728 *Gleditsia triacanthos* **HONEY LOCUST.** Spreading deciduous tree to 20m; stems and trunk armed with long stout *spines*. Leaves pinnate, deep glossy green, with 20 or more oblong-lanceolate leaflets. Flowers *greenish*, unisexual, the male in downy racemes to 5cm long, the female fewer. Fruit a pod, scimitar-shaped, twisting, to 50cm long, remaining on the tree during the winter. July-Aug. (North America). A yellow-leaved form, 'Sunburst' is often grown.

729 *Delonix regia* **FLAMBOYANT TREE.** Spreading tree to 15m at maturity, deciduous. Leaves large, 2-pinnate, with numerous small elliptical leaflets. Flowers red or orange, *large*, 70-90mm, with one of the 5 spoon-shaped petals pink with darker blotches; stamens projecting, curved. Pod large and woody, to 60cm long. June-Aug. (Madagascar). Widely cultivated in the tropics and subtropics and only hardy in the mildest frost-free parts of the Med as a park and street tree.

730 *Cassia corymbosa* **CASSIA.** Vigorous evergreen or semi-evergreen shrub to 2m, with rather erect stems. Leaves pinnate with 2-3 pairs of oblong-oval leaflets, rounded at the base. Flowers yellow, in small terminal clusters about, 25-30mm, across, with 5 slightly unequal petals; stamens curved, *not* longer than the petals. July-Aug. (Tropical America).

731 *Cassia didymobotrya.* Like the previous, but more robust; leaves with 4-18 pairs of oval-oblong leaflets. Flowers borne in raceme-like heads, *blackish-brown* in bud. (Tropical Africa).

732 *Caesalpinia pulcherrima [Poinciana pulcherrima]* **BARBADOS PRIDE.** Prickly evergreen shrub or small tree to 6m, though often less, with spreading to erect branches. Leaves 2-pinnate, with numerous small, oblong green leaflets. Flowers borne in erect, dense terminal racemes, orange-yellow, cup-shaped, with long protruding, *red-stalked*, stamens. July-Aug. Grown in parks and gardens mainly. (Tropics).

SORREL FAMILY Oxalidaceae

A medium-sized family of tropical and temperate plants, some shrubby but the majority herbs with tubers or bulbs. Leaves various, but pinnate or palmate, often clover-like with 3 leaflets.

Oxalis **SORRELS.** Herbs, sometimes with a bulbous stock. Leaves stalked, usually trifoliate, the leaflets untoothed. Flowers solitary or in long-stalked, umbel-like clusters, 5-parted, with 5 separate sepals and petals; stamens 10. Fruit a capsule, exploding when ripe.

733 *Oxalis corniculata [O. repens]* **PROCUMBENT YELLOW SORREL.** Low creeping, hairy perennial; stems *rooting* at the nodes. Leaves alternate; leaflets broadly oval, notched at the apex. Flowers yellow, in clusters of 1-7, petals 4-7mm long. Capsule 10-25mm long, hoary, on reflexed stalks. Cultivated and waste ground, roadsides, generally in dry open habitats. Apr-Dec. T – a widespread cosmopolitan weed. Country of origin uncertain.

734 *Oxalis europaea.* Similar, but stems not rooting at the nodes and leaves mostly sub-opposite or whorled. Fruit-stalks *not* reflexed. Cultivated and waste places. Apr-July. European Med.

735 *Oxalis pes-caprae [O. cernua]* **BERMUDA BUTTERCUP, CAPE SORREL.** Slightly hairy, tufted, low to, short bulbous perennial, without an aerial stem, often carpeting. Leaves long-stalked, at ground level; leaflets broadly heart-shaped. Flowers large, yellow, funnel-shaped, the petals 20-25mm long, borne in broad umbels. Capsule rarely formed. A widespread weed of cultivated and waste land, olive groves, vineyards, plantations and orchards. Nov-May. T – except parts of the E Med and N Africa. (South Africa). Double-flowered forms, sometimes coppery-yellow in colour, are found throughout the region. This widespread weedy species is generally believed to have been introduced to Malta *c.* 1806, and within 50 years had become widespread in the Med region. It is particularly resistant to modern herbicides.

736 *Oxalis articulata* **PINK OXALIS.** Low to short, hairy, tufted perennial, with a swollen rhizomes. Leaves all basal, long-stalked; leaflets heart-shaped, covered in orange or brown dots. Flowers *pink*, borne in broad umbel-like clusters; petals 12-20mm long. Capsule 9—10mm long. Waste and cultivated land – sometimes grown in gardens. May-Oct. W European Med. (E temperate South America).

737 *Oxalis purpurea.* Similar, but leaves not dotted, often purplish beneath and flowers *solitary*, purplish-pink with a white centre. Capsule 5mm long. Cultivated and waste ground, gardens. Spain, Portugal, Corsica and Sicily.

GERANIUM FAMILY Geraniaceae

Herbs, mostly with alternate leaves, palmately-lobed in *Geranium*, but pinnately-lobed in *Erodium*. Flowers in cymes or umbels, sometimes solitary, 5-parted, regular to somewhat irregular; sepals separate; stamens in two whorls of 5. Fruit with 5, one-seeded, portions, united together into a prominent beak, springing apart from the base when ripe.

Geranium **CRANE'S-BILLS**. Leaves palmately-lobed. Flowers regular with 5 even petals.

738 *Geranium tuberosum* **TUBEROUS CRANE'S-BILL**. Short to medium, tuberous-rooted, hairy perennial; stem *solitary*, branched above. Leaves greyish-green, mostly basal, long-stalked, with 3-6 pinnately-lobed segments. Flowers purplish-pink with darker veins, 14-24mm, borne in branched clusters (cymes); petals notched. Cultivated and waste ground, roadsides, rocky slopes. Feb-Apr. Sardinia eastwards, including Cyprus and the E Med. Widely grown in gardens.

739 *Geranium macrostylum*. Similar, but the stem with a *pair of leaves* and the flower-stalks with glandular hairs. Flowers larger, 22-32mm. Similar habitats and flowering time. Greece and Albania.

740 *Geranium malviflorum* **MALLOW-FLOWERED CRANE'S-BILL**. Like *G. tuberosum*, but with more broadly lobed leaves and *larger* flowers, 32-42mm. Rocky slopes. S Spain and NW Africa.

741 *Geranium molle* **DOVE'S-FOOT CRANE'S-BILL**. Low to short, densely tufted, sprawling to prostrate, usually greyish-green annual; stems branched from the base, softly hairy. Basal leaves rounded or kidney-shaped in outline, divided into 5-7 wedge-shaped, 3-lobed segments; upper leaves more deeply divided, short-stalked or unstalked, alternate. Flowers pinkish-purple, 7-10mm, borne in lax clusters, the petals deeply notched. Fields, rocky slopes, roadsides, gardens and sand-dunes. Feb-May. T.

742 *Geranium brutium*. Similar, but usually perennial, green and less hairy; stems *erect*, to 70cm. Flowers bright reddish-purple, 12-18mm. S Italy and Sicily to the Balkans and Turkey.

743 *Geranium rotundifolium* **ROUND-LEAVED CRANE'S-BILL**. Like *G. molle*, but with erect or ascending stems with more shallowly lobed leaves and bright pink flowers, 10-12mm; *petals* unnotched or only slightly notched. Similar habitats. Feb-July. T.

744 *Geranium pusillum* **SMALL-LEAVED CRANE'S-BILL**. Like *G. molle*, but flowers *smaller*, only 4-6mm, pale lilac and half the stamens without anthers (staminodes). Grassy and rocky places, hillsides, garrigue. Mar-May. T.

745 *Geranium dissectum* **CUT-LEAVED CRANE'S-BILL**. Short to medium, spreading or rather sprawling, hairy annual, with ascending flowering stems. Leaves rounded in outline, *split* almost to the base into 5-7 narrow-lobed segments, stalked; upper leaves opposite and less lobed. Flowers bright purplish-pink, 8-10mm, with shallowly notched petals; flower-stalks not more than 15mm long; sepals spreading. Fruit hairy and ridged. Fields and waste ground, roadsides, generally on rather moist soils. Feb-May. T.

746 *Geranium columbinum* **LONG-STALKED CRANE'S-BILL**. Similar, but flowers larger, 12-18mm, with *unnotched* petals; flower-stalks at least 20mm long. Fruit often hairless and not ridged. Damp pastures, scrub and banks. Mar-May. T.

747 *Geranium robertianum* **HERB ROBERT**. Short to medium, hairy annual or biennial, often red or bronze flushed; with a strong and rather *unpleasant smell*. Leaves

palmate, the lower with 5 pinnately-lobed segments, the upper with only 3. Flowers bright pink, occasionally white, 14-18mm, the petals slightly notched, with a distinct claw; pollen orange; sepals erect, often reddish. Fruit usually hairy, ridged. Shaded habitats, banks, rocks, woodland, walls and courtyards, sometimes on coastal cliffs or shingle. Mar-Sept. T – not Balearic Is. Coastal forms are often rather depauperate and can be readily mistaken for similar forms of *G. purpureum*.

748 *Geranium purpureum* **LITTLE ROBIN**. Similar, but an aromatic, less reddish plant. Flowers smaller, 7-14mm, with *yellow* pollen; petals usually not notched. Damp, usually shaded habitats, rocks, often in the maquis; occasionally along hedgerows or walls. Feb-May. T.

749 *Geranium lucidum* **SHINY CRANE'S-BILL**. Short, erect to spreading, hairless annual. Leaves *shiny*, green, often red-flushed, rounded in outline, divided under halfway into oval, blunt-toothed lobes; upper leaves opposite, short-stalked. Flowers bright pink, 10-14mm, often in pairs; sepals erect. Fruit hairless. Shaded habitats, cliffs, rocks, walls, hedgerows, occasionally on cultivated land. Mar-May. T.

750 *Geranium lanuginosum*. An annual or biennial, short to medium, hairy. Leaves deeply divided into 5-7 oblong or diamond-shaped, irregularly lobed segments. Flowers bright *violet-blue*, 13-16mm, generally with darker veins and a whitish centre. Apr-June. Spain eastwards to Italy and Greece, but not Balearic Is. or Yugoslavia.

Erodium **STORK'S-BILLS**. Like *Geranium*, but leaves mostly pinnately-lobed or pinnate and flowers often somewhat irregular (zygomorphic), with 2 petals slightly or markedly larger than the other 3. Stamens 5.

751 *Erodium chium*. Robust low to medium, hairy annual or biennial. Leaves oval, *divided* for half or slightly more into blunt, toothed lobes. Flowers purplish, 10-18mm, in 2-8-flowered umbels; flower-stalks generally not glandular. Fruit with short white hairs; beak 30-40mm long. Dry, open habitats, rocky places, roadsides, tracks. Mar-June. T – not Cyprus and parts of the E Med.

    751a Subsp. *littoreum*. Similar, but a slenderer perennial with pinnately-lobed leaves; flower-stalks usually glandular. SE Spain to France, Corsica and the Balearic Is.

752 *Erodium malacoides [E. subtriflorum, Geranium malacoides]* **SOFT or MALLOW-LEAVED STORK'S-BILL**. An erect to sprawling, short to medium, hairy, often glandular annual or biennial. Leaves oval to oblong in outline, heart-shaped at the base, toothed, occasionally 3-lobed or pinnately-lobed, *covered with tiny shiny glands*. Flowers purplish, 11-18mm, in 3-7-flowered umbels; bracts lanceolate, at least 3 below each umbel; flower-stalks usually glandular-hairy. Fruit beak 18-35mm long. Dry open habitats, roadsides, waste and cultivated land. Jan-May. T.

753 *Erodium laciniatum*. Similar, but the leaves indistinctly glandular beneath and flowers 4-9 to an umbel; bracts only 2, oval to kidney-shaped, below each umbel. Fruit beak 35-90mm. Dry habitats, especially coastal sands. Mar-May. T – not Balearic Is. or Yugoslavia.

754 *Erodium crassifolium [E. hirtum]*. Like *E. malacoides*, but a perennial with a tuberous rootstock and leaves 2-pinnately-lobed; flowers pale pink; fruit beak long and slender, 50-100mm long, *very hairy* internally. Coastal cliffs, rocky habitats, margins of salt lakes or brackish waters. Mar-May. N Africa, Crete, Cyprus and the E Med.

755 *Erodium maritimum*. Like *E. malacoides*, but a smaller plant with leaves less than 30mm wide and flowers pink or white, *only 5-6mm*, occasionally without petals. Fruit beak only about 10mm long. France to Italy and Sicily.

756 *Erodium corsicum*. Like *E. maritimum*, but leaves grey-green (not green) and plant a perennial. Flowers solitary or 2-3 together, 10-18mm; beak 10-15mm long. Coastal rocks. Corsica and Sardinia.

757 *Erodium gruinum* [*Geranium gruinum*] **LONG-BEAKED STORK'S-BILL**. Rather robust, short to medium, hairy annual. Leaves oblong in outline, lobed (not pinnately-lobed). Flowers large, violet, 35-45mm, in 2-6-flowered umbels; bracts whitish. Fruit rough hairy, with deep pits; beak *very long*, 60-110mm. Hillslopes, stony, grassy and waste places, wall, ruins, coastal sands. Feb-May. Sicily and Crete eastwards, including Cyprus.

758 *Erodium botrys* [*Geranium botrys*]. Similar, but often less robust with the upper leaves deeply pinnately-lobed and toothed; the umbels 1-4-flowers; bracts *brown*. Flowers 20-30mm. Dry grassy, rocky and stony habitats, roadsides. Feb-May. T – rarer in the E Med.

759 *Erodium hoefftianum*. Like *E. gruinum*, but flowers smaller, only 14-16mm and fruit beak 50-75mm long. Similar habitats and flowering time. Yugoslavia, Greece and Turkey.

760 *Erodium ciconium*. Short to medium, hairy annual or biennial. Leaves pinnate, at least in the lower part, with small leaflets between the main ones. Flowers lilac or bluish, with darker veins, 14-16mm; umbels 3-10-flowered; bracts oval, densely hairy. Fruit with whitish hairs; beak 60-100mm long. Roadsides, cultivated and waste places, fields. Feb-Apr. T – not Portugal.

761 *Erodium cicutarium* **COMMON STORK'S-BILL**. A very variable, low to medium, erect, sprawling to prostrate, hairy annual, often rather foetid. Leaves *pinnate*, without small leaflets between the main ones. Flowers purplish-pink, lilac or white, 7-18mm, with up to 12 in an umbel, the upper two petals often larger and with a dark basal blotch; bracts brownish. Fruit hairy, the beak 10-40mm long. Cultivated, waste and disturbed ground, stony and rocky places, garrigue, roadsides, old walls, sand-dunes. Feb-June. T. An extremely variable species within which many variants have been recognised in the past. Plants growing on very poor thin soils may be very small.

761a Subsp. *jacquinianum*. Similar, but the upper petals never with a dark blotch and *beak* 40-70mm long. Sandy habitats. N Africa, S Spain, Portugal and Sardinia.

762 *Erodium moschatum* **MUSK STORK'S-BILL**. Similar, but plant *smelling of musk*, sometimes almost stemless; leaflets only shallowly lobed (less than a half) and flowers larger, violet or purple, 16-28mm. Cultivated and waste ground, roadsides. Jan-June. T.

763 *Erodium acaule* **STEMLESS STORK'S-BILL**. Like *E. cicutarium*, but *stemless*. Flowers lilac, with darker blotches, 14-22mm. Fruit with white hairs; beak 25-50mm long. Dry habitats. T – not Balearic Is., Cyprus or much of the extreme E Med.

CALTROP FAMILY Zygophyllaceae

Herbs or shrubs, often with pinnate leaves; stipules present. Flowers hermaphrodite, 5-parted, with a disc and twice as many stamens as petals. Fruit dry or fleshy, often capsular.

fruit

764 *Zygophyllum fabago* **SYRIAN BEAN CAPER.** Medium to tall hairless perennial, with erect stems to 1m. Leaves with *two* oval to elliptical, rather fleshy leaflets, the leaf-stalk extending beyond the leaflets. Flowers white with an orange centre, 9-11mm, solitary in the upper leaf-axils; petals oblong, longer than the sepals. Fruit a pendent capsule, oblong-cylindrical, 20-35mm long. Dry rocky and sandy habitats, waste ground. May-Aug. E Med – not Cyprus; naturalised in S France, Spain and Sardinia.

765 *Zygophyllum album.* Similar, but a small *downy* shrub to 40cm; fruit smaller, 5-10mm long. Rocky places and salt marshes. NE Spain, N Africa, Crete and E Med, including Cyprus.

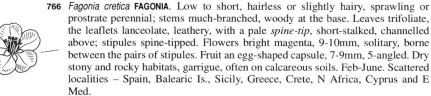

766 *Fagonia cretica* **FAGONIA.** Low to short, hairless or slightly hairy, sprawling or prostrate perennial; stems much-branched, woody at the base. Leaves trifoliate, the leaflets lanceolate, leathery, with a pale *spine-tip*, short-stalked, channelled above; stipules spine-tipped. Flowers bright magenta, 9-10mm, solitary, borne between the pairs of stipules. Fruit an egg-shaped capsule, 7-9mm, 5-angled. Dry stony and rocky habitats, garrigue, often on calcareous soils. Feb-June. Scattered localities – Spain, Balearic Is., Sicily, Greece, Crete, N Africa, Cyprus and E Med.

767 *Peganum harmala* **PEGANUM.** An erect, hairless, tough, tufted perennial; stems erect to ascending, much-branched, woody at the base. Leaves alternate, greyish green, rather fleshy, *irregularly divided* into narrow, pointed lobes. Flowers whitish or greenish, 10-20mm, solitary, opposite the leaves on stout stalks; petals oblong. Fruit a globose, 3-lobed capsule, 10-15mm. Rocky and sandy habitats, waste ground, roadsides. May-July. Scattered localities throughout the Med, but absent from many of the islands – commoner in the E, including Cyprus. Frequently a relict of former cultivated land. A widespread plant in western and central Asia.

768 *Tribulus terrestris* **MALTESE CROSS, SMALL CALTROPS.** Variable, usually hairy, spreading or sprawling, much-branched annual. Leaves pinnate, with 5-6 pairs of oblong leaflets – *no end leaflet*. Flowers yellow, 8-10mm, solitary and lateral. Fruit star-shaped, 8-10mm, spiny, hard and woody. Dry open habitats, often a weed of cultivated land, waste places and gardens, occasionally in garrigue. May-Oct. T. The hard spiny fruits can be be extremely painful to stand or sit upon.

FLAX FAMILY Linaceae

Herbs or small shrubs with simple untoothed leaves. Flowers 5-parted, in a branched inflorescence, occasionally spike-like; petals usually free, clawed. Stamens 5, alternating with 5 staminodes. Fruit a 10-valved capsule.

769 *Linum arboreum* (incl. *L. caespitosum*) **SHRUBBY FLAX.** A hairless shrub to 1m, with woody stems *terminated* by leafy-rosettes. Leaves alternate. spatula-shaped, thick and persistent, 1-veined, with a thickened horny margin, crowded; leaves with a pair of glands at the base. Flowers yellow, borne in compact, few-flowered heads; petals 10-18mm long. Capsule 6-8mm. Limestone rocks. Mar-May. Crete, SW Aegean, Greece, Rhodes and Turkey.

770 *Linum capitatum.* Similar, but only the base woody and leaf-rosettes, if present, basal, producing annual flowering stems to 40cm; petals 15-20mm long. Rocky slopes, mainly in the mountains. C and S Italy, mainland Balkans.

771 *Linum flavum* **YELLOW FLAX.** Robust, short to medium, hairless perennial, with a woody stock, with few or no non-flowering leafy rosettes. Leaves lanceolate to spatula-shaped, *3-5-veined*, with a pair of glands at the base. Flowers yellow, borne in lax clusters with 25 or more flowers; petals 18-20mm long, short-clawed. Capsule 5-6mm, short-beaked. Dry rocky and grassy habitats, garrigue. Apr-July. Albania, Italy and Yugoslavia.

772 *Linum thracicum.* Similar, but sepals 8-10mm long (not 6-8mm) and twice as long as the capsule (not equal to). Balkans and Turkey.

773 *Linum nodiflorum* (incl. *L. luteolum*). A short to medium, hairless annual; stems solitary or few, *winged.* Leaves spatula-shaped, with brown glands at the base and with a rough margin; upper leaves linear, 1-veined. Flowers pale to bright yellow, borne in a lax, rather rigid, inflorescence; petals 15-20mm, long-clawed. Capsule 5-6mm. Dry habitats, rocky ground, sandy places, garrigue, open pine forest. Mar-May. S France eastwards to Cyprus and the E Med, including Crete.

774 *Linum campanulatum.* Similar, but plant usually with non-flowering *leaf-rosettes* and leaves all 1-veined. Flowers in clusters of 3-5; petals 25-35mm long, bright lemon-yellow with orange veins towards the base. E Spain to Italy – absent from the islands.

775 *Linum narbonense* **BEAUTIFUL FLAX.** Short to medium, hairless perennial; stems erect to ascending. Leaves greyish, alternate, without basal glands, linear to lanceolate, long-pointed, mostly 1- or 3-veined; *bracts* with membranous margins. Flowers bright azure-blue, large, the petals 25-40mm long; sepals 10-14mm long. Grassy and rocky habitats. Apr-June. W Med from NW Africa and Portugal, eastwards to Yugoslavia – not Crete.

776 *Linum pubescens* **HAIRY FLAX.** *Hairy,* low to short annual, generally with only 1-2 stems, slender, erect. Leaves lanceolate, without basal glands. Flowers pink, often tinged with blue in the centre, few in a cluster; petals 20-30mm long. Capsule 3.5-4.5mm. Rocky and grassy places, scrub, garrigue, fields and vineyards, occasionally in olive groves. Mar-June. Crete, Albania, Greece and the E Med, including Cyprus.

777 *Linum bienne* [*L. angustifolium*] **PALE FLAX.** A tufted, low to medium, hairless biennial or perennial; stems erect or ascending, generally *branched* at the base. Leaves linear-lanceolate, 1-3-veined; margin smooth. Flowers pale blue or lilac-blue, in lax clusters; petals 7-9mm long, about twice the length of the sepals; stigma linear. Capsule 4-6mm. Rocky ground, garrigue, marshy ground, fields and open forests. Jan-June. T.

778 *Linum perenne* **PERENNIAL FLAX.** Similar, but leaves wider, 1-3mm (not 0.5-1.5mm) and flowers *dark blue,* the petals 3 or 4 times longer than the sepals; stigma capitate. Dry grassy habitats, roadsides, bushy places. Mar-June. Scattered localities in Spain, France, Italy and the Balkans – a primarily central European species.

779 *Linum austriacum* subsp. *collinum.* Like *L. perenne,* but flower-stalks *deflexed* in fruit (not erect and straight). Grassy and rocky habitats. Spain eastwards to Greece – absent from the islands, except Sicily.

780 *Linum usitatissimum* **FLAX, LINSEED.** Like *L. bienne,* but an annual, generally with a *solitary* unbranched stem. Flowers blue or white; petals 13-18mm long. Capsule 6-9mm, often not dehiscing. Fields, cultivated and waste ground, roadsides. Mar-June. T – often casual. Not known to be indigenous anywhere and presumed to have arisen from *L. bienne* in the first instance. Still cultivated in some parts of Europe and W Asia, mainly for oil extraction from the seed rather than its fibres as in former times. Today frequently seen in W Europe, fields becoming a pale blue haze when the plants are in flower.

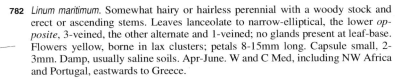

781 *Linum decumbens.* Hairless annual, rather like the previous species, but leaf-margin *rough* and flowers red or pink. S Italy, Sicily and Sardinia.

782 *Linum maritimum.* Somewhat hairy or hairless perennial with a woody stock and erect or ascending stems. Leaves lanceolate to narrow-elliptical, the lower *opposite*, 3-veined, the other alternate and 1-veined; no glands present at leaf-base. Flowers yellow, borne in lax clusters; petals 8-15mm long. Capsule small, 2-3mm. Damp, usually saline soils. Apr-June. W and C Med, including NW Africa and Portugal, eastwards to Greece.

783 *Linum trigynum [L. gallicum].* Similar, but an annual with *all leaves* alternate. Flowers smaller, petals 4-6mm long. Dry, generally stony habitats. Mar-May. T.

784 *Linum strictum* **UPRIGHT YELLOW FLAX.** Like *L. trigynum,* but leaves with rough, often *inrolled* margins. Flowers in a crowded, rigid, often spike-like inflorescence; petals 6-12mm long. Dry rocky hillslopes, coastal sands and vineyards. Mar-May. T. The plant in the E Med, including Cyprus, is often called subsp. *spicatum,* distinguished by its pronounced spike-like inflorescence.

785 *Linum corymbulosum [L. strictum* subsp. *corymbulosum].* Like *L. strictum,* but stems *often* branched below and inflorescence lax and spreading. Dry places, stony slopes, often in garrigue. Similar distribution and flowering time.

786 *Linum suffruticosum* subsp. *salsaloides* **WHITE FLAX.** Short to low, tufted, hairless perennial, generally with *numerous non-flowering* leafy shoots, spreading to ascending. Leaves linear, not more than 1mm wide, with a rough inrolled margin. Flowers white, generally with a violet or pink centre; petals 10-20mm long; sepals 3-veined. Dry rocky and grassy habitats, often exposed. Apr-July. C Spain to NW Italy – not on the islands.

787 *Linum tenuifolium.* Similar, but often taller, with few non-flowering shoots; leaf-margin generally flat; flowers smaller, pinkish or white, sepals all pointed, *1-veined.* Similar habitats and flowering time. Spain eastwards to Turkey – not Balearic Is. or Crete.

SPURGE FAMILY Euphorbiaceae

A very large family distributed throughout the world and containing herbs, shrubs, trees, lianas. There are in excess of 7000 species, 1600 in *Euphorbia* alone.

Euphorbia **SPURGES.** Annual or perennial herbs or shrubs with milky latex. Flowers in umbel-like clusters, each stalk (ray) of the umbel bearing bracts (often yellowish), with one or several flower-clusters. Male and female flowers separate, but in discrete groups (cyathia), with several male and a solitary female set in a cup-shaped involucre, with glistening, kidney-shaped glands, the male flowers with a single stamen, the female with an ovary and 3 styles. Fruit a 3-lobed capsule.

788 *Euphorbia peplis* **PURPLE SPURGE.** Low prostrate, grey-green, hairless annual, usually with *4-branches* at the base; stems purple. Leaves opposite, oblong, with a rounded lobe on one side at the base, sometimes notched at the tip, short-stalked. Flowers greenish, with semicircular, reddish-brown glands, lateral or clustered, not borne in umbels. Capsule 3.5-4mm, nearly smooth and purplish. Seeds smooth, pale grey, sometimes mottled. Sandy or shingly seashores, above high water mark, rarely inland. May-July. T. Often associated with other foreshore species like *Salsola kali.*

flower

789 *Euphorbia prostrata.* Similar, but with *many branches* from the base; stems usually hairy above. Capsule hairy on the keels; seeds rough. A weed of cultivated and waste ground, sandy places. Naturalised in Spain, Portugal, France, Italy and Sicily.

790 *Euphorbia chamaesyce [E. canescens]*. Like *E. prostrata*, but plant hairy or hairless, with capsule hairy all over; floral-glands with white appendages. Dry stony places, fields, irrigated land and river gravels. May-Nov. T.

791 *Euphorbia nutans*. Like *E. chamaesyce*, but stems ascending to erect and leaves longer, to 36mm long (to 11mm long in previous species). Weed of arable land, orchards, vineyards and waste land. July-Sept. T – scattered localities. (North and South America).

bract

792 **Euphorbia dendroides TREE SPURGE.** Tall, hairless, rounded shrub to 2m, regularly branched and with a thick trunk. Leaves oblong-lanceolate, borne during the autumn and winter and falling in the late spring to leave bare branches. Umbel with 5-10 rays; bracts yellowish, broader and shorter than the leaves; glands suborbicular, irregularly lobed. Capsule 5-6mm, smooth. Seeds grey, smooth. Rocky coastal habitats, often forming large colonies. Apr-June. T – but local; not Cyprus.

bract

793 *Euphorbia hierosolymitana*. Similar, but taller, to 3m, sparingly branched, with leaves *broadest* above the middle. Umbel usually with 5 rays. Seeds smooth, brown and shiny. Similar habitats, usually on limestone. Jan-Apr. Cyprus and E Med, including Cyprus.

794 **Euphorbia acanthothamnos GREEK SPINY SPURGE.** An intricately branched, hairless shrub forming dense mounds to 40cm high; branches regularly forked, *spine-tipped* (spines formed from the previous years rays which become stout, woody and persistent). Leaves elliptical, bright green, untoothed. Umbels often with 3 rays; bracts broader and shorter than the leaves, bright golden. Capsule 3-4mm, warted. Rocky lowland habitats, hillsides, cliffs, garrigue. Mar-May. Greece, Aegean Is., Crete and W Turkey. The characteristic golden hummocks are a striking feature of open hillslopes in the spring.

795 *Euphorbia spinosa*. Similar, but making a laxer bush, the branch-tips weakly spiny, *not sharp*, and leaves bluish-green, lanceolate. Bracts much broader than the stem-leaves; umbels with 1-5 rays. Rocky and stony places, lowland and mountains. Apr-June. S France to Albania – not Crete or Greece.

796 *Euphorbia glabriflorum*. Like *E. spinosa*, but not spiny, the dead twigs *not persisting*; shrub to only 20cm. Leaves linear-lanceolate to elliptical; rays 3-5. Capsules 4mm, warted. Rocky and stony habitats, in the mountains. Yugoslavia, Albania and Greece.

bract

797 *Euphorbia segetalis [E. tetraceras]*. Short, hairless annual; stem simple or branched. Leaves alternate, *narrow* linear to linear-lanceolate. Rays 5. Bracts diamond-shaped, yellowish-green; glands with 2-4 horns. Capsule 2.5-3mm, rough, granular; seeds pale grey. Open, generally sandy habitats, often close to the sea. Mar-May. Portugal and NW Africa, eastwards to Yugoslavia – not Sardinia or Sicily.

798 *Euphorbia pinea [E. segetalis* subsp. *pinea]*. Similar, but a perennial, often *much-branched* from the base, to 50cm. Sandy seashores. Similar distribution, as well as Sardinia, Sicily and Albania.

flower

799 **Euphorbia helioscopia SUN SPURGE.** Short to medium, more or less hairless annual; stem usually solitary, erect. Leaves oval, broadest above the middle, *finely toothed* in the upper half. Umbel with 5 rays; bracts yellowish, similar in shape to the leaves. Capsule 2.5-3.5mm, smooth and unwinged. seeds brown and netted.

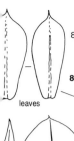

leaves

bract

flower

bract

flower

Cultivated and waste ground, roadsides, occasionally seashores. Jan-July. T. A common weed of arable land and gardens in many parts of Europe and Asia.

800 *Euphorbia arguta*. Similar, but leaves more sharply toothed, *all along* the margin and seeds smooth. Arable land and fallow fields. Feb-Apr. S Greece (Peloponnese), Aegean, Cyprus and the E Med.

801 *Euphorbia myrsinites* **BROAD-LEAVED GLAUCOUS SPURGE**. Low to short, spreading to prostrate perennial, with simple, thickened, densely leafy stems radiating from a central point. Leaves *thick and fleshy*, grey- or bluish-green, oval to rounded, with a short point. Rays 5-12; bracts bright yellowish-green, heart- or kidney-shaped; glands weakly horned. Capsule 5-7mm, smooth or minutely warted. Seeds smooth, grey-brown. Rocky habitats, scrub and open woodland, often in garrigue. Mar-June. Balearic Is. and Corsica, eastwards to Turkey. Frequently grown in gardens.

802 *Euphorbia rigida* [*E. biglandulosa*] **NARROW-LEAVED GLAUCOUS SPURGE**. Similar, but with *erect to ascending* stems and narrower, lanceolate, pointed leaves, often flushed with purple. Capsule 3-sided; seeds whitish when ripe. Rocky slopes, roadsides, scrub. Mar-May. N Africa, Italy and Sicily eastwards – not Cyprus.

803 *Euphorbia veneris*. Like *E. rigida,* but less robust and with smaller leaves. Rocky mountain habitats. Feb-June. Cyprus – endemic.

804 *Euphorbia broteri*. Like *E. rigida,* but leaves linear-lanceolate and seeds rough. Portugal and Spain.

805 *Euphorbia lathyris* **CAPER SPURGE**. Medium to tall, erect, hairless, bluish-green biennial, to 1.5m. Leaves *opposite*, linear to oblong, untoothed and unstalked. Umbels with 2-6 rays; bracts oval-triangular, pointed, bright green; glands kidney-shaped with blunt horns. Capsule 13-17mm, smooth; seeds rough, brown or grey. A weed of cultivated and waste ground, gardens, occasionally on hillslopes and along roadsides. Apr-July. Native to the C Med from S France and Corsica to Greece, but widely naturalised elsewhere in the region. Poisonous. The fruits look similar to the flower buds of the true Caper, *Capparis spinosa*, which are edible.

806 *Euphorbia marginata* **VARIEGATED SPURGE**. Short to medium erect, hairless annual; stem simple, branched above. Leaves alternate, oval or oblong. Umbels with a variable number of rays; bracts like the leaves but with conspicuous broad *white margins*; glands with white horns. Cultivated land, gardens, occasionally along roadsides. June-Sept. Scattered widely in the Med – mainly cultivated for its ornamental features. (North America).

807 *Euphorbia peplus* **PETTY SPURGE**. Medium, hairless, green annual; stem erect, with two or more branches from the base. Leaves oval to almost rounded, untoothed, short-stalked. Umbels with 3 main rays; bracts triangular-oval, *green*; glands kidney-shaped, with long slender horns. Capsule 2.8-3mm, smooth, with two ridges on the back of each valve; seeds pale grey, grooved and somewhat pitted. Cultivated, fallow and waste ground, dry slopes, marshy places, shingle, occasionally by roadsides. Mar-Sept. T.

808 *Euphorbia falcata*. Similar, but less tall, the leaves often with a rather *waxy bloom*, unstalked. Capsule not ridged. Similar habitats and flowering time. T.

809 *Euphorbia aleppica*. Like *E. peplus,* but lower leaves linear, *densely overlapping*; bracts sometimes toothed. Seeds warted. Cultivated and stony ground, damp fields. June-Oct. C and E Med from S France eastwards, including Cyprus.

810 *Euphorbia biumbellata* **WHORLED SPURGE**. Robust, medium, erect, hairless perennial, branched from the base. Leaves alternate, spreading to deflexed, linear to linear-

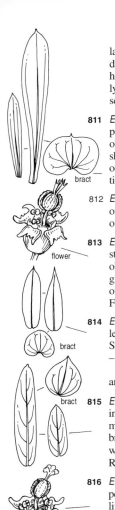

bract

flower

bract

bract

flower

flower

lanceolate. Umbels 2-3, one above the other, each with 8-21 rays; bracts oval to diamond-shaped or kidney-shaped, bright yellowish-green; glands with two horns. Capsule 3-4mm, finely warted, ridged on the valves; seeds pale grey, finely wrinkled. Rocky or sandy coastal habitats, occasionally in open woods or scrub. Apr-June. W Med, NW Africa and Spain, eastwards to Italy and Sicily.

811 *Euphorbia nicaeensis.* Medium to short, hairless, occasionally minutely papillose perennial, bluish-green, *often red-flushed.* Leaves thick and fleshy, lanceolate to oblong, 3-veined. Umbels with 9-18 rays; bracts yellowish, oval to kidney-shaped; glands notched, sometimes with 2 short horns. Capsule 3-4.5mm, rough, occasionally hairy; seeds pale grey, pitted. Dry open habitats, often rocky, sometimes in scrub. Apr-July. S France to Greece – not on the islands.

812 *Euphorbia barrelieri.* Similar, but to only 40cm, the bracts often *purple-tinged*; rays only 3-5; glands with 2 horns. Capsule smooth; seeds smooth. Rocky habitats, often shaded. S France, Italy, Yugoslavia, Greece and Turkey.

813 *Euphorbia paralias* **SEA SPURGE.** Short to medium, hairless, fleshy, tufted perennial; stems erect, branched below. Leaves grey-green, numerous and *overlapping*, oblong, concave above. Umbels with 3-6 rays; bracts oval, concave, green; glands kidney-shaped, with long horns. Capsule 3-5mm, granular along the back of the valves; seeds pale grey, smooth. Rocky and sandy coastal habitats, dunes. Feb-Sept. T.

814 *Euphorbia pithyusa.* Similar, but a bluish-green plant with linear-lanceolate, *pointed* leaves. Capsule smaller, 2-3mm. Inflorescence often overtopped by leafy shoots. Similar habitats and flowering time. Balearic Is. and S France eastwards to Italy – not Sicily.

814a Subsp. *cupanii.* Similar, but without non-flowering branches. Rocky places and scrub inland. W Med islands, including Sicily.

815 *Euphorbia terracina.* Medium, hairless, very fleshy perennial; stems erect to ascending, with non-flowering lateral branches. Leaves oblong to linear-lanceolate, minutely toothed, closely overlapping along the·stem, *flat.* Umbels with 4-5 rays; bracts oblong to diamond-shaped, green, sometimes coarsely toothed; glands with two long, slender horns. Capsule 3-5mm, smooth; seeds pale grey, smooth. Rocky and stony coastal habitats, dunes, ruins and pathsides. Feb-June. T – local.

816 *Euphorbia cyparissias* **CYPRESS SPURGE.** Short to medium, hairless, rhizomatous perennial, often tuft-forming; stems generally branched from the base. Leaves linear, crowded, alternate, untoothed; leafy shoots *resembling young pine trees.* Umbels with 9-18 rays; bracts rounded to kidney-shaped, greenish-yellow; glands kidney-shaped, with two short horns. Capsule 3mm, granular; seeds grey, slightly shiny. Grassy and rocky habitats, scrub and waste places, often on calcareous soils, rarely at sea level. Mar-June. European Med and Turkey – absent from the islands except the Balearics. Widely grown in gardens.

817 *Euphorbia serrata.* Short to medium, greyish- or bluish-green perennial, with a woody stock. Leaves narrow-oblong, to lanceolate, with a finely *toothed margin.* Umbels within 3-5 rays; bracts lanceolate to almost rounded, yellow; glands oval with a truncated end. Rocky places, scrub, garrigue. May-June. Iberian Peninsula eastwards to Italy and Sicily.

818 *Euphorbia characias* **LARGE MEDITERRANEAN SPURGE.** A medium to tall perennial – imposing, stout and hairy; stems thick and leafy, ascending to erect, to 1m, unbranched. Leaves blue- or grey-green, linear to lanceolate, untoothed, generally crowded towards the stem tips which arch over before flowering. Umbels with 10-20 rays, forming large rounded or oblong heads; bracts bluish-green, circular-triangular, *fused* to form 'cups' around the flowers; glands dark reddish-brown, notched or with a pair of short horns. Capsule 4-7mm, smooth, softly hairy; seeds silvery grey. Rocky habitats, scrub, garrigue, maquis, open woodland. Feb-June. NW Africa to Cyrenaica, Portugal eastwards to Italy and Yugoslavia. Widely grown in gardens.

flower

819 *Euphorbia wulfenii [E. characias* subsp. *wulfenii, E. veneta].* Very similar, but a larger plant, sometimes reaching 1.8m tall with yellow or yellowish-green bracts and *yellowish glands* with a pair of long horns. Similar habitats and flowering time. Italy eastwards to Turkey, including the Aegean Is. and Rhodes. Widely grown in gardens.

820 *Mercurialis annua* **ANNUAL MERCURY.** Short to medium, hairless or slightly hairy annual; stems branched from the base. Leaves opposite, oval to lanceolate, toothed, short-stalked. Male and female plants on separate plants; male in upright, stalked spikes, greenish, female flowers few, 3-4mm, in small lateral clusters. Fruit 2-3mm, 2-lobed, *bristly.* Cultivated land, orchards, groves, plantations, waste places, grassy hills and rocks. Oct-Apr. T. The bristly fruits attach themselves to clothes, fur etc and the plant is easily distributed in this way. A British native and a widespread weed of cultivation.

821 *Andrachne telephioides* **ANDRACHNE.** Small shrub to 30cm tall, green, the stems arising from a much-branched stock. Leaves grey-green, oval to elliptical, often broadest above the middle, closely spaced, short-stalked; stipules silvery, often with a reddish base. Male and female flowers yellowish-green, separate, but borne on the same plant, solitary or in small lateral clusters; male with 5-6 stamens, female with a 3-parted ovary. Capsule globose, 2-3mm, 3-lobed, hairless, borne on *reflexed* stalks. Dry habitats, roadsides, waste places. Apr-July. Scattered localities from Spain to Greece – absent from the islands except for Sicily.

822 *Chrozophora tinctoria [C. hieroscolymitana]* **TURN-SOLE.** A low to short, spreading, generally grey-green annual, covered with *star-shaped* hairs – without milky juice. Leaves oval to diamond-shaped, untoothed or wavy-edged and toothed. Flowers yellowish-green, rather inconspicuous, male and female separate, but on the same plant; male with 9-11 stamens, borne in small erect racemes, the female solitary or several together on long recurved stalks at the base of the male. Fruit a trilobed capsule, 5-8mm, purplish, warted. Dry coastal habitats, cultivated and fallow ground. May-Oct. T. Formerly cultivated as a dye plant.

823 *Chrozophora obliqua [C. verbascifolia].* Very similar, but a whitish, more densely hairy plant, the leaves truncated or heart-shaped at the base. Male flowers with 4-5 *stamens.* Similar habitats and flowering time. N Africa, Spain, Crete, Italy, Greece and Turkey. Often regarded as only a form of *C. tinctoria.*

824 *Ricinus communis* **CASTOR OIL PLANT.** Bold and handsome annual or a shrub, to 5m, green or often flushed with purple, bronze or red. Leaves large, *palmate,* with 5-9, coarsely toothed lobes, shiny. Flowers in large terminal panicles, the male below the female; male with numerous yellowish stamens, the female with bright red stigmas; petals inconspicuous, membranous. Fruit up to 20mm long, a 3-parted capsule, covered in spines usually; seeds bean-like, usually mottled, but very variable in colour, with a lump (caruncle) on one end. Cultivated and waste ground, gardens, roadsides, stream banks. Feb-Oct. T. Grown as a garden or house plant, but also commercially in other parts of the world for its oil-bearing seeds. They are highly poisonous, and the oil has to be refined before it is safe for use.

RUE FAMILY Rutaceae

A large and cosmopolitan family or trees, shrubs and herbs. Leaves usually alternate, simple to pinnate, dotted with translucent glands. Flowers generally in cymes or racemes; calyx often 5-parted; corolla usually of 4-5 petals, sometimes more. Fruit a capsule, berry or drupe, often very glandular and aromatic.

Ruta **RUES.** Pungent sub-shrubs with pinnately-divided leaves. Flowers 4-, occasionally 5-parted. Fruit a 4-5-parted capsule.

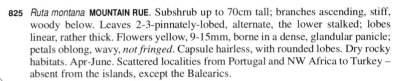

825 *Ruta montana* **MOUNTAIN RUE.** Subshrub up to 70cm tall; branches ascending, stiff, woody below. Leaves 2-3-pinnately-lobed, alternate, the lower stalked; lobes linear, rather thick. Flowers yellow, 9-15mm, borne in a dense, glandular panicle; petals oblong, wavy, *not fringed.* Capsule hairless, with rounded lobes. Dry rocky habitats. Apr-June. Scattered localities from Portugal and NW Africa to Turkey – absent from the islands, except the Balearics.

826 *Ruta graveolens* **RUE.** Hairless evergreen subshrub to 45cm, densely branched, often rather rounded. Leaves bluish-green, very pungent when crushed, the lower long-stalked, the upper almost stalkless; lobes lanceolate to oblong. Flowers dull yellow, 14-18mm, borne in lax panicles with bract-like leaves; petals oblong to oval, *toothed.* Capsule hairless. Dry rocky habitats and scrub. Apr-July. Spain, France, Albania, Yugoslavia and Turkey, but naturalised in other parts of the European Med. Much grown in gardens, but one should beware: it can seriously blister and pigment bare skin if touched in hot sun. In classical times it was considered to be a panacea for curing all manner of ailments, as well as having profound aphrodisiac properties. Today its use is confined to flavouring *grappa,* an Italian brandy.

827 *Ruta chalepensis [R. bracteosa]* **FRINGED RUE.** Similar, but a greener more laxly branched plant to 70cm tall. Flowers rather smaller, the petals bright yellowish-green, *fringed* with long 'hairs'. Capsule with pointed lobes. Similar habitats and flowering time. T. Possibly the rue mentioned in the Bible; used medicinally in the E Med.

828 *Ruta angustifolia.* Like *R. chalepensis,* but the inflorescence *glandular-hairy* with narrower bracts, lanceolate, not heart-shaped. Similar habitats and flowering time. W and C Med, eastwards to Sicily and Yugoslavia.

829 *Haplophyllum buxbaumii [Ruta buxbaumii]* **HAPLOPHYLLUM.** A hairy, short to medium perennial; stems solitary or few, unbranched. Leaves alternate, linear-lanceolate to oblong, sometimes 3-lobed, untoothed, short-stalked. Flowers yellow, 11-14mm, borne in broad, branched clusters; *petals 5,* concave, untoothed. Fruit a 5-lobed capsule, margined with pale glands, each compartment with 2 ovules. Dry grassy places and scrub, fields and waste places. May-July. Crete, Rhodes, Turkey and the E Med, including Cyprus.

830 *Haplophyllum suaveolens [H. ciliatum].* Similar, but leaves rarely lobed, the uppermost *often* forming a whorl below the flowers; inflorescence compact, the sepals lanceolate (not triangular). Ovary with 4 ovules in each compartment; capsule warted. Dry grassy habitats. May-July. Yugoslavia and Turkey.

831 *Haplophyllum linifolium.* Like *H. suaveolens,* but leaves *not reaching* the inflorescence, leaving a bare length of stem above the uppermost leaf. Capsule hairy or not. Dry grassy and rocky habitats. May-July. Spain.

Citrus **CITRUS FRUITS.** Evergreen trees or bushes, with the young twigs with single spines in the leaf-axils. Leaves alternate, thin but leathery, aromatic when crushed, with or without a winged stalk. Flowers white, powerfully scented, with 4-5 sepals and 5-8 petals; stamens 4-10, sometimes many. Fruit large and succulent with a thin or thick gland-pitted rind, with a number of fleshy segments, with or without seeds. All the species described below are widely cultivated in the Med region, in orchards and gardens, or planted as street trees. Many forms and cultivars exist. The origin of many is obscure, but the species are generally thought to have originated in Asia. Most flower in the late winter and early spring, but some flowers are often to be seen throughout the summer.

832 *Citrus limon* **LEMON.** Tree to 4-5m with stout spines and angular twigs. Leaves elliptical to lanceolate, shallowly toothed, with a narrowly winged stalk. Flowers white, often flushed with pink or purple on the outside, few, in short racemes, sometimes solitary, with 25-40 stamens. Fruit the common lemon, 6-13cm long, oval with a *nipple-like* end; rind thick, rough and warty, yellow when ripe; fleshy, acid-tasting. Jan-Dec.

833 *Citrus medica* **CITRON.** Similar, but leaf-stalks *unwinged*. Fruit large, 15-24cm, globose, with a thick, rough warty rind, yellow when ripe; flesh acid or sweetish. Jan-Sept. The rind is candied. Occasionally cultivated, more especially in Corsica and Israel. The species name *medica* indicates not a medical use but that the plant comes from Medea.

834 *Citrus limetta* **SWEET LIME.** Like *C. limon*, but flowers *pure white* and fruit smaller and sweeter-tasting. Seldom grown. The true Lime, *Citrus aurantifolia* (**835**) is not very hardy and is seldom grown in the Med, except in the mildest, most favoured areas.

836 *Citrus sinensis* **ORANGE.** Tree with a rounded crown to 10m, with angular young twigs and thin, rather flexible spines. Leaves elliptical to lanceolate with a *rounded base*, the stalk narrowly winged. Flowers white, sometimes flushed with pink on the outside, borne in short lateral racemes, occasionally solitary; stamens about 20. Fruit the common sweet orange, almost globose, 7-12cm, with a rather smooth thin to thickish, pitted, rind, orange or orange-yellow when ripe, with a solid core; flesh sweet. The most widely cultivated species – many different forms are grown. As with most citrus types the flowers appear as the fruits ripen – often in the late winter and early spring. The word orange is derived from the Arabic *narandj* (fruit favoured by the elephants).

837 *Citrus aurantium* **SEVILLE or SOUR ORANGE.** Similar, but leaf-stalk *widely winged* and fruit with a very rough, pitted rind and bitter flesh. Locally cultivated, especially in Spain. The Sour Orange is known to have been cultivated in Cyprus since as early as 1394. It is far too sour to eat raw and is generally used in flavouring and, most important of all, as the main constituent of marmalade. The flowers are also used in perfumery and the plant is sometimes used as a stock onto which sweet orange varieties are grafted. The Bergamot Orange, *Citrus bergamia* (**838**), is generally considered to be a form of this species; the inedible pear-shaped fruits are cultivated for their sweet smelling ethereal oil – cultivated primarily in Sicily and Calabria.

839 *Citrus paradisi* **GRAPEFRUIT.** Like *C. sinensis*, but the leaf-stalk very broadly winged, to 15mm wide. Fruit large, 10-15cm, depressed globose to almost pear-shaped, with a thick smooth rind, *pale yellow* when ripe; flesh acid to sweetish. Cultivated occasionally in the region for its large and tasty, though here generally somewhat sour fruits.

840 *Citrus grandis* **POMELO, SHADDOCK.** Like *C. paradisi*, but a larger tree, to 12m with few spines; twigs and leaf-midrib *hairy*. Fruit large, to 25cm, globose to pear-shaped,

very pithy, and with a thick rind, green or yellow when ripe; flesh sweetish. Occasionally cultivated, more especially in parks and gardens.

841 *Citrus deliciosa* **MANDARINE, TANGERINE.** Small spreading tree, to 4m, occasionally more. Leaves narrow-elliptical. Flowers solitary or in small clusters. Fruit 5-8cm, depressed globose, with a thin, pitted rind, rather loose and *easily removed*, bright orange when ripe; flesh sweet. Increasingly grown in the region. The easiest citrus to peel. The Satsuma belongs to this group.

TREE OF HEAVEN FAMILY Simaroubaceae

A small family of tropical and subtropical trees or shrubs, often with bitter-tasting bark, related to Sapindaceae.

842 *Ailanthus altissima* **TREE OF HEAVEN.** Large deciduous tree to 20m, suckering freely; bark bitter-tasting, smooth, grey. Leaves alternate, pinnate, more or less hairless; leaflets 13-25, lanceolate to oval, with a few coarse teeth near the base, the teeth each with a large gland beneath. Flowers greenish or creamish, 7-8mm, borne in large terminal panicles, mostly 5-parted, male and female on different trees. *Fruit a group* of reddish-brown samaras (wings), each 30-40mm long. Widely planted as an ornamental tree, but also used in soil conservation, sometimes naturalised. May-July. Scattered localities, especially in the European Med, including many of the islands. (China). In some places this tree has become a serious 'weed' problem, competing successfully with the natural vegetation.

PERSIAN LILAC FAMILY Meliaceae

A medium-sized family of trees, occasionally shrubs, mostly in the tropics and subtropics, often with bitter-tasting bark.

843 *Melia azedarach* **INDIAN BEAD TREE, PERSIAN LILAC.** A deciduous tree to 15m with furrowed bark. Leaves alternate, 2-pinnate; leaflets elliptical to oval, toothed or lobed. Flowers lilac, sweetly fragrant, 15-18mm, borne in broad panicles. Fruit a globose berry, 6-14mm, yellow when ripe, *remaining* on the tree long after the leaves have fallen, eventually becoming wrinkled. Widely planted in the region, and occasionally becoming naturalised. May-June. Naturalised in S France, Crete and Yugoslavia, perhaps elsewhere, but a widely planted tree for streets and gardens. (N India and China). The hard seeds have long been used for making beads and rosaries.

CNEORUM FAMILY Cneoraceae

A tiny family with only 3 species, one each from Cuba, the Canary Is. and the Med.

844 *Cneorum tricoccon* **CNEORUM.** An almost hairless small evergreen spreading shrub, to 1m, though often less. Leaves thick, oblong, blunt but with a short point, unstalked; veins indistinct. Flowers yellow, solitary or in clusters of 2-3 at the upper leaf-axils; petals 3-4. 5mm long. Fruit *trilobed*, each portion rounded, 4-5mm, red at first but becoming black. Rocky habitats in maquis, woodland or sometimes in more exposed places. Mar-June. Spain eastwards to Italy – not Corsica or Sicily.

MILKWORT FAMILY Polygalaceae

Herbs and small shrubs with simple, usually alternate leaves; no stipules. Flowers hermaphrodite, irregular, in slender racemes or spikes; sepals 5, separate, the inner 2 (wings) larger and petal-like; corolla with 3 fused petals, fringed at the apex; stamens 8. Fruit a compressed, usually 2-lobed capsule.

845 *Polygala rupestris* **ROCK MILKWORT**. Small bushy, low to short perennial with a woody stock; stems minutely hairy. Leaves rather leathery, linear to oblong with *inrolled margins* (revolute). Flowers white with a purple tip, 6-8mm long, generally solitary or 2-3 together in a short more or less terminal raceme, the keel petal with a large crest; wings greenish, longer than the petals. Capsule narrowly winged. Rock crevices, lowland and mountains. Apr-June. Spain, France and Balearic Is.

846 *Polygala myrtifolia*. An erect *shrub*, 1-2.5m tall. Leaves oblong, often broadest above the middle, blunt. Flowers lilac with a deep violet apex to the keel, 15-20mm long, borne in short racemes; wings violet-purple, slightly longer than the petals. Locally naturalised in the W Med; grown in gardens. May-Aug. S France, Corsica and Sicily. (South Africa).

847 *Polygala monspeliaca*. An erect, low to short annual. Leaves large, 10-25mm long, linear-lanceolate to lanceolate. Flowers *whitish*, 6-8mm long, with greenish-white wings that are up to twice as long as the petals; keel with a large crest. Garrigue, maquis and open woodland, rocky places, roadsides. Feb-July. T.

848 *Polygala exilis*. Similar, but flowers lilac, with a deep violet tip, smaller, 3-3.5mm long. Similar habitats. Apr-July. E Spain, S France and Italy.

849 *Polygala nicaeensis* **NICE MILKWORT**. Very variable, short to medium, generally spreading perennial, woody at the base and with ascending flowering stems. Leaves spatula-shaped to linear-lanceolate, the upper longer than the lower, hairy or not. Flowers pink, blue or sometimes white, 8-11mm long, borne in *long*, 7-40-flowered racemes; wings with 3 or 5 veins. Garrigue, maquis and open woodland, dry grassy and stony places. Apr-July. S France, NW Italy and NW Africa.

850 *Polygala vulgaris* **COMMON MILKWORT**. Similar, but a shorter, often low plant with denser racemes of *smaller* flowers, 5-8mm long; wings usually 3-veined. Grassy and stony places, scrub and occasionally on sand-dunes. Apr-July. T – not Balearic Is., Crete or Cyprus and rather rare in the E Med.

851 *Polygala comosa* **TUFTED MILKWORT**. Like *P. vulgaris*, but flowers lilac-pink, 4-6mm long, with *bracts* exceeding the flower-buds (not shorter); wings 1-3-veined. Dry grassy habitats, open woodland and scrub. Apr-July. From France eastwards to Turkey, but absent from most of the islands.

852 *Polygala venulosa* **EASTERN MILKWORT**. Low to short tufted perennial, with a woody stock, hairy. Leaves variable, the lower oblong to spatula-shaped, the upper linear-lanceolate, minutely hairy. Flowers pale mauve, pale pink or whitish, 12-17mm long, borne in rather dense racemes; wings green-veined, *very much shorter* than the petals. Dry grassy places, scrub, garrigue and open pine forest, rocky hillsides. Feb-May. Crete, S Greece, Aegean Is., Rhodes and Cyprus.

853 *Polygala preslii*. Similar, but less hairy and with *slightly toothed* leaves; flowers with rather larger wings. Similar habitats and flowering time. Italy and Sicily.

854 *Polygala sardoa*. Like *P. venulosa*, but a smaller, usually hairless, plant. All leaves linear-lanceolate and wings whitish, only 5-7mm long (not 7.5-9mm). Sardinia.

CORIARIA FAMILY Coriariaceae

A family of only 5 species scattered in Europe, Asia, the Americas and New Zealand, often with rather frond-like leaves.

fruit

855 *Coriaria myrtifolia* **MEDITERRANEAN CORIARIA**. Hairless shrub, 1-3m tall; stems 4-angled. Leaves *opposite or in 3-4s*, leathery, oval-lanceolate, pointed and somewhat shiny. Flowers small, greenish but the petals becoming dark reddish-brown in fruit, 5-parted, borne in racemes 20-50mm long; flowers harmaphrodite, male or female. Fruit 5 shiny-black achenes, surrounded by the persistent and fleshy petals. Open woodland, thickets. occasionally in hedgerows. May-Aug. W Med from Portugal to N Italy – not Corsica or Sardinia.

MAPLE FAMILY Aceraceae

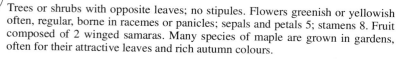

Trees or shrubs with opposite leaves; no stipules. Flowers greenish or yellowish often, regular, borne in racemes or panicles; sepals and petals 5; stamens 8. Fruit composed of 2 winged samaras. Many species of maple are grown in gardens, often for their attractive leaves and rich autumn colours.

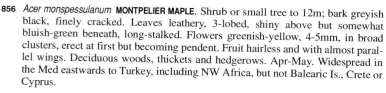

856 *Acer monspessulanum* **MONTPELIER MAPLE**. Shrub or small tree to 12m; bark greyish black, finely cracked. Leaves leathery, 3-lobed, shiny above but somewhat bluish-green beneath, long-stalked. Flowers greenish-yellow, 4-5mm, in broad clusters, erect at first but becoming pendent. Fruit hairless and with almost parallel wings. Deciduous woods, thickets and hedgerows. Apr-May. Widespread in the Med eastwards to Turkey, including NW Africa, but not Balearic Is., Crete or Cyprus.

857 *Acer sempervirens [A. creticum]*. Similar, but an evergreen twiggy shrub to 5m, with pale bark. Leaves green beneath, *short-stalked*, only shallowly lobed, leathery. Racemes few-flowered. Fruit wings diverging at an acute angle or subparallel. Rocky slopes and open woodland, garrigue. S Greece, Aegean Is., Crete and SW Turkey.

858 *Acer obtusatum [A. aetnense]*. Like *A. monspessulanum*, but leaves with *five* short, wide, blunt lobes, lower surface densely hairy. Rocky places, scrub and open woodland. Corsica eastwards to the Balkans, including Sicily.

859 *Acer granatense*. Like *A. obtusatum*, but leaves with five long, *parallel-sided* lobes, hairy or hairless beneath. Similar habitats. Yugoslavia, Albania and Greece.

860 *Acer obtusifolium [Acer orientale var. obtusifolium, A. syriacum]*. Like *A. monspessulanum*, but leaves variable from obscurely to distinctly 3-lobed and fruit with spreading to subparallel wings, strongly veined. Rocky places, open pine forest, field and stream borders. Feb-Apr. Cyprus, Lebanon and Syria.

PISTACIO FAMILY Anacardiaceae

A large family, primarily of tropical and subtropical trees and lianas; wood often gummy. Leaves alternate, usually pinnate. Flowers usually 5-parted; stamens 5 or 10. Fruit a drupe.

Pistachia. Trees with resinous bark and pinnate leaves. Flowers borne in lateral panicles, without petals, the male and the female borne on separate trees. Fruit a drupe.

861 *Pistacia terebinthus* **TURPENTINE TREE, TEREBINTH.** Small deciduous, aromatic (resinous), tree or shrub, to 6m. Leaves pinnate, with an end leaflet, shiny deep green; leaflets 3-9, oval, with a short abrupt point, with hairless stalks; rachis *not* winged. Flowers brownish, in rather dense long-branched panicles. Fruit egg-shaped, 5-7mm long, reddish at first, becoming brown. Maquis, dry open woods, pine forest and rocky slopes and gullies. Mar-July. T. Occasionally, forms are reported in which the leaves are reduced to a single leaflet. Plants are often galled.

862 *Pistachia palaestina.* Similar, but with oval, *long-pointed*, leaflets, slightly hairy along the margins, the terminal leaflets often absent; flower-clusters more spreading. E Med – not Cyprus.

863 *Pistachia vera* **PISTACHIO NUT.** Similar, but leaves thin, minutely hairy when young. Fruit *larger*, 15-25mm long, with a thin hard, pale brown, shell. Cultivated for its edible fruit. Apr-July. Locally naturalised in Spain, S France, Greece, Sicily and Turkey. Commercially this species is often grafted onto a stock of *P. terebinthus*; sometimes both male and female grafts are placed onto a single stock.

864 *Pistachia atlantica.* Like *P. terebinthus,* but to 10m, sometimes more. Leaves with hairy stalks and rachis *narrowly winged*; leaflets lanceolate. Rocky habitats, open woodland, maquis. Feb-Apr. NE Greece, Turkey and the E Med, N Africa. Sometimes cultivated for mastic – a yellowish gum-resin (see below).

865 *Pistacia lentiscus* **MASTIC TREE, LENTISC.** Small evergreen tree or shrub to 8m, occasionally more; young twigs and leaf-stalks rough. Leaves pinnate, *without* an end leaflet; leaflets usually 6-18, oval, leathery, untoothed; rachis winged. Flowers in rather dense panicles or spikes, the male with dark red anthers, the female greenish. Fruit globose, 4-5mm, red but becoming black, shiny. Garrigue, maquis and dry rocky slopes, sometimes on sand-dunes. Feb-May. T – not Egypt. Resin, mastic, is obtained from the tree and in some regions, especially on the island of Chios, it is cultivated for this purpose. The mastic is used as a chewing gum. Other products from the berry-like fruits, including *mastiche* (a liqueur) and *masticha* (a sweet) are made in Arab countries.

866 *Pistacia × saportae [P. lentiscus × P. terebinthus].* An evergreen hybrid like the former species, but the female inflorescence paniculate, not clustered or racemose. Fruit whitish. Rocky hillsides. Often as an isolated plant in close proximity to the parent species. Mar-May. Scattered localities – recorded from S France, Sardinia, Italy, Cyprus, Palestine and NW Africa.

867 *Rhus coriaria* **SUMACH.** An almost evergreen shrub or small tree to 3m; young twigs and leaf-stalks hairy. Leaves alternate, pinnate, with an end leaflet; leaflets 7-21, ovate, toothed, sometimes lobed at the base; rachis winged. Flowers in a large, rather narrow panicle, greenish-white, 6-7mm; petals longer than the sepals. Fruit brownish-purple or crimson, almost globose, 5mm, *hairy*. Mountainsides, open woodland, thickets, vineyards, occasionally cultivated. May-July. T – not Balearic Is., Corsica and Sardinia. Formerly widely used for tanning and dyeing, less so today.

868 *Rhus pentaphylla. Spiny* shrub or small tree to 7m, often less, generally with rather contorted greyish branches. Leaves palmate, with 3-5 oblong to oblong-triangular leaflets; leaflets lobed or unlobed, but often with 3 teeth at the apex. Flowers greenish-yellow, tiny, borne in small lateral racemes which may be slightly branched; racemes shorter than the leaves. Fruit small and berry-like, 6-8mm, with 3 warts at the apex, red when ripe. Dry calcareous soils, generally in rocky habitats. Sicily and N Africa. The juice is poisonous like that of other species of *Rhus*.

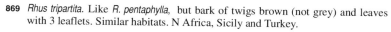

869 *Rhus tripartita.* Like *R. pentaphylla,* but bark of twigs brown (not grey) and leaves with 3 leaflets. Similar habitats. N Africa, Sicily and Turkey.

870 *Cotinus coggygria [Rhus cotinus]* **SMOKE-TREE, VENETIAN SUMACH.** Rounded, hairless shrub to 5m, aromatic. Leaves simple, oval, untoothed, long-stalked, bluish-green. Flowers in large lax panicles, 15-20cm, small pale green; inflorescence with many thread like-sterile branches which, as the flowers develop, become silky with spreading hairs, giving the bush a *smoky appearance.* Fruit kidney-shaped, 3-4mm. Garrigue, open woods, thickets and dry rocky slopes. May-July. From SE France to Turkey – absent from most islands except Crete. Formerly used for tanning and dyeing and as a medicine (for gargling and to staunch blood). This attractive plant is widely grown in gardens – the leaves take on rich red autumn tints and there is a purple-leaved cultivar.

871 *Schinus molle* **CALIFORNIAN PEPPER TREE, PERUVIAN MASTIC TREE.** A rather graceful evergreen shrub or tree to 15m, with slender *pendent* branches. Leaves pinnate with 7-13 pairs of linear-lanceolate leaflets, usually toothed, hairy when young; rachis not winged. Flowers white, small, 3-4mm, borne in lax, generally terminal panicles; sepals and petals 5. Fruit pink, globose, 6-7mm. Planted for ornament and occasionally naturalised. Apr-Aug. Spain, Portugal, Sardinia, Italy, Sicily, Greece and Cyprus, but probably elsewhere. (SW Brazil and Paraguay).

872 *Schinus terebinthifolia.* Similar, but branches *not* pendent and leaflets only 2-7 pairs. Fruit 4-5mm, shiny-red. Resembles *Pistacia terebinthus* in general appearance.

873 *Maytenus senegalensis [Catha europaea]* **MAYTENUS.** A much-branched, *very spiny,* evergreen shrub; stems grey. Leaves alternate, oval to diamond-shaped with a wedge-shaped base, untoothed, greyish-green. Flowers in cymose clusters, tiny, white. Fruit red and shiny, a globose capsule, 5-7mm; seed with a conspicuous fleshy aril at one end. Rocky habitats. S Spain and NW Africa (also in tropical Africa and Asia).

SAPINDA FAMILY Sapindaceae

A large family of tropical and subtropical trees, shrubs and climbers, the latter often with tendrils; few in temperate regions. Leaves alternate, simple to pinnate. Flowers small, 4-5-parted; stamens often 8. Fruit fleshy or dry.

874 *Cardiospermum halicacabum* **BALLOON-VINE.** Tall clambering annual, somewhat hairy, to 2m though often less, climbing by branched tendrils. Leaves trifoliate with the main segments deeply lobed and toothed. Flowers small, greenish or whitish, with 4 petals and sepals, borne in small, long-stalked clusters with tendrils inter-mixed. Fruit an inflated *bladder-like* capsule, 20-30mm; seeds black with a white heart-shaped hilum. Cultivated and occasionally becoming naturalised. May-Aug. Spain, Greece and Yugoslavia, probably elsewhere. (Widespread in tropical and subtropical regions).

875 *Dodonaea viscosa* **DODONAEA.** An erect evergreen shrub, 1-3m tall. Leaves simple, oblong, generally broadest above the middle, sticky, untoothed. Flowers small and greenish, borne in short terminal and lateral racemes. Fruit a capsule, membranous, with 2-3 broad *wings,* often suffused with pinkish-purple. Widely grown in some regions of the Med as a hedging plant, being sometimes found as a relict of former cultivation, or as an escape. May-July. (Tropical and subtropical regions of the world).

BALSAM FAMILY Balsaminaceae

More than 1000 species in temperate and tropical regions of the world, mostly in Africa, India and Asia. The African *Impatiens walleriana* (876) with a wide range of flower colours from pink to red, orange, mauve and white, is widely grown as a summer bedding plant and pot plant.

877 *Impatiens balfourii* **KASHMIR BALSAM.** Medium to tall hairless annual, generally branched. Leaves alternate, oval, pointed, toothed, the upper rather larger than the lower, all stalked. Flowers pinkish-purple with a white helmet, 25-40mm, in racemes of 3-8, held just above the foliage; spur slender, straight or curved. Capsule narrow, club-shaped, *exploding* suddenly when ripe to expel the seeds. Moist semi-shaded places and gardens. June-Oct. Naturalised in S France; cultivated and possibly naturalised elsewhere in S Europe. (W Himalaya).

BOX FAMILY Buxaceae

Shrubs or small trees with opposite leaves, untoothed. Flowers small, often greenish or whitish, with a 4-parted perianth, not petal-like. Fruit usually a 3-parted capsule.

fruit

878 *Buxus sempervirens* **BOX.** Dense, much-branched, foxy-smelling, evergreen shrub to 5m; young stems 4-angled. Leaves small, opposite, oval, 15-30mm long, shiny dark green above but paler beneath; margin somewhat revolute. Flowers in small lateral clusters, greenish-yellow, with a terminal female flower and several males below; no petals. Fruit a small capsule, 6-7mm long, oblong with 3 short horns (styles); seeds black. Rocky habitats, woodland, maquis, on dry calcareous soils. Mar-May. Spain eastwards to Turkey – not Balearic Is., Sicily or Crete. Grown in gardens since medieval times, often for hedging and topiary, and many different forms exist.

fruit

879 *Buxus balearica.* Similar, but a stouter-stemmed plant with *larger* leaves, 25-40mm long. Flower-clusters larger, to 10mm and styles the same length as the capsule (not half the length). Similar habitats and flowering time. NW Africa, Balearic Is., S and E Spain, Sardinia and Turkey. The Turkish plant is sometimes assigned to a distinct species, *B. longifolia* (880).

BUCKTHORN FAMILY Rhamnaceae

Trees or shrubs with simple leaves; stipules present. Flowers in cymes, 4-5-parted, the petals often small, sometimes absent, often hooded over the stamens; ovary with 2-4 cells. Fruit a fleshy berry.

881 *Paliurus spina-christi* **CHRIST'S THORN, JERUSALEM THORN.** Much-branched, almost hairless shrub, to 3m, with zig-zag stems; stipules spiny, one in each pair straight, the other curved. Leaves alternate, arranged in two opposing ranks, oval, toothed, with 3 longitudinal veins, shiny-green, short-stalked. Flowers small yellow, 4-5mm, borne in small lateral clusters, 5-parted. Fruit a conspicuous *disc*, 18-35mm, with a wavy, membranous wing, dry and yellowish-brown when ripe. Dry habitats, maquis and garrigue, plains and hills, open woodland, streamsides. Apr-Sept. T – but absent from many of the islands. One of the plants reputed to have been used for Christ's crown of thorns. A typical shrub of the Med region, often forming dense thickets.

882 *Zizyphus zizyphus [Z. jujuba, Rhamnus zizyphus]* **JUJUBE.** A much-branched deciduous shrub, to 8m, with whitish or pale brown bark and zig-zag flexuous young, hairless, green stems; stipules spiny, one straight and one curved in each pair. Leaves alternate, oblong, blunt, with 3 longitudinal veins, *glandular-toothed* along the margin, short-stalked. Flowers tiny, yellowish, in small lateral clusters, the petals shorter than the sepals. Fruit egg-shaped, 15-30mm long, dark red or black, edible. Hedgerows and cultivated land – nearly always close to habitation. May-June. Cultivated for its fruits in scattered localities and locally naturalised T. (Temperate Asia).

883 *Zizyphus lotus [Rhamnus lotus]*. Similar, but a low bush to 2m with *grey* twigs, often forming an impenetrable thicket. Leaves shallowly and bluntly toothed. Fruit almost globose, 10-15mm, yellowish-orange when ripe. Dry habitats, fields, hedgerows, roadsides and waste ground. May-July. N Africa, Spain, Sicily, S Greece, Cyprus and Palestine.

884 *Zizyphus spina-christi [Rhamnus spina-christi]*. Like *Z. zizyphus*, but a round-headed tree to 14m, although often less, with flower-stalks and sepals *densely hairy*. Fruit globose, 13-18mm, yellowish or reddish-brown when ripe. Very dry plains and hillslopes. May-July. Cyprus and E Med. Sometimes planted. A non-spiny form, var. *inermis* (884a), is sometimes seen.

885 *Rhamnus alaternus* **MEDITERRANEAN BUCKTHORN.** Very variable, rather holly-like, but non-spiny evergreen shrub, to 5m, almost hairless. Leaves alternate, leathery, oval to lanceolate, shiny dark green, untoothed or slightly toothed. Flowers greenish-yellow, tiny, 2-3mm borne in dense cylindrical racemes, each flower 4-5-parted, male and female on separate plants. Fruit a berry, 4-6mm, not particularly fleshy, reddish, but ripening black. Maquis, garrigue, coniferous woodland, streamsides, occasionally cultivated. Mar-Apr. T – rarer in the E Med. The white wood has an unpleasant smell, but is sometimes used for furniture.

886 *Rhamnus ludovici-salvatoris*. Similar, but leaves *spiny-edged*. A shrub to 2m. E Spain and Balearic Is.

887 *Rhamnus lycioides*. Densely branched, spiny deciduous shrub to 1m, sometimes more. Leaves leathery, *linear*, opposite or clustered. Flowers tiny, greenish-yellow, 4-parted; petals very small or absent. Fruit rounded, 4-6mm, slightly compressed, black when ripe. Rocky places and scrub. Mar-May. Spain and Balearic Is.

888 *Rhamnus oleoides*. Similar, but leaves oval, broadest above the middle, with distinct lateral veins. Fruit yellowish when ripe. Garrigue, maquis and rocky hillslopes. Mar-Apr. Scattered localities T.

888a Subsp. *graecus*. Similar, but deciduous, the leaves thin with *inconspicuous* veins. S Greece, Aegean Is., Cyprus and E Med.

VINE FAMILY Vitaceae

A fairly large, primarily tropical and subtropical family; mostly climbers with tendrils opposite the alternate leaves. Flowers small, generally 4-5-parted, borne in clusters, racemes or panicles; calyx very small; petals present. Fruit a berry.

889 *Vitis vinifera* **GRAPE, COMMON VINE.** A climbing or scrambling shrub to 35m (often far less when cultivated). Leaves alternate, most with *opposing* branched tendrils, long-stalked, palmately 5-7-lobed, the lobes coarsely toothed. Flowers small, greenish, occasionally purplish, hermaphrodite, borne in panicles which become pendent as the flowers develop. Fruit a juicy berry, globose to oblong, 8-40mm,

green, pink, purple or black when ripe, often with a bluish bloom. Cultivated since very early times in vineyards, gardens, and against buildings, sometimes naturalised or a relict of former cultivation. Many different varieties exist. May-June. T.

889a Subsp. *sylvestris*. Similar, but with separate male and female flowers borne on distinct plants, the male plant generally with more deeply lobed leaves. Fruit small, 6mm, bluish-black. Damp wooded areas, thickets, river banks. Corsica, Italy and the Balkans; perhaps Cyprus.

OLEASTER FAMILY Elaeagnaceae

A small family of trees and shrubs. Leaves and stems often covered in tiny silvery scales. Flowers 4-5-parted, without petals. Fruit berry-like.

890 *Elaeagnus angustifolia [E. orientalis]* **OLEASTER**. A spiny shrub or small tree to 7m, the twigs at first silvery-scaly, but becoming brown and shiny with age. Leaves alternate, oblong to linear-lanceolate, untoothed, greenish above, but *silvery with scales* beneath. Flowers yellow, 8-10mm long, silvery with scales on the outside, with a short tube and 4 lobes, sweetly scented; flowers borne in small lateral clusters or solitary, on the current years shoots. Fruit berry-like, oblong in outline, 15-25mm, olive-like, yellowish-brown, shiny or somewhat scaly. Rocky slopes, river gravels, hedgerows, cultivated ground, gardens, roadsides. May-June. Scattered localities T. (Temperate Asia). Grown for ornament in gardens. The fruits are edible, but hardly delicious. They are sometimes fermented into an alcoholic liquor.

MALLOW FAMILY Malvaceae

Herbs or shrubs, often with stellate (star-shaped) hairs; stipules present. Leaves alternate, usually palmately-lobed. Flowers regular, hermaphrodite; sepals and petals 5, separate; epicalyx often present; stamens many, fused together into a column surrounding the 5-lobed style. Fruit with a ring of closely packed nutlets (mericarps) or a capsule.

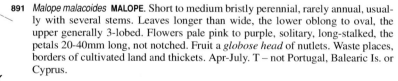

891 *Malope malacoides* **MALOPE**. Short to medium bristly perennial, rarely annual, usually with several stems. Leaves longer than wide, the lower oblong to oval, the upper generally 3-lobed. Flowers pale pink to purple, solitary, long-stalked, the petals 20-40mm long, not notched. Fruit a *globose head* of nutlets. Waste places, borders of cultivated land and thickets. Apr-July. T – not Portugal, Balearic Is. or Cyprus.

892 *Malope trifida*. Similar, but annual, almost hairless, to 1.5m, with a single erect stem. Flowers *deep* satiny purple-red, the petals broad, 35-60mm long. Spain, Portugal and NW Africa. Widely grown in gardens and occasionally naturalised.

Malva **MALLOWS**. Annuals or perennials. Epicalyx of 1-3 free lobes. Petals notched to 2-lobed. Fruit a ring of mericarps.

893 *Malva cretica*. An erect, rather delicate-looking, short to medium annual with long hairs. Lower leaves rounded, toothed or slightly lobed, the upper leaves deeply 3-5-lobed, toothed. Flowers solitary, bluish-lilac to pale pink, the petals 8-20mm long; epicalyx of 3 linear to narrow-triangular lobes, similar to the sepals. Nutlets hairless. Garrigue, fallow and waste ground, stony ground. Apr-June. T – not Portugal, France, Balearic Is. or Yugoslavia.

894 *Malva aegyptia* **EGYPTIAN MALLOW**. Similar, but stems usually spreading with the sepals *much broader* than the epicalyx lobes. Petals lilac, 7-11mm long, equal in length to the sepals. Rocky places, roadsides and open pine forest. Mar-Apr. Spain, N Africa, Greece, Crete and the E Med, including Cyprus.

seed

calyx

895 *Malva moschata* **MUSK MALLOW**. Sparsely hairy, medium to tall, erect perennial. Leaves palmate, with 5-7 pinnately-lobed segments, pointed. Flowers solitary at the upper leaf-axils, bright pink, the petals 20-35mm long, twice as long as sepals; epicalyx lobes 3, linear to narrowly oval. Nutlets with long white hairs. Pastures and field boundaries, roadsides, rocky places, generally on dry fertile soils. May-July. European Med – absent from the islands except for Corsica and Sicily.

896 *Malva tournefortiana*. Similar, but flower-stalks with stellate (not simple) hairs and nutlets *hairless*. Similar habitats and flowering time. France, Spain, Portugal and NW Africa.

calyx

897 *Malva parviflora* **LEAST MALLOW**. Short to medium, hairy or hairless annual, with erect or ascending stems. Leaves rounded-heart-shaped in outline, with 3-7 shallow, rounded, toothed lobes. Flowers in groups of 2-4, pale lilac-blue or mauve, *small*, the petals only 4-5mm long, short-stalked; epicalyx lobes linear to lanceolate. Fruit with enlarged spreading sepals; nutlets hairy or not, strongly netted. Cultivated, fallow and waste ground, roadsides. Feb-June. T.

fruit

898 *Malva sylvestris* [*M. erecta*, *M. mauritiana*] **COMMON MALLOW**. Very variable medium to tall, hairy biennial or perennial to 1.5m, often with rather sprawling stems. Leaves kidney-shaped to rounded-heart-shaped, with 3-7 rounded, toothed lobes. Flowers in clusters of 2 or more, pink or purple, with *darker* veins, the petals 15-30mm long, bearded; epicalyx lobes elliptical, hairy. Nutlets hairy or not, netted. Meadows, cultivated, fallow and waste ground, roadsides, occasionally on coastal rocks and sand-dunes. Apr-Sept. T. Often confused with *Lavatera cretica*, but with mixed simple and stellate hairs, broader epicalyx lobes and more strongly marked flowers.

899 *Malva neglecta* **DWARF MALLOW**. Similar, but an annual to only 60cm tall, densely stellate-hairy. Flowers pale lilac to whitish, the petals only 9-13mm long. Nutlets smooth and only faintly netted. Similar habitats and flowering time. T.

fruit

900 *Malva nicaeensis*. Like *M. sylvestris*, but annual or biennial to only 40cm tall, the petals pale lilac, *without* darker veins, 7-12mm long, usually unbearded. Differs from *M. parviflora* in having longer fruit-stalks, 10mm long or more (not less). Similar habitats. Feb-May. T.

901 *Malva verticillata* **CHINESE MALLOW**. Like *M. neglecta*, but the flowers with petals only 6-7mm long, twice (not three times) as long as the sepals. France, Italy, Yugoslavia and Greece, perhaps elsewhere. (E Asia). Cultivated locally as a salad plant and occasionally naturalised.

calyx

902 *Malvella sherardiana* [*Malva sherardiana*] **MALVELLA**. A low to short, prostrate to erect, hairy annual. Leaves kidney-shaped to rounded, with an untoothed, toothed or slightly lobed margin. Flowers solitary, pink, with oval, *unnotched* petals. Nutlets inflated, densely hairy. Cultivated, waste and fallow land. May-July. Spain, Balkans and Crete eastwards, including Cyprus.

Althaea **MARSH MALLOWS**. Like *Malva*, but epicalyx with 5-9 lobes which are united below.

903 *Althaea hirsuta* [*Malva althaeoides*] **ROUGH MARSH MALLOW**. Short to medium, occasionally semi-prostrate, annual; stems with simple bristles as well as stellate

calyx

fruit

hairs. Leaves rounded-heart-shaped in outline, toothed, the lower shallowly lobed, the upper more deeply 3-5-lobed. Flowers bluish- or pinkish-lilac, solitary but forming leafy racemes, with yellow anthers, petals 10-20mm long, about the same length as the sepals; epicalyx lobes 6-9, lanceolate. Nutlets hairy, ridged. Dry places, fallow land, often a weed of cultivation, more rarely along seashores or in garrigue. Mar-May. T.

904 *Althaea officinalis* **MARSH MALLOW.** Tall, soft *grey-woolly* perennial, to 2m, tufted. Leaves triangular-oval in outline, toothed, mostly slightly 3-5-lobed. Flowers pale lilac-pink, solitary or in clusters, forming leafy racemes or panicles, the petals 15-20mm long; epicalyx with 8-9 linear lobes. Nutlets hairy; sepals curved outwards in fruit. Damp habitats, salty and brackish marshes, ditches and stream margins. July-Sept. T – not Balearic Is., Crete, Cyprus or parts of the E Med. Edible marsh mallow was originally obtained from the root mucilage and the plant was previously used as an ingredient of various soothing ointments.

905 *Althaea rosea [Alcea rosea]* **COMMON HOLLYHOCK,** widely grown in gardens, is sometimes found as a casual, or perhaps naturalised in the Med.

fruit

906 *Althaea pallida [Alcea pallida].* Medium to tall hairy perennial, with erect stems. Leaves rounded-heart-shaped to diamond-shaped, toothed, with 3-5 shallow lobes, *grey-hairy*, especially beneath. Flowers pale pink with a yellowish centre, forming long, spike-like racemes, the petals 30-45mm long, not overlapping. Nutlets deeply furrowed, hairy in part. Rocky places, scrub, occasionally cultivated. June-Aug. Balkans and Turkey – absent from most of the islands.

    906a Subsp. *cretica [Althaea cretica].* Similar but a more densely hairy plant with flowers bright pink or purple, with a yellow centre. S Greece and Crete.

907 *Althaea setosa [A. pontica].* Similar, but stems sparsely hairy, *often* purple-spotted and flowers rosy-purple or violet with a yellowish centre, the petals 35-50mm long. Waste and rocky ground. May-June. Crete, Turkey, Cyprus and E Med. Cultivated and naturalised occasionally – in Italy and Yugoslavia, for instance.

908 *Althaea cannabina.* Like *A. setosa,* but flowers pink, the *petals* 15-30mm long. Sepals erect in fruit and nutlets hairless. Similar habitats and flowering time. From Portugal and NW Africa eastwards to Turkey – not Balearic Is., Corsica, Crete or Cyprus.

fruit

909 *Abutilon theophrasti* **ABUTILON.** Short to tall, erect, hairy annual to 1m. Leaves long-stalked, rounded-heart-shaped, slightly toothed, not lobed. Flowers *yellow*, in small lateral clusters at the upper leaves, short-stalked, the petals 7-13mm long; epicalyx absent. Nutlets black and hairy. Waste and damp places, fallow land. Apr-June. Corsica eastwards to the Balkans – not Sicily; naturalised in France and the Iberian Peninsula.

Lavatera **LAVATERAS.** Like *Althaea*, but epicalyx of only 3 lobes. Herbs or shrubs, often with stellate hairs.

fruit

910 *Lavatera cretica* **CRETAN MALLOW, SMALL TREE MALLOW.** Medium to tall, hairy annual or biennial, to 1.5m. Leaves rounded-heart-shaped in outline, with 5-7 shallow, toothed lobes. Flowers lilac, in clusters of 2-8 on unequal stalks, petals 10-20mm long; epicalyx lobes triangular-oval, shorter than the sepals, but *enlarging* in fruit. Nutlets smooth or slightly ridged. Waste and fallow land, roadsides, occasionally on cultivated land or sand-dunes. Feb-June. T. Often confused with *Malva sylvestris,* but with broader epicalyx-lobes and an absence of simple (unbranched) hairs on the flower-stalks. A rare British native.

fruit

calyx

911 *Lavatera mauritanica.* Similar, but sepals much enlarged in fruit and nutlets markedly ridged. Flowers purple, the petals 8-15mm long. Coastal rocks. Portugal, S Spain and NW Africa.

912 *Lavatera arborea* **TREE MALLOW.** Sturdy tall biennial to 3m; stem woody below, hairy when young. Leaves large (to 20cm), rounded, with 5-7 toothed lobes. Flowers lilac with purple veins at the base, in clusters of 2-7, the petals 15-20mm long; epicalyx lobes oval, longer than the sepals. Nutlets hairy or not, sharply angled. Rocky habitats, cliffs, stony ground, hedges and waste places, generally coastal, but sometimes inland. Apr-July. From Portugal and NW Africa eastwards to the Balkans. Grown in gardens and sometimes naturalised in the E Med. Native to S Britain.

913 *Lavatera maritima* **SEA MALLOW.** Similar, but young parts of the plant *white-felted* and flowers solitary, occasionally paired; petals pale pink with a purplish base, 15-30mm long. Similar habitats. Feb-May. W Med from Portugal and NW Africa to Italy – not Sicily.

914 *Lavatera olbia* **TREE LAVATERA.** Laxly branched *shrub* to 2m, the stems and leaves felted when young. Leaves variable, the lower 3-5-lobed, the upper oblong to lanceolate, often slightly 3-lobed. Flowers solitary, short-stalked, pink to purplish, the petals 15-30mm long, forming a spike-like inflorescence; epicalyx lobes oval, slightly shorter than the sepals. Nutlets hairy or bristly. Damp places, hedgerows, field boundaries, along rivers and streams. May-Aug. W Med from Portugal and NW Africa eastwards to Italy and Sicily. This handsome and floriferous shrub is widely grown in gardens and is sometimes naturalised in the E Med.

915 *Lavatera bryonifolia.* Similar, but leaves *spear-shaped*, 3-lobed and the nutlets hairless. Garrigue, stream margins and hillsides, or along irrigation ditches. May-July. Sicily, Crete, S Greece, Aegean Is., Cyprus and Palestine.

916 *Lavatera thuringiaca.* Like *L. olbia,* but perennial, the leaves generally 5-lobed the flowers purplish-pink, 20-45mm long; flower-stalks 13mm long or more (not up to 10mm). Hillslopes, thickets and woodland margins, roadsides. May-July. Italy, the Balkans and Turkey.

917 *Lavatera trimestris* **ANNUAL LAVATERA.** An erect, rather rough annual. Leaves long-stalked, rounded-heart-shaped, toothed, the upper often shallowly 3-7-lobed, deep green, somewhat shiny. Flowers large, bright satiny-pink, occasionally white, the petals 20-45mm long, solitary; epicalyx baggy and the sepals fused for most of their length, *enlarging* in fruit. Nutlets ridged, hairless, concealed by the ridge like expansion of the central axis. Cultivated, fallow and waste land, waysides. Apr-June. Portugal and NW Africa eastwards to Greece – not Crete. Widely grown in gardens.

fruit

918 *Lavatera punctata.* Similar, but a smaller annual, the stem usually flushed with purple-red, the lower leaves 5-lobed. Petals lilac-pink, 15-30mm long. Fruit *without* a disk concealing the nutlets. Field boundaries, waste ground, cultivated places, orchards and olive groves. May-Aug. T.

fruit

919 *Lavatera triloba* **MUSK-SCENTED LAVATERA.** *Musk-scented,* glandular, greyish or whitish hairy perennial, woody at the base. Leaves rounded-heart-shaped, long-stalked, slightly 3-lobed, flat or slightly wavy. Flowers in clusters of 3-7, purple, sometimes flushed with yellow, the petals 15-30mm long; epicalyx lobes lanceolate, shorter than the sepals which enlarge in fruit. Nutlets hairless or glandular-hairy. Damp and saline soils, sandy soils, ditches and streamsides. May-July. S Portugal, Spain and Sardinia.

919a Subsp. *agrigentina*. Like the type, but flowers pure *yellow*. Italy (Calabria) and Sicily.

919b Subsp. *pallescens*. Similar, but leaves markedly wavy and flowers pink or purple. Menorca and San Pietro (by Sardinia).

920 *Gossypium herbaceum* **LEVANT COTTON**. Rather woody annual, to 1.5m, though often less, slightly hairy or not. Leaves heart-shaped, with 3-7 lobes. Flowers erect, yellow, the petals with a purple claw; calyx cup-shaped, with 5 short teeth, the epicalyx lobes 3, heart-shaped, short-toothed. Fruit a capsule, 20-35mm, splitting open widely to reveal the seeds embedded in a *mass of cotton*. Cultivated in hot, dry places and sometimes casual or naturalised on waste ground. June-Aug. Scattered localities in the Med. (Pakistan). Cultivated for cotton and for its oil-bearing seeds – used for margarines and other purposes. Cotton growing in the Med has generally declined in recent years.

921 *Gossypium hirsutum* **AMERICAN UPLAND COTTON**. Similar, but a hairier plant, the epicalyx lobes with long *pointed teeth*. Capsule 40-60mm. Remarks as for *G. herbaceum*. (Peru). More commonly cultivated in the Med than *G. herbaceum* and widely grown in tropical and subtropical regions of the world.

fruit

922 *Hibiscus trionum* **BLADDER HIBISCUS**. Rather bristly, low to short annual, erect to, prostrate. Leaves deeply divided into 3 pinnately-lobed segments. Flowers pale yellow with a deep violet *centre*, the petals 18-22mm long, solitary, long-stalked; epicalyx with 10-13 linear lobes, the calyx with united sepals and prominent deep purple, bristly veins. Fruit a capsule, concealed by the expanded, membranous calyx. Cultivated, fallow and waste ground. June-Sept. Crete and the Balkans eastwards, including Cyprus; sometimes naturalised in the W Med. Grown in gardens, including extra-large-flowered forms.

923 *Hibiscus syriacus* **COMMON HIBISCUS**. Stiffly branched, rather upright shrub to 2-3m. Leaves diamond-shaped, toothed, often somewhat 3-lobed, short-stalked. Flowers variable in colour from rose to lilac or white, with a deep purple centre, solitary or paired at the upper leaf-axils, the petals 45-60mm long; epicalyx with 7-9 linear lobes, the sepals fused together in the lower half. Capsule 20-25mm, yellow-hairy. Planted for ornament and hedges, or a relic of former cultivation. Double-flowered forms are sometimes seen. July-Oct. T – particularly in Europe. (Asia).

924 *Hibiscus rosa-sinensis* **HIBISCUS**. Large deciduous shrub to 3m, hairless. Leaves deep green and shiny, oval, irregularly toothed, stalked. Flowers bright rose-red, the petals 60-80mm long, solitary at the upper leaf-axils, with a prominent protruding red staminal column and stigmas. Widely planted in parks and gardens, or along roads. June-Oct. T. (China). A very popular, exotic looking shrub. Various colour forms are seen besides the common red ones – apricot, salmon, white, cream, pink, yellowish and multicolored, as well as some with double flowers.

VIOLET FAMILY Violaceae

Small herbs or shrubs with alternate leaves, stalked and often in a basal tuft; stipules present. Flowers zygomorphic, solitary; sepals 5 separate, often extended backwards into a short appendage; petals 5, separate, the lowermost forming a lip and extending backwards into a spur; stamens 5, held in a close ring around the ovary. Fruit a 3-valved capsule.

Viola **VIOLETS**. Although a widespread European and Asian genus, few species are found at low altitudes in the Med region; several of the common mountain ones are included here. The genus contains both violets and pansies.

925 *Viola alba* subsp. *dehnadtii [V. thessala]* **MEDITERRANEAN WHITE VIOLET**. A low, somewhat hairy perennial, with short *non-rooting runners*. Leaves in a basal tuft, sparsely hairy to hairless, oval to triangular-heart-shaped, pointed, dark green, often with convex margins; stipules linear-lanceolate, deeply fringed. Flowers violet or mauve, 15-20mm, fragrant, with a short upturned spur; lateral petals bearded. Fruit slightly hairy or not. Damp and shaded places, among rocks and bushes, close to streams; not at sea level. Feb-Apr. T – not Balearic Is., N Africa or much of the extreme E Med.

925a Subsp. *scotophylla*. Similar, but flowers white with a violet spur. Balkans.

926 *Viola odorata* **SWEET VIOLET**. Similar, but with long *rooting* runners and leaves more rounded; stipules shortly fringed. Flowers dark violet or white, 13-15mm, fragrant. Similar habitats and flowering time. Distribution the same.

927 *Viola hirta* **HAIRY VIOLET**. Like *V. alba,* but a hairier plant without stolons and stipules shortly fringed. Flowers violet, 10-15mm, not fragrant. Fruit-capsule hairy. Similar habitats and flowering time. Europe from Spain to Greece – not Balearic Is.

928 *Viola cretica* **CRETAN VIOLET**. Like *V. alba,* but with very long stolons, leaves roughly hairy and fruit *hairy*; lateral petals not bearded. Rocky places scrub and woodland in the mountains. Mar-May. Crete – endemic.

929 *Viola jaubertiana* **MALLORCAN VIOLET**. Like *V. alba,* but a hairless plant with stout stolons and rather leathery, *shiny*, deep green leaves and larger bright violet flowers. Damp rocks and ravines. Mar-Apr. Mallorca – endemic.

930 *Viola hymettia*. Low, roughly-hairy annual. Leaves tufted, the lower rounded to oval, the upper narrower, oblong to spatula-shaped, somewhat toothed; stipules *pinnately* divided, with a large terminal lobe. Flowers yellow, the upper petal often becoming violet, or all violet, 10-15mm, the petals twice as long as the sepals; spur stout, 3-4mm long. Grassy and stony meadows, at lower altitudes than the preceding species. Mar-May. Portugal eastwards to Greece and Turkey – not Balearic Is., Corsica, Sardinia, Crete or Cyprus.

931 *Viola kitaibeliana [V. arvensis* subsp. *kitaibeliana]* **DWARF PANSY**. Low, hairy annual – stem simple or branched. Leaves rather small, the lowermost rounded, the others oblong to spatula-shaped, blunt-toothed; stipules pinnately-lobed, with a large end lobe. Flowers creamy-white or yellow, nearly always with a deeper yellow centre, concave, 4-8mm; sepals lanceolate, pointed, *longer* than the petals; spur short. Dry open habitats, fields, vineyards, olive groves, gardens, hills and bare sandy places, at low and high altitudes. Mar-May. T – not Balearic Is. or Sardinia.

932 *Viola scorpiuroides [V. methodiana]*. Low, often prostrate perennial, often forming a small mat, sometimes more tufted, grey, hairy. Leaves elliptical to spatula-shaped, slightly toothed, stalked; stipules small, linear. Flowers small, 4-7mm, yellow, with two *brown spots* on the lower petal. Rocky places at low altitudes, generally close to the coast. Crete, Kythera (Aegean), N Africa.

933 *Viola arborescens* **SHRUBBY VIOLET**. Short, grey-hairy perennial, woody in the lower part, often rather corky; stems distinct, ascending to erect. Leaves oval to linear-lanceolate, pointed, slightly toothed; stipules small, narrow, pinnately-lobed. Flowers whitish or pale violet, 10-15mm; spur 3-4mm long, curved and blunt. Fruit erect at maturity, hairless. Rocky places, low scrub, thickets, often growing up through low shrubs, on calcareous soils. Mar-June. W Med from Portugal to France and Sardinia, including the Balearic Is.

WATERWORT FAMILY Elatinaceae

A small family of aquatic or water-margin plants with entire leaves and insignificant flowers. Terrestrial·and aquatic forms of the same species exist in many instances.

934 *Elatine alsinastrum.* Low to short hairless annual. Leaves in *whorls* of 3-18, linear in aquatic habitats, lanceolate or oval in terrestrial plants. Flowers tiny, reddish or greenish, 4-parted, unstalked; stamens 8. Fruit a small 4-parted capsule. Muddy habitats, pools, ditches. Apr-July. T – not Balearic Is., Cyprus or many of the Aegean Is.

935 *Elatine macropoda [E. campylospermum].* Similar, but leaves *opposite* and flowers borne on slender stalks. Plants often forming a flat mossy creeping patch. Similar habitats, often shallow pools close to the sea. Feb-May. T – apparently absent from the Balkans and Turkey.

DAPHNE FAMILY Thymelaeaceae

Small shrubs, rarely herbs, with simple untoothed leaves. Flowers in clusters, racemes or umbels, hermaphrodite; calyx with a tube and 4 spreading lobes, petal-like; true petals absent; stamens 8, fused to the side of the calyx-tube; style solitary. Fruit a small berry or nut. The berries are often extremely poisonous.

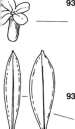

936 *Daphne gnidium.* An erect, little-branched, almost hairless shrub to 2m, often less; branches slender and leafless. Leaves bluish-green, rather leathery, oblong to linear, pointed. Flowers creamy-white, 4-6mm, borne in dense terminal *panicles*; flower-stalks and corolla-tube hairy. Berry deep red, becoming black eventually. Maquis, garrigue, woods and rocky places. Mar-Sept. T – except the extreme east Med, including Cyprus; rarer in the east of its range. Very poisonous in all its parts; though it was used medicinally in ancient times.

937 *Daphne oleoides.* Very variable plant, not unlike the previous species, with ascending to almost prostrate stems, much-branched, to 60cm high at the most. Flowers white or cream, in *groups* of 2-6, with longer, pointed lobes, fragrant. Rocky mountain habitats, scrub and open woodland, never at low altitudes. Apr-June. Spain eastwards to Turkey – not Balearic Is. or Cyprus.

938 *Daphne sericea [D. collina, D. vahlii].* Rather dense, rounded, upright to spreading evergreen shrub, to 70cm; young shoots hairy. Leaves crowded, deep green and leathery, oblong, broadest above the middle and narrowed to a very short stalk, hairy beneath. Flowers pink, rarely cream, 8-12mm, borne in dense terminal heads, fragrant; tube with whitish hairs. Berry red-brown when ripe. Maquis, open woodland, rocky places, generally fairly close to the coast. Feb-Apr. S Italy, Sicily, Crete, S Greece, Turkey and the Lebanon. Very poisonous. Grown in gardens.

939 *Daphne gnidioides.* Similar, but with bluish-green, *sharply pointed*, erect leaves. Flowers pink, in heads of 5-8 (not 5-15). Berry scarcely fleshy, hidden within the persistent corolla-tube. Rocky and bushy habitats. Mar-Apr. Aegean Is. and S Turkey (S Anatolia).

940 *Daphne rodriguezii.* Like *D. gnidioides*, but leaves with hairy revolute margins and flowers purple tinged with yellow, in groups of 2-5. Coastal scrub. Feb-Mar. Minorca only.

Thymelaea **THYMELAEA.** Dwarf evergreen shrubs, occasionally annual herbs with small unstalked leaves. Flowers male and female on different plants or at least some hermaphrodite, yellow, solitary or in small clusters in the upper leaf-axils. Fruit dry and indehiscent.

941 *Thymelaea sanamunda [Passerina thymelaea].* Short, hairless perennial with *annual stems* arising from a woody base, erect. Leaves elliptical to oblong, pointed. Flowers yellow, 7-9mm long, with a long slender tube and short pointed lobes, borne in small lateral clusters, but the whole forming a leafy spike-like structure. Fruit hairless. Rocky places and scrub, garrigue. May-June. C and E Spain and S France.

942 *Thymelaea hirsuta [Passerina hirsuta].* Small shrub to 1m, though often less, erect, spreading or prostrate; stems white-downy. Leaves small and scale-like, thick, *densely overlapping* along the stem, shiny green and hairless outside, but white-downy inside. Flowers yellowish, 3-4mm, borne in small, partially concealed, clusters of 2-5, hairy outside. Garrigue, dry grassy and sandy places, semi-desert. Oct-May. T. The tough stem fibres, common to many members of the family, have been used for making rough twine in the past.

943 *Thymelaea tartonraira [Passerina tartonraira].* A small, much-branched, erect or more or less prostrate dwarf shrub, to 50cm, generally *silkily hairy*. Leaves spreading, narrow-oblong to oval, often broadest above the middle. Flowers yellowish, 3-4mm, inconspicuous, borne in small clusters of 2-5 at the base of the upper leaves. Garrigue, rocky and sandy habitats, open scrub, often close to the coast. Feb-Apr. From Spain and NW Africa to Turkey – not Balearic Is., Crete or Cyprus.

943a Subsp. *argentea [Thymelaea argentea].* Like the type but leaves densely silver with hairs, *narrow*, usually only 1.5-3mm wide. N Africa, Crete, Rhodes, SW Turkey and Cyprus.

943b Subsp. *thomasii.* Like subsp. *argentea*, but young shoots and leaves hairless. Corsica.

944 *Thymelaea myrtifolia [Daphne myrtifolia, Thymelaea velutina].* Like *T. tartonraira*, but always with erect stems and *felted*, oblong to elliptical leaves. Flowers solitary or clustered, slightly smaller. Similar habitats and flowering time. Balearic Is.

945 *Thymelaea lanuginosa [Daphne lanuginosa, T. canescens].* Like *T. myrtifolia*, but leaves elliptical, grey-hairy. Flowers larger, 4-6mm, borne in clusters on *short* lateral shoots. Coastal sands. S Spain.

946 *Thymelaea passerina [Lygia passerina, Passerina annua]* **ANNUAL THYMELAEA.** Short to medium, erect, more or less hairless annual. Leaves linear-lanceolate, alternate, pointed. Flowers greenish, tiny, 2-3mm, solitary or 2-3 together at the leaf-axils, bell-shaped, the tube hairy outside. Dry rocky and waste places, cultivated and fallow fields, grass steppes. Apr-July. T.

HYPERICUM FAMILY Guttiferae (Hypericaceae)

Shrubs or herbs with simple, untoothed, opposite or whorled leaves, often with translucent glands, or red or black gland dots. Flowers regular, generally with 4-5 sepals and petals, all free, the petals contorted in bud; stamens numerous, often in 3 or 5, more or less distinct bundles; ovary with 3 or 5 styles. Fruit a capsule.

947 *Hypericum hircinum [Androsaemum hircinum]* **STINKING TUTSAN.** Hairless shrub to 1m; stems erect, branched, 2-lined or 4-angled. Leaves opposite, narrow-lanceolate to oval, unstalked, *goat-scented* when crushed, without dark glands. Flowers large, 25-30mm, borne in lax clusters at branch ends; petals longer than the sepals; stamens longer than the petals; styles 5. Capsule red or green, 8-13mm long. Damp habitats, often along stream and river banks. June-Aug. T – naturalised in the Iberian Peninsula and France.

948 *Hypericum aegyptiacum [Triadenia maritima]* **EGYPTIAN ST. JOHN'S-WORT.** Low spreading shrub to 30cm. Leaves small, bluish-green, rather crowded, narrow-oblong to el-liptical, leathery. Flowers *solitary*, bright yellow, 11-14mm, rather flax-like, per-sistent; stamens in 3 bundles. Cliffs and rocks, generally coastal. Jan-Apr. N Africa, Sardinia, Sicily, Crete, S Greece and the E Med – not Cyprus.

949 *Hypericum aciferum.* Similar, but leaves linear to spatula-shaped and flowers mostly in 3's. Cliffs. Oct-Mar. SW Crete – endemic.

950 *Hypericum empetrifolium.* Very variable dwarf shrub to 50cm tall, stems erect to spreading or prostrate, sometimes rooting below. Leaves small, linear to lanceo-late, borne in 3s. Flowers yellow, often flushed with red in bud or on the outside in flower, 14-18mm, borne in panicles or small clusters, solitary in some high mountain forms; sepals with marginal black dots, deciduous. Rocky habitats, cliffs, scrub, sometimes in garrigue. Mar-June. Greece, Albania, Crete and Turkey.

951 *Hypericum amblycalyx.* Similar, but leaves in 4s and sepals without black glands. Cliffs and rocky habitats. Mar-Apr. E Crete – endemic.

952 *Hypericum olympicum [H. dimoniei].* Short to medium, hairless perennial, often rather woody at the base; stems with 2 lines. Leaves opposite, narrow-oblong to lanceo-late, bluish-green. Flowers large, bright yellow, 30-60mm, on erect stems, the petals sometimes with marginal dark glands; sepals leaf-like. Dry stony, grassy and rocky places. May-July. Balkans and Turkey.

953 *Hypericum perfoliatum.* Medium to tall erect to spreading, usually hairless perennial; stem with 2 raised lines. Leaves bluish-green, opposite, oval to lanceolate or linear-lanceolate, with an unstalked *clasping* base. Flowers yellow, 16-26mm; sepals blunt, with black dots and streaks. Fruit with oil glands and orange warts. Damp meadows, bushy places, or shady rocky places. Apr-June. T. One of the commonest hypericums in the region.

954 *Hypericum australe.* Similar, but a shorter plant to 40cm; stems often semi-prostrate and rooting at the base. Leaves ascending or pressed to the stem. Similar habitats and flowering time. Balearic Is., S France, Corsica, Sardinia, Italy and Sicily.

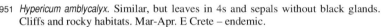

955 *Hypericum balearicum* **BALEARIC ST. JOHN'S-WORT.** Shrub to 1.2m, but sometimes very dwarf, without any black dots; stems and leaves with *prominent* resinous warts. Leaves opposite, oval to oblong, with a wavy margin, leathery. Flowers solitary, pale to deep yellow, 15-40mm; sepals rounded. Rocky and dry wooded habitats. July-Oct. Balearic Is. – endemic.

956 *Hypericum tetrapterum [H. acutum, H. corsicum, H. quadrangulum]* **SQUARE-STALKED ST. JOHN'S-WORT.** Short to tall, generally erect, sometimes spreading or more or less prostrate perennial; stems with 4 narrow *wings*. Leaves oblong or elliptical to rounded, unstalked, with translucent dots. Flowers pale yellow, not red-tinted, 9-12mm, many in a spreading panicle; sepals usually with 1-2 black dots; styles 3. Damp habitats, stream margins, open woodland, roadsides, meadows. May-

Aug. T – not Balearic Is. or Portugal. A form from Corsica with red-veined flowers is distinguished as var. *corsicum* (956a) .

957 *Hypericum perforatum* **PERFORATE ST. JOHN'S-WORT**. Very variable, short to tall, hairless perennial, spreading and rooting at the base; stems erect, with 2 raised lines. Leaves opposite, linear to oval, unstalked, with *large* translucent dots. Flowers yellow, 18-22mm, in broad panicles; sepals narrow, with or without black dots, much shorter than the petals; petals with few to many black dots; styles 3. Dry habitats, cultivated ground, hillsides, roadsides, scrub, hedgerows, rarely at sealevel. May-July. T. A common species in many parts of Europe and western Asia.

958 *Hypericum repens* [*H. tenellum*]. Similar, but stems *prostrate* and leaves smaller, 5-7mm long (not 13mm or more); styles 5. Dry stony places and grazed pastures. May-July. Cyprus – endemic.

959 *Hypericum triquetrifolium* [*H. crispum*] **CRISPED ST. JOHN'S-WORT**. Like *H. perforatum*, but shorter, rarely more than 50cm tall, with erect or spreading stems. Leaves clasping the stem, with prominently *wavy* margins, sometimes without translucent dots; petals without black dots. Cultivated and waste ground, olive groves, vineyards, roadsides. May-Aug. N Africa, Italy and Sicily eastwards.

ROCKROSE FAMILY Cistaceae

Shrubs or herbs with simple, generally opposite, leaves; stipules often present. Flowers hermaphrodite, solitary or in cymes, racemes or panicles; sepals 3 or 5; petals 5; stamens numerous. Fruit a small capsule splitting with 3, 5, 6 or 10 valves. A showy family; many are ornamental and are grown in gardens.

Cistus **CISTUS**. An important genus of colourful evergreen shrubs centred upon and typical of the Med region. Plants have opposite leaves and large showy flowers with rather crumpled petals; sepals 3-5; stamens numerous, all fertile; stigma with or without a well defined style. Fruit a woody capsule. Species are often parasitised by *Cytinus hypocistis* (q.v.). Most species of *Cistus* are grown in gardens for ornament.

960 *Cistus crispus*. An aromatic rounded bush, erect or spreading, to 50cm. Leaves oblong to elliptical, 10-40mm long, with a distinct *undulate* margin, 3-veined, grey-green and hairy. Flowers purplish, 30-40mm, borne in few-flowered cymes; sepals 5, hairy; style distinct, slender. Garrigue, low maquis, open woodland, rocky places. Apr-June. NW Africa and Portugal eastwards to Italy and Sicily – not the islands.

961 *Cistus albidus* **GREY-LEAVED CISTUS**. Similar, but leaves flat, 20-50mm long, *greyish-white* with hairs. Flowers larger, 40-60mm, purplish-pink. Similar habitats and flowering time, usually on calcareous soils. Similar distribution but including Balearic Is., Corsica and Sardinia.

962 *Cistus creticus* [*C. corsicus, C. incanus, C. villosus*]. An erect or spreading shrub to 1m, though often less; young stems clothed in reddish glandular or non-glandular hairs, often sticky. Leaves flat, oval to elliptical, 10-50mm long, pinnately-veined (without 3 or 5 main veins from the base), green or greyish, hoary with stellate hairs, short-stalked, the veins impressed above. Flowers purplish-pink, 40-60mm, in few-flowered cymes; sepals 5, oval, long-pointed. Maquis, garrigue, bushy and rocky places, dry hillslopes, woodland margins. Feb-May. T. Cistus exudes a gum, Ladanum, which is said to be collected from the leaves in hot weather by dragging a rake-like implement through the bushes (it was probably a source of myrrh). The resultant dark brown gum is fragrant and bitter-tasting and is used in perfumes and medicinal pastes. A very variable species in leaf size and in the presence or absence of glandular or stellate hairs – various subspecies and varieties have been recognised in the past.

963 *Cistus heterophyllus*. Similar, but leaves generally smaller, 5-20mm long, elliptical, the veins *not* impressed above; sepals not long-pointed. SE Spain and NW Africa.

964 *Cistus parviflorus*. Like *C. creticus*, but leaves 3-veined, 10-30mm long, and flowers smaller, 20-30mm, pink; no style. Coastal garrigue, rocky places, open woodland and dry stony slopes, on calcareous soils. Jan-May. From Italy and Sicily eastwards to Turkey and Cyprus. Occasionally hybridises with *C. salvifolius* where the two grow in close proximity.

965 *Cistus salvifolius* **SAGE-LEAVED CISTUS**. Spreading to almost prostrate shrub to 1m tall, though often less. Leaves oval to elliptical, with a rounded or wedge-shaped base, 10-40mm long, 3-veined, deep green, rough, hairy on both surfaces, often somewhat undulate along the margins, short-stalked. Flowers white, 30-50mm, solitary or in groups of up to 4; sepals 5, the outer 2 with a *heart-shaped* base; styles very short. Maquis, garrigue, rocky places, stony dry hillsides, open woodland, especially of pine, waste places; often forming large colonies. Feb-June. T. Together with *C. creticus*, the commonest species in the region.

966 *Cistus monspeliensis* **NARROW-LEAVED CISTUS**. Similar, but lower, to 50cm at the most, sticky, the leaves *narrow*, linear to linear-lanceolate, unstalked. Flowers 20-30mm; the outer 2 sepals narrowed at the base. Rocky and scrubby places, generally in garrigue. Mar-June. T – except the extreme E Med, but including Cyprus; commoner in the W. Occasionally hybridises with *C. parviflorus* where the two species grow in close proximity.

967 *Cistus varius [C. pouzolzii]*. Like *C. monspeliensis*, but leaves oblong, grey-hairy, and flowers in a *one-sided* cyme; style slender, distinct. S France and NW Africa. Sometimes thought to be a natural hybrid between *C. crispus* and *C. monspeliensis*.

968 *Cistus psilosepalus*. Like *C. monspeliensis*, but leaves oblong, 20-60mm long, and flowers *larger*, 40-60mm; outer 2 sepals with a heart-shaped base. Portugal and W Spain.

969 *Cistus clusii*. Much-branched slender shrub to 1m. Leaves linear, 10-25mm long, with *revolute margins*, dark green above, but white-hairy beneath. Flowers white, 20-30mm, borne in umbel-like cymes of up to 12 flowers, the stalks white-hairy; only 3 sepals. Rocky places and scrub, maquis. Mar-May. Spain, NW Africa, Balearic Is., S Italy and Sicily.

970 *Cistus libanotis [C. bourgeanus]*. Similar, but leaves 20-35mm long and, like the flower-stalks, sticky, almost hairless. Ovary 6-valved, not 10 as in most *Cistus* species. SW Portugal.

971 *Cistus ladanifer* **GUM CISTUS**. An *aromatic* and very sticky, rather erect shrub to 2.5m. Leaves linear-lanceolate, 40-80mm long, 3-veined in the lower third, deep green above, paler with white hairs beneath, scarcely stalked. Flowers large, 70-100mm, white, often with a crimson blotch at the base of each petal, solitary; sepals 3; style very short. Fruit 10-valved. Maquis, garrigue, woods and open forest, dry rocky slopes. Apr-June. Spain, Portugal, S France and NW Africa; introduced and naturalised in Cyprus and perhaps elsewhere.

972 *Cistus palhinhae*. Similar, but lower, to only 50cm, with leaves broadest above the middle, 20-60mm long. Flowers plain white. Fruit 6-valved. Similar habitats and flowering time. SW Portugal.

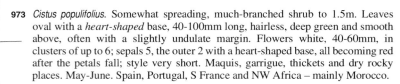

973 *Cistus populifolius.* Somewhat spreading, much-branched shrub to 1.5m. Leaves oval with a *heart-shaped* base, 40-100mm long, hairless, deep green and smooth above, often with a slightly undulate margin. Flowers white, 40-60mm, in clusters of up to 6; sepals 5, the outer 2 with a heart-shaped base, all becoming red after the petals fall; style very short. Maquis, garrigue, thickets and dry rocky places. May-June. Spain, Portugal, S France and NW Africa – mainly Morocco.

974 *Cistus laurifolius.* Rather erect shrub to 1.5m. Leaves oval to lanceolate, 30-80mm long, *3-veined*, dark green and hairless above but white downy beneath, stalked. Flowers white, 50-60mm, borne in umbel-like cymes; sepals 3; style very short. Maquis, garrigue and dry rocky habitats. May-July. Spain, Portugal, S France, Corsica, Italy, Turkey, Morocco.

Halimium **HALIMIUM.** Like *Cistus*, but capsule with 3, not 5 or 10 valves; sepals 5, occasionally 3, the outer 2 much smaller than the others.

975 *Halimium halimifolium [Helianthemum halimifolium].* Much-branched, silvery-grey, erect shrub, to 1m. Leaves elliptical to oblong, often broadest above the middle, 10-40mm long, white downy when young, greenish or greyish above when mature, with *silvery scales* and stellate hairs. Flowers yellow, often with a black spot at the base of each petal, 20-30mm, borne in panicle-like cymes; sepals 5. Sandy coastal habitats, maquis and open woodland. Apr-June. Portugal, S Spain, Balearic Is., Corsica, Sardinia and Italy. A dwarfer form, to 40cm and with petals rounded, not wedge-shaped at the base is sometimes distinguished as subsp. *multiflorum* (975a). Confined to Portugal and SW Spain.

976 *Halimium atriplicifolium.* Similar, but often taller, the leaves of non-flowering shoots 3-veined, short-stalked, those of flowering-shoots pinnately veined, with a heart-shaped base and unstalked. Flowers 40-50mm; sepals 3, hairy. Thickets and open pine forest. May-June. C and S Spain, Morocco.

977 *Halimium ocymoides [Helianthemum ocymoides].* An erect, occasionally spreading shrub, to 1m. Leaves of non-flowering shoots oval, broadest above the middle, grey-hairy, 1-3-veined, those of flowering shoots longer, 12-30mm, lanceolate to oval, green, almost hairless and unstalked. Flowers bright yellow, 20-30mm, the petals usually with a dark spot at the base, borne in terminal panicles; sepals 3. Sandy habitats, heaths and open pine forest. Apr-June. W and C Spain, Portugal.

978 *Halimium lasianthum [H. eriocephalum, H. occidentale].* Similar, but leaves *all alike*, dark green above, but white-downy beneath. Petals unspotted or with a brown spot at the base of each; sepals with purplish bristles. Sandy habitats and Cork Oak woods. S Spain and S Portugal.

979 *Halimium alyssoides.* Like *H. lasianthum,* but petals always unspotted and sepals *without* purple bristles. Portugal and NW Spain.

980 *Halimium commutatum [H. libanotis, Helianthemum commutatum].* Low-growing, much-branched shrub to 50cm. Leaves *linear*, 10-35mm long, with revolute margins, shiny and hairless above, white-downy beneath; reminiscent of Rosemary. Flowers pale yellow, 10-15mm, solitary or in terminal cluster of 2-3; sepals hairless. Coastal sands. Apr-June. Portugal and S Spain.

981 *Halimium viscosum.* Similar, but a glandular-hairy shrub with *white* flowers; sepals very hairy. Oak and pine woods, heathland. E Portugal and Spain.

982 *Halimium verticillatum.* Like *H. viscosum,* but branches covered in stellate hairs and flower-stalks (pedicels) equal, not unequal. SW Portugal.

Tuberaria **TUBERARIA**. Shrubs or herbs, often with basal leaf-rosettes. Leaves opposite, although the upper few sometimes alternate. Flowers yellow; sepals 5, the outer 2 much smaller; style absent. Fruit capsule 3-valved.

983 *Tuberaria lignosa*. Short perennial with a branched woody stock, bearing *plantain-like* leaf-rosettes from which arise the flower stems to 30cm. Leaves elliptical to oval, sometimes broadest above the middle, 3-veined, white-hairy beneath; bracts lanceolate. Flowers yellow, unspotted, 20-30mm, in cymes of 3-7. Woodland and scrub, garrigue and sandy habitats. Mar-June. Portugal, Spain and NW Africa eastwards to Italy and Sicily.

984 *Tuberaria globularifolia*. Similar, but the leaves distinctly stalked and the petals with a *dark spot* at the base. Sandy habitats. N Portugal and NW Spain.

985 *Tuberaria guttata [T. variabilis, Helianthemum guttatum]* **ANNUAL ROCKROSE, SPOTTED ROCK-ROSE**. Very variable, often rather delicate, hairy, low to short annual; stem often unbranched, with a leaf-rosette at the base at flowering-time. Leaves narrow-elliptical to oval, often broadest above the middle; upper leaves linear-lanceolate, generally with a recurved (revolute) margin. Flowers yellow, 10-20mm, with a small to large purplish-brown blotch at the base of each petal, borne in a raceme-like inflorescence. Maquis, garrigue, grassy, sandy and waste places, open woodland, sand-dunes. Feb-June. T. A very variable plant, especially as regards leaf shape and hairiness. A common Med species, sometimes forming large scattered colonies.

986 *Tuberaria bupleurifolia*. Similar, but leaves *all* narrow, the upper bright green and with strongly revolute margins. Flowers 10-13mm. Coastal sands. Portugal and S Spain.

987 *Tuberaria praecox*. Like *T. guttata*, but a small grey-hairy annual, with the petals scarcely longer than the sepals, *unspotted*. Corsica, Sardinia, Italy, Sicily and Yugoslavia.

988 *Tuberaria echioides*. Like *T. guttata*, but more robust, the flowers *unstalked*, borne in a spiralled cyme. Sandy habitats and waste ground. SW Spain and NW Africa.

Helianthemum **ROCKROSES**. Dwarf shrubs or annual herbs with opposite leaves. Flowers in one-sided raceme-like cymes; sepals 5, the outer 2 smaller; stamens numerous, all fertile; style short or long and often S-shaped. Fruit-capsule 3-valved. Characteristic plants of the Med garrigue.

989 *Helianthemum lavandulifolium* **LAVENDER-LEAVED ROCKROSE**. An erect dwarf shrub to 50cm, often less; stems felted. Leaves *linear-lanceolate*, to 50mm long, greyish-green, white-woolly beneath and with revolute margins. Flowers yellow 15-20mm, borne in 3-5-branched inflorescences, the tips of which are tightly coiled in bud but straightening out as the flowers open; sepals fringed with hairs, the 3 inner much larger than the 2 outer. Maquis, garrigue, rocky and stony places, open woodland, on calcareous soils. Apr-June. Spain, S France eastwards to Turkey – not Balearic Is., Corsica, Sardinia, Sicily or Cyprus.

990 *Helianthemum syriacum [H. racemosum]*. A stout dwarf shrub to 50cm, though often far less, densely grey-hairy. Leaves lanceolate to linear-lanceolate, pointed and with revolute margins, greyish-green above but white with down beneath. Flowers yellow, 10-18mm, numerous borne in *branched*, dense cymes, not raceme-like. Rocky habitats, open woodland, sand-dunes and pathsides. Apr-June. T – but absent from many of the smaller islands and Portugal.

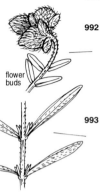

flower
buds

991 *Helianthemum squamatum.* Similar, but sepals scaly and with flat margins. Flowers yellow, the petals with a *dark spot* at the base. Gypsum soils. S and E Spain.

992 *Helianthemum caput-felis* **CAT'S-HEAD ROCKROSE.** White-felted compact dwarf shrub to 30cm, with erect flowering branches. Leaves broadly elliptical to lanceolate, thick, with strongly revolute margins. Flowers yellow, 16-22mm, in few-flowered congested cymes; sepals covered in long silky hairs which gives the buds a *cat's head-like* appearance, which continues after the petals have fallen. Maquis, garrigue, open woodland, coastal cliffs, often of limestone, dry inland habitats. Mar-Apr. SE Spain (Alicante), Balearic Is. and N Africa; rather rare.

993 *Helianthemum apenninum* [*H. polifolium*] **WHITE ROCKROSE.** Rather lax spreading, much-branched low shrub; stems prostrate to ascending. Leaves oblong to lanceolate, grey- or white-woolly, at least beneath, with revolute margins. Flowers *white* with a yellow centre, 14-20mm, borne in cymes of up to 10 flowers. Rocky and grassy habitats, dry hills. May-July. European Med and NW Africa. A form with pink flowers occurs in the Balearic Is. and NW Italy.

994 *Helianthemum pilosum.* Similar, but sepals with stellate (not simple) hairs, or hairless. Scrub and open forest. Portugal, Spain, S France and Italy.

995 *Helianthemum virgatum.* Like *H. pilosum*, but flowers *pink*. N Africa; perhaps S Spain.

fruit

996 *Helianthemum nummularium* [*H. chamaecistus, H. vulgare*] **COMMON ROCKROSE.** Very variable prostrate to ascending dwarf shrub. Leaves oblong to lanceolate to almost rounded, with flat or slightly revolute margins, grey- or white-hairy, at least beneath; all leaves with small leaf-like stipules at the base. Flowers pale to bright yellow or orange, 12-20mm, sometimes with an orange spot at the base of each petal, borne in cymes of up to 12, sometimes solitary; sepals hairy or hairless between the ribs. Fruit capsule pendent (as in most other species). Grassy and rocky habitats, garrigue. T – except much of N Africa, Cyprus and the extreme E Med. Widely grown in gardens. A widespread species, especially in the mountains of Europe where a number of subspecies are recognised, though mostly not in the Med region.

996a Subsp. *glabrum* has leaves hairless, except sometimes for the margin. European Med – mainly in the mountains.

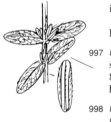

997 *Helianthemum stipulatum* [*H. ellipticum*]. Stouter, more erect plant than the previous species with revolute-margined leaves and *stalkless* flowers; flowers only 6-8mm, the petals yellow, not longer than the sepals. Sandy and rocky coastal habitats, sometimes inland. S Greece, Turkey, Cyprus and Egypt.

998 *Helianthemum sessiliflorum.* Like *H. stipulatum*, but leaves linear, whitish, and flowers *tiny*, 2-4mm, the petals shorter or slightly longer than the sepals. Dry coastal hills. S Italy and Sicily.

999 *Helianthemum croceum.* Like *H. nummularium*, but leaves rather fleshy, the upper surface covered in white *stellate* hairs; flowers bright yellow, orange yellow or white, 14-20mm. Open woodland, scrub and rocky mountainsides. May-July. Portugal and Spain eastwards to Italy and Sicily – not Balearic Is. or Corsica.

1000 *Helianthemum obtusifolium.* Like *H. nummularium*, but flowers pale creamy-yellow, 20-28mm; sepals with prominent purple-black *veins*. Garrigue and dry rocky hills. Cyprus – endemic.

1001 *Helianthemum salicifolium* [*H. intermedium*] **WILLOW-LEAVED ROCKROSE.** Low to short hairy annual, very variable, but usually much-branched, erect or spreading. Leaves oval to lanceolate or oblong, flat, short-stalked. Flowers yellow to golden-yellow, 10-22mm, borne in 5-20-flowered lax cymes; petals rather narrow, as long as the sepals, occasionally absent; bracts large and leaf-like; flower-stalks spreading in fruit, upturned at the end. Maquis, garrigue, sandy and rocky ground, grassy and waste places, semi-desert. Feb-May. T.

1002 *Helianthemum ledifolium [H. niloticum]*. Similar, but a hairier plant to 60cm and petals *shorter* than the sepals; flower-stalks *erect* and straight in fruit. Similar habitats and flowering time. T – not Balearic Is.

1003 *Helianthemum aegyptiacum*. Like *H. salicifolium*, but little-branched and with linear-lanceolate to oblong leaves with strongly *revolute* margins; inner sepals membranous. Dry sandy habitats, in hills and mountains. Mar-June. T – not Balearic Is., Portugal or Yugoslavia.

ower

1004 *Helianthemum sanguineum*. Like *H. salicifolium*, but a *sticky* plant, never more than 10cm tall, sometimes tiny, the stem often purple-tinged; stalks deflexed in fruit. Portugal, Spain, Italy and Crete.

1005 *Helianthemum canum* **HOARY ROCKROSE**. Low to short hairy dwarf shrub. Leaves el-liptical to linear with a narrowed base, often clustered in rosettes at the apex of the vegetative shoots, usually greyish with branched hairs. Flowers *small*, 8-15mm, borne in small racemes of 3-5. Dry meadows and grassy places, rocks and cliffs, often on limestone. Apr-July. Spain eastwards to Turkey – not Balearic Is., Cor-sica or Crete. One of the common rock-roses in the Med region.

1006 *Helianthemum hymettium*. Similar, but with even smaller flowers, 6-8mm, and upper leaves of flowering shoots with prominent stipules. Crete and S Greece.

1007 *Helianthemum origanifolium*. Low, generally spreading or ascending, dwarf shrub. Leaves broad-oval to almost rounded with a heart-shaped base, green on *both* surfaces, with at least some stellate hairs on the lower surface. Flowers yellow, 5-8mm, borne in branched inflorescences, almost panicle-like. Rocky and sandy habitats, often on limestone. Apr-June. S Portugal, Spain and N Africa.

1007a Subsp. *serrae*. Leaves with stellate hairs on both surfaces. Balearic Is.

1007b Subsp. *molle*. Flowers larger, 5-13mm, borne in a single, unbranched cyme. S and NE Spain.

1008 *Helianthemum marifolium [H. myrtifolium]*. Similar, but leaves grey- or white-woolly beneath, with a heart-shaped base; flowers 10-15mm. Rocky and stony habitats. S Portugal, S and E Spain, S France and NW Africa.

1009 *Helianthemum cinereum [H. rubellum]*. Like *H. marifolium*, but inflorescence paniculate (not simple or branched only at the base) and leaves of flowering shoots with small *stipules* at the base. Rocky and bushy habitats. Spain, Italy, Sicily and Greece.

Fumana **FUMANA**. Like *Helianthemum*, but upper leaves usually alternate, often linear; outer stamens often sterile and style filiform.

uit

1010 *Fumana arabica* **ARABIAN FUMANA**. Much-branched dwarf shrub, with prostrate or ascending stems to 25cm. Leaves all *alternate*, oval to almost lanceolate, pointed, green or greyish, flat, almost hairless to glandular-hairy, equally spaced along the stem. Flowers yellow, 12-18mm, the petals often with a pale orange blotch at the base, solitary or up to 7 in a lax raceme; outer 2 sepals much smaller than the 3 inner membranous ones, green-veined. Maquis, garrigue, stony hillslopes, dry pastures, generally on calcareous soils. Feb-June. Sardinia and Italy eastwards, including Crete, Cyprus and N Africa.

1011 *Fumana ericoides*. An erect or straggling, much-branched dwarf shrub to 20cm. Leaves alternate, linear, hairless or glandular-hairy, evenly spaced along the stems; no stipules. Flowers yellow, 8-16mm, in small clusters; flower-stalks

fruit

longer than the leaves, spreading in fruit and with a *deflexed* apex. Similar habitats and flowering time as *F. arabica*. Portugal and NW Africa eastwards to Greece; apparently not Crete.

1012 *Fumana procumbens* [*F. vulgaris, Cistus fumana*]. Similar, but a prostrate plant with the fruit-stalks shorter than the subtending leaves and *recurved* from the base. Similar habitats and flowering time. T – not Cyprus and parts of the extreme E Med.

1013 *Fumana scoparia*. Like *F. ericoides*, but an ascending bush with the leaves *crowded* below; inflorescence distinctly glandular-hairy. Spain, Italy, Crete and Albania.

1014 *Fumana thymifolia* [*F. glutinosa, F. viscida, Helianthemum viride*] **THYME-LEAVED FUMANA**. Small, much-branched dwarf shrub to 20cm, with erect or ascending branches. Leaves *opposite* at least below, linear to narrowly elliptical, hairless or glandular-hairy, with a revolute margin; stipules present as well as short lateral shoots in the leaf-axils. Flowers yellow, 9-14mm, occasionally with a reddish blotch at the base of each petal, borne in 3-9-flowered raceme-like cymes; inner 3 sepals much larger than the outer 2, membranous, green-veined. Dry rocky habitats, fixed sand-dunes, garrigue, open forest. Apr-June. T – not Cyprus or parts of the extreme E Med.

1015 *Fumana laevipes*. Similar, but leaves all alternate, without stipules, very narrow, almost round in cross-section, bluish-green or bright green. Portugal and NW Africa eastwards to Greece and Crete.

TAMARIX FAMILY Tamaricaceae

Shrubs or small trees with simple, alternate, small scale-like leaves. Flowers often in catkin-like spikes or racemes, rarely solitary, 5-parted (rarely 4), with separate sepals and petals; stamens 4 or more. Fruit a capsule containing numerous hairy seeds that float in the wind like willow down. The species of *Tamarix* are often confused and are difficult to identify. The branches of tamarisks are sometimes used for making brooms.

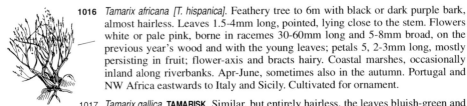

1016 *Tamarix africana* [*T. hispanica*]. Feathery tree to 6m with black or dark purple bark, almost hairless. Leaves 1.5-4mm long, pointed, lying close to the stem. Flowers white or pale pink, borne in racemes 30-60mm long and 5-8mm broad, on the previous year's wood and with the young leaves; petals 5, 2-3mm long, mostly persisting in fruit; flower-axis and bracts hairy. Coastal marshes, occasionally inland along riverbanks. Apr-June, sometimes also in the autumn. Portugal and NW Africa eastwards to Italy and Sicily. Cultivated for ornament.

1017 *Tamarix gallica* **TAMARISK**. Similar, but entirely hairless, the leaves bluish-green and the racemes only 3-5mm broad; petals 1-2mm long. Spain eastwards to Italy and Sicily – not Balearic Is. or Sardinia. Frequently planted.

1018 *Tamarix canariensis*. Like *T. africana*, but a minutely hairy shrub or bushy tree with reddish-brown bark. Racemes 15-45mm long, 3-5mm broad, dense; petals pale pink, 1-1.5mm long. Portugal and Spain eastwards to Sicily – not Corsica or Italy.

stamens

ovary

1019 *Tamarix parviflora* [*T. cretica*]. Shrub or small tree to 5m, often less, with brown or purple bark, hairless or slightly and minutely hairy. Leaves pointed, 3-5mm long, with a membranous margin. Flowers usually white, *4-petalled*, borne in racemes to 30mm long and 3-5mm broad, on the previous year's wood; sepals finely toothed; petals 1.5-2mm long; styles 4. Riverbanks, hedges and roadsides. Apr-June. Crete and Yugoslavia eastwards to Turkey – not Cyprus. Widely cultivated and naturalised in Spain, Corsica and Italy.

seed

1020 *Tamarix hampeana [T. haussknechtii].* Similar, but a more sprawling bright green shrub, often with smaller leaves and flowers with 4 or 5 petals and 3 styles; racemes 20-60mm long, 10-12mm *broad*; petals 2.5-4mm long, pink. River-banks, coastal sands, roadsides. Mar-May, occasionally later. Greece, Aegean Is., Turkey, Cyprus and Palestine.

1021 *Tamarix tetrandra.* Like *T. parviflora,* but with *black* bark, the racemes white or pale pink, 6-7mm wide; petals 2.5-3mm long. Damp places, especially river beds rocky and gravelly ground, but rarely at low altitudes. Mar-Apr. Yugoslavia and Greece eastwards, including Cyprus.

1022 *Tamarix smyrnensis [T. hohenackeri].* Like *T. tetrandra,* but flowers borne on the *current* year's growths, usually 5-parted, the racemes 3-5mm wide; styles usually 3. Mar-shy ground, riversides, coastal rocks and sand-dunes, lowland and in the mountains. Apr-June. Greece, Crete, Turkey, Cyprus and the E Med.

1023 *Tamarix dalmatica.* Like *T. hampeana,* but racemes 8-10 broad with bracts longer than the flower-stalks (pedicels); petals 2.5mm long narrow, widest above the middle and with a distinct *claw* (not elliptical and clawless). Coastal marshes and river-banks. Apr-June, occasionally in the autumn. Italy and Sicily eastwards to Greece, including Crete.

1024 *Tamarix tetragyna [T. meyeri].* Spreading large shrub or small tree, to 15m, with red-dish-brown bark. Leaves bluish-green, lanceolate, 5-6mm long, much smaller on flowering shoots. Flowers pink or white, 4-parted, borne in *long racemes,* 50-120mm long, 5-8mm broad; petals 3-4mm long; styles 4. Fresh and brackish mar-shes, streamsides, more rarely in gullies or along sandy seashores. Feb-Apr. Turkey, Cyprus and the E Med.

1025 *Reaumeria vermiculata [R. mucronata]* **REAUMERIA**. A hairless shrub to 30cm with erect branches. Leaves semi-cylindrical, to 12mm long, bluish-green, crowded near the base of the branches, but widely spaced above; stems with leafy lateral shoots. Flowers white, *solitary,* 5-parted, the calyx hidden by numerous overlapping bracts; stamens in 5 bundles; styles 5. Coastal banks, often on gypsum soils. S Sicily and N Africa.

SEA HEATH FAMILY Frankeniaceae

Dwarf shrubs or herbs with usually 5 partly fused sepals and 5 separate petals, solitary or in leafy cymes; petals clawed; stamens often 6. Fruit a small capsule.

1026 *Frankenia pulverulenta.* Low prostrate, often mat-forming, annual, occasionally as-cending, often minutely hairy. Leaves tiny, 1-5mm long, oval to elliptical, broadest above the middle, not white-encrusted. Flowers pale to deep violet, in short lateral, or terminal spikes, crowded; petals 3.5-5mm long. Rocky, and sandy coastal habitats, shingle, saline areas inland. Mar-Sept. T.

1027 *Frankenia laevis* **SEA HEATH**. Low prostrate, minutely hairy, much-branched peren-nial, forming dense mats. Leaves linear-lanceolate, 2-5mm long, with *revolute* margins, often with a whitish crust. Flowers purplish or whitish, solitary or in small clusters, borne all over the plant; petals 4-6mm long, oval or rounded. Coastal sands and shingle, stabilised dunes. May-Sept. Portugal and NW Africa eastwards to Italy and Sicily.

1028 *Frankenia hirsuta.* Similar, but stems often hairy, especially near the top and flowers *confined* to dense terminal clusters; plant not white-crusted, but sometimes with a slightly powdery deposit on the surface. Similar habitats as well as the margins of salt lakes. Apr-Sept. T – not Spain or Portugal.

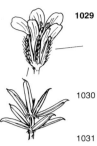

1029 *Frankenia thymifolia [F. reuteri]* **THYME-LEAVED SEA HEATH.** Dwarf bush, much-branched, to 30cm, woody at the base; branches erect or ascending. Leaves small, 2-6mm long, narrow-elliptical, needle-like and with a somewhat recurved tip, completely *covered* in a white crust; margins revolute. Flowers purplish, solitary or in small one-sided spikes, at the branch tips; petals 7mm long. Saline soils and salt steppes. Apr-June. C and S Spain, NW Africa – always local.

1030 *Frankenia corymbosa.* Similar, but plant only partially white encrusted and flowers in *dense* terminal cymes; petals 4-6mm long. Similar habitats and flowering time. S Spain and N Africa.

1031 *Frankenia boissieri.* Like *F. corymbosa,* but plant not white-encrusted and calyx larger, 4-6mm long (not 2-3mm). Coastal saline habitats. S Portugal, SW Spain and N Africa.

CUCUMBER FAMILY Cucurbitaceae

Herbs, often climbers with alternate leaves, generally with stem tendrils. Flowers unisexual, usually 5-parted, the corolla deeply lobed; stamens usually 3. Fruit fleshy, berry-like.

1032 *Ecballium elaterium* **SQUIRTING CUCUMBER.** Low to short spreading, bristly perennial, with a tuberous rootstock – without tendrils. Leaves rough, heart-shaped to triangular, long-stalked, rather fleshy and with an undulate surface. Flowers yellow, 16-20mm, male and female separate but on the same plant, male in short racemes, the female solitary. Fruit small, green and oblong, like a small cucumber, 40-50mm long, bristly, recurved on the ends of long erect stalks; *exploding* suddenly when ripe at the point of attachment, squirting the seeds out in a pulpy liquid. Sandy and stony ground, old walls, grassy places, waste and fallow land. Feb-Sept. T. The liquid around the seeds can cause skin irritation or inflammation. Root extracts have long been used in herbal medicines. The exciting fruits are always an amusement to catch the uninitiated observer.

1033 *Bryonia cretica* **WHITE BRYONY.** A tall climbing, hairy perennial, to 4m, with *coiled* tendrils. Leaves palmately 5-lobed, the lobes untoothed or with a few blunt teeth, green, often with irregular white marks. Flowers greenish-white with darker veins, 10-18mm, the female in small lateral clusters the male in drooping racemes on separate plants. Fruit a berry, green with white marks at first, becoming red when ripe, 6-10mm. Scrub, hedgerows, woodland margins, generally on calcareous soils. Apr-Sept. Aegean Is., Cyprus and E Med. Once cultivated as a medicinal plant.

    1033a Subsp. *dioica [Bryonia dioica]*. Similar, but leaves and young flowers plain green. W Med eastwards to Greece and Crete.

1034 *Citrullus colocynthis [Colocynthis vulgaris]* **BITTER CUCUMBER, BITTER APPLE.** Rough, bristly, *prostrate* perennial, with long trailing stems to 2m, without tendrils. Leaves dull green, triangular in outline, pinnately-lobed, 3-5-lobed, with undulate margins; short-stalked. Flowers yellow, or greenish-yellow, 15-20mm, solitary in the leaf-axils, male and female separate but on the same plant. Fruit globose, 4-12cm, smooth, yellow or variously mottled. Sandy and stony, dry habitats, semi-desert, especially near the coast. N Africa, S Spain, Sicily, Greece and the E Med, including Cyprus. The fruits were used in former times as a powerful purgative.

Various cucurbits are cultivated throughout the region for their edible fruits. They include various forms of **Melon,** *Cucumis melo* (1035), **Watermelon,** *Citrullus lanatus* (1036), **Cucumber,** *Cucumis sativus* (1037), **Marrow,** *Cucumis pepo* (1038) and **Pumpkin,** *Cucumis maxima* (1039).

CACTUS FAMILY Cactaceae

A large family of mostly succulent plants from the Americas, often spiny. Flowers often large and showy with many petals and numerous stamens. Many species are cultivated.

Opuntia **PRICKLY PEARS**. Plants somewhat woody, with flattened jointed green stems and small, rather inconspicuous, leaves that soon fall. Areoles bearing many short hooked bristles and often a few much longer straight spines.

1040 *Opuntia ficus-indica* **PRICKLY PEAR, BARBARY FIG**. Plant stout, to 3-5m tall, with spreading bluish-green branches; joints 20-50cm long; areoles small and whitish, with yellowish hooked bristles, generally without straight spines – if present then only 1-2, not more than 10mm long. Flowers bright yellow, 70-100mm long; filaments pale yellow. Fruit egg-shaped, 50-90mm long, yellow when ripe, occasionally red or particolored. Rocky hillslopes, cliffs, roadsides, hedges. Mar-July. Probably T. (Tropical America). Widely cultivated for its edible fruits and for hedging and often naturalised. This familiar plant was apparently introduced from the Americas by Christopher Columbus; plants self propagate themselves easily when sections of the stems fall onto the ground. The fruits are often seen for sale in markets, although nowadays it is not so frequently cultivated.

1041 *Opuntia monacantha*. Similar, but joints shiny green, the *spines* 10-40mm long. Flowers golden-yellow with greenish stamen filaments. Fruit reddish-purple. Iberian Peninsula, S France and S Italy, perhaps elsewhere. (E South America).

1042 *Opuntia stricta*. Like *O. ficus-indica*, but a smaller plant to 1m, the joints only 8-15cm long; spines, if present, 1-2, 10-40mm long. Flowers yellow, 60-70mm long. Fruit red, 40-60mm long. SE France, perhaps elsewhere. (W Cuba and SE USA).

1043 *Opuntia compressa* [*O. humifusa, O. vulgaris* – a confused name]. Like *O. stricta*, but *aerioles* brown-downy and spines brownish-white. Flowers often rather larger, bright yellow, sometimes with a reddish centre. Fruit red, 25-50mm long. S France eastwards to Greece, Crete and Cyprus. (E North America). Cultivated for its edible fruits.

1044 *Cereus uruguayanus* [*C. peruvianus*] **CEREUS**. A large tree-like, much-branched cactus, to 16m; *branches* not flattened or jointed, 6-9-ribbed; spines 5-7, 10-30mm long, brown or black. Flowers large trumpet-shaped, white inside, reddish or brownish on the outside, 12-15cm long. Fruit sub-globose, 35-35mm, orange-yellow when ripe. Naturalised on coastal rocks in SE France, perhaps elsewhere. (SE South America).

LOOSESTRIFE FAMILY Lythraceae

Herbs with simple, alternate or opposite leaves; stipules tiny or absent. Flowers hermaphrodite, regular, 4-6-parted, solitary or in small lateral clusters; epicalyx often present; petals separate, often pink or purple, inserted on the rim of a cup-like hypanthium; stamens 2-12. fruit a many-seeded capsule.

1045 *Lythrum junceum*. Hairless short to medium perennial, rarely annual; stems much-branched from the base and with rather straggly stems. Leaves mostly alternate, broadly elliptical to narrow-oblong. Flowers purple, sometimes white or cream, solitary, the 6 petals 5-6mm long; *stamens* 12, some or all protruding. Wet habitats, marshes, pools and damp meadows. Mar-Sept. T. Flowers are heterostylous, some with short, some with intermediate and others with long protruding

ole

ariole

stamens, often two levels within the same flower, the different types borne on separate plants.

1046 *Lythrum hyssopifolia* **GRASS-POLY**. Similar, but smaller, all of the same type, with 4-6 stamens, *not* protruding; petals 4-6, pink, 2-3mm long. Moist places, streams, brackish pool margins, seasonally flooded land; a frequent weed, sometimes casual often. May-July. T.

1047 *Lythrum tribracteatum*. Like *L. hyssopifolia*, but leaves usually oval to oblong and epicalyx lobes very small, *shorter* than the sepals (not longer). Similar habitats as well as salt marsh depressions. Apr-June. Scattered localities from S France and Spain, N Africa, Italy to much of the Aegean region and Cyprus.

1048 *Lythrum thymifolia*. Like *L. hyssopifolia*, but leaves mostly less (not more) than 2mm wide, flowers with 4 petals and 2-3 stamens; petals 1-2mm long. Similar habitats and flowering time. From Portugal and NW Africa eastwards to Italy – not Corsica or Sicily.

1049 *Lythrum portula [Peplis portula]* **WATER PURSLANE**. Low, more or less prostrate, creeping, hairless annual; stems *rooting* at the nodes. Leaves opposite, rather fleshy, sometimes reddish, oval, tapered to a short stalk. Flowers purple, tiny, 1-2mm, solitary at the leaf-bases, with 6 petals, sometimes petals absent. Wet open places, bare muddy ground, pool margins, seasonally flooded ground, generally on acid soils. Apr-Oct. T – absent from most of the islands except for Corsica and Sardinia.

1050 *Lythrum borysthenicum [Middendorfia borysthenicum, Peplis boraei, P. erecta]*. Like *L. portula*, but a low, rather rough annual with ascending to erect stems, scarcely rooting at the nodes. Leaves alternate or opposite. Flowers with minute or no petals. Similar habitats and flowering time. T – absent from most of the islands except for Corsica and Sardinia.

(1048)

1051 *Lagerstroemia indica* **CRAPE MYRTLE**. Deciduous tree or large shrub to 10m, often less, with angled hairless shoots. Leaves alternate, opposite or in threes, oblong to elliptical, short-stalked, untoothed. Flowers pink to deep red or purplish, occasionally white, 25-35mm, borne in large terminal panicles; petals 6, very undulate, with a long claw. Planted in parks and gardens, occasionally along roads, in hot sheltered areas. June-Sept. Scattered, mostly in European Med. (China).

MYRTLE FAMILY Myrtaceae

A primarily tropical and subtropical family, generally with opposite, simple leaves. Flowers 4-5-parted, with numerous stamens fused at the base into 4-5 bundles; ovary inferior, located below the other flower parts. Fruit often a berry.

1052 *Myrtus communis* **COMMON MYRTLE**. An erect, much-branched, evergreen shrub to 5m, though often less; twigs glandular-hairy when young. Leaves opposite, shiny deep green, oval-laneolate, pointed, untoothed, *aromatic* when crushed. Flowers white, occasionally pink-tinged, 20-30cm, with rounded petals and a mass of protruding white stamens, solitary, long-stalked. Berry oblong in outline, bluish-black when ripe. Maquis, woods, scrub, roadsides, occasionally by streams. May-Aug. T. A symbol of peace and love since classical times. The bark, leaves and flowers contain an aromatic oil, Eau d'Anges, used in perfumery and medicinally. The berries are sometimes fermented into an acid-tasting drink. Many forms are grown in gardens, including dwarf, variegated-leaved and double-flowered.

    1052a Subsp. *tarentina* **TARENTINE MYRTLE**. Similar, but a more compact shrub, not more than 2m with narrower leaves, less (not more) than 20mm long; berry almost globose, often whitish. Mainly coastal habitats – rocks, maquis and garrigue. From Portugal and Spain eastwards to Yugoslavia and Crete – not Balearic Is.

1053 *Callistemon citrinus* **BOTTLEBRUSH.** An evergreen shrub to 2-3m with stiff arching stems. Leaves leathery, grey-green, narrow-elliptical, untoothed, scented of lemon when crushed; young leaves bronzy-red. Flowers bright crimson-red, borne in bottlebrush-like heads towards the shoot tips; perianth small, but stamens prominent, long and protruding. Widely planted in parks and gardens in the mildest places, occasionally along streets. June-Aug. (Australia). One of a number of similar species grown in gardens. *C. sieberi* (1054), is a bushier plant with rigid, sharply pointed leaves and yellow flowers. *C. speciosus* (1055), has long narrow, grey-green leaves and deep red flowers in spring and autumn. *C. viminalis* (1056) makes a large bush or small tree to 5m, with narrow-oblong leaves that are bronzed when young, and with bright red flowers in the summer. All come from Australia.

Eucalyptus **GUMS.** Evergreen trees, often with peeling bark. Leaves of two types, often much broader and erect on plants in their juvenile state, narrower and pendent on mature branches. Flowers generally in umbel-like lateral clusters, rarely solitary; sepals fused into a conical cap (operculum) that falls away in one piece when the flowers open; stamens numerous and prominent. Fruit capsule opening by valves which project beyond the rim of the capsule. A large and complex Australasian genus. A number of are widely cultivated, some for timber, others for soil conservation, wind breaks or for ornament.

1057 *Eucalyptus robustus* **SWAMP MAHOGANY.** Tree to 30m, with a rough, fibrous, *persistent* bark. Juvenile leaves broad-lanceolate to elliptical; mature leaves shiny, green, lanceolate with a long tapered tip, 10-18cm long. Flowers white, 18-25mm, in clusters of 5-10. Fruit broadly bell-shaped, 10-12mm across, longer than wide. Planted in swampy ground and semi-saline areas. May-Aug. Portugal, France, Sardinia and Italy, probably elsewhere. (E Australia).

1058 *Eucalyptus resinifera.* Similar, but to 40m, with reddish bark and smaller egg-shaped fruits, 5-8mm. Same areas, plus Spain. (E Australia).

1059 *Eucalyptus torquata.* Like *E. robustus,* but a small tree to 12m, readily distinguished by its red, pink or orange flowers. Planted mainly for ornament. S France, Portugal and Cyprus, probably elswhere. (SW Australia).

1060 *Eucalyptus globulus* **BLUE GUM.** Tree to 40m with smooth deciduous bark. Juvenile leaves oval to broadly lanceolate, with a heart-shaped base, markedly blue-green; mature leaves lanceolate to sickle-shaped, 10-30cm long, bright glossy green, balsam-scented. Flowers white or pink, usually *solitary*, 30-40mm, unstalked. Fruit top-shaped 15-30mm across, wider than long. Widely planted since the nineteenth century to help drain swampy areas, but also planted for timber and ornament, especially for its attractive juvenile foliage. Feb-July. European Med, perhaps elsewhere. (Tasmania). An antiseptic oil is obtained from the leaves.

1061 *Eucalyptus viminalis* **MANNA GUM.** Large pyramidal tree to 50m with pendulous branches; bark smooth, white, *peeling* away in long, ribbon-like strips. Juvenile leaves oval, unstalked and with a clasping base, pale green; mature leaves lanceolate, pale green, 11-18cm long. Flowers white, 14-15mm, usually borne in clusters of 3. Fruit globose to top-shaped, 7-8mm across. Planted for timber and ornament. May-Sept. Portugal and Spain eastwards to Italy and Sicily. (S and E Australia and Tasmania).

1062 *Eucalyptus camaldulensis [E. rostrata]* **RIVER RED GUM**. Similar, but flowers yellowish-white, in clusters of 5-10 and leaves somewhat bluish-green. Fruit longer than wide, 5-6mm across, with a broad raised *rim*. Cultivated for timber, shelter and ornament. T. (Australia). A valuable timber tree and one of the most commonly planted of all Eucalypts.

1063 *Eucalyptus maidenii.* Like *E. viminalis,* but umbels 3-7-flowered and mature leaves larger, 18-20cm long. Fruit bluish-green, 10-12mm across, wider than long, with 1-2 *ribs*. Planted for timber and ornament. Mainly in the European Med. (SE Australia).

POMEGRANATE FAMILY Punicaceae

A small family with a single genus and only two species, one in the Med.

1064 *Punica granatum* **POMEGRANATE**. Deciduous shrub or small tree to 5m, often spiny; young stems 4-angled. Leaves opposite, shiny, rather bright green, oblong to elliptical, untoothed, very short-stalked. Flowers bright red, 30-40mm, with a waxy calyx and 5-7 rather crumpled petals; stamens numerous. *Fruit* large and globose, 50-80mm (more in some cultivated forms), with the persistent sepals on the end, reddish-brown when ripe; inside the leathery rind the numerous seeds are embedded in a sweet, translucent, purplish, pink, yellowish or whitish edible pulp. Widely grown throughout for its fruits and as an ornament and thoroughly naturalised in some places, in scrub, hedgerows and garrigue. May-Sept. T. (SW Asia). Often mentioned in the Bible, pomegranates have long been used – in drinks, for a red dye, medicinally against tapeworms, and as a fertility symbol. Cultivated forms include dwarf and double-flowered types.

WILLOWHERB FAMILY Onagraceae

Herbs with simple, alternate or opposite leaves. Flowers hermaphrodite, regular, usually with 4 sepals and 4 petals, stamens various, but 8 in our species; ovary conspicuous below the sepals. Fruit a capsule, occasionally a berry, splitting lengthways to expel numerous fluffy seeds.

1065 *Epilobium hirsutum* **GREATER WILLOWHERB**. *Robust,* softly hairy, tall perennial, to 2m. Leaves opposite, sometimes whorled, oblong to lanceolate, unstalked and half-clasping the stem, coarsely toothed; bracts leaf-like, alternate. Flowers bright purplish-pink, 15-25mm, borne in a leafy raceme; petals notched; stigma 4-lobed. Damp and waste places, ditches, river margins, irrigation channels. June-Oct. T.

1066 *Epilobium parviflora* **HOARY WILLOWHERB**. Similar, but a less robust plant, with mostly opposite or whorled leaves, not clasping the stem. Flowers *smaller,* 7-12mm, pale purplish-pink. Damp soil, waste and fallow ground, streamsides, marshes, rarely at sea-level. June-Oct. T.

1067 *Epilobium palustre* **MARSH WILLOWHERB**. Short to medium, hairy or hairless perennial, with slender underground stolons; stems erect. Leaves mostly opposite, lanceolate, *untoothed* and unstalked. Flowers pale pink or white, 8-12mm, in a lax raceme, often somewhat bristly; stigma club-shaped. Wet habitats, marshes, woodland flushes, damp meadows, generally on slightly acid soils. June-Aug. T – not Balearic Is., Sardinia, Sicily, Crete, most Aegean Is. and Cyprus.

CORNUS FAMILY Cornaceae

Trees or shrubs with simple, opposite leaves. Flowers usually hermaphrodite, 4-parted; sepals small; petals valvate, the stamens alternating with the petals. Fruit a drupe or a berry.

1068 *Cornus mas* **CORNELIAN CHERRY**. Deciduous shrub or small tree, to 8m, with greenish-yellow twigs. Leaves oval to elliptical, pointed, untoothed, dull green beneath; main veins 3-5 pairs. Flowers yellow, small, 4-5mm, borne in small clusters *before* the leaves emerge. Fruit oval in outline, 12-15mm long, shiny and scarlet when ripe. Open woodland, scrub and sometimes along hedgerows. Feb-Mar. Italy, the Balkans and Turkey. Widely cultivated for ornament. The fruits are edible, although rather acid-tasting, and are sometimes seen for sale in eastern European and Turkish markets. They are also pickled and used in the preparation of an alcoholic drink, and in jellies.

1069 *Cornus sanguinea [Thelycrania sanguinea]* **DOGWOOD**. A deciduous shrub to 4m, with *dark red* twigs, stiffly erect. Leaves elliptical to oval, pale green and hairy, untoothed, with 3-4 pairs of main veins; short-stalked. Flowers dull white, 8-10mm, borne in dense, umbel-like clusters. Fruit almost globose, 5-8mm, black when ripe. Woodland margins, scrub, hedgerows, margins of ditches, roadsides. May-July. European Med and Turkey – not Balearic Is. and Crete.

CARROT FAMILY Umbelliferae.

A large and complicated family of annual, biennial or perennial herbs, occasionally shrubs, with alternate leaves. Leaves often large and pinnately divided, sometimes simple, often with inflated, sheathing bases. Flowers borne in distinctive umbels, generally compound, the primary umbel with or without bracts, its main branches (rays) supporting secondary umbels with or without secondary bracts (bracteoles). Flowers often rather small, 5-parted and usually hermaphrodite; calyx with 5 teeth, usually inconspicuous, sometimes absent; petals separate, often notched and with an incurved tip, all the same size or markedly uneven so that the outer flowers in an umbel may have its outer petals considerably enlarged (radiate).

Carpels 2, joined along a central axis, each terminating in a style, flattened or rounded in section, often ribbed or winged and with resin canals (vittae) between the primary ridges. Characters of the fruit are often very important in distinguishing genera, as well as closely related species; flowers and fruit can often be found on the plant at the same time.

1070 *Hydrocotyle vulgaris* **MARSH PENNYWORT**. Low prostrate, somewhat hairy perennial, with *creeping* stems rooting at the nodes. Leaves circular in outline, blunt-toothed, erect on long stalks. Flowers pinkish-green, tiny, borne in small whorls, sometimes one above another, hidden below the leaves. Fruit rounded, 2mm, ridged, almost unstalked. Moist habitats, marshes, bogs, grassy places, stream and pond margins, woodland flushes. Apr-July. T – absent from most of the extreme E Med and many of the islands, except Corsica and Sicily.

1071 *Hydrocotyle bonariensis*. Similar, but the inflorescence consisting of *whorled* branches. Fruit heart-shaped at base, 1.5-3.5mm, stalked. Brackish dune slacks. Apr-June. Naturalised in Portugal, Spain, S France and Italy. (Temperate South America).

1072 *Naufraga balearica* **NAUFRAGA**. Low hairless perennial. Basal leaves crowded. tri-foliate or pinnate, with 5 leaflets; leaflets oval, untoothed or with 1-2 small lobes;

stalk clasping and sheathing at the base; stem leaves usually trifoliate, borne in a single *whorl*. Flowers white, tiny, in small simple umbels; no bracts. Fruit globose, 0.8mm, with narrow ridges. Steep, shaded, crevices in north or north-east facing sea cliffs; restricted to areas inaccessible to goats. Majorca – endemic.

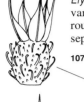

Eryngium **SEA HOLLIES**. Hairless annual or perennial herbs. Leaves simple to variously pinnately-divided, the upper often spiny. Flowers unstalked, in dense rounded or cylindrical, thistle-like heads, surrounded by spiny, showy bracts; sepals rigid; petals small. Fruit egg-shaped to globose, often scaly.

1073 *Eryngium maritimum* **SEA HOLLY**. Short to medium, rather stiff, tufted perennial, sometimes monocarpic. Leaves leathery, *bluish-green*, 3-5-lobed, with an undulate spiny margin, the veins and margins whitish; stalk unwinged. Flowers powder blue, in dense rounded heads, 15-30mm, forming a spreading inflorescence; bracts 4-7 oval, coarsely spiny (often with 3 spines to a bract) and like the upper stem often suffused with metallic blue. Coastal sands and dunes. June-Sept. T. A scarce British native.

1074 *Eryngium aquifolium*. Similar, but bracts lanceolate to linear. with 6 or more pairs of spines (not 1-3 pairs); flower-heads 10-20mm. Dry rocky and sandy habitats. May-July. S Spain and N Africa.

1075 *Eryngium ilicifolium*. Like *E. aquifolium*, but a low annual with *prostrate stems*, branched from the base. Flower-heads 10-15mm, the bracts with 2-3 pairs of spines. Similar habitats and flowering time. S Spain and N Africa.

1076 *Eryngium creticum* **SMALL-HEADED BLUE ERYNGO**. Medium to tall perennial, occasionally annual or biennial, to 1m, with erect violet-blue stems, much-branched above. Leaves very variable in outline from oval to rounded, with a heart-shaped or truncated base, toothed to 3-lobed, long-stalked, leathery, the lower decaying early. Inflorescence violet-blue, spreading, the flowers borne in globose heads, 5-10mm; bracts 5-7, linear-lanceolate, up to 30mm long, with 1-2 pairs of spines near the base. Dry habitats, hillsides, roadsides, cultivated fields, waste places, cliff crevices. May-Nov. Crete and the Balkans eastwards, including Cyprus. This plant often grows in extensive colonies and the stems may break off in the autumn to become 'tumble weeds' which scatter the seeds as they move.

1077 *Eryngium dichotomum*. Similar, but flower-heads larger, 10-15mm; bracts 20-40mm long and sepals 2-3mm long (not 1.5mm). Dry habitats. May-July. Spain, Italy and Sicily.

1078 *Eryngium tricuspidatum*. Like *E. creticum*, but basal leaves soft and persistent and inflorescence *greenish*, not spreading, the flower-heads small, usually 8-10mm. Dry habitats. May-July. SW Spain, Sardinia, Sicily and N Africa.

1079 *Eryngium dilatatum*. Like *E. creticum*, but basal leaves persistent, pinnately-lobed to 3-lobed and usually softly spine-toothed; stalk *winged*. Flower-heads 5-15mm; bracts with 3-6 pairs of spines. Dry habitats. May-July. Spain and Portugal.

1080 *Eryngium amethystinum* [*E. glomeratum*] **BLUE ERYNGO**. Short to medium erect perennial. Basal leaves *pinnately-lobed*, with spine-toothed margins; stalk broadly winged. Inflorescence usually blue, rather narrow, with numerous flower-heads, each 10-20mm; bracts 20-50mm long, linear-lanceolate, with 1-4 pairs of spines. Dry habitats, grassy places, stony pastures, garrigue. July-Oct. Italy and Sicily eastwards, including Crete and Cyprus.

1081 *Eryngium campestre* **FIELD ERYNGO**. Short to medium erect perennial. Basal leaves leathery and usually persistent, oval in outline, 3-lobed, spine-toothed, the stalks unwinged; stem leaves unstalked, clasping the stem. Flowers *pale* greenish-white or greenish-yellow, borne in dense rounded or rather spreading heads, 10-15mm; bracts 6-7, linear-lanceolate, 15-45mm long, with or without one pair of spines. Dry habitats, grassy or stony, coastal, or inland. June-Oct. T – not Cyprus or parts of the extreme E Med.

1082 *Eryngium corniculatum.* Similar, but basal leaves undivided, with a long segmented stalk and flower-heads bluish, with a *bract-like* appendage on the top. Habitats subjected to winter flooding. May-August. SW Spain, Portugal and Sardinia.

1083 *Lagoecia cuminoides* **LAGOECIA**. Slender short annual. Leaves simple-pinnate, the basal with oval, toothed lobes, the upper with more deeply divided and narrower lobes. Umbels white, dense, globose, 5-15mm, with numerous rays; bracts like the leaves; secondary bracts 42-pinnately-lobed, with bristle-like lobes; *sepals* like the bracteoles. Fruit 2mm, with brittle hairs. Cultivated fields, pastures, waste and fallow land, roadsides, hillsides. Mar-May. Scattered localities in Portugal, Spain, Italy and Crete, commoner from Greece eastwards, including Cyprus.

1084 *Echinophora spinosa* **ECHINOPHORA**. More or less hairy, short to medium, rather robust perennial. Leaves 2-3-pinnate, rigid; lobes thick, grooved above, *spine-tipped.* Umbels white, occasionally pink with 4-8 hairy rays; bracts and secondary bracts 5-10, oblong to linear, spiny; each partial umbel consisting of an hermaphrodite flower surrounded by several male ones whose stalks unite together around the fruit. Fruit egg-shaped with indistinct ridges. Coastal sands. June-Oct. Spain and NW Africa eastwards to the Balkans – not Crete.

1085 *Echinophora tenuifolia.* Similar, but a grey-felted plant with fleshy, flat, leaf-lobes and *yellow* flowers; umbels with 2-5 rays. Dry habitats, cultivated and fallow fields, waste ground, vineyards, roadsides. June-Aug. Italy and Sicily eastwards, including Crete and Cyprus.

1086 *Scaligeria cretica* **SCALIGERIA**. Medium, erect perennial, sometimes biennial, with *bright green* stems. Leaves 2-3-pinnate; lobes oval-diamond-shaped, toothed, those of the upper leaves narrower, linear and often untoothed. Inflorescence repeatedly branched, the umbels white, rather lax, with 6-15 slender rays; bracts absent; secondary bracts linear, rather inconspicuous. Fruit egg-shaped with a heart-shaped base, 1.5-2mm, with slender ridges; oil glands 2-3. Dry habitats, scrub, rocks and open pine forest. Apr-June. Crete, Yugoslavia and S Greece eastwards, including Cyprus.

Smyrnium **SMYRNIUM**. Biennial herbs with 2-3-ternate leaves the uppermost often simple and undivided. Umbels yellow, the flowers without sepals. Fruit egg-shaped to subglobose, with slender ridges and numerous scattered oil glands.

1087 *Smyrnium olusatrum* **ALEXANDERS**. Tall, pungent, hairless biennial, to 1.5m; stem stout, becoming hollow when old, the upper branches usually opposite. Leaves deep green and shiny, *all* 1-2-pinnate, with oval or diamond-shaped, toothed lobes, the upper leaves smaller than the lower and less divided, chrome yellow. Flowers yellow, in dense rounded umbels, with 7-15 rays; bracts few. Fruit 7-8mm long, black when ripe. Damp places, roadsides, hedgerows, woodland margins, damp dunes, coastal cliffs, often near the sea. Feb-May. T. The young shoots were formerly eaten as a vegetable in some parts of the W Med.

1088 *Smyrnium perfoliatum* **PERFOLIATE ALEXANDERS**. More or less hairless, tall biennial, to 1.5m; stems angled, narrowly winged on the angles, solid, hairy at the nodes only, the upper branches alternate. Basal leaves 1-2-ternate with oval, toothed lobes; upper leaves simple, oval, *clasping* the stem with heart-shaped bases, bright yellowish-green, toothed. Umbels yellow, rounded, with 5-12 rays; no bracts. Fruit

3-3.5mm long, broader than long, brownish-black. Grassy and rocky places, scrub, open woodland. From Portugal and Spain eastwards to Turkey – not Balearic Is. or Cyprus.

1089 *Smyrnium apiifolium.* Similar, but upper leaves and branches *opposite*, not alternate and rays 15-20; lower stem leaves trifoliate. S Greece, Crete and the Aegean Is.

1090 *Smyrnium orphanidis.* Like *S. apiifolia,* but lobes of basal leaves with a *heart-shaped* (not narrowed) base and lower stem leaves simple, heart-shaped with a short inflated stalk. Greece, Aegean Is. and Turkey.

1091 *Smyrnium rotundifolium.* Like *S. perfoliatum,* but stem ridged, not winged, and upper leaves *untoothed,* occasionally minutely toothed. Moist shaded habitats, open forest, thickets, generally in the mountains. May-June. Sardinia, Italy and Sicily eastwards, including Cyprus.

1092 *Smyrnium connatum.* Like *S. perfoliatum,* but upper stem leaves opposite, *fused* in pairs along their basal margins, vivid yellow-green. Rocky mountainsides. Apr-May. Cyprus, Turkey, Syria and Palestine.

1093 *Bunium ferulaceum* **BALKAN PIGNUT.** Short to medium perennial with a globose tuberous rootstock; stem erect to ascending. Leaves 2-3-pinnate, with *linear,* acute lobes, the basal often withered by flowering time. Umbels white, lax, with 6-15 spreading rays; bracts 1-2, occasionally absent, lanceolate; secondary bracts 3-6, similar but smaller; anthers purplish. Fruit oblong, 4-6mm long, with thick ridges; oil glands solitary. Cultivated, fallow and waste ground, roadsides, sometimes in scrub or open forest. Mar-May. Balkans, including Crete, eastwards.

1094 *Bunium pachypodum [Bulbocastanum incrassatum].* Similar, but *bracts* 6-8 amd leaf-lobes blunter. Iberian Peninsula and Balearic Is.

1095 *Bifora testiculata* **BIFORA.** Short to medium, hairless annual; stems freely branched, ridged or angled. Leaves 1-2-pinnate, oblong in outline, the lobes oblong to linear, flat or with very slightly revolute margins, only the lower leaves stalked. Umbels white, leaf-opposed or terminal, with 1-3, rather irregular rays, each up to 10mm long; bracts solitary or absent; secondary bracts thread-like, usually 2-3. Fruit 2.5-3.5mm long, with 2 rounded *lobes,* rough and with rather obscure ridges, short-beaked. Cultivated and fallow fields, waste ground. Feb-May. T.

1096 *Bifora radians.* Similar, but lobes of upper leaves thread-like and umbels with 3-8 rays, each up to 25mm long; outer petals of marginal flowers much *larger* than the others. Similar habitats. Mar-July. T – but absent from parts of the E Med and most of the islands, except the Balearics and Sicily.

Scandix **SHEPHERD'S NEEDLES.** Slender annual herbs with 2-3-pinnate leaves; lobes rather slender. Umbels few-rayed, occasionally with only one ray. Flowers white, without sepals; petals oblong, often markedly unequal in the outer flowers (radiate). Fruit long and needle-like, with a long cylindrical beak, much longer than the seed-bearing lower portion; ridges prominent and resin canals very slender.

1097 *Scandix pecten-veneris* **SHEPHERD'S NEEDLE.** Very variable, short, almost hairless annual. Leaves 2-3-pinnate, with linear lobes, toothed. Umbels white, opposite the leaves, with 1-3 rays, some petals of the outer flowers usually larger, to 2-3mm long; bracts absent or few; secondary bracts with membranous, untoothed or few-toothed margins, usually hairy. Fruit subcylindrical, 20-80mm long overall, erect, with a *very long* beak; styles short and erect. Cultivated, fallow and waste land, hillslopes, roadsides, sometimes in garrigue. Jan-July. T.

1097a Subsp. *brachycarpa*. Distinguished primarily by its smaller fruits, about 15mm long and *short-beaked*. Italy, Sicily and Greece.

1098 *Scandix stellata [S. pinnatifida]*. Similar, but secondary bracts *pinnate*, with narrow spreading lobes. Usually on rocky hillslopes. Scattered localities throughout, but especially S Spain, the Balkans and the E Med, including Cyprus.

1099 *Scandix australis*. Like *S. pecten-veneris* and equally variable, but secondary bracts usually untoothed, sometimes notched at the apex. Marginal petals scarcely larger than the others, to 1.5mm long. Fruit cylindrical, not compressed, 15-40mm long overall. Rocky and grassy hillsides, open pine forests, often in semi-shaded places. Mar-May. T – not Balearic Is. or Corsica.

1100 *Seseli bocconii* **SESELI**. Short to medium hairless perennial. Leaves 1-3-*trifoliate*, the lobes lanceolate to linear, often 2-3-lobed at the apex. Umbels white, with 4-18 rays, no bracts; secondary bracts small, linear. Fruit oblong, 4-6mm, with prominent ridges and 1-3 resin canals. Rocks and cliffs. Apr-June. Corsica, Sardinia and Sicily.

1101 *Crithmum maritimum* **ROCK SAMPHIRE**. Short to medium, greyish, hairless, branched perennial, often woody at the base. Leaves 1-2-pinnate, with slender, almost cylindrical, *fleshy*, untoothed lobes, the base membranous and sheathing the stem. Flowers yellowish-green, in umbels 30-60mm across, with 8-36 rays; bracts and secondary bracts triangular-lanceolate to linear-lanceolate. Fruit oblong, 5-6mm long, yellowish or purplish, with prominent thick ridges and several resin canals. Coastal rocks, occasionally on sand or shingle. July-Nov. T. A widespread coastal species that is readily identified by its fleshy (succulent) leaves.

1102 *Oenanthe globulosa* **MEDITERRANEAN WATER DROPWORT**. Much-branched medium perennial, the roots with egg-shaped tubers; stems hollow, grooved. Basal leaves 2-pinnate, with oval to linear lobes, the upper leaves often less divided and with narrower lobes. Umbels white, terminal or leaf-opposed, with 3-16 rays which become thickened in fruit; flowers male or hermaphrodite; sepals persistent. Fruit *globose*, 4-5mm, with thickened lateral ridges. Marshes, usually close to the sea. May-July. W Med from Portugal and NW Africa eastwards to Italy and Sicily.

1103 *Oenanthe crocata* **HEMLOCK WATER DROPWORT**. Similar, but *more robust*, to 1.5m, with broader lobes to the basal leaves and terminal umbels with 10-40 rays. Fruit cylindrical, 4-6mm long. Wet habitats, ditches, woodland margins. May-July. Similar distribution – not Balearic Is.

Other species occasionally found in the European Med are *O. aquatica* (1104), **Fine-leaved Water Dropwort**, *O. fistulosa* (1105), **Tubular Water Dropwort**, *O. pimpinelloides* (1106), **Corky-fruited Water Dropwort**, *O. silaifolia* (1107), **Narrow-leaved Water Dropwort** – all are more widespread in C and W Europe, away from the Med coast.

1108 *Foeniculum vulgare [F. officinale, Anethum foeniculum]* **FENNEL**. Tall greyish, hairless, strongly pungent perennial, forming large tufts, to 2.5m; stems tough, shiny, hollow when old. Leaves feathery, 3-4-pinnate, with numerous *thread-like* lobes and sheathing bases. Umbels yellow, flattish, with 12-30 rays, without bracts of any sort. Fruit oblong, 4-10mm long, ridged, sweet-tasting. Roadsides, riverbanks, ditches, cultivated and fallow ground, often coastal. Apr-Sept. T. Widely cultivated as a culinary herb and often naturalised; some forms have attractive bronze or purplish foliage. The form widely grown as a vegetable, var. *azoricum*, **Florence Fennel**, has broad, closely overlapping, leaf-bases.

1108a Subsp. *piperitum [Foeniculum piperitum]*. Similar to the type, but leaf-lobes fleshier and more rigid and umbels with 4-10 rays. Fruit *sharp-tasting*. Dry rocky habitats. T.

1109 *Peucedanum anisum [Anethum graveolens, Anisum vulgare]* **DILL**. A strongly aromatic, greyish, short to medium annual, finely hairy. Leaves 3-4-pinnate with long slender divisions. Umbels yellow, with 15-30 unequal rays; no bracts of any sort. Fruit elliptical, strongly compressed, 5-6mm long, dark brown with pale wings, ridged. Gardens, cultivated and waste ground, occasionally on sand-dunes, frequently naturalised. Apr-July. Probably T. (India and SW Asia). Widely grown as a culinary herb.

1110 *Kundmannia sicula [Brignolia pastinacifolia]* **KUNDMANNIA**. A medium, hairless perennial, with erect stems. Lower leaves usually 2-pinnate, with *an extra* pair of lobes at the base of each primary lobe; lobes oval, toothed; upper leaves 1-pinnate, sharply toothed. Umbels yellow, with 5-30 rays; bracts numerous, linear, reflexed. Fruit almost cylindrical, 6-10mm long, with slender ridges and numerous, irregularly arranged resin canals. Dry hills and fields. May-June. Portugal and NW Africa eastwards to Greece and Crete.

Cachys **CACHYS**. Perennial herbs with 2-4-pinnate leaves, generally with narrow lobes. Umbels yellow, the flowers with or without sepals; petals oval with an incurved apex. Fruit 2-lobed, thick-ridged and with undulate wings and numerous resin canals.

1111 *Cachys ferulaceum*. Medium to tall, slightly rough, bluish-green perennial; stems erect, to 1.8m, solid, lined with opposite or whorled branches. Leaves 2-3-pinnate with linear lobes, margins rough or minutely hairy. Umbels yellow, with 20-30 rays; all bracts linear-lanceolate; secondary bracts linear. Fruit swollen, 10-25mm long, with rounded ridges, toothed or crested. Dry habitats, hillsides, rocks and coastal sands. Apr-June. Italy, Sicily and the Balkans.

1112 *Cachys libanotis*. Similar, but smaller and stouter with *rigid* leaf-lobes that are often slightly toothed; leaves only 2-3-pinnate; main umbels with unlobed or 2-3-lobed bracts; rays 8-15. Pine forests, scrub, dry slopes. Portugal, Spain, Sardinia, Italy and Sicily.

1113 *Cachys sicula*. Like *C. ferulaceum*, but to 1.5m and margins of leaf-lobes smooth. Bracts of terminal umbel 1-2-pinnately-lobed. Fruit 10-15mm. Iberian Peninsula, Sardinia, Italy and Sicily.

1114 *Cachys trifida [C. laevigata]*. Like *C. ferulaceum*, but to 1.2m tall at the most, with few or no bracts. Umbels with 10-20 rays; flowers *without sepals*. Fruit 12-15mm long, with wide, smooth ridges. W Med; Portugal, Spain, S France and Italy.

1115 *Cachys scabra [Ferula scabra]*. Like *C. ferulaceum*, but plant *pleasantly aromatic* when crushed, rough-hairy. Umbels with 2-12 rays. Fruit globose, 5mm. Coastal sands and shingle, field margins. Apr-June. Cyprus, SE Turkey and the E Med.

Bupleurum **HARE'S-EARS, THOROW-WAXES**. Hairless annual or perennial herbs, or shrubs, with simple undivided leaves. Flowers usually green or yellow, borne in small umbels surrounded by a ruff of 'petal-like' bracts; no sepals, but petals present, not notched. Fruit usually oblong or egg-shaped, with prominent ridges and 1-5 resin canals.

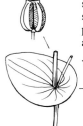

1116 *Bupleurum rotundifolium* **THOROW-WAX**. Short to tall, erect, bluish-green, often purple-tinged annual. Leaves elliptical to almost rounded, the lower short-stalked the upper unstalked and closely *encircling* the stem. Umbels yellow, small, with 5-10 rays; secondary bracts 5-6, oval, yellowish-green, forming a cup around the flower-clusters, becoming whitish in fruit. Fruit oblong, 3-3.5mm, smooth. Dry open habitats, especially arable land and waste places. May-July. Spain and NW

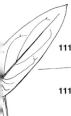

Africa eastwards to Turkey, but absent from most of the islands, except Corsica and Sardinia.

1117 *Bupleurum subovatum [B. intermedium, B. protractum]* FALSE THOROW-WAX. Similar, but leaves usually oval to oblong, greener, and umbels with only 2-3 rays. Fruit egg-shaped, 3-5mm, warted. Similar habitats. Feb-June. T.

1118 *Bupleurum lancifolium.* Like *B. subovatum,* but leaves generally with a *tapered* tip and flowers in clusters of 6-16 (not 15-25) in each partial umbel. Similar habitats. Apr-Aug. T.

1119 *Bupleurum aureum.* Medium to tall, rather slender, branched annual. Leaves *narrow,* linear-lanceolate to linear, the lower distinctly stalked, the upper unstalked, 3-5-veined. Umbels yellowish-green, with 3-6 rays; secondary bracts lanceolate, long-pointed, yellowish-green, semi-translucent, with membranous, finely toothed, margins. Fruit 1.6-2mm long, narrowly ridged. Dry rocky habitats, especially near the sea. Apr-June. Greece and Turkey.

1120 *Bupleurum gracile [B. glumaceum].* Similar, but secondary bracts *not* toothed and fruit smaller, 1.3-1.8mm long. Garrigue, open pine forests. Apr-June. Crete, Aegean Is., Turkey, Cyprus and the Lebanon.

1121 *Bupleurum nodiflorum.* Like *B. gracile,* but all umbels virtually *unstalked* (stalk not more than 5mm long at the most) and petals very pale. Cultivated and fallow fields. Apr-June. Turkey and the E Med, including Cyprus.

1122 *Bupleurum semicompositum [B. glaucum].* Low to short, much-branched, spreading, bluish-green annual. Lower leaves linear to spatula-shaped, stalked, the upper linear, half-clasping the stem with unstalked bases, 3-5-veined. Umbels brownish-yellow, with 3-6, slender, unequal rays; *all bracts* linear-lanceolate, 3-veined, bluish-green. Fruit subglobose, 1.5-2mm, with whitish warts. Dry habitats, especially on sandy soils, pastures and dry salt marshes. Apr-May. T.

1123 *Bupleurum tenuissimum.* Similar, but taller, to 75cm, and leaves 5-7-veined. Umbels with 1-3 rays and very narrow pointed bracts, *minutely toothed* along the margins and veins. Saline habits, mostly coastal, sometimes inland. T – not parts of the E Med, Balearic Is., Crete or Cyprus.

1124 *Bupleurum fontanesii.* Like *B. semicompositum,* but secondary bracts lanceolate, *becoming* whitish and semi-translucent in fruit, 3-9-veined. Dry open habitats. Apr-July. Sardinia and Sicily eastwards to the Balkans and Turkey.

1125 *Bupleurum falcatum [B. exaltatum, B. olympicum, B. parnassicum]* SICKLE-LEAVED HARE'S-EAR. Very variable medium to tall perennial; stems hollow. Basal leaves oblong to elliptical, stalked, 5-7-veined; stem leaves lanceolate to linear, often *sickle-shaped,* unstalked and half-clasping the stem. Umbels yellow, with 3-15 rays; all bracts linear-lanceolate, pointed, 3-5-veined, greenish. Fruit oblong, 3-4mm long, narrowly ridged. Grassy and stony habitats, waste places, field boundaries, hedgebanks. June-Aug. European Med – absent from the islands, except Corsica.

1126 *Bupleurum rigidum.* Similar, but taller, to 1.5m, with leathery leaves, variable in shape, but *all* stalked and clasping the stem with their stalked bases; veins 3-11. Umbels with 2-5 rays and short slender bracts. Fruit 4mm long, with prominent ridges. Dry rocky habitats. Iberian Peninsula, NW Africa, S France, Italy.

1127 *Bupleurum spinosum* SPINY HARE'S-EAR. Short, much-branched, bluish-green perennial, with a stout woody base; upper part of stem and umbel rays dying and persistent, becoming hard and *spiny.* Basal leaves linear, 3-5-veined, the veins conspicuous beneath; upper leaves similar, few. Umbels greenish, with 2-7 rays which become rigid and spinose after fruiting; all bracts small and 1-veined,

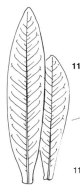

deciduous. Fruit egg-shaped, 3-4.5mm long, prominently ridged. Rocky places and scrub, generally in the mountains. June-Aug. S and E Spain, NW Africa.

1128 *Bupleurum fruticosum* **SHRUBBY HARE'S-EAR.** An aromatic, evergreen *shrub*, to 2.5m tall, with rather erect stems. Leaves leathery, deep bluish-green, shiny, oblong, often broadest above the middle, evenly spaced along the stem. Umbels greenish-yellow or yellow, with 5-25 stout rays; all bracts elliptical or oval, reflexed, 5-7-veined, deciduous. Fruit 7-8mm long, with narrowly winged ribs. Garrigue, scrub and rocky habitats, roadsides. Apr-Sept. Iberian Peninsula eastwards to Greece – not Balearic Is. or Crete. Widely cultivated and sometimes naturalised in the region.

1129 *Bupleurum foliosum.* Similar, but leaves *crowded* near the tops of the woody stems, from which arise annual flowering stems. SW Spain (Gibraltar) and Morocco.

1130 *Bupleurum gibraltaricum.* Like *B. fruticosum,* but leaves narrower, the lateral veins not reaching the margin and the bracts persistent. C and S Spain, including Gibraltar, and NW Africa.

1131 *Apium graveolens* **WILD CELERY.** Medium to tall, yellowish-green, rather stout, hairless biennial, to 1m, with a strong *celery* smell; stem solid, grooved. Leaves shiny, 1-2-pinnate, with diamond-shaped to lanceolate, toothed and lobed segments. Umbels greenish-white, with 4-12 rays, often with a trifoliate leaf immediately below, but no bracts. Fruit egg-shaped, 1.5-2mm long. Damp habitats, river margins, ditches, irrigation channels, brackish soils, mainly coastal, sometimes on saline meadows inland. May-July. T – except parts of the E Med. var. *dulce* (1131a) is edible **Celery** and var. *rapaceum* (1131b) **Celeriac.**

1132 *Apium nodiflorum [Helosciadium nodiflorum]* **FOOL'S WATER-CRESS.** Similar, but with hollow, prostrate or spreading stems, *rooting* at the lower nodes; bracts 0-2. Wet meadows, ditches, riversides. Apr-July. T.

1133 *Apium repens [Helosciadium repens]* **CREEPING MARSHWORT.** Very similar to *A. nodiflorum,* but stems creeping and rooting at *every node*; bracts 3-7. Similar habitats and flowering time. Iberian Peninsula, France and Italy. Hybridises with *A. nodiflorum.*

1134 *Ridolfia segetum* **RIDOLFIA.** Medium to tall, bluish-green, hairless annual, *unpleasant* smelling when crushed. Leaves 4-pinnate, with long, spreading, thread-like lobes; upper leaves reduced to sheathing stalks without a blade, or with a very reduced one. Umbels golden-yellow, with 10-60 slender, curved rays; no bracts at all, or sepals. Fruit oblong, 1.5-2.5mm long, with slender ridges. Cultivated and waste land. Apr-June. T.

1135 *Ammi majus* **FALSE BISHOP'S WEED.** Medium to tall, hairless annual, or occasionally biennial; stems erect, branched. Leaves 1-2-pinnate, with crowded elliptical to oval, toothed lobes. Umbels white, with 15-60 rays; bracts several, often more than half the length of the rays, pinnately-lobed. Fruit oval, 1.5-2mm, pale, with 5 slender ridges. Cultivated, fallow and waste land, roadsides, rocky places. Apr-Sept. T. Dwarf variants occur on some Med islands. An important medicinal plant used in the treatment of asthma and angina.

1136 *Ammi visnaga.* Similar, but much more robust, to 1m, the upper leaves with linear lobes. Umbels with up to 150 rays arising from a thickened disk, spreading at first, but become *erect* in fruit. Similar habitats and flowering time. T. A widespread weed in many parts of the world.

1137 *Ptychotis saxifraga [P. heterophylla]* **PTYCHOTIS.** A medium, hairless biennial, with a basal rosette of leaves in the first year. Rosette and lower leaves pinnate, with 3-9 oval, few-toothed lobes; upper leaves 1-2-pinnately-divided, with pronounced sheathing bases. Umbels whitish, with 6-12 unequal, slender rays; sepals conspicuous; bracts small, linear, soon falling. Fruit oblong, 2-3mm, with slightly winged ridges. Dry habitats, waste and rocky ground, banks. May-July. Spain, S France, Corsica, Sardinia and Italy.

1138 *Ammoides pusilla [Ptychotis ammoides]* **AMMOIDES**. Slender, short to medium annual. Leaves greyish-green, the lower 2-pinnate, with 7-11 pairs of very short lobes, the upper leaves with 2-3 pairs of long thread-like lobes. Umbels whitish, with 5-11 unequal rays; bracts absent or few; secondary bracts 4-6, linear-lanceolate, inflated distally. Fruit oblong, 1mm, with slender ridges. Dry habitats. May-July. Iberian Peninsula eastwards to Greece – not Balearic Is. or Crete.

1139 *Bonannia graeca* **BONANNIA**. Medium annual. Leaves mostly basal, 2-pinnate, with oblong-lanceolate, irregularly toothed lobes; stem leaves with sheathing stalks. Umbels yellow, with 6-20 rays. Bracts variable in number, short and linear. Fruit egg-shaped, 5-6mm long, ridged, with a plum-coloured bloom. Grassy and stony places. May-July. S Italy, Sicily, S Greece and the Aegean Is.

1140 *Krubera peregrina [Capnophyllum peregrinum, Tordylium peregrinum]* **KRUBERA**. A short to medium, hairless annual; stem solitary, grooved. Leaves 3-pinnate, *fumitory-like*, with lanceolate to linear, untoothed or lobed segments. Umbels white, with 2-5 rays; bracts few or none; secondary bracts 4-6, triangular. Fruit egg-shaped, 4-6mm long, with prominent, rough, ridges. Cultivated fields, fallow land. Mar-May. Scattered localities from the S Iberian Peninsula to Sardinia, S Italy, Sicily and N Africa and much of the E Med, including Cyprus.

1141 *Ferula communis* **GIANT FENNEL**. Giant perennial herb to 3m, occasionally more, very robust, rather pungent, with stout, hollow stems. Leaves 3-4-pinnate, with numerous bright green thread-like lobes and prominent sheathing bases; upper leaves becoming progressively reduced to a large sheath with or without a small blade, conspicuous especially just before flowering. Umbels large and rounded, bright yellow-green, the terminal umbel stalkless, surrounded by smaller, stalked, umbels, with 20-40 rays; bracts absent; secondary bracts, few, linear-lanceolate. Fruit elliptical, rather flattened, 12-15mm long, with thin dorsal wings and numerous resin canals. Garrigue, grassy and waste places, rocky ground, roadsides, edges of ditches, occasionally in sandy places or on cliffs. Mar-June. T. The largest and most distinctive umbel in the Med region. The stems become hard and woody on drying and have been used in some places for making furniture. The pith, when dry, burns slowly inside the stem and can be carried alight – it may well have been the original olympic torch.

    1141a Subsp. *glauca*. Distinct on account of the leaves which are bright green above, but bluish-green beneath. Similar distribution.

1142 *Ferula tingitana*. Similar, but less robust, the leaf-lobes shorter, to 10mm long (not up to 50mm), with revolute margins. Rocky habitats, hedges and damp habitats. Apr-June. Portugal, S Spain and NW Africa.

1143 *Ferulago nodosa* **FERULAGO**. Medium, erect, hairy perennial; stem erect, conspicuously swollen at the nodes. Leaves triangular in outline, 2-3-pinnate, with linear lobes. Umbels yellow; all bracts oval-lanceolate, well developed. Fruit oblong, 8-10mm long, with narrow undulate lateral wings as well as narrow dorsal wings. Dry rocky and grassy habitats, scrub. May-July. Sicily, Albania, Greece and Crete.

1144 *Ferulago campestris*. Similar, but a more robust plant, to 2m; stems little swollen at the nodes, angled. Fruit 10-12mm long, with broad lateral wings. S France, Italy, Sicily, Yugoslavia and Albania.

1145 *Ferulago lutea [Ferula sulcata]*. Like *F. campestris*, but with short (not long) leaf-lobes. Spain and Portugal.

1146 *Opopanax chironium* **OPOPANAX**. Robust, tall perennial, to 2m; stem stout and solid, with sub-opposite or whorled branches, often very close below the terminal umbel. Leaves large, 2-pinnate, with oval lobes, up to 12cm long, with a heart-shaped or wedge-shaped base, stellate-hairy beneath; upper leaves simple, some-times reduced to an inflated leaf-stalk. Umbels large, greenish-yellow, with 9-25 rays; bracts few, bristle-like. Fruit elliptical, 6-7mm long, with a narrow thick-ened, whitish border. Rocky and damp habitats. Apr-July. Spain eastwards to the Balkans – not Balearic Is. or Corsica. Often rather rare and local.

1147 *Opopanax hispidus [Ferula hispida, Pastinaca opopanax]*. Similar, but even more robust, to 3m, with oval-lanceolate leaf-lobes. Umbels with 6-13 rays. Fruit 7-9mm, with a wide but thin border. Rocky ground, olive groves and vineyards. May-June. Italy and Sicily eastwards, including N Africa, Crete and Cyprus.

1148 *Heracleum sphondylium* **HOGWEED**. Very variable, rather robust, medium to tall, rather *bristly* biennial or short-lived perennial, to 2.5m, though often less; stem hollow, ridged. Leaves large, pinnate, with often 5 toothed and lobed segments; upper leaves reduced, with large inflated bases which enfold the developing in-florescence. Umbels large and rather flat, up to 15cm across, white, occasionally pink, with 15-45 rays; petals of outer flowers very unequal, markedly radiate, notched. Fruit elliptical to rounded, 7-10mm long, flattened and broadly winged. Open woodland, grassy places, banks, roadsides, river margins. Apr-July. Scat-tered localities in the European Med and Turkey, but generally rather rare in the Med region as a whole. A common plant in C and N Europe.

    1148a Subsp. *verticillatum [Heracleum verticillatum]*. Similar, but leaves softly hairy, especially along the veins; upper branches *whorled*. Balkan Peninsula.

Tordylium **TORDYLIUM**. Annual or biennial herbs with pinnately-lobed leaves. Flowers with obvious, but often unequal sepals; petals often unequal, the outer larger, sometimes markedly so, notched or 2-lobed. Fruit rounded to elliptical, flattened, with a thickened, beaded or lobed margin.

1149 *Tordylium apulum* **TORDYLIUM**. Short to medium, fairly stout, somewhat hairy annual; stems erect, hairier at the base, ridged and branched. Leaves pinnate, with oval, toothed lobes; upper leaves with linear, untoothed lobes. Umbels white, with 3-8 rays; bracts present, not more than 10mm long; outer flowers with one large, equally 2-lobed petal (appearing to be two large petals), 5-9mm long, and 4 smaller petals, 4-6mm long. Fruit 5-8mm, with a thick, pale, beaded margin. Cul-tivated, fallow and waste ground, roadsides, seashores, occasionally in rocky places. Mar-June. T. Common – often seen together with with the following species.

1150 *Tordylium officinale*. Similar, but stems more densely hairy, umbels with 8-14 rays and outer flowers with *two* enlarged, unequally 2-lobed petals. Fruit 2-3mm long, with short swollen hairs along the margin. Similar habitats and flowering time. Italy, the Balkans, including Crete, and Turkey.

1151 *Tordylium pestalozzae*. Like *T. officinale,* but a shorter plant, not more than 15cm tall. Fruit 3.5-5mm long, with soft flexuous *hairs*. Greece (Cyclades and Karpathos), Crete, S and W Turkey.

1152 *Tordylium maxima*. Like *T. officinale,* but plant up to 1.3m and fruit larger, 5-8mm long, bristly. Flowers white or occasionally purplish, the largest petals 2-4mm long. Similar habitats. Apr-July. T – not Balearic Is. and rarer in the E Med. Com-mon in the rest of the Med region.

1153 *Tordylium syriacum.* Like *T. apulum*, but secondary bracts long and conspicuous, to 20mm long. Largest petals to only 2.5mm long. Cultivated and fallow land, occasionally in maquis and dry hills. Feb-Apr. Cyprus and the E Med.

1154 *Tordylium aegyptiacum.* Like *T. apulum*, but segments of upper leaves pinnately-lobed. Umbels with the central flower-cluster (partial umbel) sterile and forming a conspicuous dense *violet* 'eye'; largest petals 4-5mm long. Similar habitats. Feb-Apr. Cyprus and the E Med.

1155 *Ainsworthia trachycarpa [A. cordata, Tordylium trachycarpa]* **AINSWORTHIA.** An erect, rather slender, short to medium, somewhat hairy annual. Basal leaves simple, heart-shaped, long-stalked; stem leaves pinnate with 3-5 oval to heart-shaped leaflets, toothed or irregularly lobed. Umbels white, with 10-25 unequal rays; bracts 12-18, thread-like, to 18mm long; petals of outer flowers markedly uneven, the largest 2-lobed, to 6mm long. Fruit rounded to oblong, 3-4mm long, the dorsal surface with a pale thickened wing. Cultivated, waste and fallow ground, pastures, roadsides, grassy hillslopes. Feb-May. Turkey, Cyprus and the E Med.

1156 *Elaeoselinum asclepium* **ELAEOSELINUM.** Tall, practically hairless perennial, to 1.3m; stock with coarse fibres. Basal leaves 3-5-pinnate, with numerous thread-like segments, often whorled; stem leaves reduced to inflated sheaths (petioles). Umbels yellow, with 8-25 rays, the petals equal, oblong, slightly notched. Fruit rounded to oblong, 8-15mm, ridged, with wide shiny-white lateral wings, extending beyond the top of the fruit. Dry, sunny, rocky hillslopes and open scrub. May-July. Spain eastwards to Greece – not France, Corsica or Yugoslavia.

1157 *Thapsia garganica [T. decussata]* **THAPSIA.** A medium to tall, somewhat bristly perennial, to 2.5m; stock with stiff fibres, the stem solid, grooved. Leaves 2-3-pinnate, green above, *blue-green* beneath, with narrow-oblong segments, often lobed, untoothed or with 1-2 small teeth; upper leaves reduced to inflated sheaths without a blade or with a very reduced one. Umbels large, yellow, with 5-25 rays; no bracts. Fruit oblong to elliptical, 12-25mm, with wide lateral wings, notched at both ends. Dry rocky hillslopes and open scrub. May-June. From Portugal and NW Africa eastwards to Greece, including Crete.

1158 *Thapsia maxima.* Similar, but leaves pinnate, with oblong or oval, toothed or shallowly lobed segments. Fruit 7-10mm long. C and S Spain and Portugal.

1159 *Thapsia villosa.* Like *T. garganica*, but to only 2m, the leaf-segments oblong, regularly toothed. Umbels occasionally with a few bracts. Fruit 8-15mm long. Similar habitats and flowering time. Iberian Peninsula, S France and NW Africa.

1160 *Rouya polygama [Thapsia polygama]* **ROUYA.** An almost hairless, short perennial; stem lined. Leaves 2-pinnate, with small oval to lanceolate lobes, often toothed, pointed. Umbels white, with 10-20 rays; bracts present, *lobed*, with a hairy margin; secondary bracts linear-lanceolate. Fruit oblong-elliptical, 7-8mm long, with narrow, undulate wings. Coastal sands. May-July. Corsica, Sardinia and N Africa.

Torilis **HEDGE-PARSLEYS.** Annual or biennial herbs with 1-3-pinnate leaves; segments jagged-toothed. Umbels often rather lax; flowers usually with inconspicuous sepals and white or pinkish petals which have a pointed and incurved tip. Fruit linear or egg-shaped, grooved, with straight or hooked spines or tubercles.

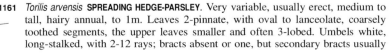

1161 *Torilis arvensis* **SPREADING HEDGE-PARSLEY.** Very variable, usually erect, medium to tall, hairy annual, to 1m. Leaves 2-pinnate, with oval to lanceolate, coarsely toothed segments, the upper leaves smaller and often 3-lobed. Umbels white, long-stalked, with 2-12 rays; bracts absent or one, but secondary bracts usually numerous, small. Fruit egg-shaped, with straight spines. Cultivated, fallow and waste land, roadsides. May-Sept. T – and in many parts of Europe and W Asia.

1161a Subsp. *elongata [Caucalis elongata]*. Distinguished by its little-branched stems and generally 2-rayed umbels; flowers often tinged with violet or purple. Restricted to the Med region.

1161b Subsp. *neglecta [Torilis radiata]*. Distinguished by the flowers which have distinctly *unequal* petals (radiate) and flowers with greyish bristles. T.

1162 *Torilis tenella [Caucalis tenella]*. Similar, but not more than 50cm tall, with leaf-segments *very narrow*, less than 1mm wide (not more than) and petals inconspicuous. Similar habitats. Feb-June. SE Greece eastwards, including Cyprus.

1163 *Torilis leptophylla [Caucalis leptophylla]*. Like *T. arvensis*, but umbels all leaf-opposed, with only 2-3 rays, the flowers white or pink-tinged. Fruit with barbed spines. Similar habitats. Feb-June. T.

1164 *Torilis purpurea [Caucalis purpurea]*. Like *T. arvensis*, but umbels 2-3-rayed and flowers pink or purple and fruits with *hooked* spines. Dry habitats, rocky places, hillslopes, often semi-shaded. Apr-July. Italy and Sicily eastwards, including Crete and Cyprus.

1165 *Torilis nodosa* **KNOTTED HEDGE-PARSLEY**. Low to short, *usually prostrate*, rough-hairy annual. Leaves 1-2-pinnate, with deeply toothed segments. Flowers pinkish-white, in stalkless or short-stalked, leaf-opposed umbels, with 2-3 *very short* rays, giving the flowers a clustered appearance. Fruit egg-shaped, 2-3mm long, with warts and straight bristles. Cultivated, fallow and waste ground, fields, roadsides, sometimes in open maquis or woodland. Mar-Sept. T.

1166 *Orlaya grandiflora [Caucalis grandiflora]* **ORLAYA**. A short to medium, erect annual; stem simple or branched, somewhat hairy at the base. Leaves 2-3-pinnate, with oval, toothed segments. Umbels white, with 5-12 rays, the flowers *markedly* radiate, some of the outer petals up to eight times longer than the others, bilobed; Bracts 2-3, long. Fruit egg-shaped, 7-8mm long, ridged, with rows of hooked spines. Dry grassy habitats, maquis, vineyards and olive groves, fallow fields. Mar-May. Spain eastwards to Turkey – absent from the islands. One of the most striking and distinctive Med umbels.

1167 *Orlaya daucoides [O. kochii, O. platycarpos]*. Similar, but umbels with only 2-4 rays, flowers less markedly radiate (the largest petals not more than three times longer than the others) and fruit larger, 10-15mm long. Similar habitats and flowering time. T – not Balearic Is.

Daucus **CARROTS**. Annual or biennial herbs with 2-3-pinnate leaves. Umbels with pinnately-lobed bracts usually; petals often unequal, some of the outer larger (radiate). Fruit elliptical to egg-shaped with slender ridges, spiny.

1168 *Daucus carota* **WILD CARROT**. Very variable, short to tall, hairy or hairless annual or biennial; stem solid, usually ridged. Leaves feathery, with linear or lanceolate segments, long-stalked; uppermost leaves often bract-like. Umbels white, many-rayed, usually with one or several flowers in the centre of the middle partial umbel, purple, occasionally the whole umbel purplish; *bracts* pinnately-lobed. Fruit oblong, 2-4mm long, shortly spiny; rays becoming *incurved* and bunched in fruit. Rough grassy habitats, roadsides, hillslopes, sandy and stony pastures, cultivated ground, seashores. Apr-Sept. T. The taproot is typically thin and white. Coastal forms of *D. carota*, which are hairless and with small terminal umbels, only 3-5cm across, are often distinguished as subsp. *maritimus* (1168b).

1168a Subsp. *sativus*, **CARROT**, is widely cultivated for its thick orange or red roots and sometimes becomes naturalised in the region.

1168c **Subsp.** *drepanensis.* Like the type, but leaves *fleshy* and shiny. A small plant seldom exceeding 30cm tall. T – except some of the islands.

1169 *Daucus muricatus.* Medium, hairy annual, branched above. Leaves 3-pinnate, with linear-lanceolate segments. Umbels white, with numerous, markedly *unequal* rays, which become contracted and incurved in fruit; flowers strongly radiate with some of the outer petals longer than the others; bracts pinnately-lobed, deflexed. Fruit oblong, 5-10mm, with silvery-white rows of long spines which are joined together near the base. Dry open habitats, grassy places, hillsides, roadsides, garrigue, especially close to the sea. May-Sept. Portugal and NW Africa eastwards to Italy and Sicily – not Balearic Is.

1170 *Daucus aureus.* Similar, but petals becoming *yellowish.* Fruit 4-6mm long. Cultivated and waste ground. May-July. S Spain, N Africa, Italy, Sicily, Cyprus and Palestine.

1171 *Daucus guttatus [D. bicolor, D. setulosus].* Like *D. muricatus,* but leaves 2-pinnate and bracts *not* deflexed. Middle flowers of umbel sterile, dark blackish-crimson. Fruit 2-4mm long. Dry habitats, especially close to the sea, sand-dunes. May-Sept. S Italy eastwards, including Crete and Cyprus, often very local.

1172 *Daucus involucratus.* Like *D. guttatus,* but a slender plant *not more* than 20cm tall, the umbels with only 3-4 rays. Petals tiny, white, often tipped with pink or red. Dry rocky hillslopes, garrigue and open pine forests, dry coastal pastures. Apr-July. Crete, Greece, Aegean Is., Turkey and Cyprus.

1173 *Artedia squamata* **ARTEDIA.** Slender, hairless, short to medium annual. Leaves 3-pinnate, with thread-like segments. Umbels white, with a central tuft of *violet bristles,* with numerous rays, the petals markedly radiate, some of those of the outer flowers much larger than the others, oval; bracts finely dissected, becoming strongly reflexed in fruit, reminiscent of those of *Nigella damascena.* Fruit egg-shaped, 10-12mm long, with papery lobed wings. Cultivated fields, waste and fallow ground, garrigue, dry hills, roadsides. Apr-July. European Turkey eastwards, including Cyprus.

1174 *Pseudorlaya pumila [Daucus pumilus, Orlaya maritima, Pseudorlaya maritima]* **PSEUDO-RLAYA.** Low to short, *densely hairy* annual, branched from the base. Leaves 2-3-pinnate with oval segments. Umbels white or purplish, with 2-5 rays, unequal; petals subequal, some of those of the outer flowers in the umbel slightly larger; bracts 2-5, linear. Fruit elliptical, 7-10mm long, ridged, with hooked spines. Coastal sands and dunes. Feb-May. T.

1175 *Pseudorlaya minuscula.* Similar, but flowers usually white and fruit *smaller,* 5-6mm long. Similar habitats and flowering time. Portugal, W Spain and Sardinia.

HEATH FAMILY Ericaceae

Evergreen trees, shrubs or undershrubs with alternate, opposite or whorled leaves, often untoothed. Flowers in racemes, often spike-like, panicles, clusters or occasionally solitary; sepals 4-5, petals 4-5, joined; stamens twice as many as petal lobes; anthers opening by pores, not slits. Fruit a many-seeded dry capsule or a berry.

1176 *Arbutus unedo* **STRAWBERRY TREE.** An evergreen shrub or small tree, to 12m, often less; bark dull brown, fissured, peeling in small flakes. Leaves oblong-lanceolate, short-stalked, toothed, sometimes obscurely so, hairless except for the base. Flowers white, often tinged with pink or green, bell-shaped with recurved lobes, 8-9mm long, borne in *drooping panicles,* honey-scented. Fruit a globose berry,

15-20mm, covered in conical swellings, ripening through yellow to scarlet and deep crimson. Maquis, evergreen scrub, woodland margins, rocky slopes, generally on acid soils. Oct-Mar. T – but rare in parts the E Med and N Africa, but widely cultivated. The fruits are edible but rather sour: an alcoholic drink is sometimes made from them. The leaves and bark are used medicinally and the hard wood makes a fine-grade charcoal.

1177 *Arbutus andrachne* **EASTERN STRAWBERRY TREE**. Similar, but generally a small tree with beautiful *orange-red* bark which peels in long papery strips; twigs hairless, not bristly. Flowers borne in erect panicles. Fruit 8-12mm diam., with a netted surface. Similar habitats. Feb-Apr. Crete and Albania eastwards.

Erica **HEATHERS**. Dwarf to large evergreen shrubs with tiny whorled leaves with revolute margins. Flowers bell-shaped to almost globular, borne in spikes or panicles, the corolla persistent in fruit, generally 4-lobed. Fruit a dry capsule. Most of the European species are grown in gardens.

1178 *Erica arborea* **TREE HEATH**. Shrub or small tree, 1-4m tall; young twigs densely hairy. Leaves in 4s, 3-5mm long, dark green and hairless. Flowers *white*, broadly bell-shaped, 2.5-4mm long, with erect lobes, borne in large terminal panicles. Maquis, evergreen woods and scrub, streamsides, embankments. May-June. T – not Cyprus or the extreme E Med. Widely grown in gardens, sometimes as a hedge or screen. An important plant for honey-bees.

1179 *Erica lusitanica* **PORTUGUESE HEATH**. Similar, but leaves paler green, 5-7mm long. Flowers larger, 4-5mm long, white tinged with pink, especially in bud. Damp heaths and woodland margins. Mar-May. Spain and Portugal.

1180 *Erica terminalis* **CORSICAN HEATH**. Bushy shrub, 1-2.5m tall, with suberect branches; young twigs minutely hairy. Leaves in 4s, 3-5.5mm long, broadly linear, spreading. Flowers bright pink, bell-shaped, with recurved lobes, 5-7mm long, borne in terminal umbels of 3-8; anthers not protruding. Maquis, woodland ravines, river banks and other damp habitats. May-Sept. W Med – Spain, Corsica, Sardinia and Italy.

1181 *Erica australis* **SPANISH HEATH**. Like *E. terminalis*, but to 2m, rather slender, with larger flowers, 6-9mm long, deep reddish-pink, tubular-bell-shaped. Heaths, scrub and open woodland. C and W Spain and Portugal.

1182 *Erica umbellata*. Like *E. australis*, but smaller, seldom more than 80cm tall, the flowers 3.5-5.5mm long; anthers without basal appendages. Similar habitats and flowering time. Portugal, W and SW Spain.

1183 *Erica sicula*. Like *E. terminalis*, but flowers pale to bright pink, *5-lobed*. Rocky garrigue, often in limestone crevices. Mar-Aug. Sicily, S Turkey, Cyprus, Lebanon and Libya.

1184 *Erica cinerea* **BELL HEATHER**. Dwarf shrub to 15cm with leaves in 3s, linear. Flowers bright reddish-purple, 4-7mm long, in terminal racemes or umbels. Heaths, rocky ground, woods and dry moorland, generally in the mountains. June-Sept. Spain, Portugal, France and Italy.

1185 *Erica manipuliflora* [*E. verticillata*]. Spreading to erect shrub to 1m tall; young stems glabrous or minutely hairy. Leaves in 3-4s, 4-8mm long, erect to somewhat spreading. Flowers pale pink, broadly bell-shaped, 3-3.5mm long, with erect lobes, borne in long leafy racemes, fragrant; *anthers protruding*. Evergreen scrub and dry rocky places, on calcareous rocks. Aug-Dec. Italy and Sicily eastwards – not Crete.

1186 *Erica multiflora.* Like *E. manipuliflora,* but a more erect and rigid bush, to 80cm. Leaves in 4-5s, 6-11mm long, narrow-bell-shaped, 5-7mm long. Rocky hillslopes, dry woods and thickets. Nov-Mar. Iberian Peninsula and NW Africa eastwards to Italy and Sicily.

1187 *Erica scoparia* **BESOM HEATH.** Slender erect shrub, 1-2.5m; young twigs hairless. Leaves in 3-4s, linear, 4-7mm long, erect or somewhat spreading. Flowers *green*, variously tinged with red, broadly bell-shaped with erect lobes, 2.5-3mm long, borne in narrow interrupted terminal racemes. Woods and heaths. Apr-June. Iberian Peninsula and NW Africa eastwards to Italy – not Sicily.

PRIMROSE FAMILY Primulaceae

Herbs, usually with simple leaves, often in basal rosettes. Flowers regular, usually 5-parted, the petals sometimes joined to form a tube; stamens opposite the petal-lobes; ovary with a single compartment (loculus) and a solitary style. Fruit a small capsule.

1188 *Primula palinuri.* Low to short plant with basal leaf-rosettes. Leaves oblong, often broadest above the middle, fleshy, sticky and somewhat fragrant, minutely hairy beneath, with a slightly thickened margin. Flowers deep yellow with a *mealy-white* ring (of farina) in the throat, 12-15mm, borne in one-sided clusters on long leafless stems; bracts farinose. Rock crevices in coastal cliffs. Mar-Apr. SW Italy – near Naples, endemic.

1189 *Androsace maxima* **ANNUAL ANDROSACE.** Low hairy annual. Leaves in a lax basal rosette, green, oblong or rounded, toothed, scarcely stalked. Flowers white or occasionally pink, small, 2-3mm, but surrounded by *large* green sepals, borne in a long-stalked umbel; corolla rather insignificant, 5-lobed. Dry open habitats, fields, waste and fallow land, hillslopes. Feb-May. Scattered localities T – not Portugal or most of the islands, but present on Cyprus.

1190 *Asterolinon linum-stellatum [Lysimachia linum-stellatum]* **ASTEROLINON.** A low, hairless annual, slender, erect or spreading; stems sharply 4-angled. Leaves *opposite*, lanceolate, pointed, stalkless and untoothed. Flowers tiny, white or pinkish, 0.5-2mm, with 5 rounded lobes, solitary in the leaf-axils. Dry open habitats, gravelly and rocky ground, dried river beds, cultivated and fallow fields, sometimes on cliff-tops. Mar-May. T.

1191 *Lysimachia atropurpurea* **PURPLE LOOSESTRIFE.** Short to medium, finely hairy, rhizomatous perennial; stems erect, few-branched. Leaves linear-lanceolate to spatula-shaped, alternate, the lower short-stalked; margin irregularly toothed and somewhat undulate. Flowers dark purple, 6-7mm, in long terminal spikes; *style* becoming stiff and spine-like. Waste ground and damp sandy habitats. May-July. Balkans and Turkey.

1192 *Lysimachia dubia.* Similar, but annual or biennial, the flowers pink; style not spine-like. Damp habitats, especially ditches. Balkans and Turkey.

1193 *Lysimachia serpyllifolia.* Low subshrub, spreading to ascending. Leaves opposite, oval, small, 3-8mm long, untoothed, scarcely stalked. Flowers yellow, *pimpernel-like*, 8-10mm, long-stalked, solitary at the leaf-axils. Open scrub and rocky places, generally in the mountains. Mar-May. C and S Greece and Crete.

1194 *Glaux maritima* **SEA MILKWORT.** Low, more or less *prostrate*, rather fleshy, hairless perennial, rooting at some of the nodes. Leaves elliptical, mostly opposite, except the uppermost, untoothed and unstalked. Flowers pale pink, purplish or white, 3-6mm, without petals, solitary at the base of the leaves. Fruit a 5-valved capsule.

Coastal habitats, sandy places, rock crevices, salt marshes, stabilised shingle, occasionally inland on saline soils. Mar-Sept. Iberian Peninsula and France – local. Often confused with members of the Caryophyllaceae but flowers with a solitary style and only 5 stamens.

1195 *Samolus valerandi* **BROOKWEED**. Low to short, creeping perennial; stems branched or unbranched, erect. Leaves oval to spoon-shaped, pale green, in a *basal* rosette and alternate up the stem. Flowers white, cup-shaped, 2-3mm, borne in lax racemes; petals joined to half way. Wet, generally saline or calcareous, habitats, wet grassland, stream margins, ditches. Apr-July. T.

1196 *Coris monspeliensis* **CORIS**. Short perennial, occasionally a biennial, with erect to ascending stems. Leaves numerous, alternate, lanceolate, unstalked, margin sub-revolute to spine-toothed, often with two rows of *black dots* on each side of the midrib. Flowers pink, purple or blue, 9-12mm, borne in dense racemes; calyx membranous, tinged with purple; corolla irregular (zygomorphic) with a short tube and 5 unequal notched lobes. Dry habitats, rocky and sandy, especially along the coast. Apr-July. Spain and NW Africa eastwards to Albania.

1197 *Coris hispanica*. Similar, but leaf-margin always distinctly revolute and flowers white or pale pink; outer calyx teeth 0-4 (not 6-21). Coastal rocks and clay soils. SE Spain – Almeria.

Anagallis **PIMPERNELS**. Hairless herbs with alternate or opposite leaves. Flowers 5-parted, solitary in the leaf-axils; sepals narrow and pointed; petals fused close to the base. Fruit a capsule, splitting equatorially with the top half falling away as a small cap.

1198 *Anagallis arvensis [A. parviflora, A. phoenicea, A. platyphylla]* **SCARLET PIMPERNEL**. A low annual or biennial, with prostrate or ascending, 4-angled stems. Leaves oval to lanceolate, opposite, occasionally whorled, *gland-dotted*, unstalked. Flowers blue, red, sometimes pink or whitish, 4-7mm, long-stalked, the stalks becoming recurved in fruit; petals with a hairy margin, occasionally slightly toothed at the apex. Cultivated, fallow and waste ground, hillslopes, roadsides, pathways, coastal sands. Apr-Oct. T. A widespread and familiar plant in many parts of Europe and western Asia.

1199 *Anagallis foemina [A. arvensis* subsp. *foemina, A. caerulea]*. Similar, but upper leaves narrower, lanceolate, and flowers blue with narrower petals *without* hairy margins; petals concealed by sepals in bud. Similar habitats, especially on arable land. Apr-Sept. T.

1200 *Anagallis crassifolia*. Similar, but a perennial *rooting* at the nodes, with alternate or sub-opposite leaves. Flowers white or cream, 3-6mm. Wet habitats. Iberian Peninsula, France and Sardinia.

1201 *Anagallis minima* **CHAFFWEED** *[Centunculus minimus]*. A tiny erect annual, seldom more than 4cm tall. Leaves oval, alternate. Flowers white or pink, more or less unstalked, 1-2mm, the petals much shorter than the sepals. Damp open habitats, especially on sandy soils, including dune slacks. Apr-Aug. T – not Balearic Is., Crete or Sicily.

1202 *Anagallis monelli [A. collina, A. linifolia]* **SHRUBBY PIMPERNEL**. Low to short perennial, with erect or spreading stems, sometimes prostrate and mat-forming; stems round, freely branched. Leaves opposite or whorled, linear-lanceolate to elliptical, unstalked, often with small lateral leafy shoots. Flowers blue, red or pink, rarely white, 5-12mm; stamens with a *tuft* of basal blue or yellowish hairs. Dry open habitats, banks and stabilised sand-dunes. Mar-June. Iberian Peninsula,

Sardinia, Sicily and N Africa. Sometimes grown in gardens. The narrow-leaved forms are sometimes distinguished as subsp. *linifolia* (1202a), but these intergrade with the wider-leaved forms.

Cyclamen **SOWBREADS**. Small tuberous perennials with basal heart- or kidney-shaped, long-stalked, leaves. Flowers 5-parted, scapose, the corolla with a short tube and reflexed, somewhat twisted, lobes, sometimes with auricles (ear-like appendages) where the lobes are reflexed. Fruit a capsule, fleshy at first, dehiscing by 5 or more teeth, the stalk (pedicel) usually coiling spirally as the fruits develop; seeds sugary-coated, often carried away by ants and other insects.

1203 *Cyclamen hederifolium* **IVY-LEAVED SOWBREAD**. Low perennial. Leaves heart-shaped, usually with short-angled lobes, *ivy-like*, sometimes unlobed, toothed, variously variegated and mottled with grey or cream, sometimes plain, purplish beneath. Flowers pink with a purple-magenta V-shaped blotch at the base of each lobe, 14-22mm long, auricled, fragrant or not, appearing before or with the young leaves. Fruit with stalk coiled from the top downwards. Maquis, garrigue, open scrub or woodland, vineyards, olive groves, usually in semi-shaded habitats. Aug-Oct. S France eastwards to W Turkey – not Crete or Cyprus. Widely grown in gardens.

1204 *Cyclamen africanum*. Very similar, but leaves and flowers generally arising *erect* from the tuber, not elbowed in the lower half; flowers larger, 18-35mm long. Scrub and rocky gullies, sun or semi-shade. Sept-Nov. N Africa – Algeria and Tunisia, possibly Sicily.

1205 *Cyclamen graecum* **GREEK SOWBREAD**. Low perennial. Leaves rounded-heart-shaped, not lobed or angled, with a thickened, rather beaded, finely toothed margin, plain green or variegated with grey, silver or cream, often with a rather satiny surface. Flowers pale pink to cerise, with 3 fine magenta streaks at the base of each lobe, the outer streaks V-shaped, the central one unbranched, 15-26mm long, auricled, the petal-lobes prominently twisted; flowers generally appearing before the leaves. Fruit with stalk coiling from the *centre* in both directions. Rocky slopes, often on red soils (*terra-rosa*), rock fissures, olive groves and scrub, usually in sunny exposed places. Sept-Nov. S Greece, Crete, Aegean Is., W and S Turkey and N Cyprus.

1206 *Cyclamen cyprium* **CYPRIOT SOWBREAD**. Low perennial. Leaves heart-shaped, the margin generally somewhat angled, sometimes markedly so, variously variegated with grey, white or silver, sometimes as a heart-shaped pattern or as flecks over the entire surface. Flowers sweetly scented, white or very pale pink, with a small M-shaped magenta blotch towards the base of each lobe, auricled, 14-21mm long; petal-lobes rather *narrow* and twisted. Fruit with stalk coiling from the top. Shaded limestone rocks, generally beneath trees and shrubs, sometimes in vineyards or on screes. Sept-early Jan. W and N Cyprus – endemic.

1207 *Cyclamen repandum* **SPRING SOWBREAD**. A low perennial. Leaves heart-shaped, coarsely toothed, sometimes somewhat angled, deep green with a heart-shaped pattern in grey or silver, sometimes plain, green or purplish beneath. Flowers sweetly scented, *deep* carmine-magenta, unmarked, not auricled, 17-24mm long, the lobes rather narrow and twisted; flowers appearing with the developed leaves. Fruit with stalk coiling from the top. Deciduous and pine woodland, or occasionally maquis, in shaded or semi-shaded situations, often in rock crevices or among tree roots. Mar-May. S France eastwards to Albania, including Corsica, Sardinia, and Corfu, but not S Italy.

    1207a Subsp. *peloponnesiacum*. Similar, but leaves *speckled* with grey, white or silver, rarely with a well-marked heart-shaped pattern and flowers pale to mid-pink, with a darker zone around the mouth (var. *peloponnesiacum*, 1207b) or a uniform deep magenta-purple (var. *vividum*, **1207c**), 20-31mm long. S Greece – Peloponnese, endemic.

    1207d Subsp. *rhodense [Cyclamen rhodense].* Like subsp. *peloponnesiacum*, but flowers white or very pale pink with a rose-pink zone around the mouth, 20-24mm long. Rhodes – endemic.

1208 *Cyclamen creticum* **CRETAN SOWBREAD**. Similar, but leaves often greyer, variously marbled with grey or silver and flowers pure white, rarely very pale pink, 15-26mm long. Shrubby maquis, rock fissures, banks along streams and gullies, occasionally on old walls, lowland and in the mountains. Mar-May. Crete and Karpathos – endemic.

1209 *Cyclamen balearicum* **BALEARIC SOWBREAD**. Like *C. creticum*, but leaves often duller, sometimes with the margins turned downwards and flowers *smaller*, 9-16mm long, white or greyish, often with pinkish or greyish translucent veins. Similar habitats and flowering time. Balearic Is. and S France.

1210 *Cyclamen persicum* **PERSIAN SOWBREAD, FLORIST'S CYCLAMEN**. Low to short perennial. Leaves heart-shaped, the margin finely toothed but not angled, plain green above or with a regular pattern in grey, pale green, cream or silver, green or purplish beneath. Flowers scented, white, sometimes with a deep pink zone around the mouth, or all pink, mauve, or occasionally red, 20-37mm long, not auricled, the lobes often narrow and markedly twisted, sometimes short and rather broad; flowers appearing with the mature leaves. Fruit with stalk arching but *not coiling*. Maquis, garrigue, or open scrub, sometimes on more open rocky hillsides. Late Dec-May. Scattered localities in S Greece, the Aegean Is., S Turkey, Rhodes, W and S Cyprus, the E Med, Algeria and Tunisia. The florist cyclamen has been developed over many years from this species; polyploid forms in cultivation have larger leaves and flowers with less twisted petals, often unscented and altogether more coarse – they are widely grown as pot plants in many parts of the world.

1211 *Cyclamen rohlfsianum* **LIBYAN SOWBREAD**. Low perennial. Leaves kidney-shaped, broader than long, lobed and toothed, with a silver or greyish band above, purplish-red beneath. Flowers pink with a deep purplish-magenta zone around the mouth, auricled, 11-26mm long, with *protruding* stamens; flowers appearing before or with the young leaves. Fruit with stalk coiling from the base upwards. Rocky and shrubby maquis, especially in limestone rock crevices. Sept-Nov. N Libya – endemic.

THRIFT FAMILY Plumbaginaceae

Perennial with alternate or basal leaves, untoothed. Flowers in lax cymes or tight heads, 5-parted; calyx lobes often persisting in fruit, usually papery; petals fused together in the lower part into a narrow tube. Fruit a capsule or dry and single-seeded with a papery wall.

1212 *Plumbago europaea* **EUROPEAN PLUMBAGO**. Medium to tall, erect, much-branched perennial. Leaves alternate, oval to oblong, somewhat undulate, the upper un-stalked and clasping the stem with a heart-shaped base. Flowers violet or lilac-pink, 7-10mm, borne in spike-like, often branched, racemes; corolla with a narrow tube and a broad limb with oval lobes. Fruit a 5-valved capsule. Fallow and waste land, roadsides, hedgerows, coastal sands. July-Nov. T – not Balearic Is.

1213 *Plumbago auriculata [P. capensis]* **PLUMBAGO, CAPE LEADWORT**. Scrambling, semi-evergreen shrub to 6m, often less. Leaves alternate, elliptical to oval, untoothed, short-stalked. Flowers *sky blue*, 16-22mm, salver-shaped, with a long slender tube, borne in condensed racemes that slowly elongate. Parks and gardens. June-Sept. (South Africa). A form with white flowers is sometimes seen.

1214 *Plumbago indica [P. rosea]*. Similar, but to 2m, with pink or red flowers. June-Sept. (E Indies).

Armeria **THRIFTS**. Tufted perennials with basal leaves and heads of flowers borne on long leafless scapes, the flower clusters with a membranous sheath extending down the stem below. Corolla funnel-shaped.

1215 *Armeria canescens*. Very variable short to medium perennial. Leaves variable, the outer linear, often broadest above the middle, the inner, *much longer*, linear to linear-lanceolate, flat or revolute, with a wide membranous margin. Flowers pink or reddish-purple in heads 15-25mm across, on scapes up to 70cm long; sheaths 7-30mm long; bracts pale brown, blunt, with papery margins. Rocks and grassy places, mainly in the mountains. May-July. Italy, Sicily and the Balkans.

1216 *Armeria ruscinonensis*. Dwarf shrub, usually with a long-branched stout stock. Leaves *all* similar, linear to linear-spatular shaped, blunt, flat or channelled, becoming rather leathery. Flowers white or pinkish, in heads 15-20mm across, on flexuous scapes, 10-30mm long; sheath 10-40mm long. Coastal cliffs and adjacent mountain rocks; usually on acid rocks. May-July. NE Spain and S France.

1217 *Armeria soleirolii*. Similar, but the inner leaves longer and narrower than the outer, calyx 5-6mm long (not 6-8mm); sheaths 8-12mm long. Coastal rocks and sands. Corsica.

1218 *Armeria pungens [A. fasciculata]*. Compact dwarf shrub; stock with many long branches. Leaves linear-lanceolate to linear-spatula-shaped, up to 10cm long, pointed. Flowers pink or white, in heads 20-30mm across; scapes up to 25cm long; *sheaths* 25-35mm long. Coastal sands. Apr-July. Portugal, S Spain, Corsica and Sardinia.

1219 *Armeria macrophylla*. Similar, but leaves large, 12-25cm long, thread-like to linear. S Portugal and SW Spain.

Limonium **SEA LAVENDERS**. Perennial herbs with simple, often rather leathery, leaves, generally in basal rosettes, occasionally a dwarf shrub. Flowers borne in corymbose inflorescences, the individual branches like a one-sided spike; corolla with a short tube and a wide limb. The corollas persist and becomes very papery in fruit and for this reason the stems are often cut for dried flower arrangements.

1220 *Limonium sinuatum [Statice sinuata]* **WINGED SEA LAVENDER**. A short to medium, rough-hairy perennial. Leaves *pinnately-divided*, with 4-7 pairs of rounded lobes, up to 15cm long, in a rather flat basal rosette. Stems with 3-4 undulate wings. Flowers yellowish-white or pink, purple when dry; calyx conspicuous, 10-14mm, bluish mauve, with a papery margin. Rocky and sandy coastal habitats and saline areas inland. Mar-Sept. T.

1221 *Limonium thouinii [Statice thouinii]*. Similar, but a short annual, stems *not winged* and flowers yellow with a whitish or pale blue calyx. Similar habitats. May-Sept. S Spain and NW Africa.

1222 *Limonium ferulaceum [Statice ferulaceum]*. Densely branched dwarf subshrub with dense brush-like tufts of flowering and non-flowering branches, to 40cm tall, with reddish-brown scales at the base. Leaves elliptical, unlobed, *absent* at flowering time. Flowers pink, 5-6mm, the branches alternate with flowers only

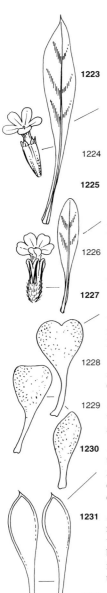

towards the tips. Rocky and sandy habitats, marshes. June-Sept. Iberian Peninsula and NW Africa eastwards to Yugoslavia – not Corsica or Sardinia.

1223 *Limonium vulgare [Statice limonium]* **COMMON SEA LAVENDER**. Short to medium, hairless perennial. Leaves oblong to spoon-shaped, generally widest above the middle, in a lax basal rosette; leaves *pinnately-veined*. Flowers crowded, reddish to lavender-lilac, 6-8mm, on stems branched in the upper half; branches spreading, short and crowded. Muddy salt flats and marshes, often forming extensive colonies. June-Oct. T – not Balearic Is., Cyprus or parts of the E Med.

1224 *Limonium hirsuticalyx.* Similar, but leaves *densely* tubercled; flowers 5-5.5mm. Similar habitats and flowering time. SE Greece – Cyclades.

1225 *Limonium bellidifolium [Statice bellidifolia]* **MATTED SEA LAVENDER**. Like *L. vulgare*, but a low to short mat-forming plant, the leaves mostly 3-veined. Inflorescence with numerous sterile, *non-flowering* branches. Flowers pale violet, 4.5-5mm. Similar habitats. June-Aug. Spain eastwards to Italy and Yugoslavia – not Balearic Is. or Crete.

1226 *Limonium cancellatum [Statice cancellata].* Like *L. bellidifolium*, but seldom more than 18cm tall, a *densely hairy* plant; bracts green, not membranous. Coastal rocks. Adriatic coasts of Italy, Yugoslavia and Greece.

1227 *Limonium graecum.* Short, rough, hairless perennial. Leaves linear-lanceolate to spoon-shaped, *1-veined*, green, but withering during the summer, borne on long woody basal branches. Flowers pink, 7-8mm, the inflorescences with numerous non-flowering branches; bracts green. Coastal rocks and sands. June-Aug. Balearic Is., Corsica, Sardinia, Sicily, Greece, Crete and Turkey.

1228 *Limonium articulatum.* Similar, but a smaller plant with warted branches that are conspicuously *constricted* at the nodes and appearing to be jointed. Coastal rocks. Corsica and Sardinia.

1229 *Limonium oleifolium [Statice oleifolia].* Like *L. graecum*, but a smooth plant to 50cm tall with linear leaves; flower-spikes 20-40mm long (not 30-60mm). Similar habitats and flowering time. T – not Cyprus or parts of the E Med.

1230 *Limonium ramosissimum [Statice globulariifolia].* Variable short perennial. Leaves oval to spoon-shaped, usually more than 10mm wide, *3-5-veined*. Flowers pale pink, 5-7mm, borne in a branched inflorescence, usually without sterile branches; calyx 4-6mm. Salt marshes, usually coastal. June-Aug. Spain and Algeria eastwards to Greece – not Crete.

1231 *Limonium echioides [Statice echioides].* Low to short slender annual. Leaves in a basal rosette, oblong to elliptical, broadest above the middle, obscurely pinnately-veined, *glandular*. Flowers pale pink, fleeting, arranged along one side of a branched inflorescence; calyx with 5-10 curved red spines; bracts with tiny swellings. Sandy and rocky coastal habitats, saline soils. Apr-June. Iberian Peninsula to NW Africa eastwards to Greece and Turkey

1232 *Limonium ocymifolium [Statice ocymifolia].* Similar, but a smaller plant not more than 30cm tall, the leaves generally *1-veined*, not more than 10mm wide; calyx 3-3.5mm. Similar habitats and flowering time. S Greece.

1233 *Limonium auriculae-ursifolium.* Like *L. ramosissimum*, but leaves 3-7-veined. Flowers violet-blue, 7-8mm. Coastal cliffs and salt marshes. Iberian Peninsula, S France and the Balearic Is.

1234 *Limoniastrum monopetalum* **LIMONIASTRUM**. Small, *fleshy shrub*, to 1.2m, though often less, silvery-blue-green; stems much-branched, leafy. Leaves fleshy, oblong to narrow spoon-shaped, covered with white scales, sheathing the stem with their bases. Flowers bright pink, drying violet, 14-16mm, borne in laxly branched spikes; corolla with 5 spreading, oval petals; bracts forming an envelope around the base of the flowers; inflorescence very fragile when dry. Coastal sands and salt marshes. June-Aug. Iberian Peninsula and N Africa eastwards to Italy, Sicily and Crete.

1235 *Goniolimon dalmaticum* **GONIOLIMON.** Low to short perennial with a stout, generally rather angular, stems. Leaves mostly in basal rosettes, leathery, lanceolate to spoon-shaped, pointed, with sparse *white dots*. Flowers reddish-purple, borne in dense, branched, one-sided spikes. Dry grassy habitats, stony hillslopes. June-Sept. Balkan Peninsula and Turkey.

EBONY FAMILY Ebenaceae

Trees with alternate leaves; no stipules. Flowers unisexual, often borne on separate plants.

1236 *Diospyros lotus* **DATE PLUM.** Round-headed deciduous tree to 14m, with furrowed bark; young twigs hairy. Leaves elliptical to oblong, shiny-green, untoothed, short-stalked. Flowers reddish- or greenish-white, bell-shaped, the male in clusters of 2-3, 5mm, the female usually solitary, 8-10mm. Fruit a globose berry, 13-16mm, yellow or bluish-black when ripe. Cultivated locally throughout the region for its edible fruits or for ornament. June-July. (Asia, from Turkey eastwards).

1237 *Diospyros kaki* **CHINESE PERSIMMON** or **KAKI.** Similar, but flowers yellowish-white, the female 28-32mm and the fruit *much-larger*, 35-75mm, yellow or orange-yellow when ripe. Grown occasionally for its handsome edible, though somewhat insipid, fruits, which persist on the branches after the leaves have fallen. Locally grown throughout the region. June-July. (NE China, Korea and Japan). Several varieties are cultivated, differing primarily in fruit colour and shape.

STORAX FAMILY Styracaceae

With only one representative in the region.

1238 *Styrax officinalis* **STORAX.** Deciduous shrub or small tree, to 7m, though often less; twigs white-woolly, with stellate-hairs. Leaves alternate, oval to oblong, blunt, untoothed, short-stalked. Flowers white, *bell-shaped* and pendent, 18-22mm, borne in small lateral clusters of 3-6, fragrant; petals 5-7, elliptical, fused together at the base. Fruit oval, white-woolly, with a persistent calyx, 1-seeded. Open woodland, thickets, river margins. Apr-May. C Italy eastwards.

OLIVE FAMILY Oleaceae

Trees and shrubs, occasionally woody climbers, with opposite leaves, rarely alternate, simple or pinnate. Flowers in cymes or panicles, 4-parted; calyx generally with 4 small teeth; corolla with 4 free or united petals; stamens usually only 2. Fruit a capsule or berry or a winged nut (samara).

1239 *Jasminum fruticans* **WILD JASMINE.** An evergreen or semi-evergreen shrub to 3m, with slender 4-angled stems. Leaves *alternate*, usually trifoliate, shiny; leaflets oval to lanceolate. Flowers yellow, 12-15mm, salver-shaped, not scented, borne in lax

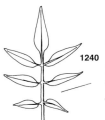

clusters of 1-5. Fruit a black, shiny berry. Woodland and scrub, river banks. Apr-June. T – absent from most of the islands. Occasionally grown in gardens.

1240 *Jasminum officinale* **WHITE** or **SUMMER JASMINE**. Vigorous twining deciduous climber. Leaves opposite, pinnate; leaflets usually 5-7, oval or elliptical. Flowers white, often purplish outside, salver-shaped, 16-22mm, with a slender tube, *intensely fragrant*, borne in rather dense clusters. Fruit a black berry. Grown in gardens and sometimes found in hedges or on old walls. June-Oct. (Himalaya and China).

1241 *Jasminum polyanthum*. Similar, but evergreen, the flowers with scarcely any calyx, generally rose on the outside in bud, becoming pure white. Extensively cultivated. Mar-May. (China). This is the jasmine most frequently grown as a house plant.

1242 *Jasminum grandiflorum*. Like *J. officinale*, but a rather straggling bush with larger white flowers, reddish on the outside; calyx-lobes *twice* as long as the tube. Grown in gardens, and in SE Europe for the perfume industry. (SE Asia). June-Oct.

1243 *Jasminum mesnyi [J. primulinum]*. A scrambling evergreen shrub with angled stems; twigs green. Leaves opposite, trifoliate; leaflets elliptical, deep green above. Flowers solitary and lateral, bright yellow, 30-40mm, with 6 or more oval petal-lobes, often appearing doubled or semi-doubled. Widely grown in gardens. Mar-Apr. (W China).

1244 *Ligustrum lucidum* **CHINESE PRIVET**. Rather upright evergreen tree to 10m. Leaves oval, *glossy dark-green*, long-pointed, short-stalked, untoothed. Flowers white, small, but borne in rather dense panicles up to 20cm long; corolla tubular with 4 spreading lobes. Berry blue-black when ripe, 8-12mm long. Widely planted in parks and gardens, sometimes as a street tree. Aug-Oct. (China). There is also a form with yellow variegations on the leaves.

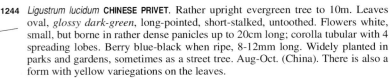

1245 *Fraxinus ornus* **MANNA** or **FLOWERING ASH**. Deciduous tree to 20m, with smooth grey bark; twigs usually hairless. Leaves opposite and pinnate, with 5-9 leaflets, dark green; leaflets lanceolate to oval, toothed. Flowers white, borne in dense, showy, rather fluffy, terminal panicles, 4-petalled; petals 5-6mm long, linear. Fruit a single-winged samara. Maquis, ravines, mixed woodland, thickets and rocky places. Apr-June. Spain eastwards to Turkey and the Lebanon, sometimes cultivated. The bark exudes a sweet and nutritious substance ('manna') when slashed, which is sometimes used as a laxative. Grown in gardens for ornament.

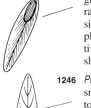

1246 *Phillyrea angustifolia*. An evergreen shrub to 2.5m, with rather upright branches and smooth grey bark. Leaves opposite, linear to lanceolate, untoothed to finely toothed, with 4-6 pairs of rather obscure veins. Flowers greenish-yellow, small, 2-3mm, 4-lobed, borne in small lateral clusters about 10mm across, *fragrant*. Fruit pea-sized, 6-8mm, fleshy, with a short apical point, bluish-black when ripe. Maquis, open woods, rocky places, ravines, roadsides. Mar-May. T – not Crete or Cyprus.

1247 *Phillyrea latifolia [P. media]*. Similar, but twigs finely hairy and leaves of two types; juvenile leaves oval with a heart-shaped base, the adult lanceolate to elliptical; all rather leathery, dark green, toothed or not and with 7-10 pairs of *distinct* lateral veins. Flowers whitish, sometimes tinged with purple. Fruit globose and fleshy, 7-10mm, without an apical point, bluish-black when ripe. Similar habitats and flowering time. T.

1248 *Olea europaea* **OLIVE**. Much-branched evergreen tree to 15m, the grey trunk and branches becoming very thick and contorted in old specimens. Leaves ashy-grey-green, silvery beneath, minutely scaly, opposite, lanceolate to oblong, untoothed,

short-stalked. Flowers small, whitish, borne in small erect clusters. Fruit oblong or egg-shaped, 10-25mm, green or black. Extensively cultivated in large groves, sometimes becoming naturalised. May-June. T. For centuries and still today the most important Med plant, though olive oil has been partly replaced by other, cheaper oils, and abandoned groves are a frequent sight in some countries. There are many culinary varieties but the wild ancestor of the olive, var. or subsp. *oleaster*, (**1248a**), can be found in maquis and woodland throughout the Med. It is distinguished by its more shrubby habit, spiny stems, smaller leaves and small bitter fruits. Where they have not been under-ploughed, olive groves are a haven for wild flowers of many sorts, especially beautiful in the spring.

GENTIAN FAMILY Gentianaceae

Hairless, bitter-tasting herbs with opposite, untoothed, leaves. Flowers 4-5-parted; calyx deeply lobed; petals contorted in bud, united into a short or long tube. Fruit a 2-parted capsule. The true gentians, *Gentiana* are plants of mountain and northerly or southerly latitudes and are not present in hot regions such as the Med.

1249 *Blackstonia perfoliata [Chlora perfoliata]* **YELLOW-WORT**. An erect, short to medium, bluish- or grey-green annual. Leaves opposite, oval, the lower narrowed at the base, but the upper fused together to completely *encircle* the stem. Flowers yellow, 8-15mm, with 6-8 petal-lobes, borne in lax-branched terminal clusters. Maquis, garrigue, sand-dunes, moist bare sandy ground, streamsides and roadsides. Apr-Sept. T. The Med plant, especially at the eastern end of its range, often has very slender stems, generally less than 30cm tall, and rather smaller flowers, few to a cluster. Such plants are often assigned to subsp. *intermedia* (1249a), although this is not clearly differentiated from the normal European form.

1250 *Blackstonia acuminata [B. perfoliata* subsp. *acuminata, Chlora acuminata, C. serotina].* Similar, but the stem-leaves *not* clasping the stem or only slightly fused together around the stem, the flower-stalks stouter, often 20-30mm long (not less than 20mm) and calyx-lobes lanceolate rather than linear. Damp habitats by streams or flushes, on banks and hillslopes. May-July.

Centaurium **CENTAURIES**. Biennial or perennial herbs with flowers in broad, often flat-topped, regularly branched, clusters; calyx with keeled lobes; petals pinkish or purple, occasionally yellow.

1251 *Centaurium erythraea [C. majus]* **COMMON CENTAURY**. Variable short to medium biennial; stem generally solitary, branched above. Leaves elliptical to oval, 3-7-veined, the lower in a distinct, persistent *rosette*, the upper leaves much smaller. Flowers pink to purplish, rarely white, 9-15mm, scarcely stalked, borne in dense to lax, flat-topped clusters. Dry grassy habitats and scrub, in garrigue, usually on calcareous soils. May-July. T. The eastern populations (from S Italy eastwards) are often more vigorous, with more widely spreading branches and flowers up to 22mm and with more pointed petals. These are generally assigned to subsp. *rhodense* (1251a).

1252 *Centaurium pulchellum [Erythraea pulchella]* **LESSER CENTAURY**. Low to short annual, *without* a basal leaf-rosette; plants sometimes very dwarf; stems branched from near the base, or unbranched. Leaves oval to lanceolate, pointed, mostly 3-veined. Flowers pinkish-purple, rarely white, 5-9mm, long-stalked, borne in lax, wide-spreading clusters, rarely solitary; petals narrow, sometimes only 4. Open habitats and damp grassy places, stony hillslopes, sand-dunes, roadsides and streamsides. Mar-June. T.

1253 *Centaurium tenuiflorum [Erythraea tenuiflora]* **SLENDER CENTAURY**. Similar, but stems generally branched towards the top and flowers very short-stalked or unstalked, borne in dense, narrow clusters. Damp, often marshy ground, springs and margins of salt lakes, often close to the sea. June-Aug. T.

1254 *Centaurium spicatum [Erythraea spicata]* **SPIKED CENTAURY**. Short to medium annual or biennial with stems usually branching from the base. Leaves oval to elliptical, 3-5-veined, the lower in a rosette but withered by flowering time. Flowers pinkish-purple, occasionally white, 8-10mm, borne in *spike-like* inflorescence with all the flowers along one side; petal-lobes 4-5. Damp grassy or sandy places close to the sea, margins of salt marshes, damp walls, sometimes in the hills. May-Aug. T.

1255 *Centaurium maritimum [Erythraea maritima]* **YELLOW CENTAURY**. Short annual or biennial; stem solitary or branched above. Leaves rather fleshy, elliptic-oblong to oval, the lower two very small and not forming a distinct rosette, the upper much longer. Flowers *pale yellow*, occasionally tinged with red, 11-18mm, borne in lax-branched clusters, occasionally solitary; petal-lobes usually 5, elliptical. Sandy or grassy coastal habitats, moist rocky banks inland. Apr-June. T.

OLEANDER FAMILY Apocynaceae

Trees, shrubs and climbers, sometimes herbs, with opposite, untoothed leaves; usually with milky latex when cut. Flowers solitary or in branched cymes or clusters, 5-parted; corolla with a distinct tube and usually 5 lobes, contorted in bud. Fruit a pair (sometimes only one develops) of follicles; seeds often with hairy tufts.

1256 *Nerium oleander* **OLEANDER**. Robust evergreen shrub to 4m, with rather erect, whippy stems. Leaves opposite or in 3-4s, linear-lanceolate, leathery, rather dull green. Flowers pink, red or white, fragrant, salver-shaped, 30-40mm, borne in large terminal clusters, with broad spreading petal-lobes. Follicles *large*, 8-16cm long, erect. Stream and river banks and gravels, rocky places and gullies. May-August. T. All parts of the plant are extremely poisonous; the milky juice contains glycosides that may affect the function of the heart. Widely grown in gardens and along roads and in parks, sometimes as an informal hedge.

1257 *Nerium indicum*. Very similar and often regarded as the same species as *N. Oleander*, with rather smaller fragrant flowers; corolla with deeply cut appendages in the throat. Cultivated forms include those with yellowish, apricot or crimson flowers as well as various shades of pink and red – they often have fully double blooms.

1258 *Rhazya orientalis* **RHAZYA**. An erect, short to medium perennial, with unbranched stems, woody at the base. Leaves lanceolate to oval, pointed, rather thin and with a *hairy* margin. Flowers blue to deep violet, 12-16mm, broad salver-shaped, with a slender tube and narrow oval, spreading lobes, borne in terminal, rather lax, clusters. Follicles 5-8cm long, erect. Wet habitats, generally close to the sea. Aug-Oct. N Greece and Turkey. Sometimes grown in gardens.

1259 *Trachomitum venetum [Apocynum venetum]* **TRACHOMITUM**. A rhizomatous, medium, hairless perennial. Leaves narrow-oblong, rough-margined, obscurely veined, with a very short stalk. Flowers pale to bright pink, or whitish, 4-5mm, bell-shaped, borne in lax, branched, terminal clusters. Follicles 8-24cm long, usually *pendent*. Sandy coastal habitats. July-Sept. Adriatic coast, Turkey and Cyprus. Always local.

fruit

Vinca **PERIWINKLES.** Perennials or subshrubs, often with trailing stems and pairs of leathery leaves. Flowers solitary at the upper leaf-axils; corolla propeller-shaped, with a short tube and obliquely truncated lobes.

1260 *Vinca major* **GREATER PERIWINKLE.** Short to medium, spreading, evergreen subshrub, with long arching or trailing stems, often rooting down at the tip. Leaves shiny bright green, oval, with a *hairy* margin, stalked. Flowering stems to 30cm, ascending. Flowers bluish-violet or purplish, 30-50mm; calyx-lobes hairy on margin. Follicles 4-5cm, rarely produced. Garrigue, woodland, banks, hedgerows, widely cultivated. Mar-May. European Med, but often naturalised. Cultivated forms include those with yellow- or white-variegated leaves.

1261 *Vinca minor* **LESSER PERIWINKLE.** Similar, but smaller with elliptical or lanceolate *hairless-margined* leaves. Flowers blue, pink or purplish, 25-30mm; calyx-lobes not hairy on margin. Similar habitats, sometimes on more open rocky ground. Feb-May. From Portugal eastwards to Turkey. Often cultivated and naturalised.

1262 *Vinca balcanica.* Like *V. minor*, but leaves *hairy* on margin and stems not more than 12cm long; flowers often slightly larger. Yugoslavia and Albania.

1263 *Vinca difformis [V. media]* **INTERMEDIATE PERIWINKLE.** Vigorous evergreen subshrub similar in general appearance to *V. major*; stems sometimes reaching up to 2m and far creeping. Leaves oval to lanceolate, with a hairless or minutely hairy margin. Flowering stems to 30cm, ascending. Flowers pale blue or whitish, 30-70mm. Shady and damp habitats, woodland and scrub, banks, roadsides and ditches. Feb-May. Iberian Peninsula and NW Africa eastwards to Italy.

1264 *Vinca herbacea* **HERBACEOUS PERIWINKLE.** Low to short, usually hairless perennial, *not evergreen*, with the stems dying back during the winter. Leaves narrow, elliptical to lanceolate. Flowers pale blue to white, 20-35mm, well spaced along the stems. Rocky places, scrub, banks and roadsides, sometimes beneath trees. Mar-May. Iberian Peninsula eastwards to Greece. Sometimes cultivated. The Sardinian plant, which can be distinguished by its larger flowers, 60-70mm, is subsp. *sardoa* (1264a).

MILKWEED FAMILY Asclepiadaceae

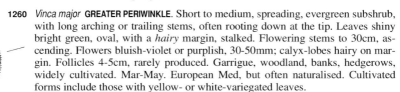

Herb, shrubs or trees, sometimes climbers, with milky latex and opposite leaves. Flowers 5-parted, the corolla with a distinctive central crown (corona); stamens fused together into a ring; pollen in bunches (pollinia). Fruit a pair of follicles; seeds with a hairy tuft at apex.

1265 *Periploca graeca* **SILK-VINE.** Vigorous *twining* deciduous shrub, to 12m. Leaves dark green, shiny, oval, stalked, usually hairless. Flowers purplish-brown, green outside, 20-25mm, with spreading oblong lobes whose margin are deflexed, borne in lax lateral clusters; corona with erect purplish-brown awns. Follicles 10-15cm long. Woodland, thickets and riverbanks. June-July. Italy, Balkans and Turkey.

1266 *Periploca laevigata.* Similar, but a thorny grey-stemmed shrub, rarely with twining stems, to 3m; leaves rather leathery. Flowers *smaller*, 10-15mm, brownish-purple and white within, greenish outside. Rocky places and scrub. May-July. N Africa, SE Spain, Crete, Sicily and Syria.

1267 *Gomphocarpus fruticosus* **BRISTLE-FRUITED SILKWEED.** An erect shrubby perennial, 1-2m. Leaves linear-lanceolate, long-pointed, hairless. Flowers white, 12-14mm, borne in hairy-stalked, lateral, umbels; corona with erect, fleshy scales. Fruit boat-shaped, inflated, 4-6cm long, erect, *very bristly*. Damp places, especially riverbanks, often close to the coast, naturalised. May-Sept. T. (South Africa). Sometimes grown in gardens – for flowers and its curious and decorative fruits.

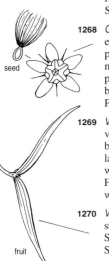

seed

fruit

1268 *Cynanchum acutum* **STRANGLEWORT.** Hairless, twining, bluish-green, woody climber, to 3m; stems slender. Leaves *arrowhead-shaped*, stalked. Flowers white or pink, 8-12mm, borne in lateral or terminal umbels, scented; corolla-lobes rather narrow; corona with 10 triangular projecting lobes. Follicles spindle-shaped, pointed, appearing like a pair of horns, 6-8cm long. Scrub, hedgerows, riverbanks, saline soils, often close to the sea. June-Sept. T – absent from Cyprus. Poisonous.

1269 *Vincetoxicum hirundinaria [V. officinale, Cynanchum vincetoxicum]* **SWALLOW-WORT.** A very variable, medium to tall perennial, hairless or slightly hairy; stems erect, unbranched, occasionally slightly twining. Leaves heart-shaped to broadly oval or lanceolate, pointed, stalked. Flowers yellow or greenish-yellow, sometimes white, 5-10mm, borne in stalked clusters of 6-8 at the base of the upper leaves. Follicles spindle-shaped, usually paired, 5-6cm long. Woodlands, rocky ground, waste places, hedgerows, grassy pastures. May-Sept. T – not Cyprus. Poisonous.

1270 *Vincetoxicum nigrum* **DARK SWALLOW-WORT.** Similar, but generally not as tall, the stems mostly twining and leaves long-pointed. Flowers *dark purple*, 6-8mm. Scrub and rocky places, riversides and waste places. May-July. Portugal, S Spain, S France, Balearic Is., Italy.

1271 *Vincetoxicum canescens [Cynanchum canescens]*. Like *V. hirundinaria*, but plant *grey-hairy*; flowers yellow, 7-8mm. Rocky and bushy habitats, generally in the mountains. May-July. Crete, Aegean Is., Turkey, Cyprus and Syria.

1272 *Cionura erecta [Cynanchum erectum, Marsdenia erecta]* **CIONURA.** A hairless or slightly hairy shrub to 1m, but occasionally climbing into large bushes or trees to 5m; stems rounded, twining or not. Leaves heart-shaped, stalked. Flowers milky-white, 8-10mm, *unpleasant smelling*, borne in large terminal or lateral, umbel-like clusters, hairless; corona segments tongue-shaped. Follicles solitary, smooth, spindle-shaped, 8-9cm long. Rocky habitats, river gravels, coastal sands and dunes. May-July. Balkans, including Crete, Turkey, Cyprus and the extreme E Med.

1273 *Caralluma europaea [Apteranthes gussoneana]* **CARALLUMA.** A short *succulent* herb, with underground stolons; stems silvery-blue-green, square, 13-21mm wide. Leaves small and scale like, quickly falling and inconspicuous. Flowers yellow with purple bands or dusky purple with a darker centre, 13-17mm, borne in rounded clusters at the stem tops, usually fringed with violet hairs. Dry rocky habitats, generally salt-rich. Mar-July. SE Spain, Sicily and N Africa.

1274 *Caralluma munbyana*. Similar, but stem-faces *grooved*, not flat; flowers brownish, 6-8mm. Similar habitats and flowering time. SE Spain and N Africa.

BEDSTRAW FAMILY Rubiaceae

Herbs or shrubs with opposite or whorled leaves; stipules present, between each pair of leaves on both sides of the stem (interpetiolar), often very leaf-like. Flowers funnel-shaped, with a short or long tube, 4-5-parted, borne in dense heads, branched cymes or panicles; ovary below the corolla and calyx (inferior). Fruit fleshy or dry, berry-like, 1-2-seeded often. A large family with many species, particularly, in the tropics and subtropics.

1275 *Putoria calabrica* **PUTORIA.** Dwarf, much-branched shrub, generally less than 15cm tall, but spreading to 1m, very *unpleasant smelling* when crushed. Leaves opposite, elliptical to oval, sometimes broadest above the middle, with revolute, minutely hairy, margins; stipules small and inconspicuous. Flowers pink, funnel-shaped, 10-15mm long, with a narrow tube and 4 spreading linear-lanceolate lobes. Fruit two-lobed, red or blackish when ripe. Garrigue on rocky ground, rock crevices, dry stony ground. May-Aug. T – not Balearic Is., Corsica, Sardinia or Portugal.

Crucianella **CRUCIANELLA**. Leaves in whorls of 4-6. Flowers borne in dense spikes; corolla with a tube longer than the lobes.

1276 *Crucianella maritima* **COASTAL CRUCIANELLA**. Prostrate to spreading, low to short shrub; stems whitish, hairless and smooth. Leaves in 4s, oval-lanceolate, leathery, *spine-tipped* with a whitish margin, closely overlapping along the woody stems. Flowers yellow, 10-13mm long, 5-lobed, protruding well beyond the bracts. Coastal rocks and sands, established dunes. May-Sept. Iberian Peninsula and NW Africa eastwards to Italy and Sicily.

1277 *Crucianella latifolia*. Similar, but an annual with leaves in whorls of 6-8, linear-lanceolate, the lower rather broader than the upper, not spine-tipped; bracts fused together in the lower half. Flowers creamy-white or purplish, 5-7.5mm long. Similar habitats, often in garrigue, sometimes below pine trees. Apr-June. T – not Portugal.

1278 *Crucianella imbricata*. Like *C. latifolia*, but flowers *smaller*, 3-4.5mm long, not exceeding the free bracts. Dry rocky places, sometimes below pine trees, most frequent in the mountains. May-July. Crete, Turkey, Cyprus and Syria.

1279 *Crucianella angustifolia*. Like *C. latifolia*, but a taller plant, to 50cm. Flowers 3-5mm long, the corolla *4-lobed*. T – not Cyprus.

1280 *Crucianella macrostachya*. Like *C. latifolia*, but a more robust erect or spreading plant with larger flowers, 8-9mm long, cream or yellowish, 4-5-lobed, greatly exceeding the bracts. Dry rocky and stony habitats, waste grounds, olive groves and roadsides. May-Aug. Crete and Aegean Is. eastwards, including Cyprus.

Asperula **ASPERULA**. Annual or perennial herbs with square stems. Leaves in whorls of 4-8. Flowers borne in panicles or heads, usually 4-parted; corolla with a tube longer than the lobes.

1281 *Asperula aristata*. Rather variable short to medium subshrub, generally rather woody at the base and with green or grey-green shoots, slightly hairy. Leaves in 4s lanceolate to linear, with a colourless apex, the margin usually slightly revolute. Flowers greenish-purple, to pale purple or yellowish, funnel-shaped, 5.5-9mm long; corolla-tube hairy. Rocky habitats. May-Aug. Iberian Peninsula and NW Africa eastwards to Greece – not Crete.

1282 *Asperula crassifolia [A. tomentosa]*. Similar, but *shoots* bluish- or purplish-green and flowers yellowish, 5-7mm long; corolla densely hairy. Similar habitats and flowering time. S Italy and Sicily.

1283 *Asperula rigida*. Like *A. aristata*, but leaves in 6s and flowers smaller, 1.5-2mm long, the corolla hairless. Dry rocky habitats. Apr-May. Crete – endemic.

1284 *Asperula laevigata*. Short to tall hairless perennial; stems ascending to erect, rather weak. Leaves in 4s, elliptical to oval, blunt, short-stalked, with a rough margin and netted veins on each side of the midrib. Flowers *white*, 11-2mm long, narrow funnel-shaped, borne in a long, pyramidal inflorescence; corolla 4-lobed. Wooded habitats. May-July. Spain eastwards to Greece – not Crete.

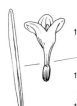

1285 *Asperula tinctoria [Galium triandrum].* Similar, but very variable and with *3-lobed* corollas, 3-4mm long. The stock bears characteristic spreading orange stolons. France, Italy and Yugoslavia.

1286 *Asperula lutea.* Like A. *laevigata*, but flowers yellowish or reddish, 3.5-5.5mm long, the corolla hairy or not. C and S Greece – endemic.

1287 *Asperula taygetea.* Like A. *laevigata*, but a lower plant, to 40cm at the most with leaves in 6s and flowers whitish, 4-6mm long; flowers and fruits hairy. Stony and rocky habitats, sometimes on coastal sands. Apr-June. S Greece, Crete and SW Aegean Is.

1288 *Asperula arvensis* **BLUE WOODRUFF.** Short, slender, hairless annual. Leaves lanceolate to linear-lanceolate, in whorls of 6-8. Flowers bright blue or bluish-violet, 4mm, borne in clusters surrounded by a ruff of leaf-like bracts. Fruit smooth, 2-3mm, brown. Fields, cultivated, waste and fallow land, vineyards. Mar-June. T.

Galium **BEDSTRAWS.** Like *Asperula*, but stems sometimes rounded. Leaves mostly in whorls of 4 or more. Flowers usually 4-parted, the corolla with a very short tube; stamens protruding. Fruit 2-lobed, often with hooked bristles.

1289 *Galium verum* **LADY'S BEDSTRAW.** Variable low to short, sprawling stoloniferous perennial; stems rounded, with 4 raised lines. Leaves dark green, shiny, linear, in whorls of 8-12, hairy beneath; margin somewhat revolute. Flowers *golden yellow,* 2-3.5mm, fragrant, borne in dense oval panicles. Fruit smooth, 1.5mm, black when ripe. Grassy habitats, open woodland, banks, roadsides, olive groves. Apr-July, sometimes later. T – not Balearic Is., Crete or Cyprus. A widespread and familiar species in much of Europe and western Asia.

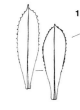

1290 *Galium rotundifolium.* Low to short, stoloniferous perennial; stem square, slender, with short scattered hairs. Leaves in 4s, oval or rounded, short-stalked, with 3 *parallel* veins. Flowers whitish or yellowish, 3-3.5mm, borne in lax broad inflorescences. Fruit 2mm, with hooked bristles. Grassy and wooded habitats. T – except Balearic Is., Cyprus and the extreme E Med.

1291 *Galium scabrum [G. ellipticum].* Like *G. rotundifolium*, but stem densely hairy (not hairless) and flowers in a longer, narrower inflorescence. Rocky and grassy habitats. Spain, Corsica, Sardinia, Italy and Sicily.

1292 *Galium corrudifolium [G. adriaticum].* Medium perennial, without stolons; stems erect, somewhat hairy. Leaves leathery, linear with a prominent midrib and revolute margins. Flowers cream, white or yellowish, 3-3.6mm, borne in dense oblong heads, with short erect branches. Fruit hairless. Dry rocky habitats. May-July. Spain eastwards to the Balkans – not Crete.

1293 *Galium cinereum.* Similar, but a bluish- or purplish-green plant, often with a *solitary* stem, taller and more robust. Flowers white, 3-5mm. Similar habitats and flowering time. Balearic Is., S France and Italy.

1294 *Galium mollugo* **HEDGE BEDSTRAW.** Very variable medium to tall, sometimes scrambling, usually hairless, stoloniferous perennial; stems square and *smooth*, the rootstock usually reddish. Leaves oblong to elliptical, in whorls of 6-8, thin and rather pale green, 1-veined. Flowers white, 2-3mm, borne in loose, branched clusters. Fruit smooth, black when ripe. Grassy habitats, hedgerows, open woodland, roadsides, olive groves. May-Aug. Iberian Peninsula and NW Africa eastwards to Yugoslavia – not Balearic Is. Widespread in Europe and western Asia.

1295 *Galium heldreichii.* Similar, but without stolons and leaves more leathery, sometimes reddish. Flowers whitish or greenish, very rarely reddish. Dry habitats, particularly scrub. Apr-July. Greece, Crete and W Turkey.

1296 *Galium litorale.* Like *G. mollugo,* but leaves rather thick and shiny and flowers white, 3-4mm, slightly *hairy* outside. Fruit rather fleshy. Coastal sands. Sicily.

1297 *Galium setaceum.* Slender, low to short annual; stem smooth or somewhat prickly. Leaves narrow-linear, in whorls of 6-8, hairless or slightly hairy. Flowers tiny, *purple,* 0.5mm, borne in oval clusters; corolla-lobes erect, pointed. Fruit usually with dense, hooked bristles. Dry open grassy and stony habitats, dried river beds, rock crevices. Mar-May. T.

1298 *Galium murale [Sherardia muralis].* Low to short sprawling annual; stems much-branched from the base, smooth to sparsely hairy. Leaves narrow elliptical, with a short *awn-tip,* in whorls of 4-6, hairy or not. Flowers yellowish, tiny, 0.7mm, borne in a lax, rather few-flowered inflorescence; corolla-lobes pointed, erect. Fruit with 2 oblong, spreading lobes, usually with hooked bristles towards the top. Fallow and waste land, roadsides, banks, vineyards, old walls. Mar-June. T.

1299 *Galium verticillatum.* Similar, but flowers in denser clusters, *whitish,* 1-1.5mm. Fruit-lobes globose. Similar habitats and flowering time. Spain eastwards to the Balkans.

1300 *Cruciata laevipes [C. chersonensis, Galium cruciata, Valantia cruciata]* **CROSSWORT.** A short to medium, softly hairy perennial, with a creeping stock; stems square, branched near the base. Leaves in whorls of *four,* oval-elliptical, 12-20mm long, 3-veined, yellowish-green. Flowers pale yellow, honey-scented, 2-2.5mm, in clusters forming whorls at the base of the leaves. Fruit globose, smooth and hairless, blackish when ripe, borne on recurved, short stalks. Grassy habitats, pastures, roadsides, open woodland, generally on calcareous soils. Mar-June. T – absent from Balearic Is., Cyprus and parts of the extreme E Med. Widespread in Europe and western Asia.

1301 *Cruciata glabra [Galium vernum].* Similar, but a shorter plant not exceeding 20cm tall, *without* lateral branches. Leaves 7-16mm long. Flowers 2.5-3.5mm. Similar habitats and flowering time. T – absent from Balearic Is., Sicily, Cyprus and much of the E Med.

1302 *Cruciata pedemontana [Galium pedemontana, Valantia pedemontana].* Like *C. laevipes,* but annual with a simple or branched stem. Leaves 3-11mm long (not 12-20mm), *1-veined.* Flowers 0.5-1mm. Dry grassy habitats and scrub, often in the mountains. Apr-June. T.

1303 *Valantia hispida* **VALANTIA.** Low to short, rather delicate and inconspicuous plant, slightly fleshy, somewhat bristly. Leaves in whorls of 4, oval, broadest above the middle, 6-10mm long, 1-veined. Flowers greenish-yellow, 1.5-2mm, borne in dense clusters at the base of the leaves, each cluster with 4-lobed hermaphrodite flowers and 3-lobed male flowers. Fruit hidden by recurved, coalescent *bristly stalks.* Rocky habitats, hillsides, sandy ground, seashores, waste ground. Mar-June. T – commonest in the E Med.

1304 *Valantia muralis.* Similar, but a more softly hairy plant, the fruit-stalks with a conspicuous horn-like appendage. Rocky habitats, dry sandy and waste places, old walls, often near the coast. Mar-May. T.

1305 *Rubia peregrina* **WILD MADDER.** Medium to tall, trailing or scrambling, hairless, rather rampant evergreen perennial, with a creeping rootstock; stems square, rough with *downturned* bristles. Leaves in whorls of 4-8, oval to elliptical, leathery, deep shiny green, 1-veined, rough on the midrib beneath. Flowers pale yellowish-green, 4-5mm, 5-lobed, forming a dense leafy terminal panicle, 40-100mm long. Fruit subglobose, 4-6mm, black and fleshy when ripe. Woodland, scrub, thickets and rocky ground, often in the garrigue, margins of cultivated fields. May-July. T – not Cyprus.

1306 *Rubia tenuifolia [R. olivieri]*. Similar, but flower-clusters 10-20mm long, *lateral*, shorter than the subtending leaves. Rocks, banks and dry scrubby hillslopes. Mar-June. S Greece and Crete eastwards, including Cyprus.

1307 *Rubia tinctorum* MADDER. Like *R. peregrina*, but leaves in whorls of 4-6, *pale green*, with prominent lateral veins. Flowers pale yellow. Fruit reddish-brown to black. Similar habitats and flowering time. Italy and the Balkans eastwards, but often naturalised within this area and also in the W Med. Formerly widely cultivated for its red dye (madder), extracted from the roots.

1308 *Rubia laurae*. Like *R. peregrina*, but a less rampant plant, the leaves tapered from a *wide* (not narrowed) base; flowers yellowish-brown. Open garrigue, rocky places, open pine forest. May-Aug. Cyprus – endemic.

1309 *Gardenia jasminioides* 'Fortuniana' GARDENIA. Slow growing, rounded evergreen shrub to 1.5m. Leaves opposite, deep glossy green, oval, blunt-tipped. Flowers white, *fully double*, 50-80mm, powerfully scented, becoming cream on ageing. Widely planted in parks and gardens, but rarely surviving prolonged cold periods. May-Aug. (China and Japan). In the wild form, which is scarcely seen in cultivation, the flowers are salver-shaped with 5 spreading lobes. The Gardenia was greatly valued as a Victorian stove plant.

THELIGONIUM FAMILY Theligoniaceae

A family with a single genus and 3 species, 2 Asian and the other in the Med region.

1310 *Theligonium cynocrambe* THELIGONIUM. Low to short, prostrate or occasionally erect, usually hairless annual, unpleasant smelling; stems with swollen nodes. Leaves somewhat succulent, alternate, or the lower opposite, oval, untoothed. Flowers green, *insignificant*, 2-3mm, borne in small lateral clusters, the male and female separate but on the same plant; perianth membranous, that of the male flowers with 2-3 lobes, that of the female tubular. Fruit 2mm, nut-like. Rocky habitats, sandy ground, old walls, often in damp and shaded places. Feb-June. T.

BINDWEED FAMILY Convolvulaceae

Herbs, often with twining or scrambling stems and alternate leaves. Flowers regular, hermaphrodite, funnel- or bell-shaped, often large (not in *Cuscuta*), 4-5-parted. Fruit a 2-4-valved capsule.

Cuscuta DODDERS. Parasitic plants with thread-like stems, no leaves and 4-5-parted tiny flowers borne in rounded clusters. Parasitic on a variety of hosts.

1311 *Cuscuta epithymum* COMMON DODDER. Scrambling and entwining parasitic plant forming a mass of slender, much-branched, *reddish or purplish*, thread-like stems. Leaves reduced to tiny scales, without chlorophyll. Flowers pale pink, 3-4mm, scented, 5-parted, with spreading pointed petals, borne in tight round clusters; styles with a cylindrical stigma. Parasitic on various shrubs and herbs, particularly legumes and heaths (*Erica*); grassy and shrubby places. May-Oct. T – not Cyprus.

1312 *Cuscuta campestris* **FIELD DODDER.** Similar, but stems *yellow* and flowers 2-3mm with a capitate stigma. Primarily parasitic on cultivated species of *Trifolium* and *Medicago*, but also on a wide variety of other herbs. Apr-Oct. Naturalised T. (North America).

1313 *Cuscuta europaea* **GREATER DODDER.** Like *C. epithymum*, but stems stouter, usually reddish and flowers usually *4-parted*, borne in dense rounded clusters, 8-12mm across. Parasitic on *Urtica*, *Humulus* and various other herbs. June-Oct. T – but absent from most of the islands except Corsica and Sardinia.

1314 *Cuscuta palaestina*. Like *C. europaea*, but a very slender plant with flowers borne in small irregular clusters only 3-7mm across. Parasitic on a wide variety of herbs and shrubs. Apr-Oct. Italy and Sicily eastwards, including Cyprus.

Calystegia **GREATER BINDWEEDS.** Perennial herbs with twining or prostrate stems, producing a white latex when bruised or cut. Flowers large and funnel-shaped; calyx enclosed by large bract-like scales; stigma 2-lobed.

1315 *Calystegia soldanella [Convolvulus soldanella]* **SEA BINDWEED.** *Low* prostrate and spreading, hairless perennial; stems sometimes twisting weakly. Leaves kidney-shaped, rather fleshy, long-stalked. Flowers pink or purplish, often with whitish stripes, 30-50mm, solitary; 'bracts' generally rather shorter than the calyx. Coastal dunes, sandy and shingly places. May-Aug. T – not Cyprus. A British native, but becoming scarce in most of its localities.

1316 *Calystegia sepium [Convolvulus sepium]* **LARGER BINDWEED, BELLVINE.** Variable vigorous climbing and twining perennial, stoloniferous, to 3m, hairy or hairless. Leaves arrow-shaped, bright green. Flowers white, rarely pale pink, 30-50mm; 'bracts' longer than the calyx, scarcely overlapping. Coastal salt-marshes, reed swamps, sandy and waste places, hedges and thickets by streams. June-Sept. T.

1317 *Calystegia silvatica [C. sylvestris, Convolvulus silvatica]* **GREAT BINDWEED.** Similar, but flowers larger, 50-90mm, white, sometimes striped with pale pink; 'bracts' widely overlapping, *pouched* at the base. Hedges, thickets, woodland margins, fences and walls. June-Sept. T – not Cyprus.

Ipomoea **MORNING GLORIES.** Like *Convolvulus*, but stigma capitate, unlobed or with only short lobes, not divided into 2 narrow lobes.

1318 *Ipomoea stolonifera [I. littoralis]* **COASTAL MORNING GLORY.** Rather fleshy *creeping* and trailing perennial, often rooting at the nodes; stems often over 1m in length. Leaves alternate, oblong, entire to 3-5-lobed, with a heart-shaped base, the apex blunt or 2-lobed. Flowers white or pale yellow, 45-60mm, sometimes with a purple centre, usually solitary. Coastal sands, generally just above the tide line. July-Nov. Naturalised in Balearic Is., Italy, Crete, N Africa and much of the E Med, including Cyprus. (Widespread in the tropics and subtropics).

1319 *Ipomoea purpurea [Pharbitis purpurea]* **COMMON MORNING GLORY.** Vigorous twining annual, slightly bristly, to 5m. Leaves *heart-shaped*, untoothed, stalked. Flowers blue, purple or pink, occasionally white, 40-60mm, borne in pairs or small clusters. Naturalised along hedgerows, fences, and in scrub, or on cultivated or waste ground. July-Sept. Scattered localities T. Often cultivated for ornament.

1320 *Ipomoea sagittata*. Similar, but stems twining or trailing and leaves *arrow-shaped*. Flowers 40-70mm, pink or purple. Damp, often saline habitats, marshes, sides of ditches. S Spain, Balearic Is., Corsica, S Italy, Sicily and Crete, N Africa and E Med. (Tropical Americas).

183

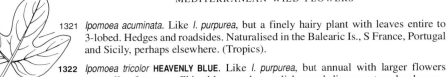

1321 *Ipomoea acuminata*. Like *I. purpurea*, but a finely hairy plant with leaves entire to 3-lobed. Hedges and roadsides. Naturalised in the Balearic Is., S France, Portugal and Sicily, perhaps elsewhere. (Tropics).

1322 *Ipomoea tricolor* **HEAVENLY BLUE**. Like *I. purpurea*, but annual with larger flowers generally of azure or China blue, rarely purplish; sepals linear, not oval or lanceolate. Grown in gardens. July-Sept. (Mexico). A source of the hallucinogen LSD, tiny amounts of which are present in the seeds.

1323 *Ipomoea batatas* **SWEET POTATO**, with white, violet or purple flowers and stems with large spindle-shaped tubers is occasionally cultivated in the region.

1324 *Cressa cretica* **CRESSA**. Erect or spreading, rather slender subshrub with a tough woody stock. Leaves greyish hairy, oval to lanceolate, with a rounded or heart-shaped base, untoothed. Flowers yellowish or pinkish, 3-5mm, borne in globose terminal clusters; corolla with a short tube equalling the calyx and 5 spreading or recurved lobes. Sandy and muddy habitats, salt flats, lake shores. June-Oct. T.

Convolvulus **BINDWEEDS**. Shrubby, climbing or trailing herbs with entire, or variously toothed and lobed leaves. Flowers solitary or in small clusters; calyx of 5 sepals; corolla funnel-shaped, rather pleated, expanding in daylight.

1325 *Convolvulus cneorum* **SILVERY CONVOLVULUS**. Erect to spreading *silvery* subshrub, to 50cm, becoming woody below. Leaves linear to elliptical, often widest above the middle, untoothed. Flowers white, occasionally pinkish, 20-35mm, borne in dense terminal heads. Fruit hairy. Calcareous rocks close to the sea. Apr-June. Italy, Sicily, Albania and Yugoslavia. A very distinctive silvery shrublet widely grown in gardens.

1326 *Convolvulus oleifolius*. Similar, but more variable, generally less robust and with thread-like to linear leaves. Flowers usually pink, 20-30mm, in laxer clusters. Garrigue, on rocky slopes. Mar-June. S Greece, Crete, Malta, Aegean Is. and E Med, including Cyprus.

1327 *Convolvulus dorycnium*. Like *C. cneorum*, but a woodier, more upright *shrub*, to 1m, though often less, densely hairy but not silvery; flowers pink, 20-25mm, in branched inflorescences but solitary or few at each branch-tip. Dry rocky places and scrub, roadsides. May-June. S Greece, Crete, Aegean Is., Tunisia and E Med, including Cyprus.

1328 *Convolvulus lanuginosus*. Silvery-grey or whitish, low to short perennial, densely hairy. Leaves linear to elliptical, untoothed. Flowers pale pink with usually deeper stripes, 15-25mm, borne in long-stalked clusters, surrounded by a *ruff* of hairy bracts; calyx with spreading whitish hairs. Dry calcareous rocks, lowlands and in the mountains. Apr-June. S and E Spain and S France.

1329 *Convolvulus cantabrica* **PINK CONVOLVULUS**. Short to medium tufted perennial; stems erect to spreading, sometimes almost prostrate, with a tough woody stock. Leaves green, linear to elliptical. often broadest above the middle, untoothed, generally covered with long spreading hairs. Flowers pink, 25-40mm, borne in lax clusters on stems longer than the accompanying leaves. Sandy and rocky habitats, banks, roadsides and waste land. Mar-June. T. One of the common bindweeds of the Med region.

1330 *Convolvulus lineatus*. Similar, but plant *silvery* with appressed, not spreading, silky hairs. Flowers pink 20-30mm on stalks shorter than the accompanying leaves. Dry rocky and sandy habitats, fields and waste land. Apr-June. Probably T, but rarer in the E Med.

1331 *Convolvulus althaeoides* **MALLOW-LEAVED BINDWEED**. Rather vigorous trailing or twining, hairy perennial, to 1m, with a slender creeping rootstock. Leaves very variable, often rather greyish, the lowest heart-shaped to kidney-shaped, often with a wavy margin, stalked; upper leaves *deeply lobed*, generally with linear, palmately arranged, divisions. Flowers deep pink, 30-50mm, solitary or paired, long-stalked. Rocky habitats, dry fields, roadsides, banks, hillslopes. Mar-July. T. Commonly seen. A form often seen in the C and E Med has silvery-hairy leaves with narrower lobes; it is generally referred to subsp. *tenuissimus [C. elegantissimus]* (1331a).

1332 *Convolvulus sabatius [C. mauritanicus]* **MAURITANIAN BINDWEED**. Vigorous trailing or scrambling perennial with a branched woody stock. Leaves rounded to oblong or elliptical, untoothed, deep green, hairy. Flowers *bright blue*, sometimes pink, 25-40mm, solitary or 2-3 together. Dry rocky habitats, often coastal, old walls. Mar-July, sometimes later. NW Italy, Sicily and NW Africa. Widely cultivated, especially in the W Med.

1333 *Convolvulus valentinus*. Similar, but leaves *narrow*, linear to narrow-oblong. Flowers slightly larger, blue, pink, white or yellowish. Dry, often rocky habitats. E Spain and NW Africa.

1334 *Convolvulus arvensis* **BINDWEED**. Variable, creeping or twining, slightly hairy or hairless, stoloniferous perennial, to 2m, though often less. Leaves arrow-shaped to oblong, stalked. Flowers white, or pink with white stripes, 15-30mm, solitary or paired, on stalks shorter than the subtending leaves, weakly scented. Cultivated, waste and fallow land, roadsides, scrub, occasionally on sand-dunes. Apr-Sept. T. A widespread weed of cultivation in many parts of the northern hemisphere.

1335 *Convolvulus betonicifolius*. Similar, but more *densely* hairy and with larger, pinker flowers, often in clusters of 3 or more. Cultivated fields, dry stony places, vineyards. Apr-July. Balkans eastwards, including Cyprus; naturalised in France, Italy and Sicily.

1336 *Convolvulus siculus* **SMALL BLUE CONVOLVULUS**. Low to short trailing or spreading, hairy annual or short-lived perennial; stems usually not twining. Leaves lanceolate to oval or heart-shaped, untoothed, stalked. Flowers blue with a yellowish centre, 9-12mm, distinctly *5-lobed*, solitary or paired, short-stalked. Dry rocky habitats, hillslopes, sandy places. Feb-June. T.

1337 *Convolvulus coelesyriacus*. Similar, but flowers larger, 15-28mm, pink or purplish, and the upper leaves *often lobed*. Similar habitats. Feb-May. Cyprus, Lebanon and Palestine.

1338 *Convolvulus tricolor* **DWARF** or **ANNUAL CONVOLVULUS**. Somewhat hairy short to medium, rather spreading annual. Leaves oval to elliptical, broadest above the middle, untoothed, unstalked. Flowers tricoloured, blue with white and a yellow centre, 20-50mm, solitary and long-stalked, lateral. Fruit hairy. Dry open habitats, fields, fallow land, sandy places, roadsides. Mar-June. T – but absent from some of the smaller islands and much of the extreme E Med. Widely cultivated for ornament.

1339 *Convolvulus pentapetaloides*. Similar, but a shorter plant with smaller blue flowers, sometimes with a yellowish centre, 10-15mm, *5-lobed*. Fruit hairless. Similar habitats and flowering time. T.

1340 *Convolvulus humilis*. Similar, but flowers more or less *unstalked* and fruit hairy. Fields, fallow land and roadsides. Mar-June. Iberian Peninsula, Italy, Sicily, N Africa and the extreme E Med, including Cyprus.

BORAGE FAMILY Boraginaceae

Herbs or small shrubs, often with bristly stems and leaves, the bristles often with swollen bases. Leaves simple and alternate. Flowers in spiralled clusters (scorpioid cymes), short-stalked, 5-parted; corolla funnel-shaped or constricted at the mouth; stamens 5, joined to the corolla. Fruit consisting of 4, occasionally fewer, nutlets, often ornamented and hidden within the persistent calyx.

1341 *Heliotropium europaeum* **HELIOTROPE.** Variable, low to short, erect or spreading, hairy annual, generally branched. Leaves oval to elliptical, grey-green, stalked. Flowers *white* with a yellow 'eye', 2-4.5mm, borne in one-sided, forked, spiralled spikes unscented; sepals linear-oblong, spreading. Fruit splitting into 4 nutlets, occasionally only 2. Cultivated, fallow and waste ground, roadsides. Apr-Nov. T.

1342 *Heliotropium dolosum.* Similar, but flowers *scented*, 3-5mm; sepals lanceolate, erect; stigma hairy (not hairless). Similar habitats and flowering time. Italy and the Balkans eastwards, including Cyprus.

1343 *Heliotropium supinum.* Like *H. europaeum*, but a rather sprawling plant with fruit with a *single* nutlet and calyx with lobes united to the top, falling with the fruit. Cultivated and fallow ground, often close to the sea. May-Nov. T.

1344 *Heliotropium hirsutissimum.* Like *H. europaeum*, but stems with long spreading, greyish or yellowish, hairs and flowers *larger*, 4-6mm, with scales in the throat. Similar habitats and flowering time. Greece eastwards, including Cyprus.

1345 *Heliotropium curassavicum.* Like *H. europaeum*, but a fleshier *hairless* plant with spreading or prostrate stems and linear-oblong leaves. Flowers 1-2.5mm, with oval sepals. Sandy and saline coastal habitats. Apr-Sept. Naturalised in the W Med, eastwards to Sicily. (The Americas).

1346 *Heliotropium suaveolens.* Like *H. europaeum*, but flowers larger, 4.5-8mm, scented, without scales in the throat. Similar habitats and flowering time. S Italy eastwards – not Cyprus.

1347 *Neatostema apulum [Lithospermum apulum]* **YELLOW GROMWELL.** Low to short annual, with a solitary or many erect, rather bristly stems, branched above. Leaves linear to oblong, bristly especially along the margins, the lower short-stalked, the upper unstalked and *erect*. Flowers yellow, 6-7mm long. Nutlets pale brown, warted. Dry open habitats, cultivated and fallow fields, rocky and stony slopes, roadsides. Feb-June. T.

1348 *Buglossoides purpurocaerulea [Lithospermum purpurocaerulea]* **PURPLE GROMWELL.** Short to medium rhizomatous perennial, hairy; stems erect, unbranched. Leaves lanceolate to narrow-elliptical, long-pointed, dark green. Flowers reddish-purple changing to dark blue, funnel-shaped, 14-19mm long, the terminal leafy cymes elongating in fruit. Nutlets white, shiny. Woodland margins and scrub, hedges. Mar-June. Spain eastwards to Turkey.

1349 *Buglossoides arvensis [Lithospermum arvense]* **CORN GROMWELL.** Very variable low to medium, somewhat bristly annual; stem often solitary, erect, little-branched. Leaves oblong, often broadest above the middle, the upper narrower, linear, pointed, and generally erect. Flowers white, blue or purplish, 6-9mm long, borne in solitary terminal cymes. Nutlets brown, hard and warted. Cultivated, fallow and waste ground, roadsides, stony slopes. Jan-June. T.

1350 *Buglossoides tenuiflora [Lithospermum tenuiflorum].* Similar, but the flowers blue, more crowded, smaller, the limb only 2mm diam. (not 3-4mm) and the bracts neatly arranged in two rows. Similar habitats and flowering time. Yugoslavia and Greece eastwards, including Cyprus.

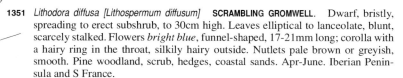

1351 *Lithodora diffusa [Lithospermum diffusum]* **SCRAMBLING GROMWELL.** Dwarf, bristly, spreading to erect subshrub, to 30cm high. Leaves elliptical to lanceolate, blunt, scarcely stalked. Flowers *bright blue*, funnel-shaped, 17-21mm long; corolla with a hairy ring in the throat, silkily hairy outside. Nutlets pale brown or greyish, smooth. Pine woodland, scrub, hedges, coastal sands. Apr-June. Iberian Peninsula and S France.

1352 *Lithodora zahnii [Lithospermum zahnii]* **GREEK GROMWELL.** Dwarf subshrub, to 40cm high, dense and much-branched with silvery-hairy young shoots; stems becoming leafless and woody with age. Leaves linear to linear-oblong, greenish or greyish, with *revolute* margins. Flowers white or pale blue, funnel-shaped, 13-15mm, solitary or in clusters of 2-3, but aggregated into heads; calyx softly hairy. Nutlets smooth. Cliffs. May-June. S Greece (SE of Kalamata) – endemic.

1353 *Lithodora hispidula [Lithospermum hispidulum]*. Similar, but leaves more or less *flat* and flowers bluish-violet, reddish, whitish or purple, smaller, 9-10mm. Nutlets white, minutely warted. Rock crevices and rocky banks, generally in garrigue, pine woodland. Feb-June. Crete, Karpathos, Turkey, Cyprus and Syria.

1354 *Lithodora rosmarinifolium [Lithospermum rosmarinifolium]* **ROSEMARY-LEAVED GROMWELL.** Densely branched subshrub to 60cm high; branches erect to spreading, grey-hairy when young. Leaves linear to lanceolate, *rigid*, dark green, but densely grey-hairy beneath, generally with a revolute margin. Flowers blue, lilac or white, 15-17mm, the corolla-throat hairless, but the tube hairy on the outside. Nutlets whitish, smooth. Rock crevices. Jan-May. S Italy and Sicily.

1355 *Lithodora fruticosa [Lithospermum fruticosum]* **SHRUBBY GROMWELL.** Similar, but the leaves oblong-linear and the corolla-tube hairless on the outside. Dry rocky habitats. Apr-June. Spain and S France.

Onosma **GOLDEN DROPS.** Bristly biennial or perennial herbs, occasionally annual, often with long narrow leaves. Flowers in terminal, sometimes branched cymes; calyx with narrow bristly lobes; corolla tubular, usually drooping, often yellow, but sometimes white or pink, with 5 very short, sometimes obscure, lobes. There are many species in the region, although the majority are confined to the higher mountains, above 1000m.

1356 *Onosma frutescens*. Slender-branched spreading, bushy perennial, with a woody stock, to 25cm, with erect flowering stems; all bristles *simple* (unbranched). Leaves linear to oblong, numerous, densely grey-hairy. Flowers pale yellow tinged with purple, 16-21mm long, hairless, about one and a half times as long as the calyx; anthers protruding. Rocks, cliffs and old walls. Apr-June. C and S Greece, Aegean Is., Turkey, to Palestine.

1357 *Onosma fruticosa*. Similar, but flowers smaller, 10-14mm long, golden-yellow, solitary or in clusters of 2-3. Dry stony hillslopes in the garrigue. Mar-May. Cyprus – endemic.

1358 *Onosma tricerosperma*. Similar, but flowering stems *branched*. Nutlets warted, generally with 3 short horns. Dry rocky and sandy habitats. Apr-June. C and S Spain.

1359 *Onosma echioides*. Short tufted perennial with several erect flowering stems; bristles *all branched* and star-shaped (stellate). Leaves linear to linear-oblong. Flowers pale yellow, 18-25mm long, twice as long as the calyx; corolla minutely hairy on the outside, cylindrical at the top but tapered towards the base. Nutlets smooth and shiny. Dry rocky and stony habitats. Apr-July. Italy, Sicily, Yugoslavia and Albania.

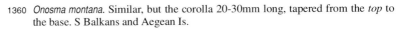

1360 *Onosma montana.* Similar, but the corolla 20-30mm long, tapered from the *top* to the base. S Balkans and Aegean Is.

1361 *Onosma heterophylla.* Like *O. montana*, but calyx with some simple (not stellate) bristles; corolla 20-30mm long. Leaves narrow-elliptic, blunt, enlarged at the base. Sandy coastal habitats and rocks. Apr-June. Balkan Peninsula and Turkey.

1362 *Onosma erecta [O. laconica].* Tufted, short, greyish perennial, with several flowering stems, becoming rather woody at the base, densely stellate-hairy. Leaves oblong to linear-lanceolate, the lower larger than the upper. Flowers bright yellow, 20-24mm long, about twice as long as the calyx; corolla minutely hairy or hairless. Rocks and cliffs, mainly in the mountains. Apr-June. S Greece and Crete. Cretan plants have a hairless corolla.

1363 *Onosma taurica.* Similar, but flowers pale yellow, or cream, 20-30mm long, the calyx with *simple* bristles; corolla two or three times longer than the calyx. Rocks and cliffs. Yugoslavia, Greece and Turkey.

1364 *Onosma visianii.* Rather robust short to medium, bristly biennial, all bristles simple; stem erect, much-branched to form a pyramid. Leaves linear-lanceolate. Flowers cream or pale yellow, 15-20mm long; corolla one and a third times as long as the calyx, narrowed below, minutely hairy, the anthers not protruding; calyx rather pale yellowish-green, very bristly. Nutlets minutely warted. Grassy and rocky habitats. May-July. Balkans and Turkey – not on the islands.

1365 *Onosma graeca.* Similar, but flowers smaller, 14-15mm long, pale yellow, tinged with purple as they age. Dry rocky and grassy habitats. Mar-May. S Greece, S Aegean Is. and Crete.

1366 *Onosma arenaria* Like *A. graeca*, but plant perennial, usually with non-flowering leaf-rosettes and leaves with simple bristles as well some branched ones. Flowers pale yellow, 12-19mm long, twice as long as the calyx. Nutlets smooth and shiny. Rocky and grassy habitats. Yugoslavia and Albania.

Cerinthe **HONEYWORTS.** Annual herbs, often with rather fleshy leaves, usually hairless or almost so. Flowers borne in simple spirals, generally branched, with large and conspicuous leaf-like bracts concealing the calyces; corolla tubular, drooping. Nutlets fused into two pairs.

1367 *Cerinthe major* **HONEYWORT.** Rather fleshy, grey-green, almost hairless short to medium annual. Lower leaves oblong, broadest above the middle, stalked; upper leaves oval, clasping the stem with a heart-shaped base; all leaves covered with *white swellings*; bracts oval to almost heart-shaped, grey-green with a reddish tinge or dark purple (var. *purpurascens*). Flowers yellow with a dark reddish-brown or reddish-purple ring at the base, occasionally all dark purple, 15-30mm long, the short oval lobes recurved. Cultivated, fallow and waste places, roadsides, stony slopes, field margins. Mar-June. T – not Balearic Is. or Cyprus. Forms with deeper prple overall are found in Portugal.

1368 *Cerinthe minor* **LESSER HONEYWORT.** Similar, but annual or biennial with smaller flowers, 10-12mm long, yellow, sometimes with 5 violet spots towards the base, the lobes pointed and *straight*. Similar habitats as well as open woodland and rocky places. Apr-July.

1369 *Cerinthe retorta* **VIOLET HONEYWORT.** Slightly bristly short to medium annual, green or bluish-green; stem erect, usually branched above. Lower leaves oval to oblong, often broadest above the middle; upper leaves oval and clasping the stem with a heart-shaped base; all leaves usually with some white swellings; bracts like the upper leaves but *deep violet*. Flowers pale yellow with a violet tip, 10-15mm long, the corolla slightly curved, with recurved lobes. Rocky places, field borders, pathways, roadsides – often forming large colonies. Balkans, including Crete.

1370 *Alkanna orientalis* **ORIENTAL ALKANET.** Bristly and glandular-hairy, medium perennial; stems erect. Leaves lanceolate to oblong, with irregular and undulate margins, the basal crowded and stalked, the upper unstalked and clasping the stem. Flowers yellow, with a tube longer than the calyx and spreading lobes, 9-12mm, borne in dense clusters which elongate in fruit; calyx glandular, elongating in fruit to 10-15mm; corolla hairles outside. Rocky habitats, stony slopes. Feb-May. S Greece eastwards, not Cyprus.

1371 *Alkanna graeca.* Similar, but leaf-margins *flat* and untoothed. Flowers slightly smaller, 8-10mm. Rocky habitats, generally in the mountains. Apr-June. S Balkans – absent from the islands.

1372 *Alkanna lutea.* Like *A. graeca*, but always annual without basal leaves and flowers smaller, 5-7mm. Similar habitats. May-July. Spain eastwards to Italy.

1373 *Alkanna lehmanii [A. tinctoria, Anchusa tinctoria, Lithospermum tinctorum]* **DYER'S ALKANET.** Bristly, short, spreading to almost prostrate perennial with many basal leaves and a woody base. Leaves linear-lanceolate to lanceolate, the lower stalked, the upper unstalked and *clasping* the stem with heart-shaped bases. Flowers bright blue, occasionally pale mauve, 6-8mm, borne in branched inflorescences that are congested at first, the lower flowers with large leaf-like bracts. Rocky garrigue and other sandy and rocky habitats, waste ground, roadsides, often close to the sea. Feb-Apr. T – not Balearic Is. or Corsica. The rootstock, like that of many borages, contains a red dye.

Nonea **NONEA.** Bristly annuals or perennials. Flowers in bracteate cymes; corolla yellow, purple, brown or white with a cylindrical tube and a funnel-shaped limb, with a tuft of hairs in the throat; style not protruding. Nutlets with a thickened, collar-like, ring at the base.

1374 *Nonea pulla* **NONEA.** Short to medium, greyish, bristly annual or perennial; stems erect, branched above. Leaves lanceolate to linear-lanceolate, pointed, untoothed, the upper clasping the stem. Flowers dark reddish-brown or blackish-purple, 10-14mm long, with short spreading lobes, borne in leafy one-sided clusters; sepals enlarging in fruit. Dry grassy habitats and stony places. Mar-July. Greece and Yugoslavia, but naturalised elsewhere, particularly in the W Med.

1375 *Nonea vesicaria [N. nigricans].* Similar, but lower leaves occasionally toothed and flowers *smaller*, the limb 3-5mm (not 5-8mm). Similar habitats and flowering time. Iberian Peninsula, Balearic Is. and Sicily.

1376 *Nonea obtusifolia.* Low to short bristly annual, seldom more than 15cm tall, with ascending stems. Leaves oblong to oval, blunt, more or less untoothed. Flowers blue or purplish, 3-6mm, borne in small clusters. Nutlets black, smooth and shiny. Dry waste and rocky habitats. Mar-July. Greece – Aegean region.

1377 *Nonea ventricosa.* Bristly low to medium annual, with ascending, little-branched stems. Leaves lanceolate, pointed to semi-blunt, the lower short-stalked, the upper half-clasping the stem. Flowers pale yellow or whitish, 2.5-5mm, borne in simple cymes with leaf-like bracts. Fruit with a large and *inflated* calyx; nutlets kidney-shaped. Cultivated and waste ground, exposed rocky hills and stony places. Jan-June. Spain eastwards to Turkey, Cyprus and Palestine, but absent from most of the islands.

calyx

1378 *Nonea philistaea.* Similar, but inflorescences 2-3-branched and flowers *larger*, 6-8mm. Similar habitats, occasionally also on sand-dunes. Jan-Apr. Cyprus, Syria and Palestine.

1379 *Nonea micrantha.* Like *N. ventricosa*, but flowers pale blue or yellowish, with a more deeply divided limb and nutlets egg-shaped (not kidney-shaped). Spain.

Echium **BUGLOSSES**. Bristly annual, biennial or perennial herbs; bristles with pimple-like bases. Flowers borne in spiralled cymes that make up a dense or lax panicle; calyx lobed almost to the base; corolla irregular (zygomorphic) without scales in the throat, with included or protruding stamens.

1380 *Echium italicum* **PALE BUGLOSS**. Robust, erect, medium to tall biennial, to 1m, with dense white or yellowish bristles; forming large leafy rosettes in the first year. Leaves lanceolate to narrowly elliptical. Flowers yellowish, pinkish or bluish-white, 10-12mm long, numerous in a symmetrically branched *pyramidal* inflorescence; stamens long-protruding, filaments pale. Rocky and grassy habitats, pastures, waste ground, roadsides, ruins, vineyards. Apr-July. T.

1381 *Echium asperrimum [E. italicum* subsp. *pyrenaicum].* Similar, but flowers flesh-pink with red filaments, 13-18mm long. Similar habitats and flowering time. Spain, Balearic Is., S France and Italy.

1382 *Echium angustifolium [E. hispidum, E. sibthorpii]* **NARROW-LEAVED BUGLOSS**. An erect to sprawling short to medium, grey-bristly perennial, with a woody stock; stems much-branched, rather irregularly so. Leaves linear to narrow-oblong, often rather undulate, usually not more than 8mm wide. Flowers red or purple, frequently changing colour from one to the other, 16-22mm long, with 4-5 protruding stamens, borne in an irregular spreading inflorescence. Rocky and sandy coastal habitats, roadsides, waste ground, hillslopes. Mar-July. Greece and Crete eastwards, including Cyprus.

1383 *Echium plantagineum [E. lycopsis* in part, *E. maritimum]* **PURPLE VIPER'S BUGLOSS**. A short to medium, erect, softly hairy annual or biennial, forming a broad dome or pyramid shape in flower. Leaves oval, the upper lanceolate, with prominent lateral veins; upper leaves unstalked and half-clasping the stem. Flowers reddish but soon changing to blue, violet-blue or purple, 18-30mm long, broadly funnel-shaped, with *two* protruding stamens; corolla hairy on veins and along margins. Fallow and waste ground, sandy places, roadsides, occasionally on the seashore. Feb-July. T. The roots yield a purple dye.

1384 *Echium vulgare* **VIPER'S BUGLOSS**. Similar, but a rough-hairy biennial, occasionally perennial, with one or several stems. Flowers smaller, 10-19mm, with 4-5 *protruding* stamens; corolla uniformly hairy. Dry open habitats, pastures, roadsides, fallow land, olive groves. Apr-July. T – not Balearic Is. or Cyprus.

1385 *Echium gaditanum.* Like *E. vulgare*, but more robust, generally with *numerous* spreading to ascending flowering stems and upper leaves oval (not narrow-lanceolate). Flowers blue to violet-blue, 11-20mm long, mostly with 3-5 protuding stamens. Coastal habitats. Apr-June. S Spain and Portugal.

1386 *Echium sabulicola.* Like *E. gaditanum*, but upper leaves with a narrowed or stalked base, with numerous white bristles. Flowers dark blue to bluish-purple, 12-22mm long, mostly with 1-2 protruding stamens. Coastal sands, dry fields and roadsides. Apr-July. Iberian Peninsula and NW Africa eastwards to Italy and Sicily.

1387 *Echium creticum.* Like *E. sabulicola*, but with one or few *erect* stems and flowers reddish-purple to pinkish-carmine, 15-40mm long. Roadsides and dry grassy and stony slopes. Apr-July. Iberian Peninsula, S France, Balearic Is., Corsica and Sardinia.

1388 *Echium parviflorum [E. calycinum]* **SMALL-FLOWERED BUGLOSS.** Short to medium bristly annual or biennial, with several or many ascending to erect stems, rarely exceeding 40cm in height. Leaves spatula-shaped to oblong, long-stalked, the upper oblong, unstalked. Flowers pale to dark blue, small, 10-13mm long, with all 5 stamens *included*. Dry rocky and sandy habitats, fields, fallow and waste ground, roadsides, occasionally on the coast. Mar-June. T – absent from Cyprus and parts of the E Med.

1389 *Echium arenarium.* Similar, but *stems* usually prostrate or sprawling and flowers violet-blue or mauve, 6-11mm long. Coastal sands and rocks, low coastal scrub, occasionally inland. Mar-May. Chiefly on Med islands, including Cyprus, also in S Italy, Greece and N Africa.

1390 *Procopiania cretica [Trachystemon creticus]* **PROCOPIANIA.** A bristly, short to medium perennial; stems usually branched. Leaves oval, often with a semi-heart-shaped base, stalked, the upper unstalked. Flowers bluish-violet, occasionally white, 12-20mm, with narrow *recurved* petal-lobes and prominent protruding stamens. Rocky habitats and cliffs, mainly in the mountains. Apr-May. S Greece, S Aegean Is., Crete.

1391 *Procopiania insularis.* Similar, but flowers rather smaller with *blunt* (not pointed) sepals and shorter petal-lobes. Similar habitats and flowering time. Aegean Is. and Crete.

1392 *Procopiania circinalis [Symphytum circinale].* Readily distinguished from the previous species by the *coiled* tips to the white petals. Greece (Euboea) and E Aegean Is.

1393 *Symphytum bulbosum* **TUBEROUS COMFREY.** Short to medium, creeping perennial with tuberous rhizomes; stems erect to ascending, with hooked hairs. Leaves oval to lanceolate, the lower stalked. Flowers pale yellow, 8-11mm long, *tubular*, with recurved lobes and somewhat protruding anthers. Damp habitats, woods and stream banks. May-July. S France, Corsica and Sardinia, eastwards to the Balkans – not Crete.

1394 *Symphytum ottomanum.* Similar, but flowers smaller, 5-7mm long. Wooded habitats. Balkans and Turkey.

1395 *Borago officinalis* **BORAGE.** Short to medium, bristly annual, occasionally overwintering; stems often rather robust, generally branched. Basal leaves oval to lanceolate, stalked, in a rosette to begin with, wavy-margined; stem leaves smaller, the uppermost clasping the stem and unstalked. Flowers bright blue with a whitish centre, 20-25mm, half-nodding and rather *star-shaped*, with spreading or somewhat reflexed pointed lobes and a prominent cone of purple-black anthers, borne in broad, branched cymes. Cultivated, waste and fallow ground, roadsides, often in dry sunny places. Mar-June. T. Grown for ornament and for flavouring drinks. Today cultivated on a field scale for its oil-rich seeds.

1396 *Borago pygmaea [B. laxiflora, Campanula pygmaea].* Somewhat like the previous species, but a rather sprawling perennial with *bell-shaped* clear, pale blue flowers, 8-12mm long. Damp habitats. Apr-July. Corsica, Sardinia and Capri.

1397 *Asperugo procumbens* **MADWORT.** Low spreading, prostrate or sprawling, bristly annual, sometimes clambering over other plants; stems angled. Leaves lanceolate, *mostly opposite*, untoothed or slightly toothed, the lower stalked. Flowers violet to purplish with a white throat, 2-3mm, solitary or paired at the base of the upper leaves. Fruit surrounded by the enlarged leaf-like sepals. Cultivated, waste and fallow ground, farmyards, vineyards, often on nitrogen-rich soils. Jan-July. T.

THE COLOUR PLATES

The following 192 pages illustrate over 1500 species of wild or commonly cultivated flowering plants in the Mediterranean region, with the more typical or conspicuous grasses, rushes, sedges and ferns. The numbers beside each Latin name refer to those in the main text. Eighteen principal families shown on the facing page, with typical plants in each, are given below. For their characteristics, see pages 16-17.

CARYOPHYLLACEAE. Spurreys, catchflies, campions, gypsophila, pinks. Page 43.

RANUNCULACEAE. Anemones, buttercups, delphiniums, larkspurs, love-in-a-mist. Page 50.

PAPAVERACEAE. Poppies, roemeria, horned poppies, hypecoum. Page 59.

CRUCIFERAE. Wallflower, stocks, candytufts, pepperworts, cresses, mustards, radishes. Page 62.

ROSACEAE. Roses, briars, hawthorn, potentilla, apple, pear, cherries, plums, laurels. Page 74.

LEGUMINOSAE. Gorse, lupins, vetches medicks, melilots and clovers. Page 78.

EUPHORBIACEAE. Spurges, mercury, andrachne, castor-oil plant. Page 117.

MALVACEAE. Mallows, hollyhocks, lavateras, cottons, hibiscus. Page 131.

UMBELLIFERAE. Eryngos, fennel, hare's-ears, hogweed, hedge-parsley, Page 153.

BORAGINACEAE. Golden drops, buglosses, borages, forget-me-nots. Page 186.

LABIATAE. Skullcaps, deadnettles, catmints, thymes, mints, salvias. Page 388.

SCROPHULARIACEAE. Figworts, verbascums, snapdragons, foxgloves, speedwells. Page 407.

CAMPANULACEAE. Bellflowers, symphanandra, Venus's looking glass, sheep's bit. Page 428.

COMPOSITAE. Daisies, marigolds, thistles, cornflowers, hawk's-beards. Page 432.

LILIACEAE. Autumn crocuses, lilies, fritillarias, squills, grape hyacinths. Page 469.

AMARYLLIDACEAE. Sternbergias, snowdrops, snowflakes, narcissi. Page 489.

IRIDACEAE. Irises, gladioli, romuleas, crocuses. Page 492.

ORCHIDACEAE. Helleborines, cephalantheras, twayblades and many other types of orchid. Page 505.

CARYOPHYLLACEAE 125-196

BORAGINACEAE 1341-1415

RANUNCULACEAE 200-267

LABIATAE 1421-1547

PAPAVERACEAE 281-298

SCROPHULARIACEAE 1585-1653

CRUCIFERAE 310-374

CAMPANULACEAE 1753-1790

ROSACEAE 404-429

COMPOSITAE 1791-2083

LEGUMINOSAE 430-732

LILIACEAE 2087-2252

EUPHORBIACEAE 788-824

AMARYLLIDACEAE 2257-2281

MALVACEAE 891-924

IRIDACEAE 2283-2348

UMBELLIFERAE 1069-1075

ORCHIDACEAE 2380-2452

1 *Pinus halepensis*

2 *Pinus brutia*

3 *Pinus pine*

4 *Pinus nigra*

5 *Pinus pinaster*

8 *Abies cephalonica*

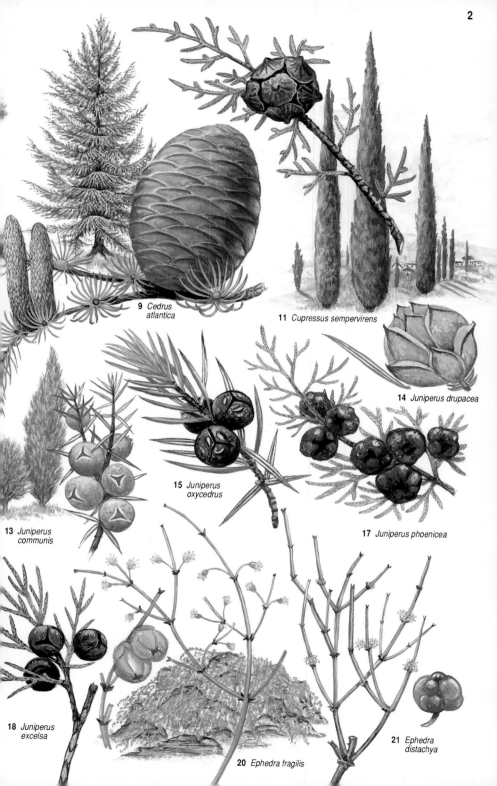

9 *Cedrus atlantica*

11 *Cupressus sempervirens*

14 *Juniperus drupacea*

13 *Juniperus communis*

15 *Juniperus oxycedrus*

17 *Juniperus phoenicea*

18 *Juniperus excelsa*

20 *Ephedra fragilis*

21 *Ephedra distachya*

3

24 *Quercus coccifera*

25 *Quercus ilex*

23 *Castanea sativa*

28 *Quercus aegilops*

33 *Cytinus ruber*

27 *Quercus suber*

31 *Quercus pubescens*

32 *Cytinus hypocistis*

34 *Cynomor coccineu*

37 Ostrya
carpinifolia

36 Carpinus
orientalis

35 Salix
pedicellata

38 Ulmus
canescens

41 Morus alba

39 Celtis
australis

44 Osyris
alba

42 Ficus
carica

43 Ficus
sycomorus

5

46 *Urtica atrovirens*

48 *Urtica pilulifera*

49 *Urtica membranacea*

50 *Parietaria judaica*

52 *Parietaria cretica*

55 *Cannabis sativa*

56 *Humulus lupulus*

57 *Aristolochia sempervirens*

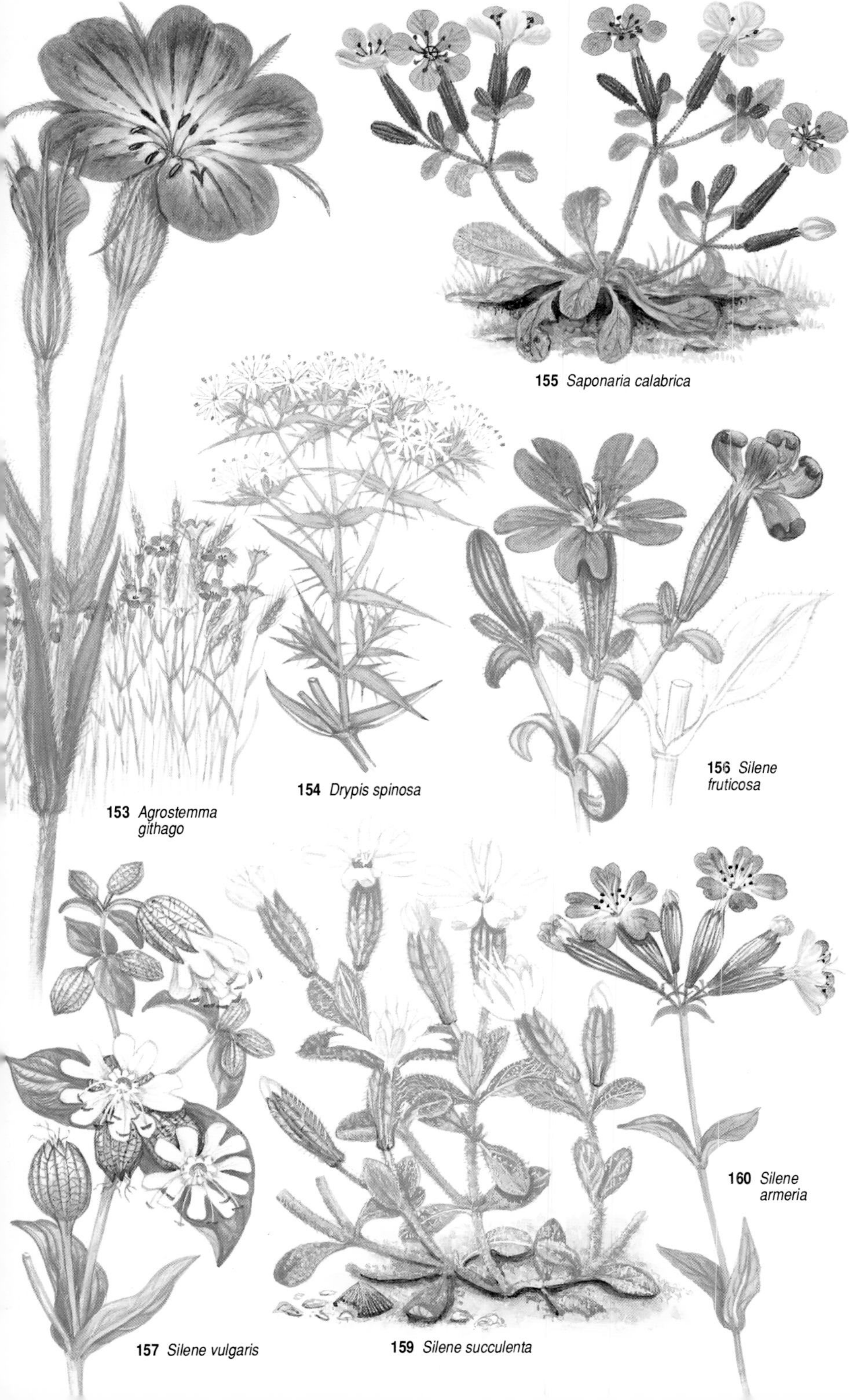

155 *Saponaria calabrica*

154 *Drypis spinosa*

156 *Silene fruticosa*

153 *Agrostemma githago*

157 *Silene vulgaris*

159 *Silene succulenta*

160 *Silene armeria*

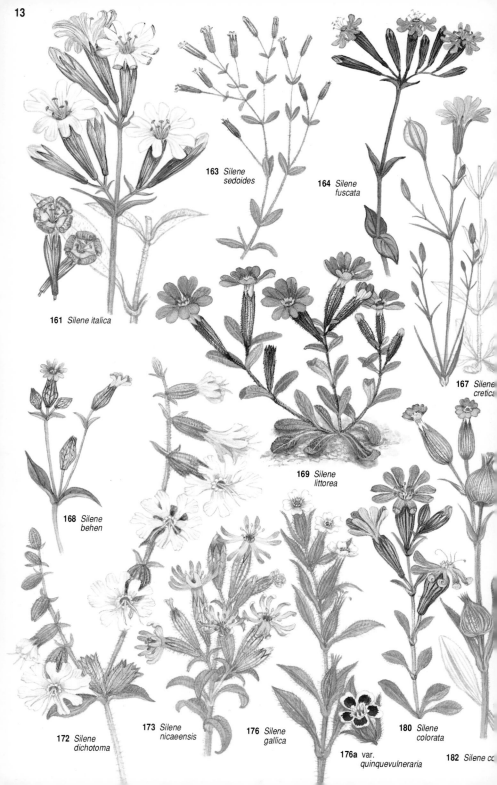

13

161 *Silene italica*

163 *Silene sedoides*

164 *Silene fuscata*

167 *Silene cretica*

168 *Silene behen*

169 *Silene littorea*

172 *Silene dichotoma*

173 *Silene nicaeensis*

176 *Silene gallica*

176a var. *quinquevulneraria*

180 *Silene colorata*

182 *Silene co*

222 *Adonis microcarpa*

224 *Ceratocephalus falcatus*

225 *Nigella arvensis*

223 *Adonis dentata*

219 *Adonis annua*

231 *Nigella damascena*

229 *Nigella sativa*

230 *Nigella hispanica*

233 *Nigella nigellastrum*

234 *Nigella ciliaris*

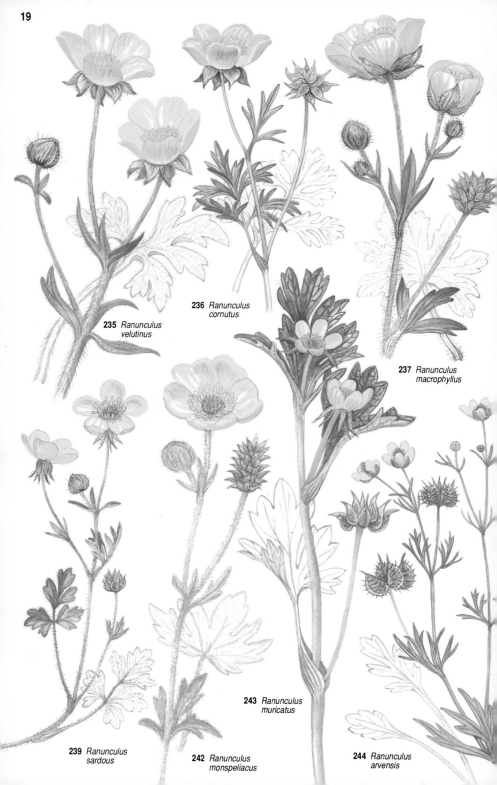

19

235 *Ranunculus velutinus*

236 *Ranunculus cornutus*

237 *Ranunculus macrophyllus*

239 *Ranunculus sardous*

242 *Ranunculus monspeliacus*

243 *Ranunculus muricatus*

244 *Ranunculus arvensis*

245 *Ranunculus parviflorus*

252 *Ranunculus ficaria*

250 *Ranunculus cupreus*

47 *Ranunculus gracilis*

249 *Ranunculus paludosus*

251 *Ranunculus sceleratus*

254 *Ranunculus millefoliatus*

256 *Ranunculus bullatus*

257 *Ranunculus asiaticus*

21

258 *Delphinium peregrinum*

262 *Delphinium pictum*

261 *Delphinium staphisagria*

264 *Consolida regalis*

266 *Consolida orientalis*

267 *Consolida ambigua*

313 *Malcolmia littorea*

315 *Malcolmia ramoisissima*

316 *Malcolmia maritima*

318 *Malcolmia chia*

319 *Ricotia cretica*

320 *Maresia nana*

321 *Cheiranthus cheiri*

322 *Arabis verna*

323 *Arabis cypria*

324 *Aubrieta deltoidea*

328 *Matthiola fruticulosa*

327 *Matthiola incana*

326 *Matthiola sinuata*

329 *Matthiola tricuspidata*

330 *Matthiola longipetala*

331 *Alyssoides sinuata*

332 *Alyssoides cretica*

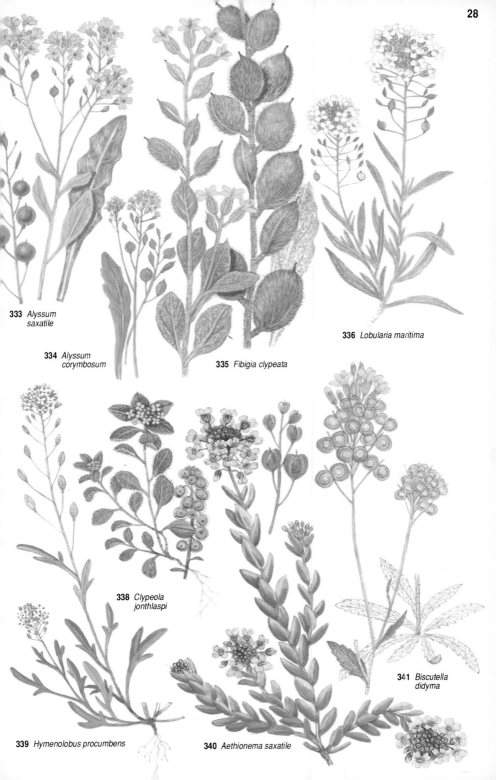

333 *Alyssum saxatile*

334 *Alyssum corymbosum*

335 *Fibigia clypeata*

336 *Lobularia maritima*

338 *Clypeola jonthlaspi*

339 *Hymenolobus procumbens*

340 *Aethionema saxatile*

341 *Biscutella didyma*

343 Iberis
sempervirens

345 Iberis
pruitii

348 Iberis
pinnata

350 Lepidium
spinosum

351 Lepidium
perfoliatum

352 Lepidium
latifolium

353 Cardaria
draba

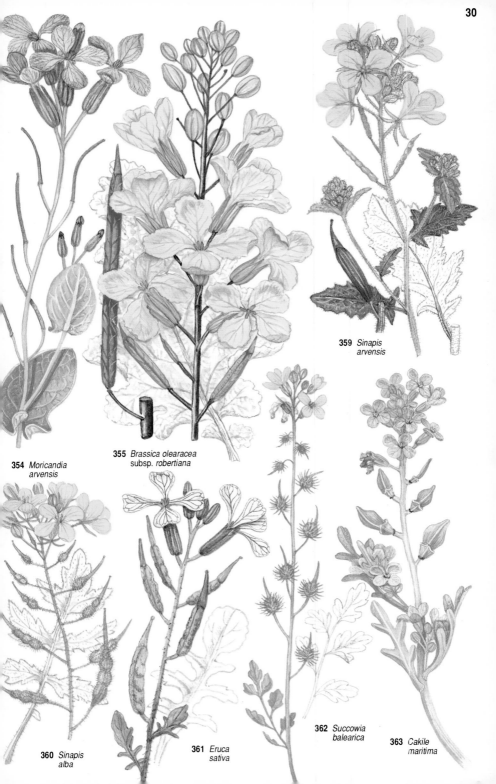

354 *Moricandia arvensis*

355 *Brassica olearacea subsp. robertiana*

359 *Sinapis arvensis*

360 *Sinapis alba*

361 *Eruca sativa*

362 *Succowia balearica*

363 *Cakile maritima*

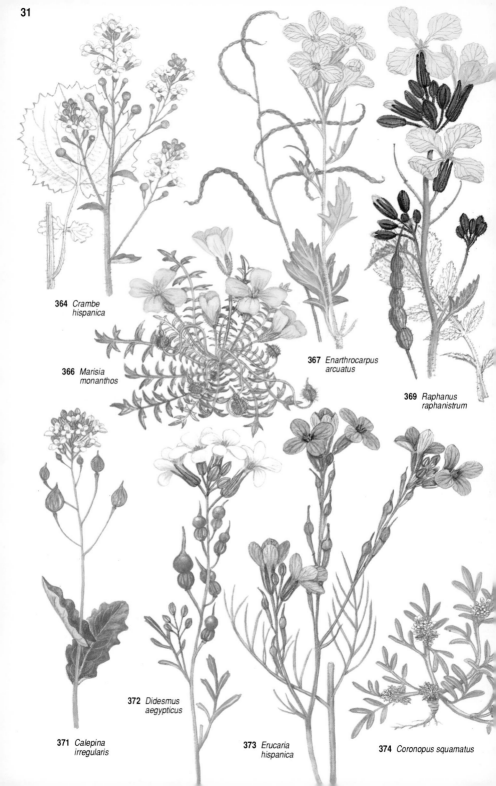

31

364 *Crambe
hispanica*

366 *Marisia
monanthos*

367 *Enarthrocarpus
arcuatus*

369 *Raphanus
raphanistrum*

371 *Calepina
irregularis*

372 *Didesmus
aegypticus*

373 *Erucaria
hispanica*

374 *Coronopus squamatus*

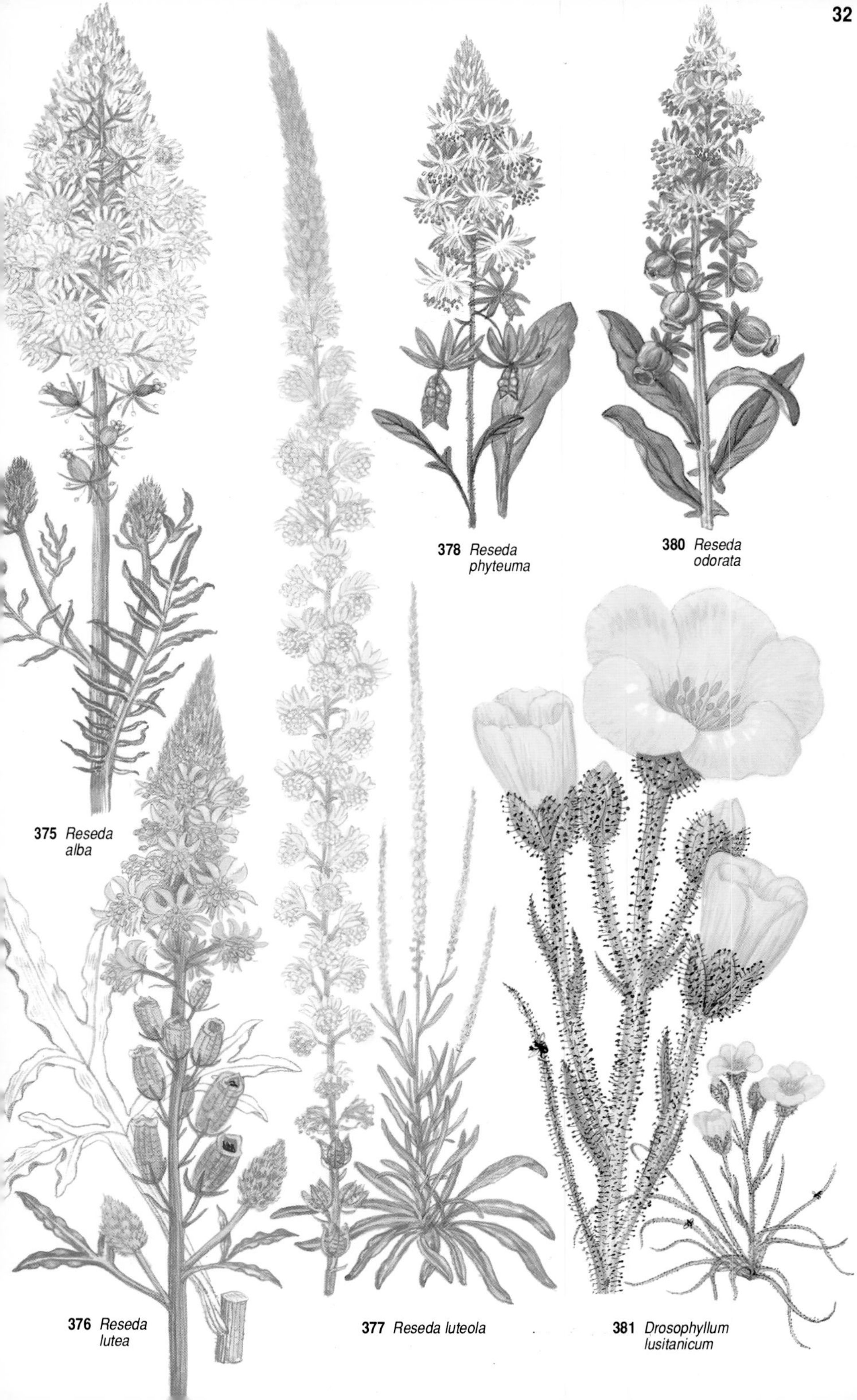

378 *Reseda phyteuma*

380 *Reseda odorata*

375 *Reseda alba*

376 *Reseda lutea*

377 *Reseda luteola*

381 *Drosophyllum lusitanicum*

33

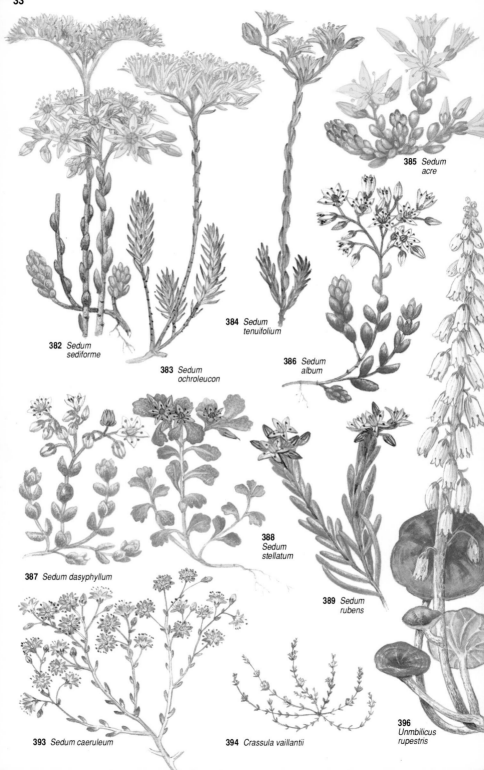

382 *Sedum sediforme*

383 *Sedum ochroleucon*

384 *Sedum tenuifolium*

385 *Sedum acre*

386 *Sedum album*

387 *Sedum dasyphyllum*

388 *Sedum stellatum*

389 *Sedum rubens*

393 *Sedum caeruleum*

394 *Crassula vaillantii*

396 *Unmbilicus rupestris*

430 *Cercis siliquastrum*

431 *Ceratonia siliqua*

436 *Acacia longifolia*

437 *Acacia melanoxylon*

432 *Acacia dealbata*

39

439 *Acacia cyanophylla*

440 *Acacia pycnantha*

438 *Acacia retinoides*

442 *Acacia armata*

443 *Albizzia julibrissin*

445 *Prosopis juliflora*

44 *Prosopis farcta*

447 *Argyrolobium zanonii*

446 *Anagyris foetida*

449 *Colutea arborescens*

451 *Podocytisus caramanicus*

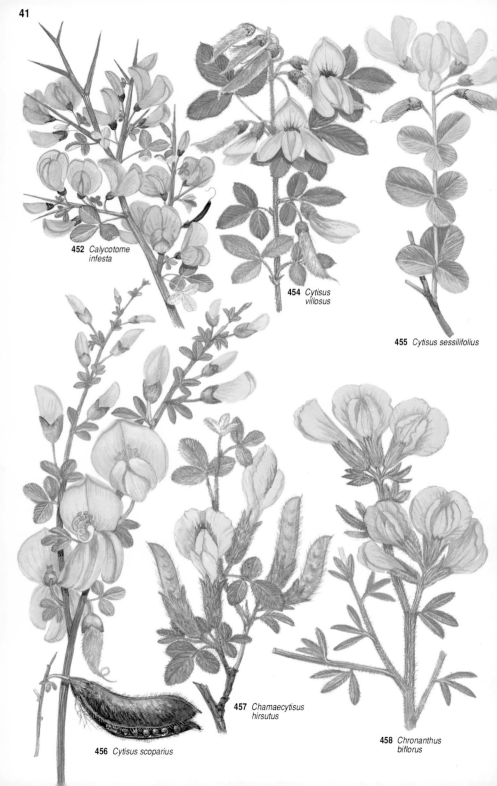

452 *Calycotome infesta*

454 *Cytisus villosus*

455 *Cytisus sessilifolius*

456 *Cytisus scoparius*

457 *Chamaecytisus hirsutus*

458 *Chronanthus biflorus*

459 *Teline monspessulana*

461 *Genista tinctoria*

462 *Genista sphacelata*

463 *Genista scorpius*

465 *Genista hispanica*

467 *Genista acanthoclada*

468 *Genista cinerea*

43

469 *Genista aetnensis*

472 *Genista umbellata*

473 *Ulex parviflorus*

475 *Ulex europaeus*

476 *Stauracanthus boivinii*

478 *Lygos sphaerocarpa*

479 *Lygos raetam*

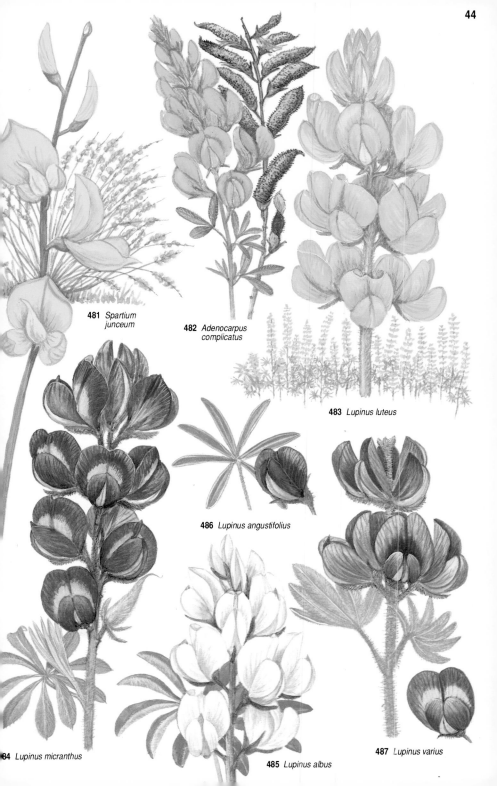

481 *Spartium junceum*

482 *Adenocarpus complicatus*

483 *Lupinus luteus*

486 *Lupinus angustifolius*

484 *Lupinus micranthus*

485 *Lupinus albus*

487 *Lupinus varius*

45

488 *Robinia pseudacacia*

490 *Galega officinalis*

491 *Astragalus boeticus*

492 *Astragalus hamosus*

493 *Astragalus stella*

496 *Astragalus massiliensis*

498 *Astragalus balearicus*

499 *Astragalus spruneri*

502 *Astragalus graecus*

501 *Astragalus echinatus*

504 *Astragalus lusitanicus*

505 *Bisserula pelecinus*

506 *Glycyrrhiza glabra*

508 *Psoralea bituminosa*

510 *Vicia villosa*

513 *Vicia benghalensis*

516 *Vicia ervilia*

520 *Vicia palaestina*

524 *Vicia sepium*

519 *Vicia hirsuta*

521 *Vicia laxiflora*

523 *Vicia tetrasperma*

525 *Vicia lutea*

526 *Vicia pannonica*

527 *Vicia hybrida*

528 *Vicia melanops*

531 *Vicia sativa*

533 *Vicia peregrina*

534 *Vicia narbonensis*

49

536 *Lathyrus tingitanus*

537 *Lathyrus latifolius*

539 *Lathyrus odoratus*

541 *Lathyrus sphaericus*

540 *Lathyrus saxatilis*

544 *Lathyrus setifolius*

545 *Lathyrus cicera*

549 *Lathyrus annuus*

547 *Lathyrus hirsutus*

546 *Lathyrus gorgonei*

548 *Lathyrus blepharicarpus*

551 *Lathyrus articulatus*

550 *Lathyrus clymenum*

552 *Lathyrus ochrus*

553 *Lathyrus aphaca*

554 *Lathyrus nissolia*

51

555 *Pisum sativum*

556 *Ononis natrix*

559 *Ononis ornithopodioides*

560 *Ononis biflora*

564 *Ononis campestris*

565 *Ononis diffusa*

562 *Ononis pusilla*

569 *Ononis variegata*

581 *Trigonella corniculata*

579 *Melilotus altissimus*

571 *Melilotus officinalis*

570 *Melilotus albus*

590 *Trigonella foenum-graecum*

587 *Trigonella caerulea*

588 *Trigonella coerulescens*

589 *Trigonella monspeliaca*

593 *Trigonella spinosa*

53

594 *Medicago lupulina*

596 *Medicago sativa*

596a subsp. *falcata*

597 *Medicago suffruticosa*

599 *Medicago orbicularis*

598 *Medicago arborea*

601 *Medicago rugosa*

600 *Medicago scutellata*

602 *Medicago intertexta*

605 *Medicago marina*

606 *Medicago littoralis*

612 *Medicago turbinata*

607 *M. truncatula*

609 *M. aculeata*

610 *M. rigidula*

613 *M. murex*

614 *M. constricta*

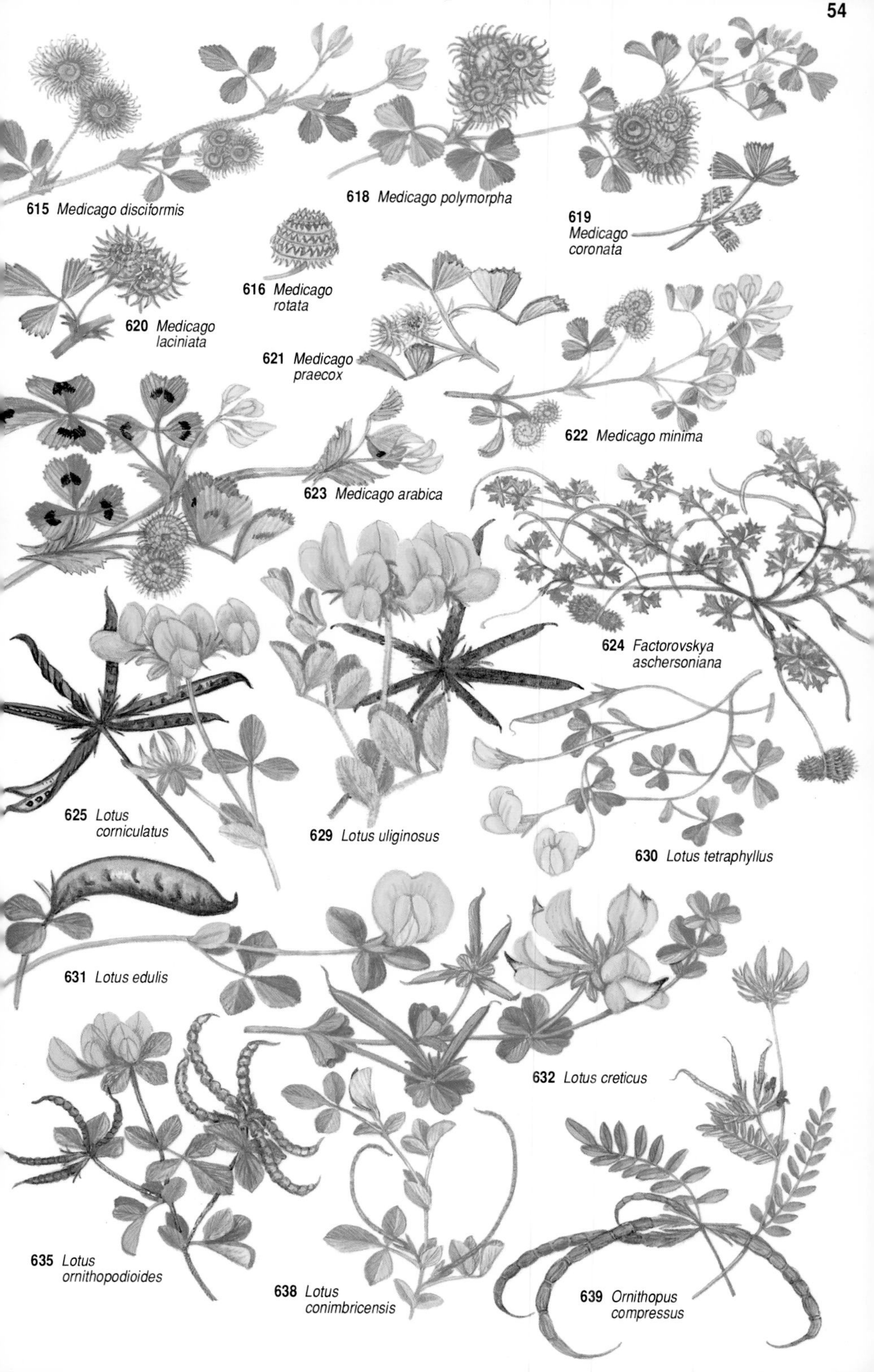

615 *Medicago disciformis*

618 *Medicago polymorpha*

619 *Medicago coronata*

616 *Medicago rotata*

620 *Medicago laciniata*

621 *Medicago praecox*

622 *Medicago minima*

623 *Medicago arabica*

624 *Factorovskya aschersoniana*

625 *Lotus corniculatus*

629 *Lotus uliginosus*

630 *Lotus tetraphyllus*

631 *Lotus edulis*

632 *Lotus creticus*

635 *Lotus ornithopodioides*

638 *Lotus conimbricensis*

639 *Ornithopus compressus*

55

642 *Trifolium repens*

643 *Trifolium hybridum* subsp. *elegans*

647 *Trifolium nigrescens*

648 *Trifolium isthmocarpum*

651 *Trifolium uniflorum*

652 *Trifolium fragiferum*

654 *Trifolium speciosum*

655 *Trifolium boisseri*

656 *Trifolium campestre*

657 *Trifolium resupinatum*

658 *Trifolium tomentosum*

659 *Trifolium pilulare*

661 *Trifolium incarnatum*

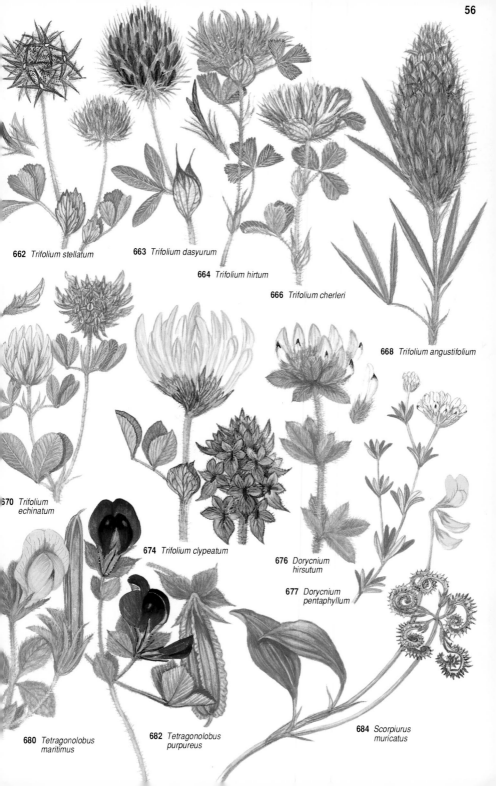

662 Trifolium stellatum

663 Trifolium dasyurum

664 Trifolium hirtum

666 Trifolium cherleri

668 Trifolium angustifolium

670 Trifolium echinatum

674 Trifolium clypeatum

676 Dorycnium hirsutum

677 Dorycnium pentaphyllum

680 Tetragonolobus maritimus

682 Tetragonolobus purpureus

684 Scorpiurus muricatus

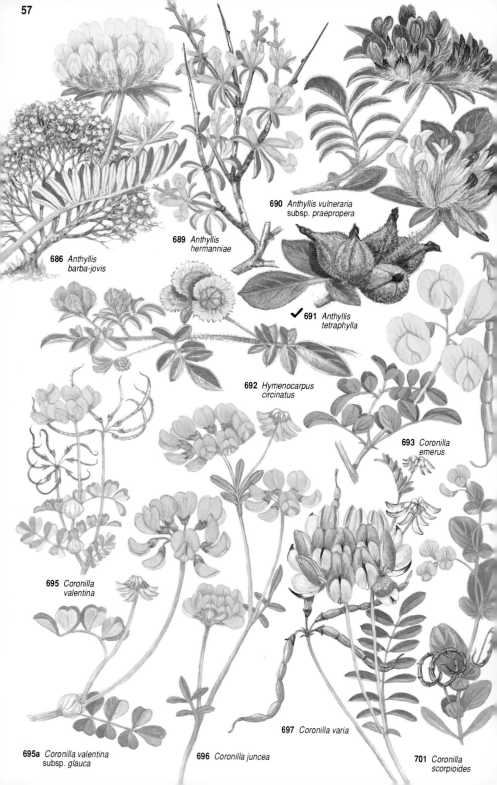

57

686 *Anthyllis barba-jovis*

689 *Anthyllis hermanniae*

690 *Anthyllis vulneraria* subsp. *praepropera*

✓ 691 *Anthyllis tetraphylla*

692 *Hymenocarpus circinatus*

693 *Coronilla emerus*

695 *Coronilla valentina*

695a *Coronilla valentina* subsp. *glauca*

696 *Coronilla juncea*

697 *Coronilla varia*

701 *Coronilla scorpioides*

706 *Hippocrepis unisiliquosa*

704 *Hippocrepis glauca*

713 *Hedysarum spinossisimum*

710 *Hedysarum coronarium*

715 *Alhagi graecorum*

720 *Onobrychis aequidentata*

718 *Onobrychis caput-galli*

722 *Ebenus creticus*

7 *Onobrychis saxatilis*

719 *Onobrychis crista-galli*

721 *Onobrychis venosa*

723 *Ebenus sibthorpii*

59

724 *Erythrina crista-galli*

725 *Wisteria sinensis*

727 *Sophora japonica*

728 *Gleditsia triacanthos*

729 *Delonix regia*

30 *Cassia corymbosa*

732 *Caesalpinia
pulcherrima*

61

733 Oxalis
corniculata

735 Oxalis
pes-caprae

736 Oxalis
articulata

738 Geranium
tuberosum

740 Geranium
malviflorum

741 Geranium
molle

743 Geranium
rotundifoli

744 Geranium
pusillum

748 Geranium
purpureum

745 Geranium
dissectum

746 Geranium
columbinum

747 Geranium
robertianum

749 Geranium
lucidum

750 Geranium
lanuginosum

751 *Erodium chium*

752 *Erodium malacoides*

757 *Erodium gruinum*

758 *Erodium botrys*

760 *Erodium ciconium*

761 *Erodium cicutarium*

764 *Zygophyllum fabago*

766 *Fagonia cretica*

767 *Peganum harmala*

768 *Tribulus terrestris*

63

769 Linum arboreum

771 Linum flavum

773 Linum nodiflorum

774 Linum campanulatum

777 Linum bienne

784 Linum strictum

775 Linum narbonense

776 Linum pubescens

780 Linum usitatissimum

778 Linum perenne

782 Linum maritimum

783 Linum trigynum

786 Linum suffruticosum subsp. salsa

788 Euphorbia
peplis

792 Euphorbia
dendroides

794 Euphorbia
acanthothamnos

795 Euphorbia
spinosa

797 Euphorbia
segetalis

799 Euphorbia
helioscopia

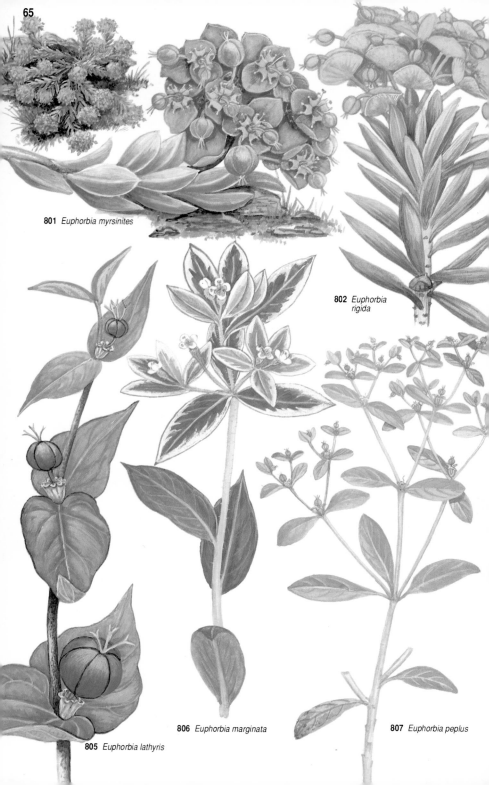

65

801 *Euphorbia myrsinites*

802 *Euphorbia rigida*

805 *Euphorbia lathyris*

806 *Euphorbia marginata*

807 *Euphorbia peplus*

811 *Euphorbia nicaeensis*

810 *Euphorbia biumbellata*

813 *Euphorbia paralias*

4 *Euphorbia pithyusa*

815 *Euphorbia terracina*

816 *Euphorbia cyparissias*

817 *Euphorbia serrata*

818 *Euphorbia characias*

819 *Euphorbia wulfenii*

820 *Mercurialis annua*

821 *Andrachne telephioides*

822 *Chrozophora tinctoria*

824 *Ricinus communis*

825 *Ruta montana*

826 *Ruta graveolens*

827 *Ruta chalepensis*

829 *Haplophyllum buxbaumii*

830 *Haplophyllum suaveolens*

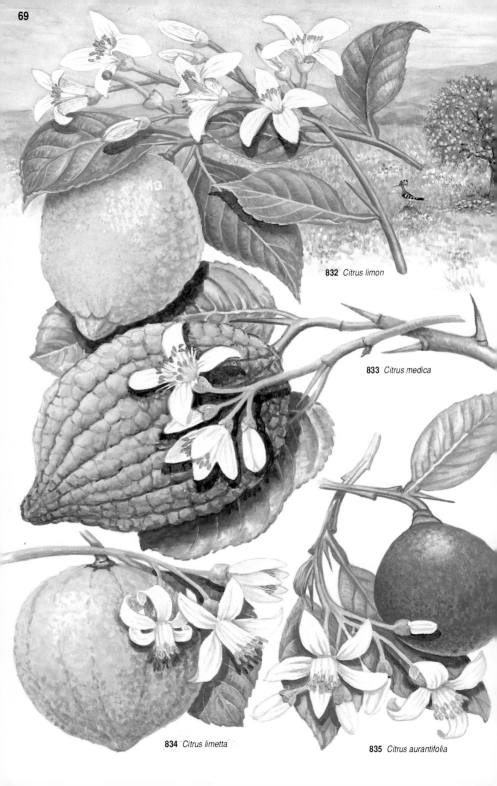

69

832 *Citrus limon*

833 *Citrus medica*

834 *Citrus limetta*

835 *Citrus aurantifolia*

836 *Citrus sinensis*

837 *Citrus aurantium*

839 *Citrus paradisi*

841 *Citrus deliciosa*

71

842 *Ailanthus altissima*

846 *Polygala myrtifolia*

843 *Melia azedarach*

845 *Polygala rupestris*

844 *Cneorum tricoccon*

847 *Polygala monspeliaca*

849 *Polygala nicaeensis*

852 *Polygala venulosa*

855 *Coriaria myrtifolia*

856 *Acer monspessulanum*

857 *Acer sempervirens*

858 *Acer obtusatum*

859 *Acer granatense*

860 *Acer obtusifolium*

73

861 Pistachia terabinthus

863 Pistachia vera

865 Pistachia lentiscus

867 Rhus coriaria

868 Rhus pentaphylla

869 Rhus tripartita

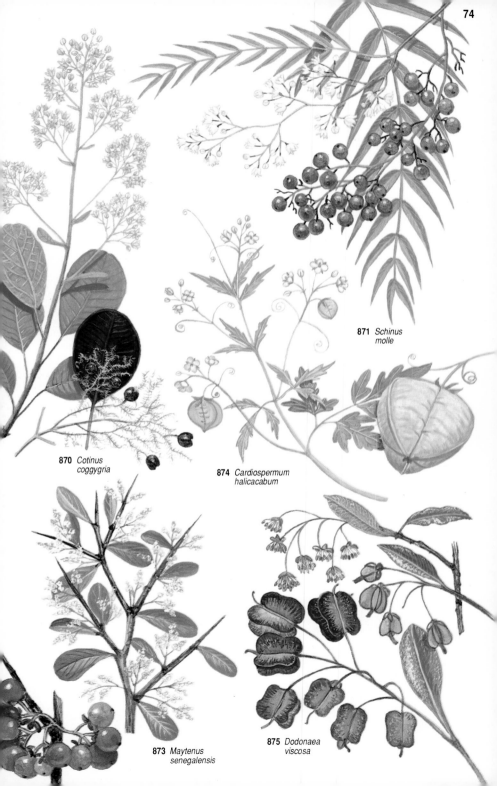

871 *Schinus molle*

870 *Cotinus coggygria*

874 *Cardiospermum halicacabum*

873 *Maytenus senegalensis*

875 *Dodonaea viscosa*

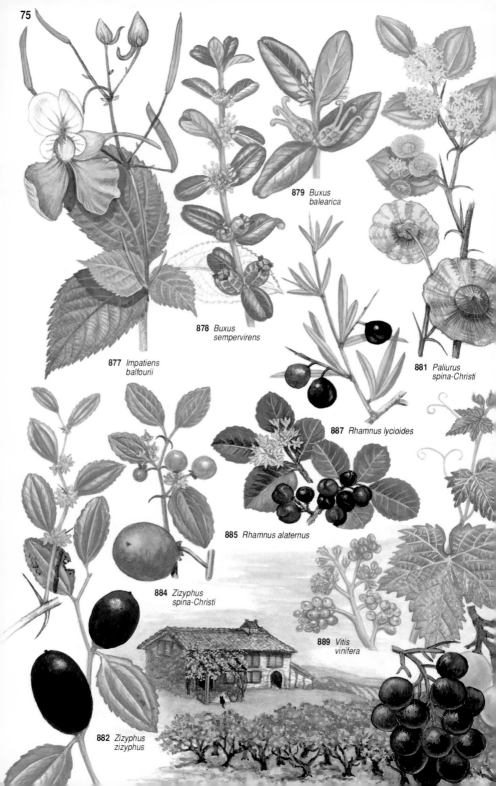

75

877 *Impatiens balfourii*

879 *Buxus balearica*

878 *Buxus sempervirens*

881 *Paliurus spina-Christi*

887 *Rhamnus lycioides*

885 *Rhamnus alaternus*

884 *Zizyphus spina-Christi*

889 *Vitis vinifera*

882 *Zizyphus zizyphus*

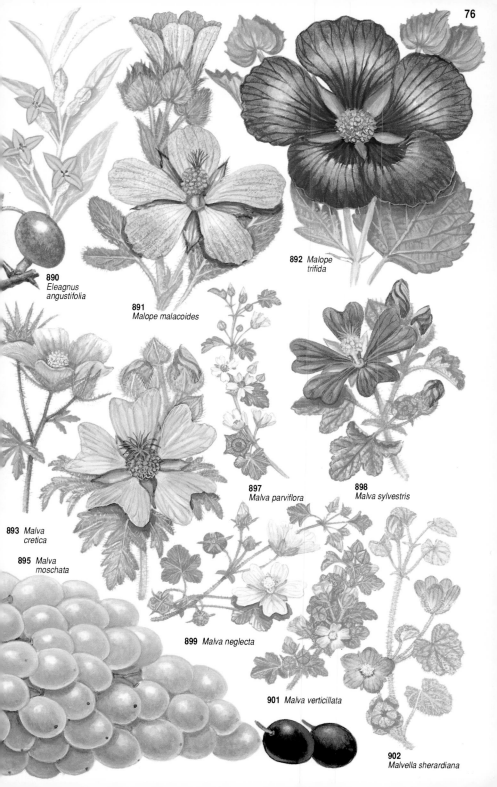

76

890
*Eleagnus
angustifolia*

891
Malope malacoides

892 *Malope
trifida*

893 *Malva
cretica*

895 *Malva
moschata*

897
Malva parviflora

898
Malva sylvestris

899 *Malva neglecta*

901 *Malva verticillata*

902
Malvella sherardiana

903 *Althaea hirsuta*

905 *Althaea rosea*

904 *Althaea officinalis*

906 *Althaea pallida*

907 *Althaea setosa*

909
Abutilon theophrasti

910
Lavatera cretica

13 *Lavatera maritima*

912 *Lavatera arborea*

914 *Lavatera olbia*

919 *Lavatera triloba*

917 *Lavatera trimestris*

920 *Gossypium herbaceum*

922 *Hibiscus trionum*

923 *Hibiscus syriacus*

924 *Hibiscus rosa-sinensis*

925 *Viola alba*
subsp. *dehnadtii*

929 *Viola jaubertiana*

930 *Viola*
hymettia

931 *Viola*
kitaibeliana

932 *Viola scorpiuroides*

933 *Viola*
arborescens

934 *Elatine alsinastrum*

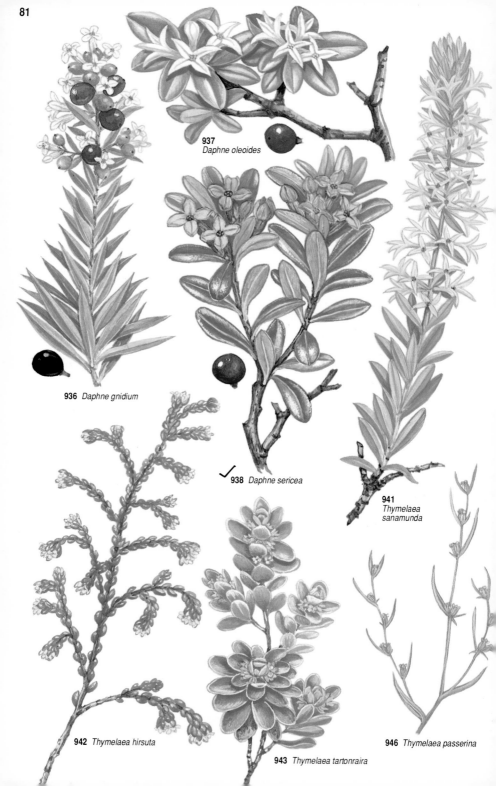

81

936 *Daphne gnidium*

937
Daphne oleoides

938 *Daphne sericea*

941
Thymelaea sanamunda

942 *Thymelaea hirsuta*

943 *Thymelaea tartonraira*

946 *Thymelaea passerina*

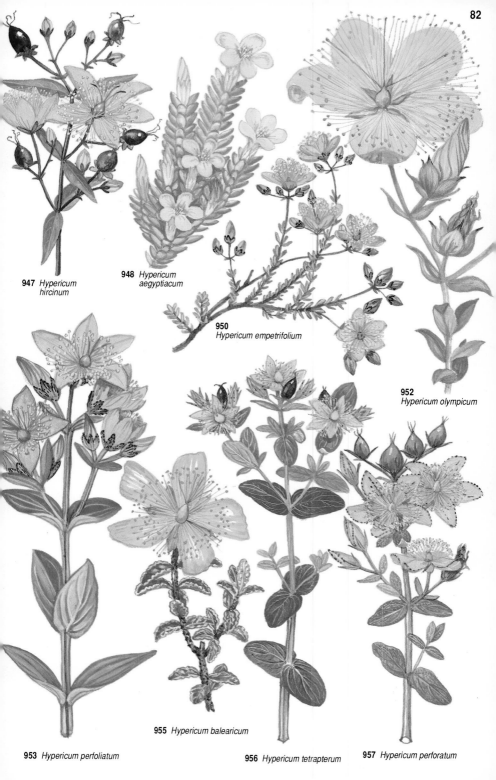

947 *Hypericum hircinum*

948 *Hypericum aegyptiacum*

950 *Hypericum empetrifolium*

952 *Hypericum olympicum*

953 *Hypericum perfoliatum*

955 *Hypericum balearicum*

956 *Hypericum tetrapterum*

957 *Hypericum perforatum*

83

960 *Cistus crispus*

961 *Cistus albidus*

962
Cistus creticus

964 *Cistus parviflorus*

965 *Cistus salvifolius*

969
Cistus clusii

966
Cistus
monspeliensis

971 *Cistus ladanifer*

973 *Cistus populifolius*

974 *Cistus laurifolius*

85

975
Halimium halimifolium

976
Halimium atriplicifolium

977
Halimium ocymoides

980 *Halimium commutatum*

989 *Helianthemum lavandulifolium*

983 *Tuberaria lignosa*

985 *Tuberaria guttata*

990 *Helianthemum syriacum*

996 *Helianthemum nummularium*

993 *Helianthemum appeninum*

992 *Helianthemum caput-felis*

1001 *Helianthemum salicifolium*

1005 *Helianthemum canum*

1007 *Helianthemum origanifolium*

1009 *Helianthemum cinereum*

1010 *Fumana arabica*

1011 *Fumana ericoides*

1014 *Fumana thymifolia*

87

1019 *Tamarix parviflora*

1016 *Tamarix africana*

1022 *Tamarix smyrnensis*

1024 *Tamarix tetragyna*

1026 *Frankenia pulverulenta*

1027 *Frankenia laevis*

1028 *Frankenia hirsuta*

1029 *Frankenia thymifolia*

1025 *Reaumeria vermiculata*

1032 *Ecballium elaterium*

1033
Bryonia cretica

1034
Citrullus colocynthis

1040 *Opuntia ficus-indica*

1044
Cereus uruguayanus

89

1049
Lythrum portula

1045
Lythrum junceum

1052 *Myrtis communis*

1051 *Lagerstroemia indica*

1057 *Eucalyptus robustus*

1060 *Eucalyptus globulus*

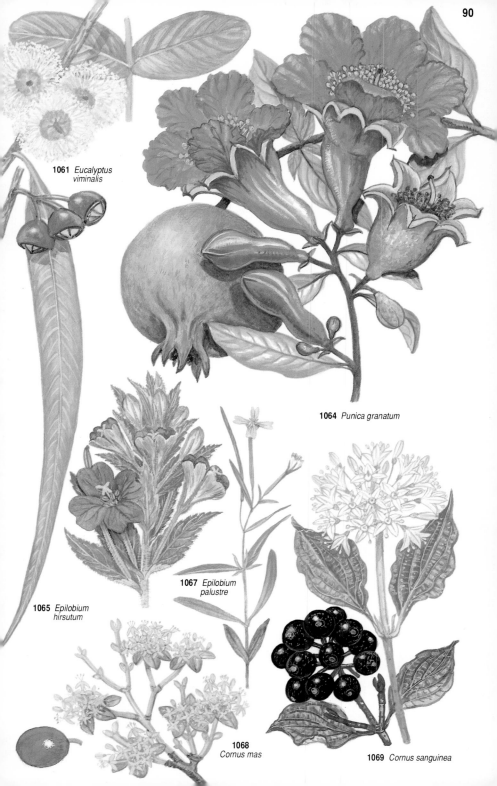

1061 *Eucalyptus viminalis*

1064 *Punica granatum*

1065 *Epilobium hirsutum*

1067 *Epilobium palustre*

1068 *Cornus mas*

1069 *Cornus sanguinea*

91

1072 *Naufraga balearica*

1070 *Hydrocotyle vulgaris*

1076 *Eryngium creticum*

1073 *Eryngium maritimum*

1080 *Eryngium amethystinum*

1081 *Eryngium campestre*

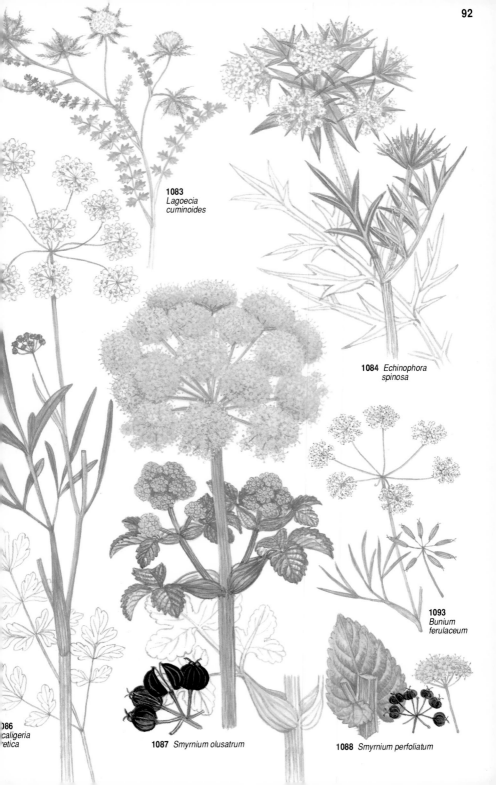

1083
*Lagoecia
cuminoides*

1084 *Echinophora
spinosa*

1093
*Bunium
ferulaceum*

086
*caligeria
retica*

1087 *Smyrnium olusatrum*

1088 *Smyrnium perfoliatum*

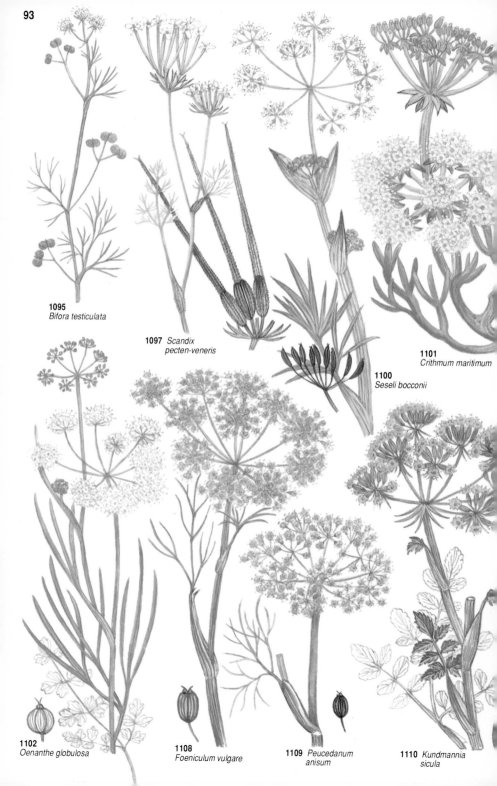

93

1095
Bifora testiculata

1097 *Scandix
pecten-veneris*

1100
Seseli bocconii

1101
Crithmum maritimum

1102
Oenanthe globulosa

1108
Foeniculum vulgare

1109 *Peucedanum
anisum*

1110 *Kundmannia
sicula*

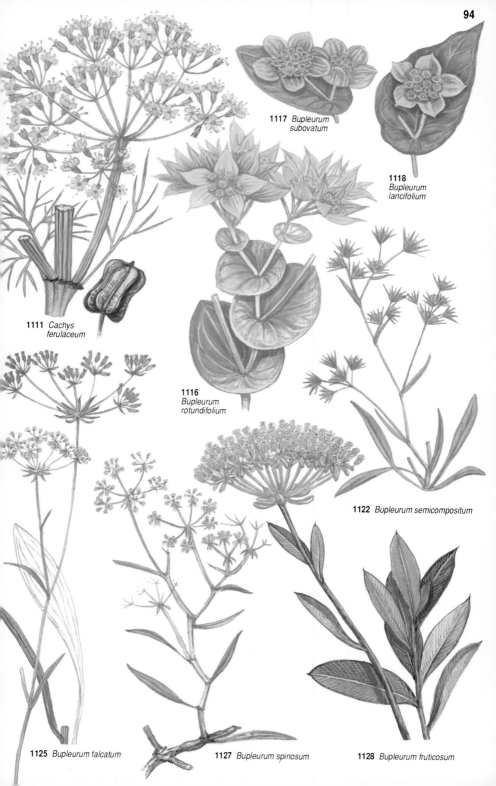

1111 *Cachys ferulaceum*

1117 *Bupleurum subovatum*

1118 *Bupleurum lancifolium*

1116 *Bupleurum rotundifolium*

1122 *Bupleurum semicompositum*

1125 *Bupleurum falcatum*

1127 *Bupleurum spinosum*

1128 *Bupleurum fruticosum*

95

1132 *Apium nodiflorum*

1131
Apium graveolens

1134
Ridolfia segetum

1135 *Ammi majus*

1137
Ptychotis saxifraga

1138
Ammoides pusilla

1139
Bonannia graeca

1140 *Krub peregrina*

1143 *Ferulago nodosa*

1141 *Ferula communis*

1148 *Heracleum sphondylium*

146 *Opopanax chironium*

1149 *Tordylium apulum*

1150 *Tordylium officinale*

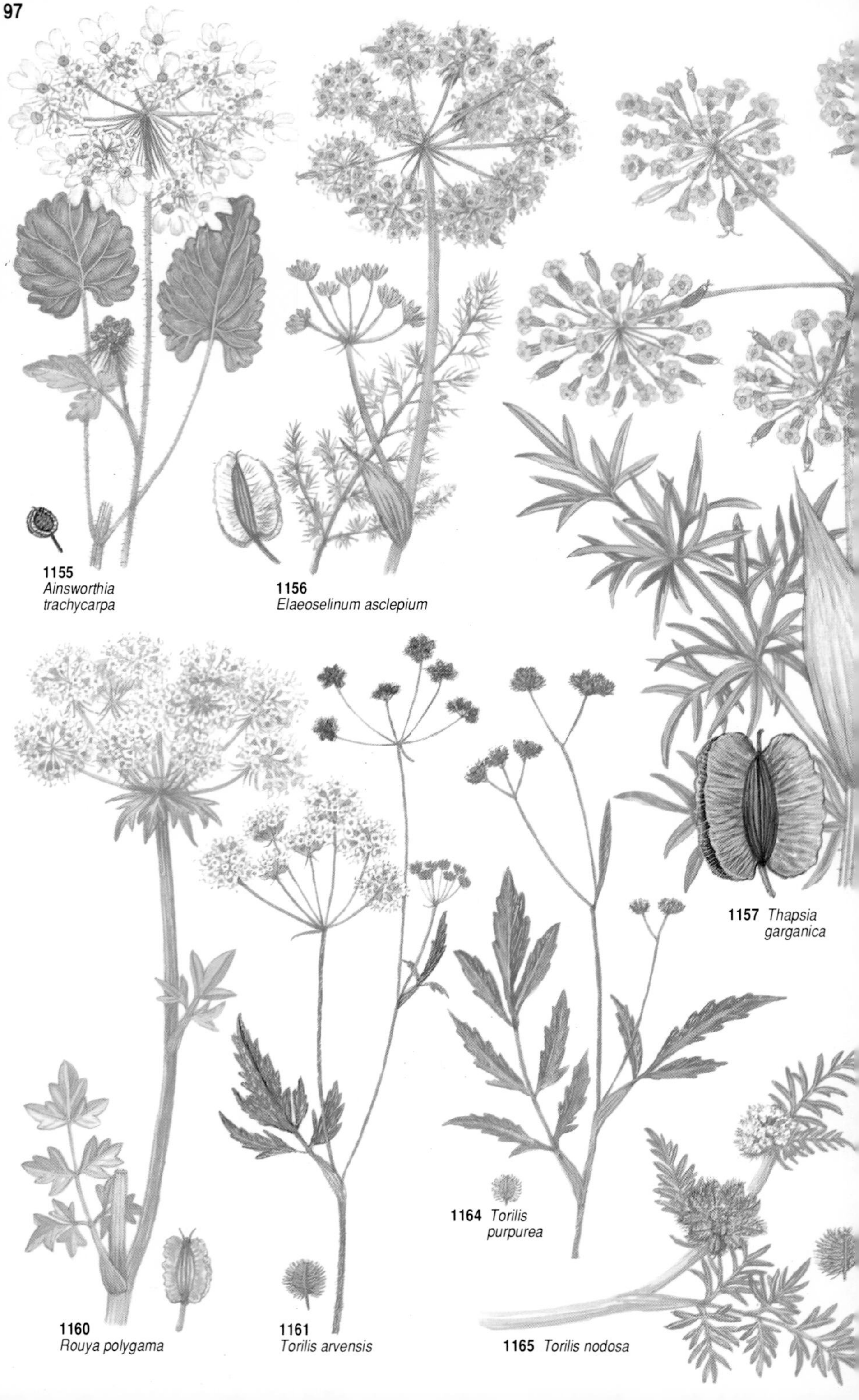

1155
Ainsworthia
trachycarpa

1156
Elaeoselinum asclepium

1157 *Thapsia*
garganica

1160
Rouya polygama

1161
Torilis arvensis

1164 *Torilis*
purpurea

1165 *Torilis nodosa*

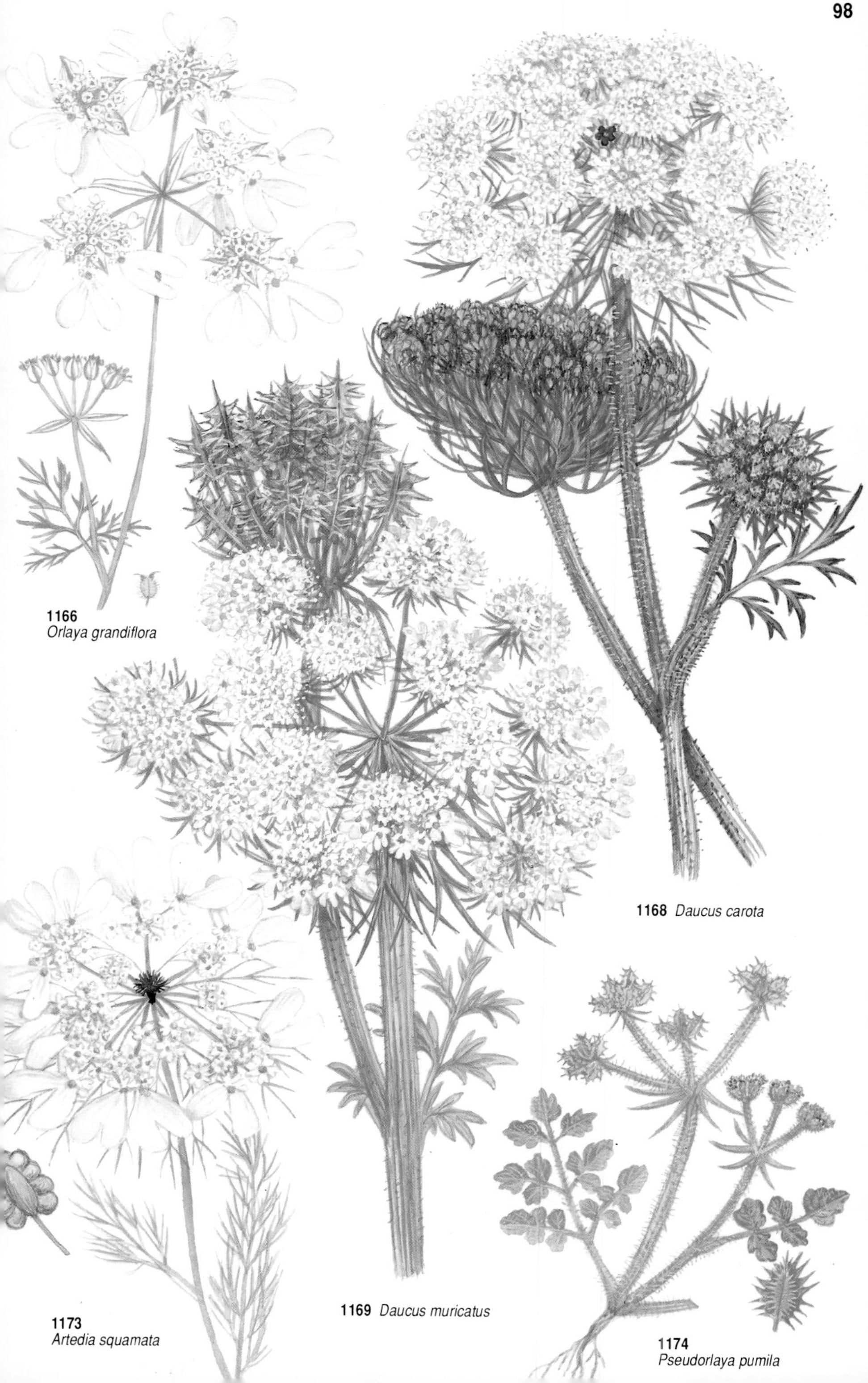

1166
Orlaya grandiflora

1168 *Daucus carota*

1173
Artedia squamata

1169 *Daucus muricatus*

1174
Pseudorlaya pumila

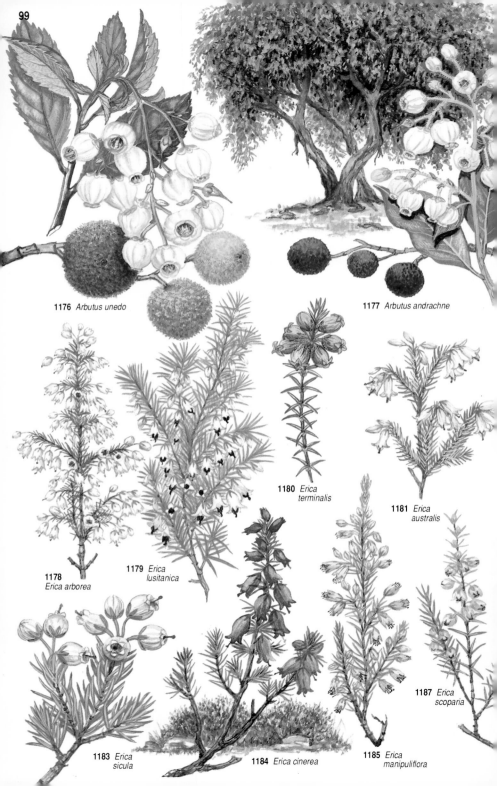

99

1176 *Arbutus unedo*

1177 *Arbutus andrachne*

1178
Erica arborea

1179 *Erica lusitanica*

1180 *Erica terminalis*

1181 *Erica australis*

1183 *Erica sicula*

1184 *Erica cinerea*

1185 *Erica manipuliflora*

1187 *Erica scoparia*

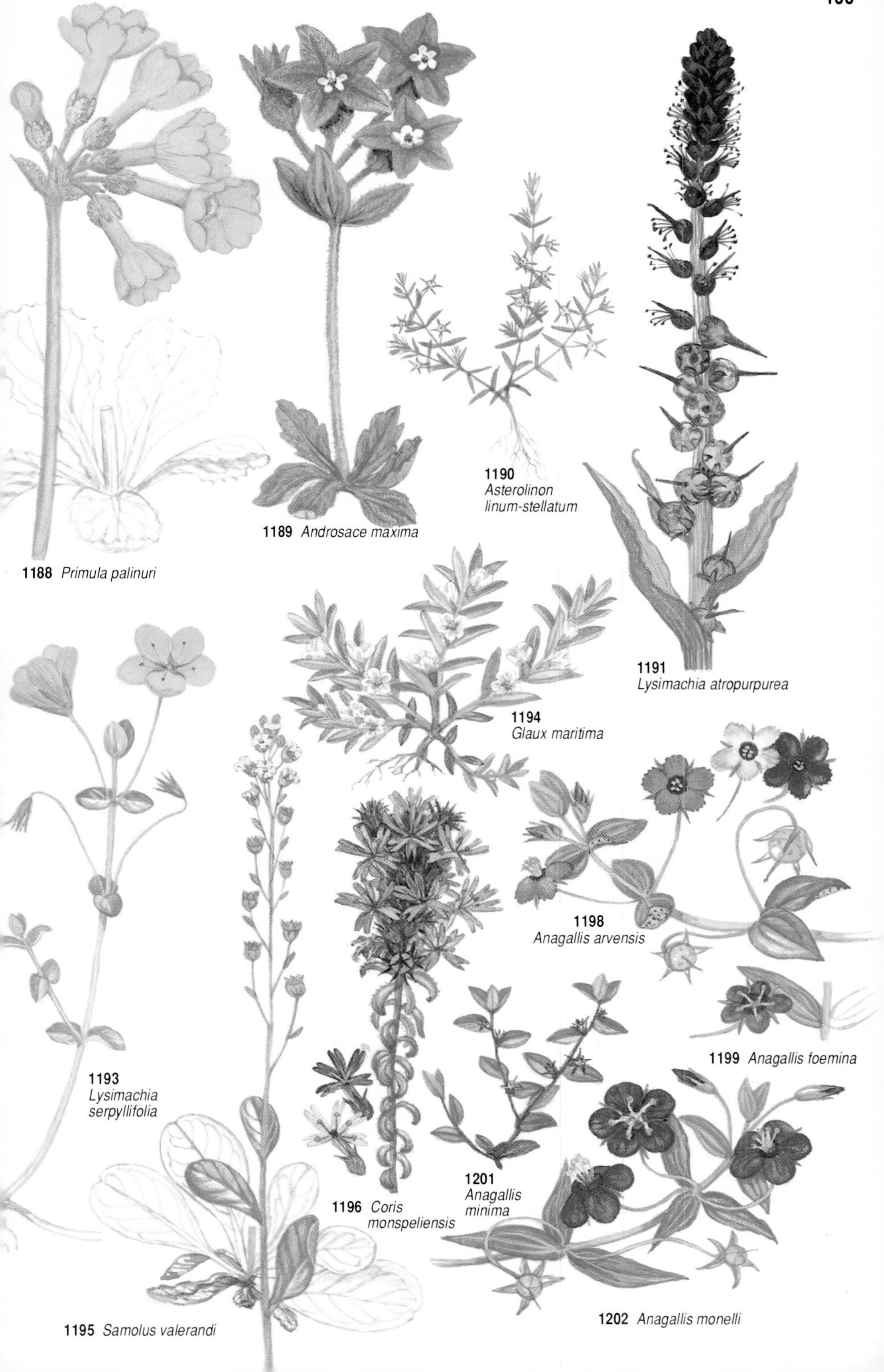

1188 *Primula palinuri*

1189 *Androsace maxima*

1190 *Asterolinon linum-stellatum*

1191 *Lysimachia atropurpurea*

1194 *Glaux maritima*

1193 *Lysimachia serpyllifolia*

1198 *Anagallis arvensis*

1199 *Anagallis foemina*

1196 *Coris monspeliensis*

1201 *Anagallis minima*

1195 *Samolus valerandi*

1202 *Anagallis monelli*

1205
Cyclamen graecum

1206
Cyclamen cyprium

1203 *Cyclamen hederifolium*

1207 *Cyclamen repandum*

1207c
Cyclamen repandum
var. *vividum*

1207d
Cyclamen repandum
subsp. *rhodense*

1207a
Cyclamen repandum
subsp. *peloponnesiacum*

1208
Cyclamen creticum

1209
Cyclamen balearicum

1210
Cyclamen persicum

1211
Cyclamen rohlfsianum

1290
Galium rotundifolium

1292
Galium corrudifolium

1294
Galium mollugo

1297
Galium setaceum

1298 *Galium murale*

1303
Valantia hispida

1309 *Gardenia jasminoides*

1300
Cruciata laevipes

1305
Rubia peregrina

1307
Rubia tinctorum

1310
Theligonium cynocrambe

109

1311
Cuscuta
epithymum

1312 Cuscuta campestris

1315 Calystegia
soldanella

1316
Calystegia
sepium

1317 Calystegia
silvatica

1318 Ipomoea stolonifera

1319 Ipomoea purpurea

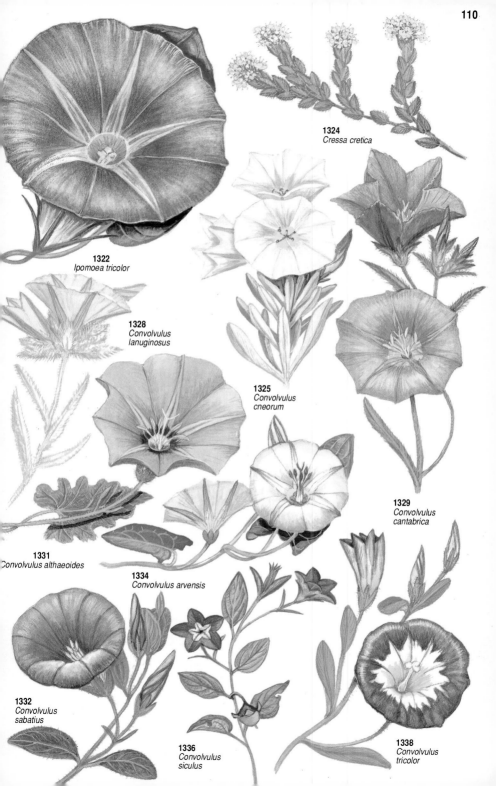

1322
Ipomoea tricolor

1324
Cressa cretica

1328
Convolvulus
lanuginosus

1325
Convolvulus
cneorum

1329
Convolvulus
cantabrica

1331
Convolvulus althaeoides

1334
Convolvulus arvensis

1332
Convolvulus
sabatius

1336
Convolvulus
siculus

1338
Convolvulus
tricolor

111

1341
Heliotropium europaeum

1351
Lithodora diffusa

1347
Neatostema apulum

1352
Lithodora zahnii

1348
Buglossoides purpurocaerulea

1349
Buglossoides arvensis

1353
Lithodora hispidula

1354
Lithodora rosmarinifolium

1355
Lithodora fruticosa

1356
Onosma frutescens

1359
Onosma echioides

1362
Onosma erecta

1364 *Onosma visianii*

1367
Cerinthe major

1369
Cerinthe retorta

1370
*Alkanna
orientalis*

1374
Nonea pulla

1377
Nonea ventricosa

1373 *Alkanna lehmanii*

1372
Alkanna lutea

113

1382 *Echium angustifolium*

1383 *Echium plantagineum*

1380 *Echium italicum*

1390 *Procopiania cretica*

1393 *Symphytum bulbosum*

1384 *Echium vulgare*

1388 *Echium parviflorum*

1395 *Borago officinalis*

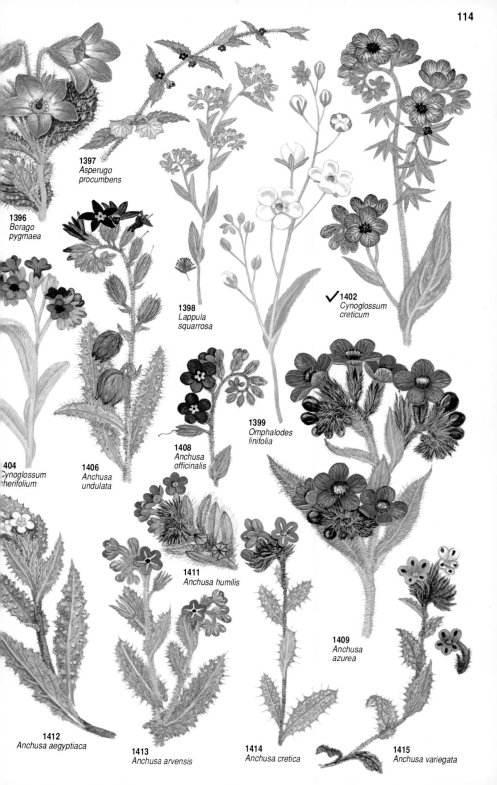

1397
*Asperugo
procumbens*

1396
*Borago
pygmaea*

1398
*Lappula
squarrosa*

✓ **1402**
*Cynoglossum
creticum*

1404
*Cynoglossum
cheirifolium*

1406
*Anchusa
undulata*

1408
*Anchusa
officinalis*

1399
*Omphalodes
linifolia*

1411
Anchusa humilis

1409
*Anchusa
azurea*

1412
Anchusa aegyptiaca

1413
Anchusa arvensis

1414
Anchusa cretica

1415
Anchusa variegata

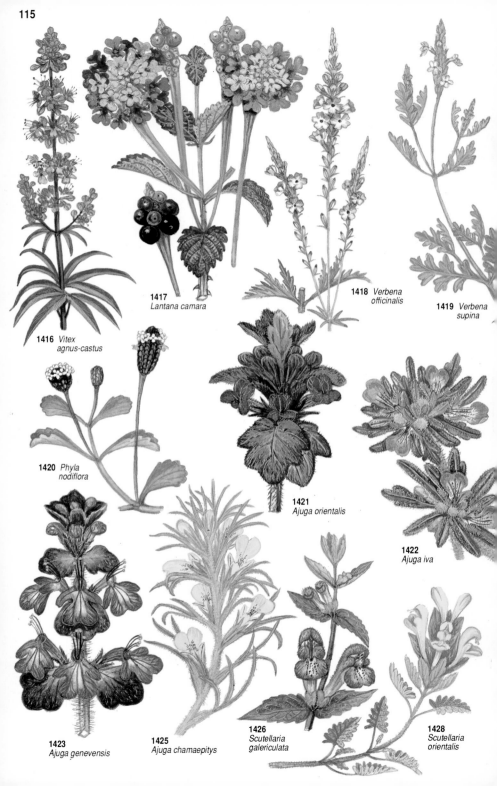

115

1416 *Vitex agnus-castus*

1417 *Lantana camara*

1418 *Verbena officinalis*

1419 *Verbena supina*

1420 *Phyla nodiflora*

1421 *Ajuga orientalis*

1422 *Ajuga iva*

1423 *Ajuga genevensis*

1425 *Ajuga chamaepitys*

1426 *Scutellaria galericulata*

1428 *Scutellaria orientalis*

1429
*Teucrium
fruticans*

1430
*Teucrium
creticum*

1431 *Teucrium
brevifolium*

1432
Teucrium marum

1433 *Teucrium
scorodonia*

1436
*Teucrium
spinosum*

1435
*Teucrium
scordium*

1438
*Teucrium
campanulatum*

1439
Teucrium chamaedrys

1442
Teucrium polium

1442a *Teucrium polium
subsp. capitatum*

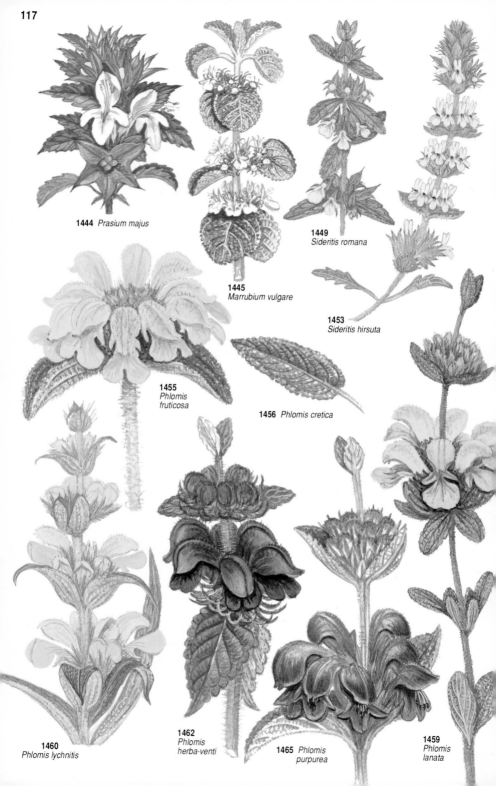

1444 *Prasium majus*

1445
Marrubium vulgare

1449
Sideritis romana

1453
Sideritis hirsuta

1455
*Phlomis
fruticosa*

1456 *Phlomis cretica*

1460
Phlomis lychnitis

1462
*Phlomis
herba-venti*

1465 *Phlomis
purpurea*

1459
*Phlomis
lanata*

1467
Molucella spinosa

1469
Ballota acetabulosa

1470 *Ballota pseudodictamnus*

1471
Ballota integrifolia

1472
Prunella grandiflora

1474
Prunella laciniata

1475
Lamium garganicum

1476
Lamium maculatum

1478
Lamium amplexicaule

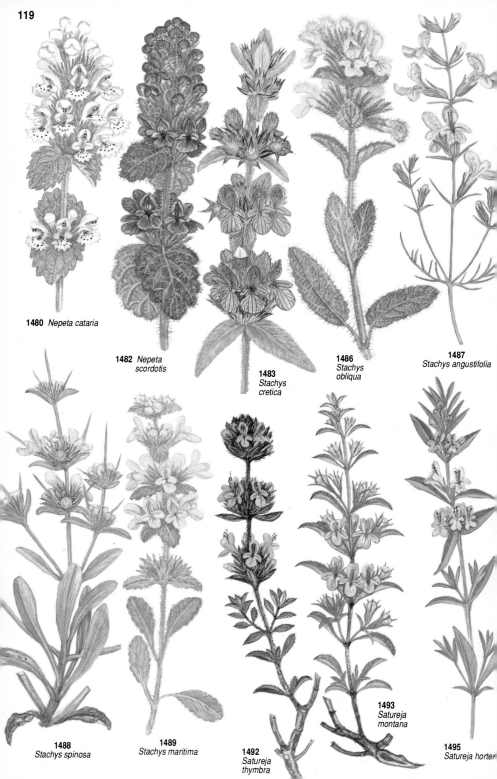

119

1480 *Nepeta cataria*

1482 *Nepeta scordotis*

1483 *Stachys cretica*

1486 *Stachys obliqua*

1487 *Stachys angustifolia*

1488 *Stachys spinosa*

1489 *Stachys maritima*

1492 *Satureja thymbra*

1493 *Satureja montana*

1495 *Satureja horter*

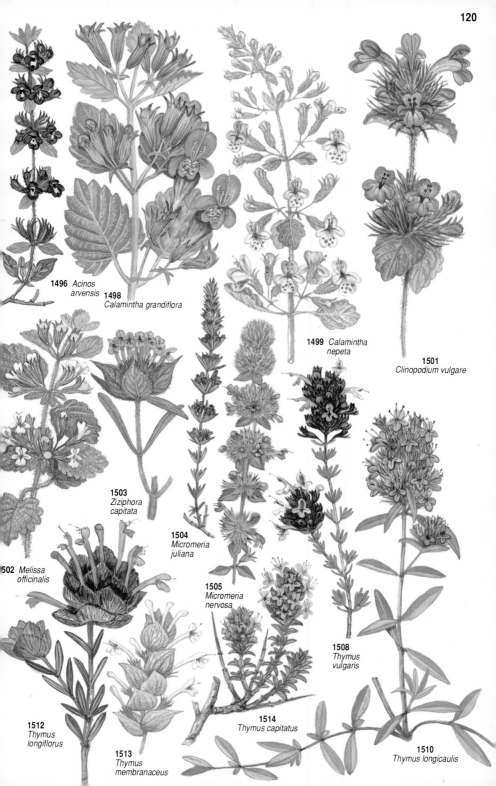

1496 Acinos arvensis

1498 Calamintha grandiflora

1499 Calamintha nepeta

1501 Clinopodium vulgare

1502 Melissa officinalis

1503 Ziziphora capitata

1504 Micromeria juliana

1505 Micromeria nervosa

1508 Thymus vulgaris

1512 Thymus longiflorus

1513 Thymus membranaceus

1514 Thymus capitatus

1510 Thymus longicaulis

121

1515
Origanum
vulgare

1518 Origanum
onites

1520
Origanum
dictamnus

1521
Mentha spicata

1522
Mentha
longifolia

1524 Mentha pulegium

1525
Mentha aquatica

1526
Rosmarinus
officinalis

1528
Lavandula
stoechas

1530
Lavandula
dentata

1531
Lavandula
multifida

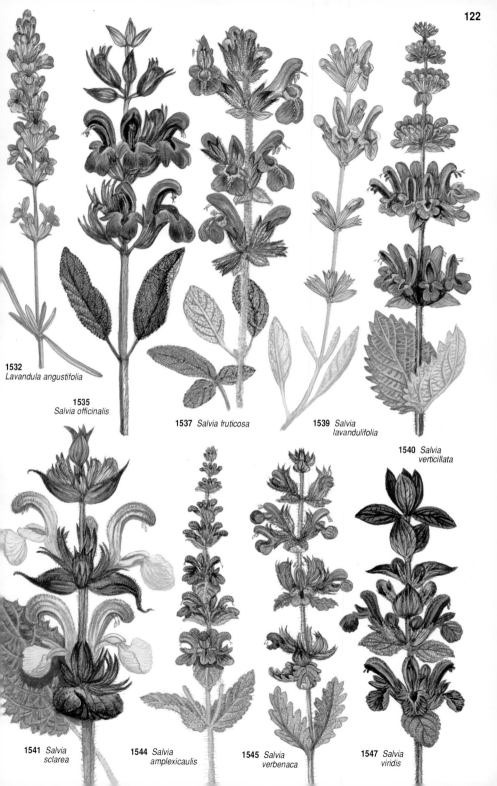

1532
Lavandula angustifolia

1535
Salvia officinalis

1537 *Salvia fruticosa*

1539 *Salvia lavandulifolia*

1540 *Salvia verticillata*

1541 *Salvia sclarea*

1544 *Salvia amplexicaulis*

1545 *Salvia verbenaca*

1547 *Salvia viridis*

123

1548
Lycium europaeum

1551
Lycium
ferocissimum

1552 Lycium
barbarum

1554
Hyoscyamus
aureus

1555
Hyoscyamus albus

1558
Withania somnifera

1556
Hyoscyamus
niger

1565 Solanum
sodomaceum

1560
Physalis alkekengi

1562
Salpichroa
origanifolia

1563
Solanum nigrum

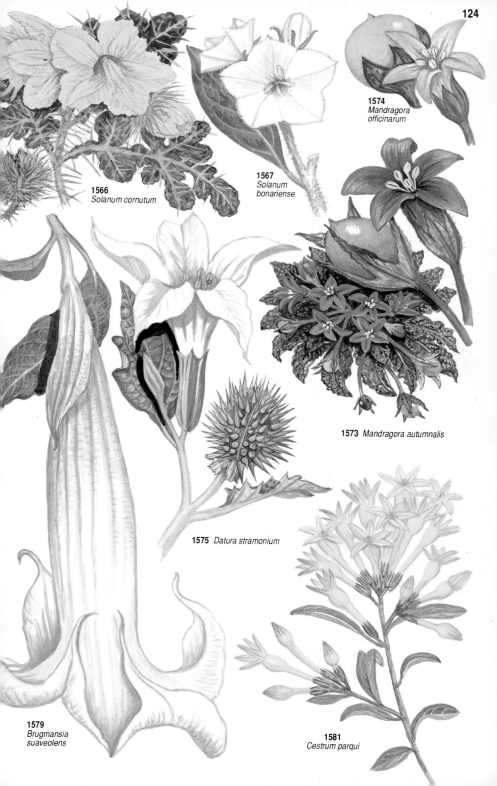

1566
Solanum cornutum

1567
Solanum bonariense

1574
Mandragora officinarum

1573 *Mandragora autumnalis*

1575 *Datura stramonium*

1579
Brugmansia suaveolens

1581
Cestrum parqui

1582
Nicotiana glauca

1583
Nicotiana tabacum

1585 *Paulownia tomentosa*

1586
Scrophularia peregrina

1587
Scrophularia lucida

1589
Scrophularia canina

1592
Scrophularia scopolii

1662
Orobanche alba

1664
Orobanche minor

1670 *Orobanche rapum-genistea*

1671 *Orobanche caryophyllacea*

1672
Orobanche gracilis

1675
Orobanche crenata

1676
Myoporum laetum

1677
Globularia alypum

1679
Passiflora caerulea

1680
Passiflora racemosa

1682
Campsis radicans

1683
Campsis grandiflora

1685
Catalpa bignonioides

1686
Jacaranda ovalifolia

1687
Tecomaria capensis

1688
Pyrostegia venusta

1689
Phaedranthus buccinatorius

133

1692 *Acanthus spinosus*

1693 *Plantago major*

1690 *Acanthus mollis*

1699 *Plantago maritima*

1696 *Plantago coronopus*

1701 *Plantago lanceolata*

1702 *Plantago lagopus*

1703 *Plantago bellardii*

1704 *Plantago cretica*

1706 *Plantago afra*

1708 *Plantago albicans*

1710
*Sambucus
edulis*

1711
*Viburnum
tinus*

1712
Lonicera etrusca

1713
Lonicera implexa

1714
*Valerianella
discoidea*

1718 *Valerianella
vesicaria*

1719
alerianella echinata

1720 *Fedia cornucopiae*

1721
Valeriana asarifolia

1723
Centranthus ruber

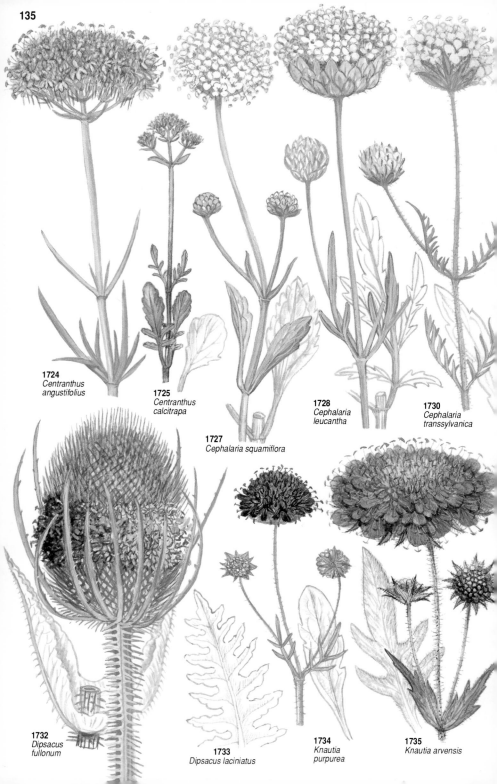

135

1724
Centranthus angustifolius

1725
Centranthus calcitrapa

1727
Cephalaria squamiflora

1728
Cephalaria leucantha

1730
Cephalaria transsylvanica

1732
Dipsacus fullonum

1733
Dipsacus laciniatus

1734
Knautia purpurea

1735
Knautia arvensis

1736
Knautia integrifolia

1739
Pterocephalus plumosus

1742
Pterocephalus perennis

1743
Scabiosa cretica

1749 *Scabiosa atropurpurea*

1751
Scabiosa brachiata

1747
Scabiosa crenata

1748
Scabiosa sicula

1750
Scabiosa prolifera

1752
Pycnocomon rutifolium

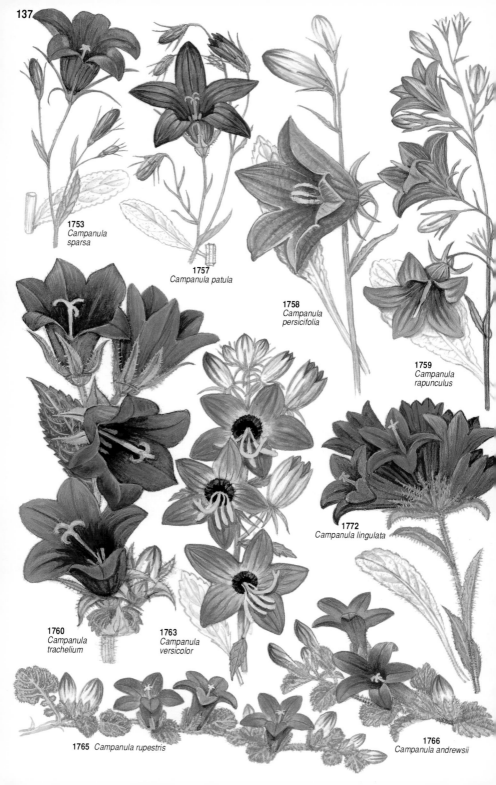

137

1753
*Campanula
sparsa*

1757
Campanula patula

1758
*Campanula
persicifolia*

1759
*Campanula
rapunculus*

1772
Campanula lingulata

1760
*Campanula
trachelium*

1763
*Campanula
versicolor*

1765 *Campanula rupestris*

1766
Campanula andrewsii

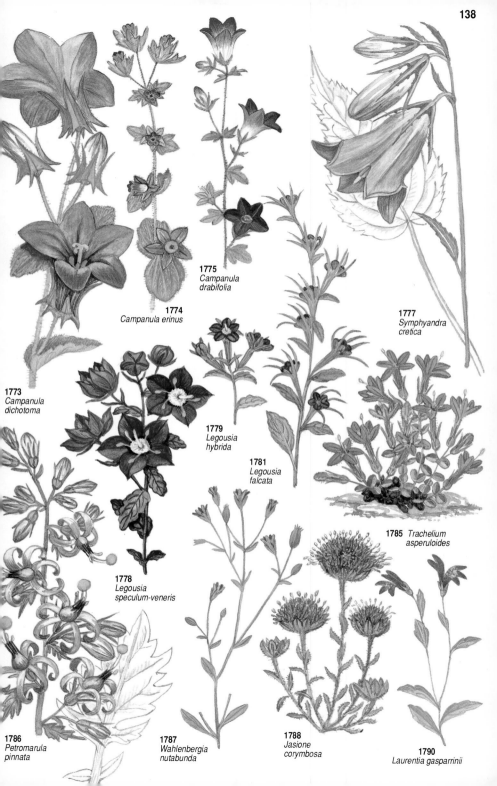

1775
*Campanula
drabifolia*

1774
Campanula erinus

1777
*Symphyandra
cretica*

1773
*Campanula
dichotoma*

1779
*Legousia
hybrida*

1781
*Legousia
falcata*

1778
*Legousia
speculum-veneris*

1785 *Trachelium
asperuloides*

1786
*Petromarula
pinnata*

1787
*Wahlenbergia
nutabunda*

1788
*Jasione
corymbosa*

1790
Laurentia gasparrinii

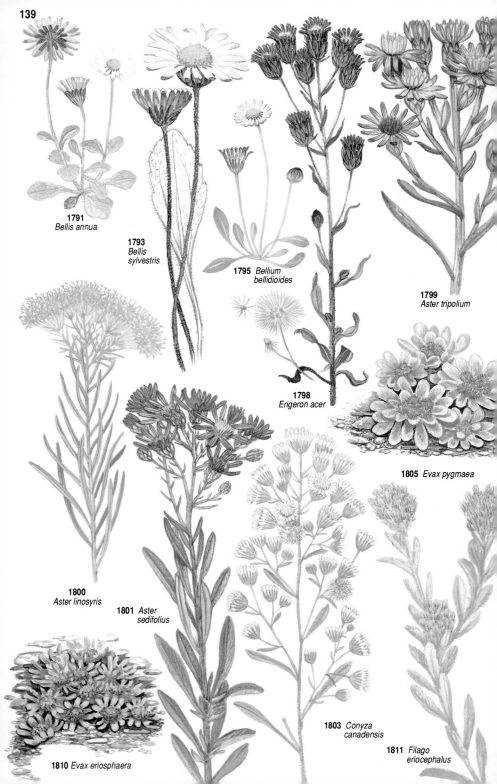

139

1791
Bellis annua

1793
Bellis sylvestris

1795 *Bellium bellidioides*

1799
Aster tripolium

1798
Erigeron acer

1805 *Evax pygmaea*

1800
Aster linosyris

1801 *Aster sedifolius*

1803 *Conyza canadensis*

1810 *Evax eriosphaera*

1811 *Filago eriocephalus*

1815
Filago pyramidata

1819
Filago minima

1813
Filago lutescens

1818
Filago arvensis

1820
Filago gallica

1822
Bombycilaena erecta

1821
Bombycilaena discolor

1823
Pseudognaphalium luteo-album

1824
Helichrysum stoechas

1828
Helichrysum italicum

1830
Helichrysum orientale

141

1831
Phagnalon
rupestre

1831a
Phagnalon
rupestre
subsp. *graecum*

1834
Inula salicina

1836 Inula
oculus-christi

1837
Inula crithmoi

1838 Inula
conyza

1841
Dittrichia
graveolens

1847 Pallenis
spinosa

1843 Pulicaria
dysenterica

1848 Asteriscus
maritimus

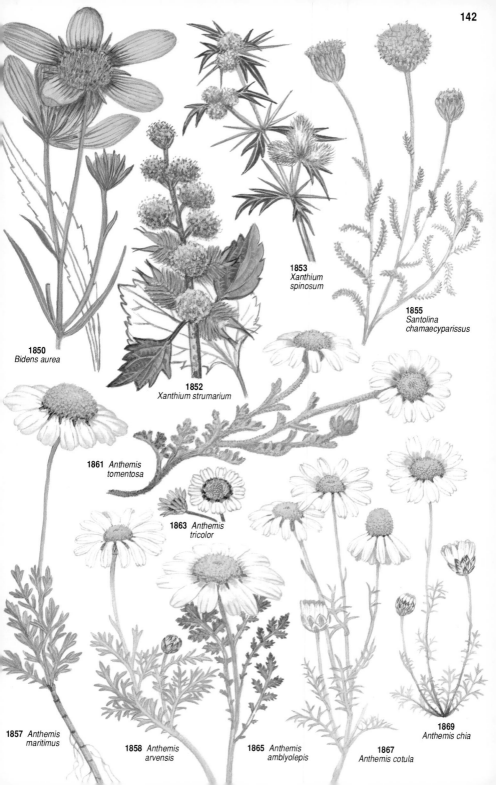

1850
Bidens aurea

1852
Xanthium strumarium

1853
Xanthium spinosum

1855
Santolina chamaecyparissus

1861 *Anthemis tomentosa*

1863 *Anthemis tricolor*

1857 *Anthemis maritimus*

1858 *Anthemis arvensis*

1865 *Anthemis amblyolepis*

1867 *Anthemis cotula*

1869 *Anthemis chia*

1870
Anthemis rigida

1872 *Achillea millefolium*

1871
Anthemis tinctoria

1875 *Achillea ligustica*

1880
Achillea santolina

1884
Chamaemelum nobile

1882
Chamaemelum mixtum

1885
Matricaria perforata

1887
Matricaria recutita

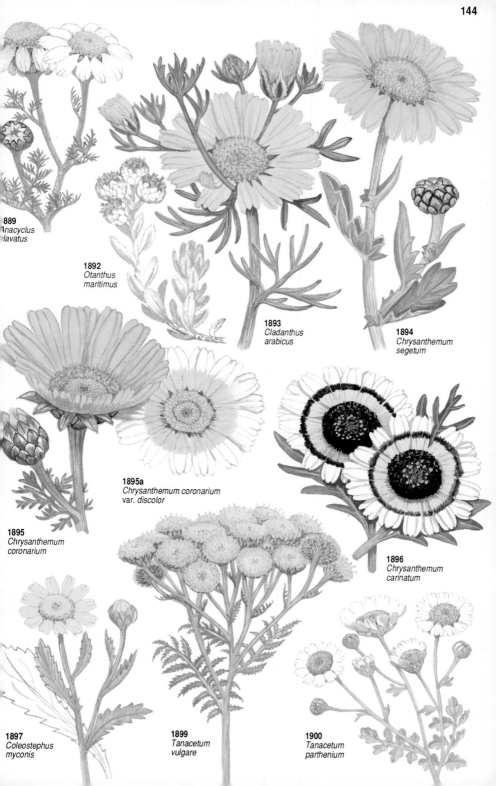

889
*Anacyclus
clavatus*

1892
*Otanthus
maritimus*

1893
*Cladanthus
arabicus*

1894
*Chrysanthemum
segetum*

1895a
*Chrysanthemum coronarium
var. discolor*

1895
*Chrysanthemum
coronarium*

1896
*Chrysanthemum
carinatum*

1897
*Coleostephus
myconis*

1899
*Tanacetum
vulgare*

1900
*Tanacetum
parthenium*

145

1902
Prolonga pectinata

1903
Leucanthemum vulgare

1905
Nananthea perpusilla

1906
Petasites fragrans

1907
Calendula suffruticosa

1908
Calendula arvensis

1911
Senecio bicolor

1913
Senecio gallicus

1920
Carlina corymbosa

1919
...undelia tournefourtii

1925
Carlina lanata

1928
Carlina acanthifolia

1929
...Xeranthemum inapterum

1931
Atractylis gummifera

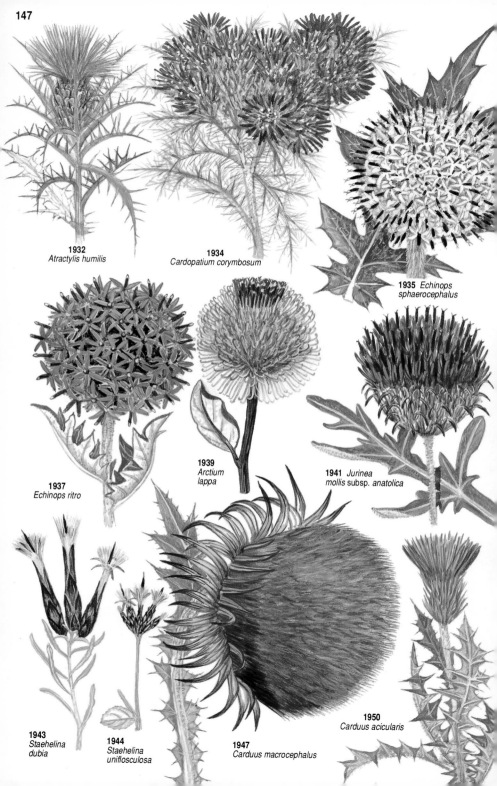

1932
Atractylis humilis

1934
Cardopatium corymbosum

1935 *Echinops sphaerocephalus*

1937
Echinops ritro

1939
Arctium lappa

1941 *Jurinea mollis* subsp. *anatolica*

1943
Staehelina dubia

1944
Staehelina uniflosculosa

1947
Carduus macrocephalus

1950
Carduus acicularis

2025
*Cichorium
spinosum*

2026
*Catananche
caerulea*

2027
*Catananche
lutea*

2023
*Cichorium
intybus*

2036
Koelpinia linearis

2028
*Hymenonema
laconicum*

2030 *Tolpis
barbata*

2032
Hyoseris radiata

2034
*Hedypnois
rhagadioloides*

2037
*Rhagadiolus
stellatus*

153

2039
Urospermum dalechampii

2041
Hypochoeris achyrophorus

2042
Hypochoeris glabra

2044
Leontodon tuberosus

2046
Picris echioides

2056
Tragopogon hybridum

2049
Picris hieracioides

2050
Scorzonera laciniata

2052
Scorzonera villosa

2055
Tragopogon porrifolius

2059
Tragopogon pratensis

2067
Crepis nicaeensis

2070
Crepis rubra

2061
Reichardia tingitana

2065
Launaea resedifolia

2073
Sonchus tenerrimus

2078
Lactuca perennis

2079
Chondrilla juncea

75
Lactuca ...inea

2076
Lactuca serriola

2080
Lapsana communis

2081
Andryala integrifolia

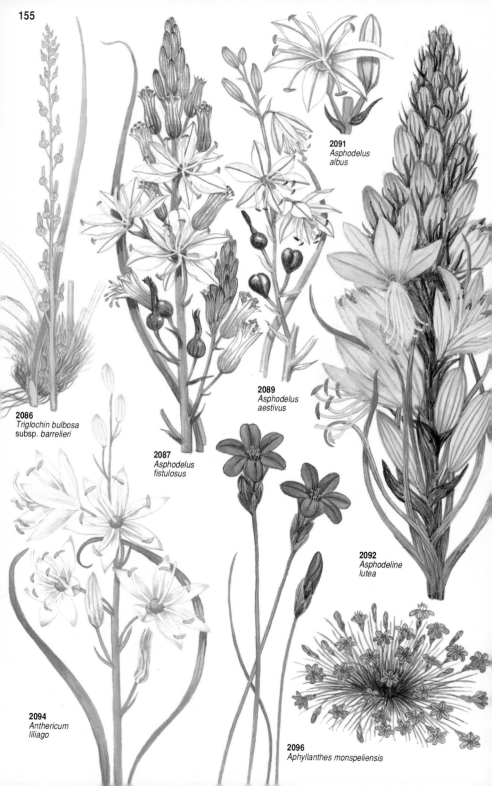

155

2086
Triglochin bulbosa
subsp. *barrelieri*

2087
Asphodelus
fistulosus

2089
Asphodelus
aestivus

2091
Asphodelus
albus

2092
Asphodeline
lutea

2094
Anthericum
liliago

2096
Aphyllanthes monspeliensis

2100
Aloe succotrina

2101
Aloe arborescens

2097
Aloe vera

2104 *Gagea
pratensis*

2105
*Gagea
fistulosa*

2106
*Gagea
arvensis*

2108
*Gagea
peduncularis*

2102 *Gagea
graeca*

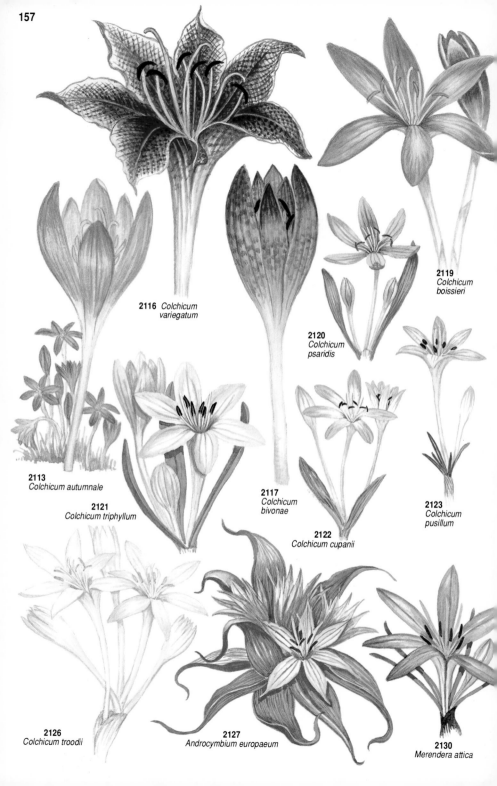

157

2116 *Colchicum variegatum*

2119 *Colchicum boissieri*

2120 *Colchicum psaridis*

2113 *Colchicum autumnale*

2121 *Colchicum triphyllum*

2117 *Colchicum bivonae*

2122 *Colchicum cupanii*

2123 *Colchicum pusillum*

2126 *Colchicum troodii*

2127 *Androcymbium europaeum*

2130 *Merendera attica*

2133
*Tulipa
aegenensis*

2134
*Tulipa
praecox*

2135
*Tulipa
undulatifolia*

2136
*Tulipa
cypria*

2137
*Tulipa
clusiana*

2138
*Tulipa
sylvestris*

2139
*Tulipa
australis*

2141
*Tulipa
orphanidea*

2146
*Tuylipa
bakeri*

2147
*Tulipa
cretica*

2145
*Tulipa
saxatilis*

159

2150 Fritillaria
acmopetala

2149 Fritillaria
persica

2148 Lilium
candidum

2151 Fritillaria
messanensis

2152 Fritillaria
lusitanica

2153 Fritillaria
graeca

2155
Fritillaria davisii

2154
Fritillaria
pontica

2156 Fritillaria conica

2158 Fritillaria
obliqua

2160 Fritillaria
ehrhartii

2161 Fritillaria
rhodocanakis

2162 Fritillaria
orientalis

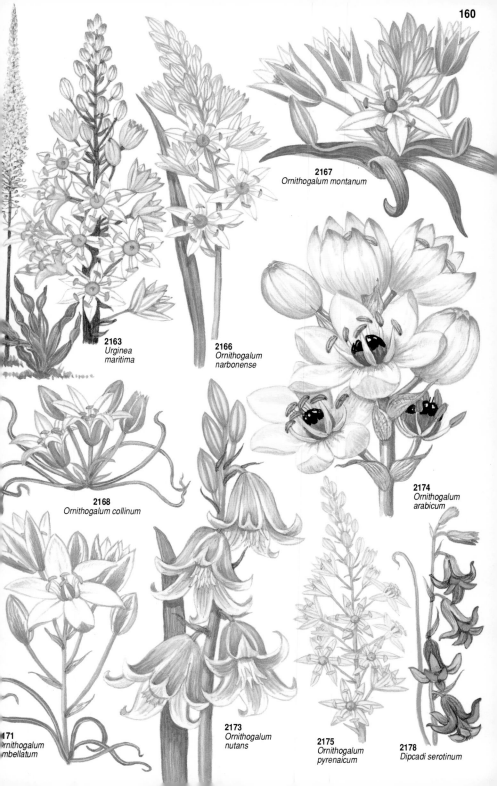

2167
Ornithogalum montanum

2163
*Urginea
maritima*

2166
*Ornithogalum
narbonense*

2174
*Ornithogalum
arabicum*

2168
Ornithogalum collinum

2171
*Ornithogalum
umbellatum*

2173
*Ornithogalum
nutans*

2175
*Ornithogalum
pyrenaicum*

2178
Dipcadi serotinum

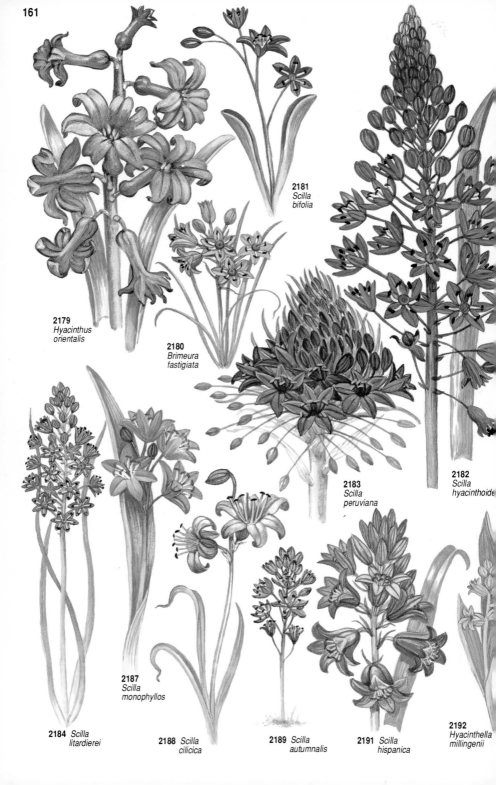

161

2181 *Scilla bifolia*

2179 *Hyacinthus orientalis*

2180 *Brimeura fastigiata*

2183 *Scilla peruviana*

2182 *Scilla hyacinthoides*

2184 *Scilla litardierei*

2187 *Scilla monophyllos*

2188 *Scilla cilicica*

2189 *Scilla autumnalis*

2191 *Scilla hispanica*

2192 *Hyacinthella millingenii*

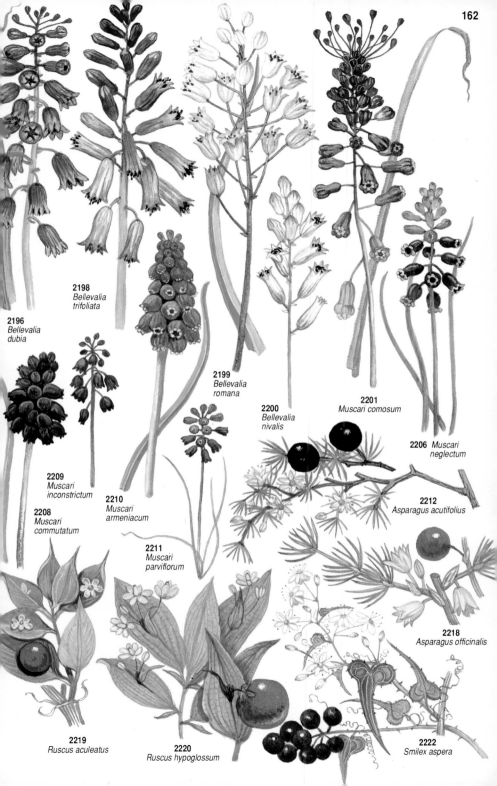

162

2198
*Bellevalia
trifoliata*

2196
*Bellevalia
dubia*

2199
*Bellevalia
romana*

2200
*Bellevalia
nivalis*

2201
Muscari comosum

2206 *Muscari
neglectum*

2209
*Muscari
inconstrictum*

2210
*Muscari
armeniacum*

2208
*Muscari
commutatum*

2212
Asparagus acutifolius

2211
*Muscari
parviflorum*

2218
Asparagus officinalis

2219
Ruscus aculeatus

2220
Ruscus hypoglossum

2222
Smilex aspera

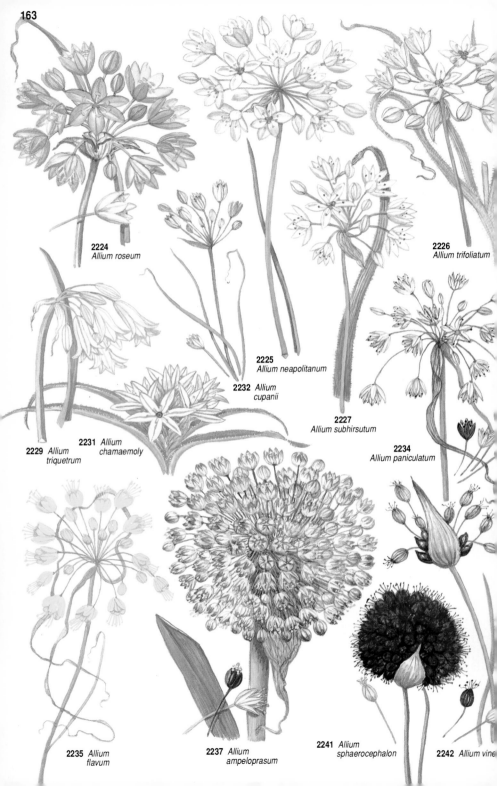

163

2224 *Allium roseum*

2225 *Allium neapolitanum*

2226 *Allium trifoliatum*

2232 *Allium cupanii*

2227 *Allium subhirsutum*

2229 *Allium triquetrum*

2231 *Allium chamaemoly*

2234 *Allium paniculatum*

2235 *Allium flavum*

2237 *Allium ampeloprasum*

2241 *Allium sphaerocephalon*

2242 *Allium vine*

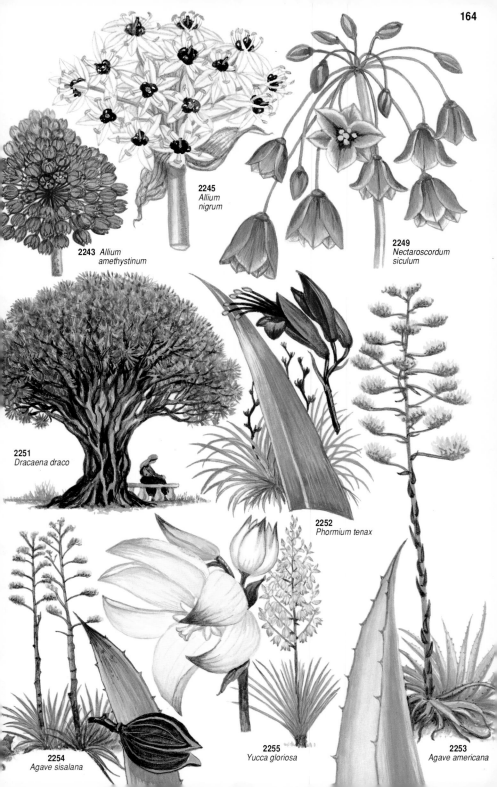

2245 *Allium nigrum*

2243 *Allium amethystinum*

2249 *Nectaroscordum siculum*

2251 *Dracaena draco*

2252 *Phormium tenax*

2254 *Agave sisalana*

2255 *Yucca gloriosa*

2253 *Agave americana*

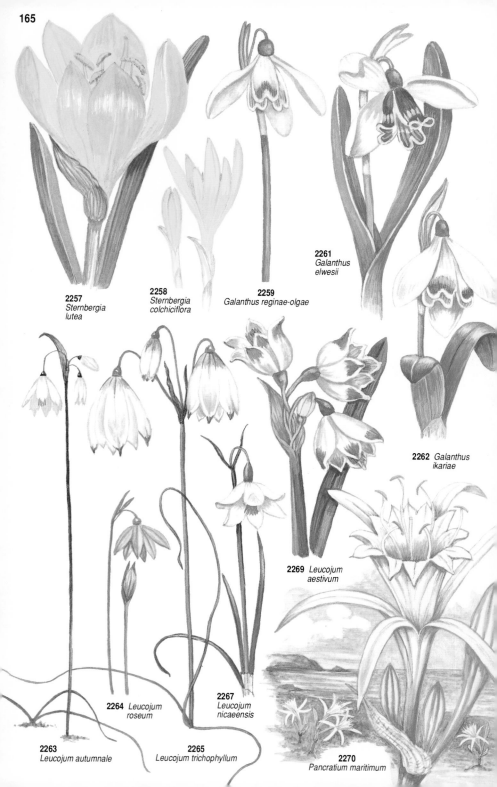

2257
Sternbergia lutea

2258
Sternbergia colchiciflora

2259
Galanthus reginae-olgae

2261
Galanthus elwesii

2262 *Galanthus ikariae*

2269 *Leucojum aestivum*

2263
Leucojum autumnale

2264 *Leucojum roseum*

2265
Leucojum trichophyllum

2267
Leucojum nicaeensis

2270
Pancratium maritimum

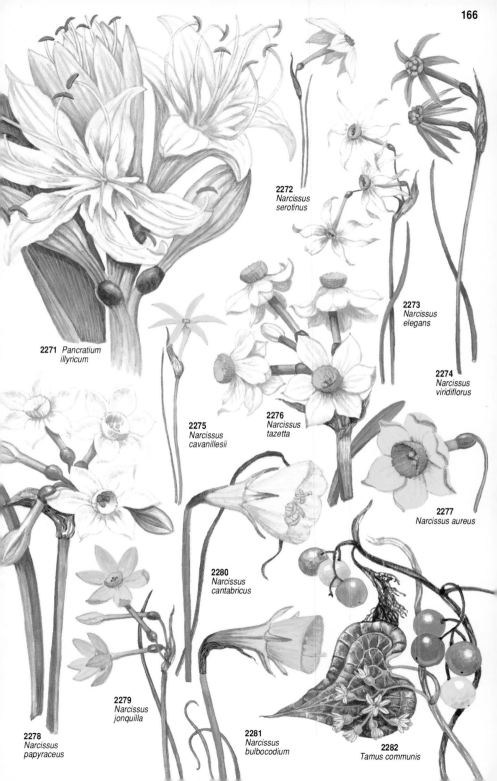

2271 *Pancratium illyricum*

2272 *Narcissus serotinus*

2273 *Narcissus elegans*

2274 *Narcissus viridiflorus*

2275 *Narcissus cavanillesii*

2276 *Narcissus tazetta*

2277 *Narcissus aureus*

2278 *Narcissus papyraceus*

2279 *Narcissus jonquilla*

2280 *Narcissus cantabricus*

2281 *Narcissus bulbocodium*

2282 *Tamus communis*

2283
*Hermodactylus
tuberosus*

2284
Iris unguicularis

2285
Iris cretensis

2286 *Iris foetidissima*

2287
Iris orientalis

2290
Iris pseudacorus

2291
Iris germanica

2292
Iris pallida

2293
Iris albicans

2294
Iris lutescens

2296
*Iris
attica*

2298
Iris planifolia

2299
Iris xiphium

2305
*Gynandriris
sisyrinchium*

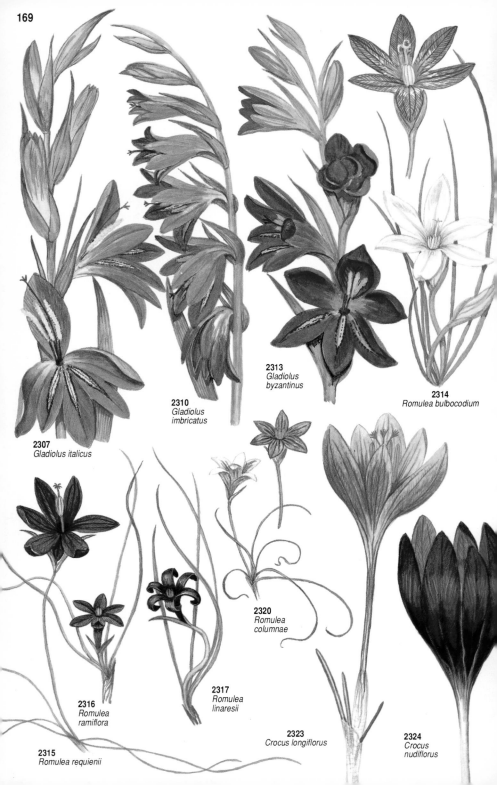

169

2313
Gladiolus
byzantinus

2314
Romulea bulbocodium

2310
Gladiolus
imbricatus

2307
Gladiolus italicus

2320
Romulea
columnae

2316
Romulea
ramiflora

2317
Romulea
linaresii

2323
Crocus longiflorus

2324
Crocus
nudiflorus

2315
Romulea requienii

2325 Crocus
serotinus

2326 Crocus
cartwrightianus

2327 Crocus
sativus

2330 Crocus
hadriaticus

2331 Crocus
tournefourtii

2332 Crocus
laevigatus

2333
Crocus
boryi

2334 Crocus
goulimyi

2335
Crocus
niveus

2336 Crocus
cancellatus

2344
Crocus
flavus

2346
Crocus
chrysanthus

2348
Crocus biflorus

2337
rocus cambessedesii

171

2349
*Phoenix
theophrasti*

2351 *Phoenix
canariensis*

2350 *Phoenix
dactylifera*

2353
Trachycarpus fortunei

2355
*Washingtonia
filifera*

2356
*Livistona
australis*

2357
*Chamaerops
humilis*

2359
*Helicodiceros
muscivorus*

2360
Ambrosinia bassii

2358
*Dracunculus
vulgaris*

2361
Arum italicum

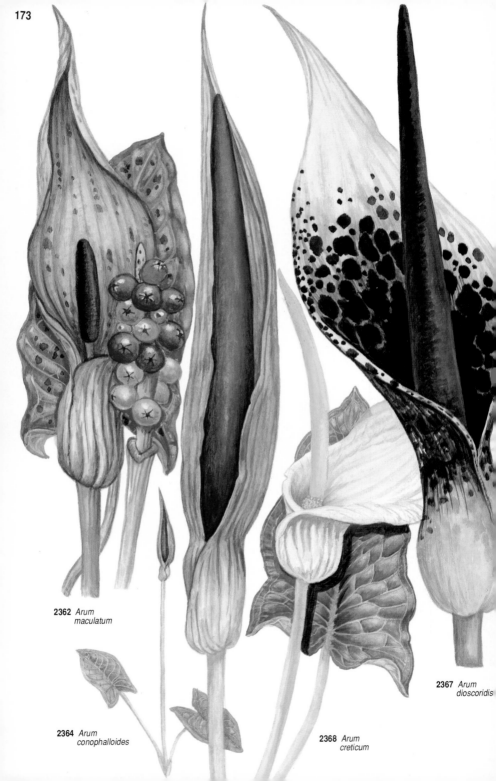

173

2362 *Arum maculatum*

2364 *Arum conophalloides*

2368 *Arum creticum*

2367 *Arum dioscoridis*

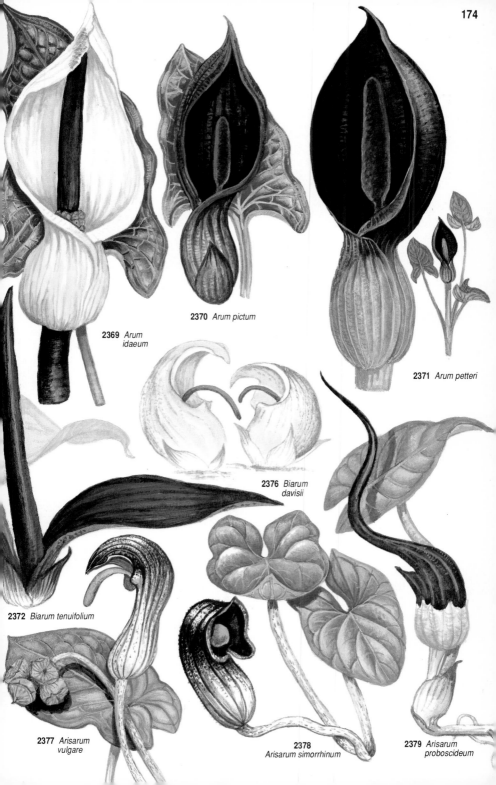

2369 *Arum idaeum*

2370 *Arum pictum*

2371 *Arum petteri*

2376 *Biarum davisii*

2372 *Biarum tenuifolium*

2377 *Arisarum vulgare*

2378 *Arisarum simorrhinum*

2379 *Arisarum proboscideum*

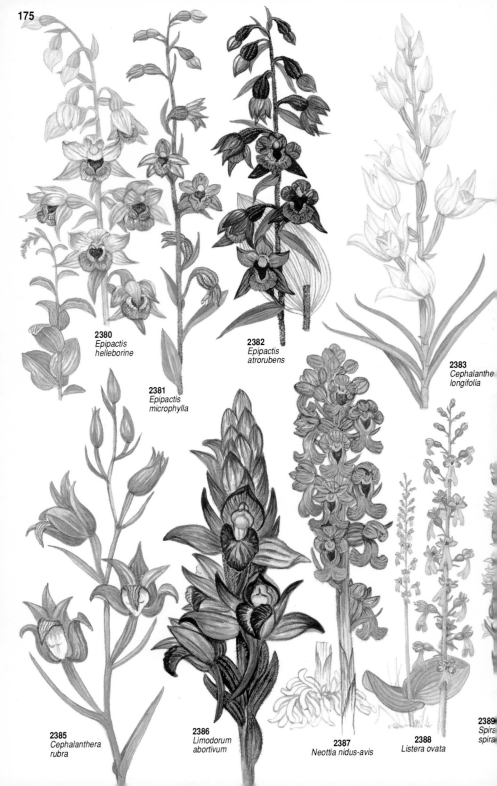

175

2380
*Epipactis
helleborine*

2381
*Epipactis
microphylla*

2382
*Epipactis
atrorubens*

2383
*Cephalanthe
longifolia*

2385
*Cephalanthera
rubra*

2386
*Limodorum
abortivum*

2387
Neottia nidus-avis

2388
Listera ovata

2389
*Spira
spira*

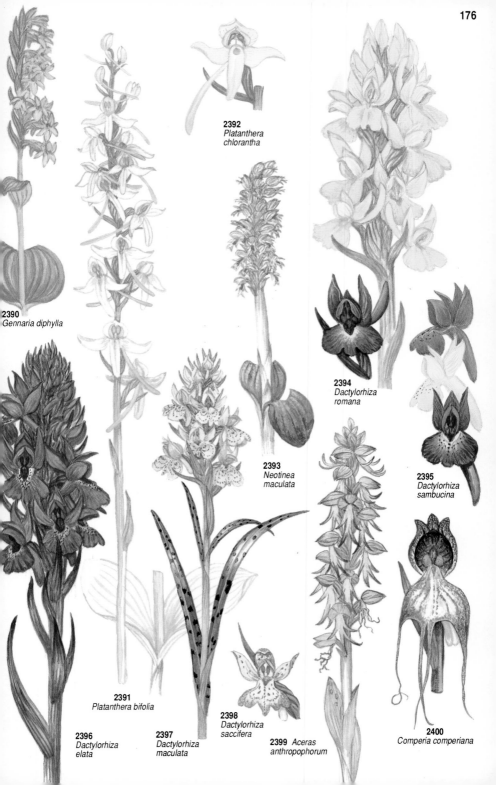

2392
Platanthera chlorantha

2390
Gennaria diphylla

2394
Dactylorhiza romana

2393
Neotinea maculata

2395
Dactylorhiza sambucina

2391
Platanthera bifolia

2396
Dactylorhiza elata

2397
Dactylorhiza maculata

2398
Dactylorhiza saccifera

2399 *Aceras anthropophorum*

2400
Comperia comperiana

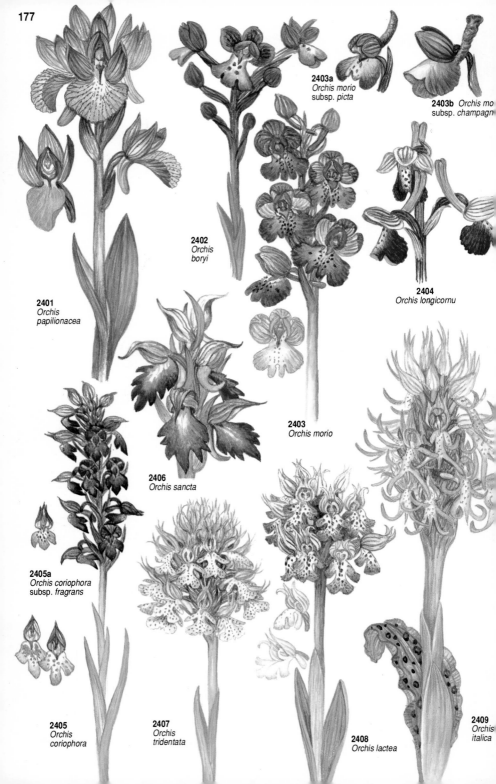

177

2401
Orchis
papilionacea

2402
Orchis
boryi

2403a
Orchis morio
subsp. *picta*

2403b *Orchis mo*
subsp. *champagn*

2404
Orchis longicornu

2403
Orchis morio

2406
Orchis sancta

2405a
Orchis coriophora
subsp. *fragrans*

2405
Orchis
coriophora

2407
Orchis
tridentata

2408
Orchis lactea

2409
Orchis
italica

2410
Orchis simia

2411 *Orchis
punctulata*

2412
*Orchis
purpurea*

2413
*Orchis
collina*

2414
*Orchis
patens*

2415
Orchis spitzelii

2416
*Orchis mascula
subsp. olbiensis*

2417 *Orchis
provincialis*

2418
*Orchis
anatolica*

2419
*Orchis
quadripunctata*

2420 *Orchis
laxiflora*

2421 *Orchis
palustris*

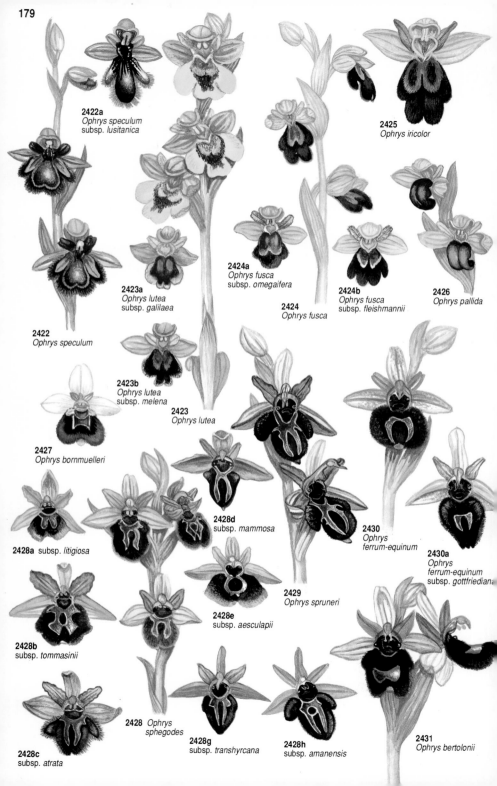

179

2422a
Ophrys speculum
subsp. *lusitanica*

2422
Ophrys speculum

2423a
Ophrys lutea
subsp. *galilaea*

2423b
Ophrys lutea
subsp. *melena*

2423
Ophrys lutea

2424a
Ophrys fusca
subsp. *omegaifera*

2424
Ophrys fusca

2424b
Ophrys fusca
subsp. *fleishmannii*

2425
Ophrys iricolor

2426
Ophrys pallida

2427
Ophrys bornmuelleri

2428a subsp. *litigiosa*

2428b
subsp. *tommasinii*

2428c
subsp. *atrata*

2428d
subsp. *mammosa*

2428e
subsp. *aesculapii*

2428 *Ophrys sphegodes*

2428g
subsp. *transhyrcana*

2428h
subsp. *amanensis*

2429
Ophrys spruneri

2430
Ophrys ferrum-equinum

2430a
Ophrys ferrum-equinum
subsp. *gottfriediana*

2431
Ophrys bertolonii

2434
Ophrys reinholdii

2435
Ophrys umbilicata

2436a
Ophrys scolopax
subsp. *cornuta*

2436b
Ophrys scolopax
subsp. *apiformis*

2433
Ophrys argolica

2435a
Ophrys umbilicata
subsp. *attica*

2436
Ophrys scolopax

2436c
Ophrys scolopax
subsp. *heldreichii*

432
Ophrys lunulata

2438
Ophrys kotschyi

2440a
Ophrys fuciflora
subsp. *candica*

2440b
Ophrys fuciflora
subsp. *exaltata*

2439
Ophrys kurdica

2440
Ophrys fuciflora

2443a
Ophrys apifera
var. *trollii*

2437
Ophrys cretica

2441
Ophrys arachnitiformis

2442
Ophrys tenthredinifera

2443
Ophrys apifera

2444
Ophrys bombyliflora

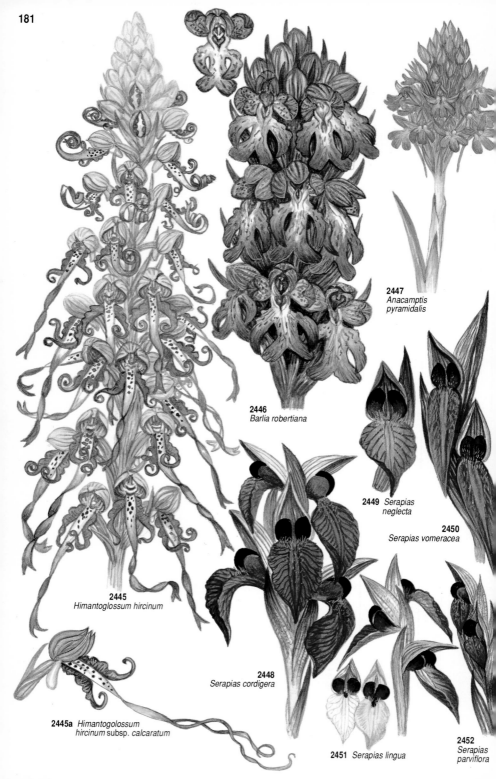

181

2447
Anacamptis pyramidalis

2446
Barlia robertiana

2449 *Serapias neglecta*

2450
Serapias vomeracea

2445
Himantoglossum hircinum

2448
Serapias cordigera

2445a *Himantogolossum hircinum* subsp. *calcaratum*

2451 *Serapias lingua*

2452
Serapias parviflora

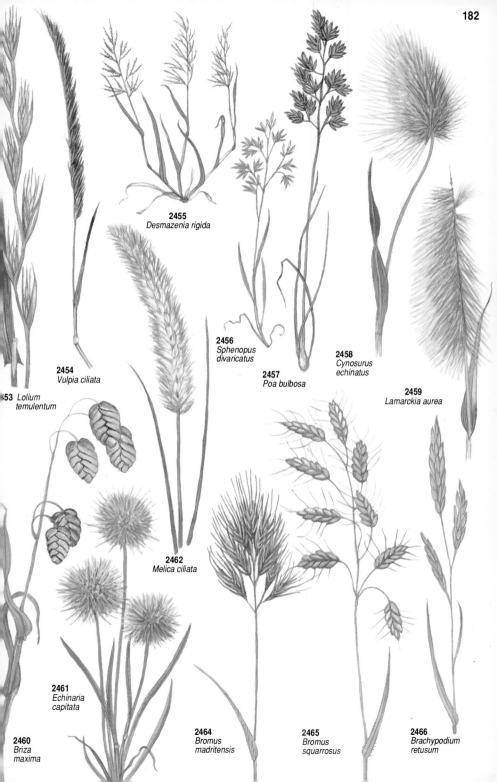

2455
Desmazenia rigida

2454
Vulpia ciliata

53 *Lolium temulentum*

2456
Sphenopus divaricatus

2457
Poa bulbosa

2458
Cynosurus echinatus

2459
Lamarckia aurea

2462
Melica ciliata

2461
Echinaria capitata

2460
Briza maxima

2464
Bromus madritensis

2465
Bromus squarrosus

2466
Brachypodium retusum

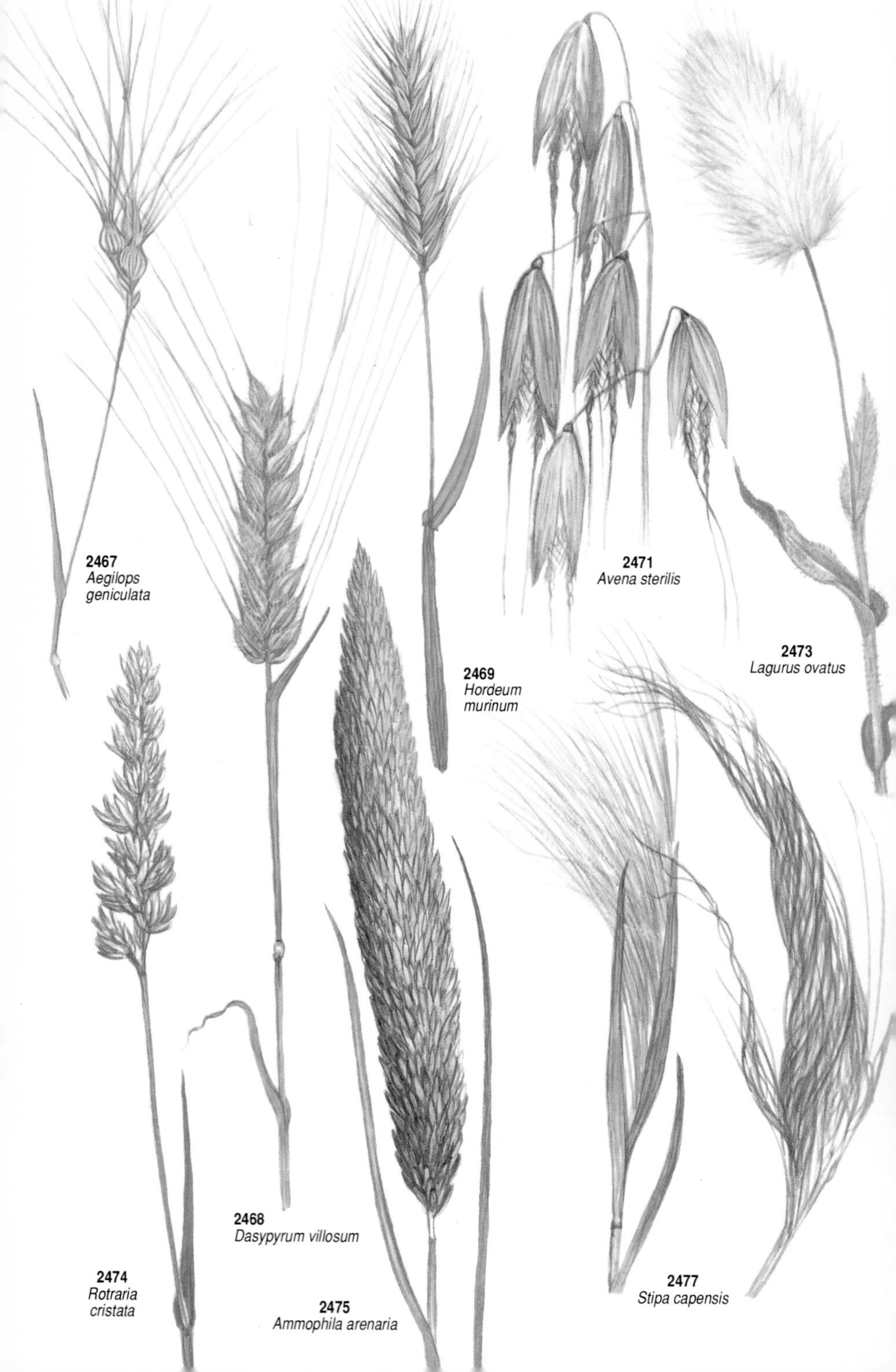

183

2467
*Aegilops
geniculata*

2471
Avena sterilis

2473
Lagurus ovatus

2469
*Hordeum
murinum*

2468
Dasypyrum villosum

2474
*Rotraria
cristata*

2475
Ammophila arenaria

2477
Stipa capensis

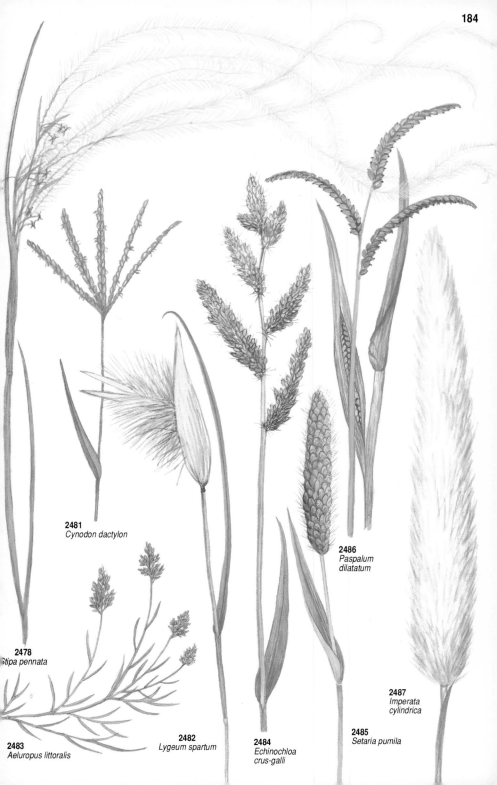

2481
Cynodon dactylon

2486
Paspalum dilatatum

2478
Stipa pennata

2483
Aeluropus littoralis

2482
Lygeum spartum

2484
Echinochloa crus-galli

2485
Setaria pumila

2487
Imperata cylindrica

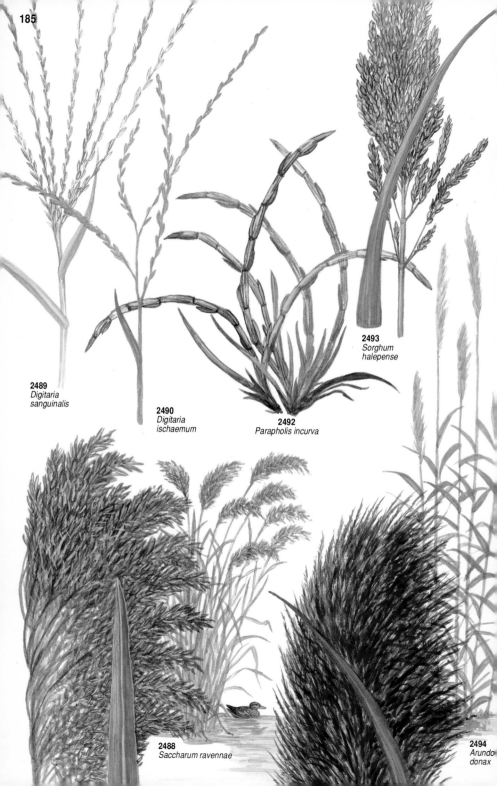

185

2489
Digitaria sanguinalis

2490
Digitaria ischaemum

2492
Parapholis incurva

2493
Sorghum halepense

2488
Saccharum ravennae

2494
Arundo donax

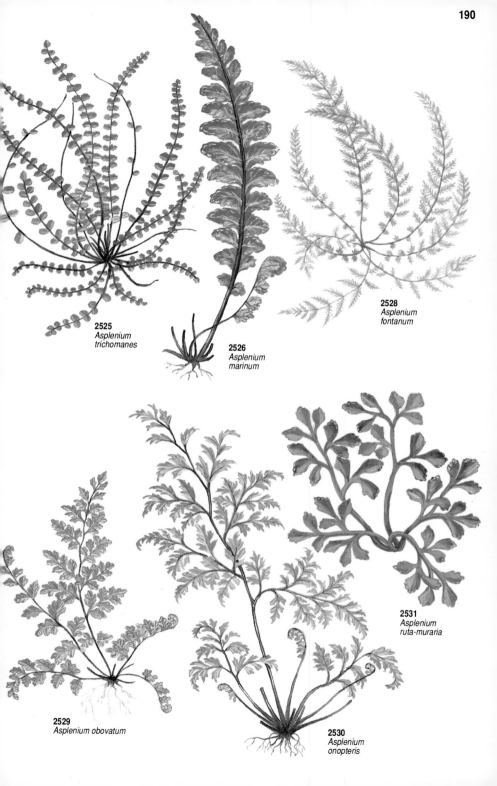

2525
*Asplenium
trichomanes*

2526
*Asplenium
marinum*

2528
*Asplenium
fontanum*

2529 *Asplenium obovatum*

2530
*Asplenium
onopteris*

2531
*Asplenium
ruta-muraria*

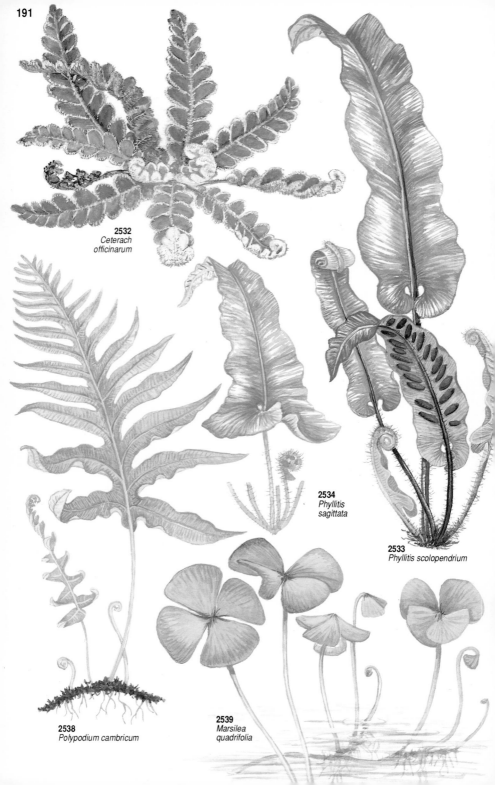

2532
Ceterach officinarum

2534
Phyllitis sagittata

2533
Phyllitis scolopendrium

2538
Polypodium cambricum

2539
Marsilea quadrifolia

1398 *Lappula squarrosa [L. myosotis, Echinospermum lappula]* **BUR FORGET-ME-NOT.** Short to medium, rough-haired, greyish annual or biennial; stems erect, usually branched, with appressed hairs. Leaves oblong to linear-lanceolate, untoothed, mostly unstalked. Flowers pale blue, 4mm, forget-me-not-like, borne in leafy clusters, often branched. Fruit on erect stalks, with an expanded calyx; nutlets covered with hooked spines in 2 rows, mitre-like. Dry habitats, disturbed, waste and cultivated land, vineyards, olive groves, roadsides and sand-dunes. Apr-July. Spain eastwards to Turkey – absent from most of the islands.

1399 *Omphalodes linifolia* **ANNUAL OMPHALODES.** Pale bluish- or whitish-green, low to short, erect annual; stem simple or branched above. Leaves variable, the lower spatula-shaped and stalked, the upper lanceolate to linear, sessile, half-clasping the stem; all leaves with a sparsely hairy margin. Flowers white or very pale blue, 5-10mm, forget-me-not-like, borne in long, branched racemes; no bracts. Nutlets smooth or hairy, cupped, with an incurved, toothed wing. Dry open habitats, fields, cultivated and fallow land, stony places, roadsides. Apr-June. Iberian Peninsula, S France, NW Africa.

1400 *Omphalodes brassicifolia [O. amplexicaulis]*. Very similar, but leaves broader and *clasping* the stem. Fruit with a narrow, erect, untoothed wing. Rocky and stony habitats in the mountains. S Spain and NW Africa.

1401 *Omphalodes kuzinskyanae*. Like *O. linifolia*, but flowers usually blue and inflorescence with *bracts*. Coastal rocks and sands. NW Spain to C Portugal.

Cynoglossum **HOUND'S-TONGUES.** Herbs, usually perennial or biennial with flowers in branched cymes, usually without bracts; corolla with a short tube and 5 spreading, often rounded lobes, with scales closing the throat; stamens not protruding. Fruit with egg-shaped nutlets covered with barbed spines.

1402 *Cynoglossum creticum* **BLUE HOUND'S TONGUE.** Fairly robust medium to tall, softly hairy biennial; stems angular, erect, branched above. Leaves oblong to lanceolate, untoothed, densely hairy, often clasping the stem. Flowers purplish in bud, but opening blue, with conspicuous deeper inky-blue or purple *net-veins*, 7-9mm, borne in branched cymes which elongate in fruit. Nutlets 5-7mm, with a thickened edge and dense hooked spines. Cultivated, fallow and waste land, olive groves, vineyards and roadsides, moist sites by streams and ditches. Feb-June. T.

1403 *Cynoglossum columnae*. Similar, but a short to medium annual with smaller, 5-6mm, deep blue or purplish flowers, *without* conspicuous net-veins. Nutlets 7-10mm. Dry open habitats, fallow and stony ground, waste places. Mar-June. Italy, Sicily and the Balkans, Turkey.

1404 *Cynoglossum cherifolium [C. heterocarpum]*. Short to medium hairy, rather *white-felted*, greyish biennial. Leaves lanceolate, unstalked and half-clasping the stem, somewhat undulate, felted on both surfaces. Flowers pale reddish-purple, becoming purple or deep blue, 5-6mm, borne in cymes that are rather congested to begin with, bracts present. Nutlets 5-8mm, with a thickened border, with dense hooked spines or almost smooth. Dry open, rocky, stony and waste places. Mar-June. Iberian Peninsula eastwards to Italy and Sicily.

1405 *Cynoglossum nebrodense*. Similar, but less hairy and rather more bristly. Flowers reddish-violet, 4-6mm, borne in cymes *without* bracts. Mountain woods. May-July. Spain, Italy. Sicily and Greece.

Anchusa **ANCHUSAS.** Annual or perennial herbs. Flowers blue, purple, white or yellow, borne in lateral or terminal cymes, with bracts; corolla with a short to medium tube and a bell-shaped limb, with 5 hairy scales in the throat; stamens not protruding. Nutlet egg-shaped to kidney-shaped with a thickened basal collar, rough or netted, sometimes finely warted.

1406 *Anchusa undulata* **UNDULATE ANCHUSA**. Short to medium, hairy or somewhat bristly biennial or perennial. Leaves elliptical, the basal in a rosette, scarcely stalked, the upper similar but unstalked and clasping the stem, all with *undulate* margins. Flowers dark blue, violet or purple, funnel-shaped, limb 3-8mm, the tube 8-13mm long; bracts oval to lanceolate. Dry hillsides in the garrigue, roadsides, waste and cultivated ground, sandy coastal habitats, olive groves. Mar-June. Iberian Peninsula.

> 1406a Subsp. *hybrida [A. hybrida]*. Very similar, but flowers *smaller*, the tube 5-8mm long and the limb 3-5mm. T – except the Iberian Peninsula.

1407 *Anchusa calcarea*. Similar, but perennial, the leaf and stem bristles with a white *pimple-like* base; corolla-tube 6.5-8mm long. Coastal sands. Iberian Peninsula.

1408 *Anchusa officinalis* **ALKANET**. Short to tall, rough-bristly perennial, occasionally biennial; stems erect, branched. Leaves long-lanceolate, 10-20mm wide, the lower stalked. Flowers bluish-red or violet, with a whitish centre, rarely all white or yellowish, 7-15mm, borne in elongating, coiled cymes; calyx divided to the middle. Nutlets conical. Meadows, banks, roadsides, cultivated ground, gardens. Apr-Sept. Balearic Is. and S France eastwards to Turkey – not Sicily or Crete.

1409 *Anchusa azurea [A. italica]* **LARGE BLUE ALKANET**. Rather like the previous species, but a more robust perennial, to 1.5m, though often less and the leaves 15-50mm wide. Flowers larger, 10-20mm, deep blue or violet with a white centre, borne in a lax, paniculate inflorescence. Cultivated, fallow and waste ground, open garrigue, roadsides, olive groves. Mar-June. T.

1410 *Anchusa strigosa*. Like *A. azurea*, but a more prickly, more densely branched plant with bluish-green (not green) stems and leaves; bristles with expanded pimple-like bases. Flowers *paler*, light blue or whitish-blue; calyx-lobes blunt (not long-pointed). Similar habitats and flowering time. Rhodes and Turkey eastwards, including Cyprus.

1411 *Anchusa humilis [Anchusa aggregata]*. Like *A. strigosa*, but annual to 30cm tall, though often less. Flowers bright cobalt blue, 3-6mm, borne in tight, white-bristled, clusters. Coastal rocks and sands, dunes, occasionally on sandy ground inland. Feb-May. Sicily, N Africa and the E Med, including Cyprus.

1412 *Anchusa aegyptiaca* **EASTERN ANCHUSA**. Low to short bristly annual; stems prostrate to ascending or sprawling. Leaves oblong-oval to lanceolate, the margin toothed to somewhat undulate, the lower with a grooved stalk, the upper unstalked, half-clasping the stem. Flowers *pale yellow*, 4-6mm, with tube equalling the limb, borne in a lax, often unbranched inflorescence; flowers appear to be solitary because of leaf-like bracts below each. Cultivated, fallow and waste ground, dry hillslopes in garrigue, sandy coastal habitats. Feb-May. Crete, S Aegean Is. eastwards, including Cyprus.

fruit

1413 *Anchusa arvensis [Lycopsis arvensis]* **BUGLOSS**. A short to medium, rough-bristly annual with ascending stems. Leaves lanceolate to linear-lanceolate, with a wavy margin, irregularly toothed, the lower stalked, the upper unstalked and half-clasping the stem. Flowers bright blue, occasionally whitish, small, 4-6mm, the tube *curved* in the middle, borne in forked cymes, the sepals enlarging somewhat in fruit; bracts leaf-like. Nutlets netted. Cultivated, fallow and waste ground, bare places, roadsides, vineyards and olive groves, sandy coastal habitats. Apr-Sept. T – except the extreme E Med and Cyprus.

1414 *Anchusa cretica.* Low to short, bristly annual; stems erect to ascending. Leaves linear-lanceolate, toothed or not, the lower short-stalked. Flowers purplish, becoming blue, with *white lines*, occasionally pure white, 6-9mm, funnel-shaped, the tube slightly shorter than the limb, curved. Nutlets, netted, rough, 3-4mm. Rocky and dry grassy habitats, roadsides, olive groves, vineyards, occasionally along sandy seashores. Mar-June. Italy, Sicily and the Balkans, Turkey.

1415 *Anchusa variegata [Lycopsis variegata].* Very similar to the previous species but prostrate, the flowers white or pale purple, becoming pale blue with reddish markings. Similar habitats and flowering time. Greece, Crete and Turkey.

VERBENA FAMILY Verbenaceae

Herbs or shrubs with opposite leaves. Flowers borne in clusters, heads or panicles; corolla with a slender tube and often a flat limb, 2-lipped or not. Fruit 2- or 4-parted, fleshy and berry-like or dry nutlets.

1416 *Vitex agnus-castus* **CHASTE TREE.** Robust deciduous shrub to 6m tall, though often less; young twigs somewhat 4-angled, finely grey hairy, becoming dull brown with age. Leaves opposite and *digitate*, with 5-7 linear-lanceolate, untoothed leaflets, white-downy beneath. Flowers blue or pink, 8-10mm long, sweetly scented, borne in branched panicles with the flowers in clusters along the branches; corolla 2-lipped with protruding stamens. Fruit 3mm, reddish-black when ripe, like a peppercorn. Riverbanks, damp places alongside streams and ditches, gravelly places. roadsides. June-Dec. T. Sometimes cultivated for ornament. Today it is used medicinally, yielding a drug used for eyes and in poultices. In the past the plant was thought to preserve chastity, so called 'Monk's Pepper': *hagnos* (Greek) and *castus* (Latin) both mean chaste. It also yields a yellow dye.

1417 *Lantana camara* **LANTANA.** Prickly shrub to 1.5m, with a strong and unpleasant smell; young twigs square, hairy as well as prickly. Leaves opposite, oval, toothed, short-stalked. Flowers yellow or orange changing to red, or all yellow or all red, sometimes mauvish, 4-5mm, congested into tight, often paired, *heads*, on long stalks; corolla weakly 2-lipped. Fruit a small black berry. May-Oct. Widely cultivated and occasionally naturalised in the region, especially in Spain and Sicily, possibly elsewhere (tropical and subtropical Americas).

1418 *Verbena officinalis* **VERVAIN.** Medium, rough-hairy perennial; stems slender, *stiffly erect*, square. Leaves opposite, diamond-shaped to lanceolate, in outline, deeply 1-2-pinnately-lobed, the lower stalked, the upper smaller and often unlobed. Flowers pink, 2-5mm, weakly 2-lipped, in slender, branched spikes up to 30cm long, clustered to begin with. Waste and rocky ground, rough grassland, waysides, ditches and streamsides. May-Sept. T.

1419 *Verbena supina.* Straggling or prostrate, low to short, often rather rough annual; stems square, much-branched from the base. Leaves opposite, triangular in outline, 1-2-pinnately divided, with slender divisions, stalked. Flowers lilac, 2.5mm long, borne in rather *crowded* spikes, sometimes branched, not more than 70mm long. Fruit with 4 faintly veined nutlets. Waste, damp and marshy places, often sandy, meadows subjected to occasional flooding. Apr-June. T – not Balearic Is. or Corsica.

1420 *Phyla nodiflora [Lippia nodiflora].* Prostrate perennial herb, with stems *rooting* at the nodes; flowering stems ascending to 30cm, often less. Leaves oval to elliptical, broadest above the middle, often somewhat toothed in the upper half. Flowers white, 2mm, borne in short, stout lateral spikes, long-stalked. Fruit 2 small nutlets.

fruit

Wet, often grassy habitats, seepage areas, often close to the sea. Mar-July. T – not France, Sardinia or Cyprus.

MINT FAMILY Labiatae

Herbs or shrubs, often aromatic from numerous glands; stems square. Leaves opposite, usually simple. Flowers irregular (zygomorphic), in distinct lateral clusters (verticillasters) which often form whorls around the stem; calyx with 5 teeth, sometimes 2-lipped; corolla 2-lipped, except in *Ajuga* and *Teucrium*, the lower lip 3-lobed and the upper 2. Stamens 4 (2 in *Salvia*). Fruit consisting of 4 nutlets hidden at the base of the persistent calyx.

Ajuga **BUGLES.** Annual or perennial herbs. Calyx with 5 even teeth. Corolla with a very reduced, inconspicuous, upper lip and a 3-lobed lower lip; stamens usually protruding.

bract

1421 *Ajuga orientalis* **ORIENTAL BUGLE.** Low to short, softly hairy, rhizomatous perennial. Lower leaves oval to oblong, deeply toothed to shallowly lobed. Flowers violet-blue or claret-red, 12-16mm long, *upside-down* (resupinate), borne in a spike-like inflorescence; corolla with a long slender tube; stamens not protruding. Mountainsides, pine forests, roadsides, fallow fields, rarely at low altitudes. Mar-July. Italy and Sicily eastwards, not Crete.

1422 *Ajuga iva.* Tufted to somewhat sprawling, low to short softly white-hairy perennial; stems woody at the base. Leaves linear to linear-oblong, unlobed or with 2-6 short lobes; bracts similar to the leaves, longer than the flowers. Flowers purple, pink or yellow, 10-14mm long, the upper lip tiny, entire. Stony pastures, waste ground, garrigue, dry grassy places, roadsides. Apr-Oct. T. The flower colour varies – on Cyprus plants appear always to have yellow flowers.

1423 *Ajuga genevensis* **BLUE BUGLE.** Low to short, hairy perennial, without runners; stems hairy all round, often rather woolly. Leaves oblong, toothed, sometimes shallowly lobed, the lower stalked and generally withered by flowering time; bracts leaf-like, *tinged* with blue or violet, the uppermost shorter than the flowers. Flowers bright blue, sometimes pink or white, 12-20mm long, borne in leafy spikes. Woodland clearings, stony and grassy places, generally on dry calcareous soils. Mar-July. Spain eastwards to Yugoslavia – absent from the islands.

1424 *Ajuga reptans* **BUGLE.** Similar, but plant with creeping and rooting *runners*; stem hairy only on two opposing sides. Similar habitats and flowering time. T – but absent from most of the islands and scarce in N Africa and the extreme E Med. A very common European plant.

1425 *Ajuga chamaepitys* **GROUND PINE.** Variable, low to short, often sprawling, greyish-hairy annual, with a faint smell of *pine-resin*. Leaves with 3 narrow, linear lobes, the lobes often further lobed or toothed. Flowers yellow, with reddish or purplish markings, 7-15mm long, partly hidden among the upper leaves. Dry open habitats, grassy and stony slopes, waste and fallow ground, roadsides, olive groves, vineyards, on calcareous soils. Jan-June. T. Used by herbalists in treating rheumatism and gout.

    1425a Subsp. *chia [Ajuga chia]* can be distinguished by being a short-lived perennial, by its wider leaf-segments, 1.5-4mm wide (not 0.5-2mm) and by its larger flowers, 18-25mm long, which are more boldly marked with red or purple. Balkans eastwards.

Scutellaria **SKULLCAPS**. Rhizomatous perennials. Flowers usually in pairs, often rather distant; calyx 2-lipped, the upper lip with a distinctive erect, often rounded appendage; corolla 2-lipped, with a long slender tube, the upper lip forming a small hood, the lower small and 3-lobed.

1426 *Scutellaria galericulata* **SKULLCAP**. Short to medium, usually hairy, shortly creeping perennial, with erect, branched or unbranched stems. Leaves oval to lanceolate, toothed, with a somewhat heart-shaped base, the upper unstalked; bracts similar to the leaves. Flowers bright violet-blue, rarely pink, with a whitish base, 10-18mm long, the corolla *abruptly upcurved*; calyx 2-lipped, the upper lip with an erect rounded appendage. Damp grassy habitats, river and stream margins, marshes, mainly in the hills and lower mountains. May-Aug. T – except Balearic Is., Sicily, Crete, Cyprus and parts of the extreme E Med. A widespread species in Europe.

1427 *Scutellaria sibthorpii*. Similar, but leaves more markedly cordate and flowers dark crimson with a whitish patch on the lower lip of the corolla. Rocky hillslopes, garrigue near the coast. Apr-May. Cyprus – endemic.

1428 *Scutellaria orientalis* **EASTERN SKULLCAP**. Low to short spreading to prostrate, somewhat hairy perennial, with a woody base. Leaves oval to oblong, deeply toothed to pinnately-lobed. Flowers *yellow*, the lower lip often reddish, occasionally all pink, 15-30mm long, borne in a rather 4-sided, oblong inflorescence; corolla abruptly upcurved from near the base. Rocky habitats, usually on limestones, sometimes in open garrigue. Apr-July. S Spain, the Balkans and Turkey.

Teucrium **GERMANDERS**. Herbs or shrubs. Flowers usually with a 2-lipped calyx and corolla with a single, 5-lobed, lower lip, rather like a small manikin.

1429 *Teucrium fruticans* **TREE GERMANDER**. Rather spreading, white- or grey-felted evergreen shrub, to 2.5m tall; twigs square. Leaves lanceolate to oval, flat, short-stalked and untoothed, white-felted occasionally reddish; bracts leaf-like. Flowers paired, blue or lilac, 15-25mm long, with the stamens long-protruding; calyx bell-shaped. Garrigue, maquis, evergreen thickets, mostly near the coast. Feb-June. Iberian Peninsula and NW Africa eastwards to Yugoslavia, not Balearic Is. or Crete. Widely grown as an ornamental shrub: some forms have deep blue flowers.

1430 *Teucrium creticum*. Similar, but leaves linear with *revolute* margins. Flowers mauve-pink. Dry rocky habitats. Mar-June. E Med from Turkey eastwards, including Cyprus – not Crete despite the name.

1431 *Teucrium brevifolium*. Like *T. creticum*, but smaller more rounded bush to 60cm, generally rather grey-downy. Leaves oblong to linear with revolute margins. Flowers *smaller*, 9-10mm long (not 17-19mm), blue. Dry rocky, mainly coastal habitats. Mar-May. S Aegean Is. and Crete.

1432 *Teucrium marum*. Like *S. fruticans*, but flowers in a denser more cylindrical inflorescence, without bract-like leaves. Flowers *smaller*, 10-12mm long, purplish. Dry rocky habitats and evergreen scrub. Mar-June. Balearic Is., S France, Corsica and Sardinia, Italy and a number of Adriatic Is.

1433 *Teucrium scorodonia* **WOOD SAGE**. Short to medium hairy perennial, sometimes almost a subshrub; stems erect, branched. Leaves oval to heart-shaped, stalked; bracts oval, short. Flowers pale greenish-yellow, occasionally whitish, 8-9mm long, hairy; stamens protruding with maroon anthers, borne in leafless spikes. Open woods, thickets, rocky places, occasionally on dunes. June-Sept. Iberian Peninsula and NW Africa eastwards to Yugoslavia – not Balearic Is. or Crete.

1434 *Teucrium massiliense.* Similar, but leaves with a truncated or rounded *base*. Flowers pink with a glandular-hairy calyx. Apr-May. Rocky habitats and scrub. Spain, S France, Corsica, Sardinia and Crete.

1435 *Teucrium scordium* **WATER GERMANDER.** Low to short, sprawling, softly hairy perennial, with a strong smell of *garlic* when crushed. Leaves oval to heart-shaped, half-clasping the stem, coarsely toothed. Flowers purplish, 7-10mm long, borne in whorls up the leafy stem; calyx downy. Damp habitats, marshes and streamsides. June-Sept. T – the normal form seen in the Med region with distinctive heart-shaped leaf-bases is generally referable to subsp. *scordioides* (1435a).

1436 *Teucrium spinosum* **SPINY GERMANDER.** Medium, much-branched, glandular-hairy annual, the branches becoming *spiny* and leafless at flowering time. Leaves oblong, sharply toothed, the uppermost small and untoothed. Flowers white, 6-8mm long, *upside-down* (resupinate), borne in small whorls; calyx with spiny teeth. Cultivated and fallow fields, sandy and gravelly places. May-July. Iberian Peninsula, mainly in the S, Sardinia, S Italy and Sicily.

1437 *Teucrium subspinosum.* Similar, but a dense shrub forming hummocks up to 50cm tall, stiffly spiny. Flowers pink. Similar habitats and flowering time. Majorca – endemic.

1438 *Teucrium campanulatum.* Short perennial, more or less hairless, with a spreading base and erect stems. Leaves *3-parted*, with narrow pinnately-lobed segments; bracts leaf-like. Flowers whitish, small, 4-5mm long, borne in small whorls; stamens slightly protruding. May-July. Open rocky habitats. SW Spain, Balearic Is., S Italy and Sicily.

1439 *Teucrium chamaedrys* **WALL GERMANDER.** Very variable, short, slightly hairy, tufted, rhizomatous perennial with a woody base. Leaves oblong, untoothed to deeply toothed, rather leathery, shiny dark green above; bracts like leaves but smaller. Flowers pale to deep purplish-pink, rarely white, 9-16mm long, borne in leafy spikes. Dry bare habitats, open woodland and scrub. Apr-Sept. T – not Crete or Cyprus. A refreshing infusion can be made from the flower-heads.

1440 *Teucrium divaricatum.* Similar, but not rhizomatous, the leaves *leathery*, oval and shallowly toothed. Flowers pink, purple or reddish. Rocky habitats in the garrigue. May-July. Crete, and Aegean Is., eastwards, including Cyprus.

1441 *Teucrium flavum.* Similar, but stems and leaves rather velvety and flowers *yellow*. Rocky and stony habitats. May-Aug. T – not Cyprus.

1442 *Teucrium polium* **FELTY GERMANDER.** Dwarf shrub or subshrub, to 45cm tall, though often less; stems with white greenish or golden hairs, often densely felted. Leaves narrow-oblong to oval, often broadest above the middle, flat or with revolute margins, bluntly toothed; bracts leaf-like, untoothed. Flowers white or pale pink, occasionally reddish, 4-5mm long, borne in globular, felted heads. Dry habitats, rocky places in the garrigue, stony pastures, open woodland and scrub. Apr-July. T – not Cyprus. A very variable species of which the following variants can be recognised in the region.

　　1442a Subsp. *capitatum.* Flowers in compound heads, stems with grey hairs. T.

　　1442b Subsp. *polium.* Flowers in simple heads and stems with grey hairs. Iberian Peninsula and S France.

　　1442c Subsp. *aureum.* As the previous, but stems with golden hairs; flowers pale yellow. Mountains of W Med.

　　1442d Subsp. *pii-fontii.* Like subsp. *capitatum*, but calyx less than 3mm long (not 3.5-7mm). Spain, Balearic Is.

1442e Subsp. *vincentinum*. Like subsp. *capitatum*, but leaves longer, more than 16mm long and stems with golden or grey hairs. Coastal rocks and sands. Iberian Peninsula.

1443 *Teucrium micropodioides [T. pseudo-polium, T. polium subsp. micropodioides]*. Similar, but only 3-20cm tall, making a domed bush, the leaves small, generally 5-10mm long and the flowers maroon, purple or brownish-pink, 6-9mm long. Garrigue in dry rocky or stony places, occasionally in open pine forest. Apr-July. Cyprus – endemic.

1444 *Prasium majus* **PRASIUM**. Much-branched evergreen shrub to 4m, though often only 1m, with rather erect branches, hairless or slightly hairy. Leaves shiny, dark green, oval to lanceolate, pointed, toothed, the lower with a heart-shaped base, the upper more truncated, all stalked; bracts leaf-like, but smaller. Flowers white or pale lilac, 17-20mm long, borne in terminal racemes; calyx 2-lipped, the teeth shortly *bristle-tipped*. Nutlets shiny-black when ripe. Maquis, garrigue, among bushes or rocks, field boundaries, olive groves, besides old walls, roadsides, rock crevices. Jan-May. T.

1445 *Marrubium vulgare* **WHITE HOREHOUND**. Medium, *white-downy* perennial, thyme-scented; stems branched, often with many short, non-flowering branches. Leaves rounded to oval, usually with a slightly heart-shaped base and a wrinkled surface, stalked. Flowers white, 12-15mm, in dense whorls up the leafy stem; calyx with 10 short, hooked teeth. Rocky and stony ground, grassy and waste places, roadsides, generally on calcareous soils. Feb-Oct. T.

1446 *Marrubium peregrinum*. Similar, but leaves oblong and calyx with only 5 teeth; flowers fewer per whorl, rarely more than 20. Dry open habitats. Balkans and Turkey; naturalised in Italy.

1447 *Marrubium incanum [M. candidissimum]*. Like *M. vulgare*, but stems and leaves more densely white-felted and stems unbranched or with erect branches; calyx 5-toothed. Garrigue, stony pastures, fallow land. May-Aug. N Africa, Italy, Sicily, Yugoslavia and Albania.

1448 *Marrubium alysson*. Like *M. peregrinum*, but leaves with a wedge-shaped, unstalked base and flowers *red*; calyx teeth protruding beyond the corolla. Similar habitats and flowering time. Spain, Sardinia and Italy.

Sideritis **SIDERITIS**. Annual or perennial herbs or small shrubs, often aromatic. Flowers generally in whorls of 4 or more; calyx bell-shaped, 5-toothed and 10-veined; corolla often yellow, 2-lipped; stamens included within the corolla-tube. Several species are dried in various parts of the Med and used for a herbal tea – in Greece called mountain tea.

1449 *Sideritis romana*. Shaggily hairy, short annual. Leaves oblong-oval, toothed, mostly unstalked; bracts similar, the upper smaller. Flowers yellow, 7-10mm long, borne in rather distant whorls, the upper lip of the corolla flat and undivided; calyx strongly veined. Dry habitats, rocky and sandy, in maquis or garrigue. May-July. Iberian Peninsula eastwards to Sicily and W Yugoslavia.

1449a Subsp. *purpurea*. Flowers purple or white. W Balkan Peninsula – endemic.

calyx

1450 *Sideritis curvidens*. Similar, but the calyx *pouched* at the base, weakly veined and with the teeth curved in fruit. Similar habitats, as well as cultivated, waste and fallow ground. Apr-May. Greece, Crete and E Med, including Cyprus.

1451 *Sideritis lanata.* Like *S. romana*, but corolla yellow with *black* tips, equalling the calyx. Cultivated, fallow and waste ground. S Balkans and Aegean Is.

1452 *Sideritis montana.* Like *S. lanata*, but leaves narrower, 2-8mm, wide (not 8-15mm). Corolla all yellow or yellow with a brownish-black upper lip. Similar habitats. T – except the islands and much of the extreme E Med.

1453 *Sideritis hirsuta.* Very variable, short to medium, hairy perennial. Leaves oblong, broadest above the middle, sharply toothed, green or grey-green. Flowers yellow with a white or pale yellow upper lip, rarely all white 8-10mm long, borne in rather distant whorls; calyx regular, *not* 2-lipped. Dry open habitats, hillslopes, vineyards, olive groves, roadsides. Apr-July. Iberian Peninsula, S France and Italy.

1454 *Sideritis incana.* Similar, but a taller and slenderer plant with *untoothed* bracts and yellow or pink flowers. Rocky habitats and screes. Spain.

Phlomis **PHLOMIS.** Herbs or shrubs with flowers in lax or dense, crowded or distant whorls. Corolla 2-lipped, the upper lip hooded and notched at the apex, the lower lip 3-lobed; stamens included or protruding; style branches unequal.

1455 *Phlomis fruticosa* **JERUSALEM SAGE.** Grey-felted evergreen shrub to 1.5m, spreading to erect. Leaves elliptical to lanceolate or oval, untoothed or slightly toothed, thick, stalked, grey-green above but white with felt beneath. Flowers yellow, 23-35mm, borne in dense whorls; whorls solitary or one above the other. Dry rocky habitats, sea cliffs, roadsides. Apr-June. Sardinia and Italy eastwards, including Crete (rare) and Cyprus. A widely cultivated ornamental shrub.

1456 *Phlomis cretica.* Similar, but a smaller shrub, rarely more than 45cm tall, with the upper leaves *pointed* and stems often with glandular hairs. Nutlets hairless (not hairy). Rocks on the lower mountain slopes. Mar-May. S Greece and Crete.

1457 *Phlomis lunariifolia.* Like *P. fruticosa*, but leaves dark green above and calyx *smaller*, 11-12mm long (not 15-20mm), the teeth ending in a distinct, spreading, spine-tip. Nutlets hairless. Garrigue, often in rocky gullies or by streams. Mar-May. Cyprus and S Turkey.

1458 *Phlomis cypria.* Like *P. fruticosa*, but leaves dull green, greyish or yellowish hairy beneath and flowers smaller, pale yellow, the calyx 7-12mm long. Garrigue and stony hillslopes. Apr-June. Cyprus – endemic.

1459 *Phlomis lanata.* Like *P. cretica*, but leaves smaller, rounded to oval, with *rounded tips*. Flowers less densely whorled, 20-23mm long. Nutlets hairy. Rocky slopes near coast and in the lower mountains. Mar-Apr. Crete – endemic.

1460 *Phlomis lychnitis.* Small evergreen shrub, white-felted, to 65cm; stems without glandular hairs. Leaves linear to narrow-elliptic or spatula-shaped, untoothed or with a few small apical teeth, thick, scarcely stalked, greyish above, white-felted beneath. Flowers yellow, 20-30mm, borne in 4-8 whorls one above the other, each cupped in a pair of oval, leaf-like bracts. Garrigue, rocky and stony slopes. Apr-July. Iberian Peninsula and S France.

1461 *Phlomis crinita.* Similar, but leaves oval to lanceolate, with a *distinct* stalk. Flowers brownish-yellow or yellow. Similar habitats and flowering time. S and E Spain, NW Africa.

1462 *Phlomis herba-venti.* Robust medium to tall perennial, greyish-hairy. Leaves oval to lanceolate, with a rounded or heart-shaped base, toothed or not, thin, scarcely hairy above but white-downy beneath. Flowers deep pink or purple, 15-20mm long, in dense whorls one above the other; calyx hairy, with bristle-tipped teeth.

Dry stony and rocky hillslopes, field boundaries, roadsides. Apr-July. Iberian Peninsula eastwards to Turkey, but absent from most of the islands except Sicily.

1463 *Phlomis tuberosa* **TUBEROUS PHLOMIS**. Similar, but tall, to 1.5m, the roots bearing tubers and the leaves felted with starry (stellate) hairs on both sides. Yugoslavia and Greece.

1464 *Phlomis samia*. Like *P. herba-venti*, but stems and branches with glandular hairs and flowers *larger*, the corolla purple, 30-35mm long; calyx 18-25mm long (not 8-15mm). Coniferous woodland and scrub, mainly in the mountains. June-Sept. S Yugoslavia, Greece and Turkey.

1465 *Phlomis purpurea*. An evergreen *shrub*, to 2m, though often less, with rather erect branches, densely hairy, but not glandular. Leaves leathery, rather wrinkled above, grey-green, lanceolate to oblong, white with stellate hairs beneath, all leaves stalked. Flowers purple or pink, occasionally white, 23-26mm long, borne in distant whorls one above the other; calyx grey-felted. Dry stony and rocky habitats, roadsides, scrub, field boundaries. Apr-June. S Portugal, C and S Spain.

1466 *Phlomis italica*. Similar, but leaves white with downy hairs on *both* surfaces. Flowers 18-20mm long. Balearic Is. – endemic.

1467 *Molucella spinosa* **MOLUCELLA**. Medium to tall, hairless annual or short-lived perennial. Leaves oval to rounded, often with a heart-shaped base, coarsely toothed. Flowers white or pale pink, 25-40mm long, borne in rather distant whorls, one above the other, the flowers subtended by spiny bracts; calyx greatly *enlarged* in fruit, funnel-shaped and papery, somewhat 2-lipped, net-veined; calyx-margin with one broad spine, the other with 7 slender spines. Hedges and ditches, cultivated fields and waste ground. May-June. Very local and decreasing in S Spain, Italy, Sicily, Greece, Cyprus and parts of the extreme E Med.

flower

1468 *Molucella laevis* **BELLS OF IRELAND**. Very similar, but calyx larger, 20-25mm long (not 13-15mm) and a regular funnel-shape, *not* 2-lipped, the margin with 5 minute teeth. Similar habitats and flowering time. Turkey, Cyprus, Syria and Palestine. Widely grown in gardens – though in no way Irish!

1469 *Ballota acetabulosa* **GARDEN HOREHOUND**. Short to medium, grey-downy perennial, with a woody base; stems erect to ascending, branched at the base. Leaves suborbicular to oval, with a heart-shaped base, stalked, with a blunt-toothed margin, thick and woolly. Flowers purple and white, 15-18mm long, borne in dense rather congested whorls; *calyx* much enlarged in fruit, goblet-shaped with a conspicuous umbrella-like, veined wing, up to 20mm across. Rocky and stony habitats, open scrub. May-July. Greece and Crete. The dried stems are collected and used as a wick for oil lamps.

calyx

1470 *Ballota pseudodictamnus*. Similar, but a lower plant, seldom more than 50cm tall, often less, *yellowish-woolly*. Flowers 14-15mm long; calyx smaller, funnel-shaped, with 5 short, pointed lobes. Rocky habitats and open scrub. Apr-May. S Aegean Is. and Crete; naturalised in Italy and Sicily. Commonly grown in gardens for its foliage.

1471 *Ballota integrifolia [Molucella frutescens]*. Slender sprawling shrub to 1m; young stems almost square, bristly. Leaves oblong, often broadest above the middle, toothed or not, stalked; bracts oval, untoothed, with a pair of straight or recurved, brownish *spines* at the base of each. Flowers white with purple or red stripes, 9-12mm long, solitary at each bract, but forming a lax, branched inflorescence; calyx funnel-shaped, with 5 short, equal teeth. Rocky hillslopes, cliff crevices, occasionally on old walls. Apr-June. Cyprus – endemic.

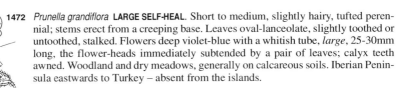

1472 *Prunella grandiflora* **LARGE SELF-HEAL**. Short to medium, slightly hairy, tufted perennial; stems erect from a creeping base. Leaves oval-lanceolate, slightly toothed or untoothed, stalked. Flowers deep violet-blue with a whitish tube, *large*, 25-30mm long, the flower-heads immediately subtended by a pair of leaves; calyx teeth awned. Woodland and dry meadows, generally on calcareous soils. Iberian Peninsula eastwards to Turkey – absent from the islands.

1473 *Prunella vulgaris* **SELF-HEAL**. Very similar, but flowers *smaller*, 13-15mm long, violet-blue or occasionally white. Moist shaded and semi-shaded ground, stream sides, meadows, open woodland, mainly in the mountains. May-July. T – not Balearic Is.

1474 *Prunella laciniata [P. alba]* **CUT-LEAVED SELF-HEAL**. Short, densely hairy, patch-forming perennial, with erect flowering stems. Leaves mostly *pinnately-lobed*, stalked, with narrow segments. Flowers yellowish-white, occasionally rose-pink or purplish, 15-17mm long, the flower-heads immediately subtended by a pair of leaves; calyx scarcely toothed. Dry grassy habitats and waste places, on calcareous soils. May-Sept. T – not Cyprus or parts of the extreme E Med.

Lamium **DEADNETTLES**. Annual or perennial herbs with crowded whorls of flowers; calyx 5-veined; corolla 2-lipped, the upper lip hooded, the lower lip with very small lateral lobes, tooth-like, the large central lobe often notched; stamens 4, with hairy filaments.

1475 *Lamium garganicum* **LARGE RED DEADNETTLE**. Short to medium spreading, hairy perennial. Leaves oval with a heart-shaped to kidney-shaped base, toothed. Flowers pink to purple, marked with reddish-purple, occasionally all white, large, 25-40mm long; corolla with a *straight tube* greatly exceeding the calyx. Rocky habitats and open scrub. Feb-Aug. S France eastwards to Turkey, Cyprus and the E Med. On some high mountains, especially in the Balkans, dwarf forms not more than 10cm tall can be found.

1476 *Lamium maculatum* **SPOTTED DEADNETTLE**. Very variable, short to tall, hairy, aromatic perennial, patch-forming. Leaves triangular-oval, coarsely toothed, often with a central whitish blotch, stalked. Flowers pinkish-purple, sometimes white or purplish-brown, 20-35mm long, with a *curved* corolla-tube, the lower lip heart-shaped; calyx shorter than the corolla-tube. Grassy habitats, woodland margins, banks, hedgerows, roadsides and olive groves. Feb-Oct. Iberian Peninsula eastwards to Turkey – absent from the islands, except Sardinia.

1477 *Lamium moschatum*. Similar, but a short annual with *white* flowers, 16-25mm long, the corolla-tube shorter than the calyx. Waste and fallow ground, field margins, sides of irrigation ditches, occasionally in rocky places. Feb-June. Greece and Crete eastwards, including Cyprus.

1478 *Lamium amplexicaule* **HENBIT DEADNETTLE**. Low to short, scarcely branched, hairy annual. Leaves rounded to oval, blunt-toothed or lobed, the lower stalked, the upper unstalked and *clasping* the stem. Flowers pinkish-purple, 14-20mm long, with a straight corolla-tube; calyx softly hairy. A weed primarily of cultivated land, fallow fields and waste places, vineyards and olive groves, occasionally on the seashore. Dec-June. T.

1479 *Lamium purpureum* **RED DEADNETTLE**. Similar, but the upper leaves and bracts *not* clasping the stem, longer than wide. Flowers pinkish-purple, 10-18mm long. Similar habitats and flowering time. T – not Balearic Is., Crete or Cyprus. A widespread and familiar European species.

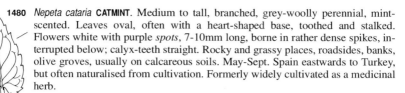

1480 *Nepeta cataria* **CATMINT.** Medium to tall, branched, grey-woolly perennial, mint-scented. Leaves oval, often with a heart-shaped base, toothed and stalked. Flowers white with purple *spots*, 7-10mm long, borne in rather dense spikes, interrupted below; calyx-teeth straight. Rocky and grassy places, roadsides, banks, olive groves, usually on calcareous soils. May-Sept. Spain eastwards to Turkey, but often naturalised from cultivation. Formerly widely cultivated as a medicinal herb.

1481 *Nepeta melissifolia.* Similar, but a short to medium plant with flowers *blue* with red dots, 12-15mm long. Rocky places and scrub. May-July. S Greece, some Aegean Is. and Crete.

1482 *Nepeta scordotis.* Short to medium, shaggily hairy perennial, with simple ascending stems. Leaves oval with a heart-shaped base, rough, mostly stalked. Flowers blue, 13-16mm long, borne in spike-like inflorescences, interrupted below; calyx with a straight tube, shorter than the corolla-tube. Dry rocky and grassy places. May-July. S Aegean Is. and Crete – endemic.

Stachys **WOUNDWORTS.** Annual or perennial herbs. Flowers 2 to many, forming dense spike-like inflorescences, often interrupted below. Flowers often pink, purple or yellow; calyx rarely 2-lipped, tubular or bell-shaped, with 5 equal teeth; corolla 2-lipped, the upper lip flat or hooded, the lower 3-lobed.

1483 *Stachys cretica [S. italica]* **MEDITERRANEAN WOUNDWORT.** Short to tall, thinly to densely *white-felted* perennial; stems erect. Leaves oblong to oval, with a wedge-shaped or somewhat rounded base, blunt-toothed, stalked, greyish above with the surface visible between the hairs and usually white beneath. Flowers pink or purple, 15-20mm long, the whorls usually rather distant, many-flowered usually; calyx usually without glands. Dry grassy habitats, roadsides, vineyards, olive groves, garrigue, fallow land. Apr-July. T – except Iberian Peninsula.

1484 *Stachys byzantina.* Similar, but leaves densely white felted on both surfaces, the upper surface *not* visible between the hairs. Flowers 15-25mm long. Rocky and grassy habitats. May-July. Turkey. Widely cultivated for ornament and sometimes naturalised in the Med.

1485 *Stachys germanica* **DOWNY WOUNDWORT.** Like *S. cretica*, but leaves with a *heart-shaped* base, green above. Similar habitats. May-July. T – not Crete or Cyprus.

1486 *Stachys obliqua* **EASTERN YELLOW WOUNDWORT.** Short to medium, rather woolly perennial, with erect stems. Leaves oblong to lanceolate, with a rounded or semi-heart-shaped base, green, sometimes greyish beneath, toothed. Flowers *pale yellow*, 14-16mm long, borne in rather crowded whorls; corolla densely hairy. Scrub, grassy places, meadows, roadsides. May-July. Balkans and Turkey – rare on the islands.

1487 *Stachys angustifolia* **GLABROUS WOUNDWORT.** Medium, erect, *hairless* perennial; stems somewhat woody at the base. Lower and middle leaves pinnately-lobed with slender segments; upper leaves linear. Flowers yellow tinged with pink, 12-16mm long, few in each, rather distant, whorl; corolla sometimes slightly hairy. Dry habitats, stony slopes, rocky places and open scrub. May-Aug. Greece and Turkey.

1488 *Stachys spinosa* **SPINY WOUNDWORT.** Short, tussock-forming perennial with *spiny*, silky-haired stems, often glandular. Leaves narrow-oblong, toothed or not, silky, soon falling. Flowers pale pink, 14-15mm long, borne in 2-3 crowded whorls, one above the other; corolla silky-haired. Dry rocky and stony places, cliffs. Apr-June. S Aegean (Cyclades), Karpathos and Crete.

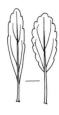

1489 *Stachys maritima* **COASTAL WOUNDWORT**. Short, hairy perennial with erect or ascending stems and *persistent* whorls of leaves. Leaves oblong to elliptical or oval, densely hairy, toothed. Flowers pale yellow, 12-14mm long, borne in fairly crowded whorls; calyx densely hairy but without glands. Coastal sands, dunes, rarely inland. Apr-June. Spain eastwards to Turkey – absent from the islands except Corsica.

1490 *Stachys pubescens*. Similar, but leaves *untoothed* and calyx with both hairs and glands. Similar habitats and flowering time. S and E Italy, Yugoslavia.

1491 *Stachys arenaria*. Like *S. maritima*, but a *prostrate*, rather bristly plant, with narrower leaves and reddish-purple flowers, 15-18mm long; calyx with hairs and glands. Coastal sands, sometimes dry sandy places inland. Apr-June. Italy, Sicily and N Africa.

1492 *Satureja thymbra* **SATUREIA**. An aromatic, *thyme-like* dwarf shrub, to 35cm tall, much-branched and grey with hairs. Leaves oblong, often broadest above the middle, pointed, rather bristly, gland-dotted. Flowers bright pink or reddish-purple, 8-12mm long, borne in dense, rounded, distant whorls; bracts bristly; calyx often reddish, bristly. Garrigue, generally in rocky dry places, roadsides, embankments. Apr-July. Sardinia, Balkans, as well as Crete and the E Med, including Cyprus. Often confused with *Thymus*, but distinguished primarily by its distant whorls of flowers rather than rounded or oblong heads.

1493 *Satureja montana* **WINTER SAVORY**. An aromatic, short to medium, generally rather spreading perennial, hairless or minutely hairy. Leaves linear to oblong, broadest above the middle, gland-dotted, hairless *except for* the margin. Flowers white, pink or purple, 6-12mm long, borne in crowded whorls, the flowers mostly facing the same direction; lower bracts longer than the flower-whorls. Stony and grassy pastures, rocky slopes. July-Sept. Spain eastwards to Turkey, but absent from the islands. A culinary herb.

1494 *Satureja cuneifolia*. Similar, but upper leaves often with *inrolled* margins and flower-whorls generally rather distant. Spain, Italy, Yugoslavia and Albania.

1495 *Satureja hortensis* **SUMMER SAVORY**. Short, finely hairy, aromatic annual. Leaves linear to linear-lanceolate, blunt, soft. Flowers white, pink or lilac, small, 4-7mm long, borne in lax or rather crowded whorls; bracts longer than the whorls. Rocky and grassy habitats, rock crevices. June-Sept. Spain eastwards to Turkey – absent from the islands. A widely cultivated culinary herb; it is an anti-flatulent herb and therefore used in bean dishes and in cucumber salads.

1496 *Acinos arvensis [Calamintha acinos, Satureja acinos]* **BASIL-THYME**. A short, hairy annual, rarely a short-lived perennial, with spreading stems branched at the base. Leaves lanceolate to oval, blunt or pointed, slightly toothed or untoothed, net-veined. Flowers violet with white markings on the lower lip, 7-10mm long, borne in lax whorls which form a fairly congested leafy raceme; bracts similar to the leaves; calyx with a curved tube, somewhat swollen at the base. Dry stony and grassy habitats, cultivated and waste land, field margins. Apr-July. T – not Portugal, Sicily, Crete or Cyprus.

1497 *Acinos rotundifolius [Calamintha rotundifolia]*. Similar, but leaves *wider*, 7-10mm wide (not 4-7mm), rounded. Similar habitats and flowering time. Spain, Italy, Sicily, the Balkans and Turkey.

1498 *Calamintha grandiflora [Satureja grandiflora]* **LARGE-FLOWERED CALAMINT**. Somewhat spreading, sparsely hairy, short to medium perennial; stems erect to ascending. Leaves oval to oblong, coarsely toothed, short-stalked. Flowers pink, *large*, 25-40mm long, borne in a lax leafy, panicle-like inflorescence, the flower clusters (verticillasters) lax and clearly stalked; calyx 2-lipped, 13-veined. Rocky places and open woodland, scrub, embankments, generally in rather shaded habitats, rarely at very low altitudes. June-Oct. NE Spain eastwards to Turkey – not Corsica, Sardinia, the Aegean Is. or Cyprus. Cultivated for ornament.

1499 *Calamintha nepeta [Calamintha glandulosa, Thymus glandulosus]* **LESSER CALAMINT.** Medium to tall, greyish, slightly to densely hairy perennial, with creeping rhizomes; stems erect and much-branched. Leaves oval, shallowly toothed, or almost untoothed, stalked. Flowers white or pale lilac, scarcely spotted, 10-15mm long, in whorls forming a leafy, narrow panicle; calyx with a tuft of hairs *protruding* from the mouth. Dry habitats, hedgerows, fallow fields and waste places, rough grassland; primarily in the mountains. June-Oct. Spain eastwards to Turkey – not Cyprus.

1500 *Calamintha incana [Thymus incanus, Satureja incana]*. Similar, but a more sprawling *grey-downy* plant with smaller pale pink flowers, 8-11mm long. Dry rocky habitats, fallow fields, waste ground, occasionally along dry stream beds. June-Dec. Greece, Aegean Is. eastwards, including Cyprus.

1501 *Clinopodium vulgare [Calamintha clinopodium, C. vulgaris, Satureja vulgaris]* **WILD BASIL.** Short to medium, softly hairy perennial, faintly aromatic; stems erect, unbranched or slightly branched. Leaves oval to lanceolate, slightly toothed, short-stalked. Flowers pinkish-purple, 12-22mm long, borne in dense, rather distant, whorls, the upper lip flat; calyx *purplish*, more or less 2-lipped, curved. Dry grassy and stony habitats, open woodland, scrub, roadsides, embankments, hedgerows. May-Sept. T – not Balearic Is. or parts of N Africa.

1502 *Melissa officinalis [M. romana, M. altissima]* **BALM.** A medium to tall, hairy, *lemon-scented* spreading perennial; stems erect and branched. Leaves oval to diamond-shaped, deeply toothed, stalked, Flowers whitish to pale yellow, often becoming pinkish, 8-15mm long, borne in leafy, whorled, interrupted spikes, the upper lip of the corolla erect, the lower 3-lobed. Scrub and shaded habitats, in open garrigue, along streambeds or roadsides. May-Sept. T. Grown since ancient times as a medicinal and culinary herb, including forms with yellow variegated leaves. Often used in pot pourris.

1503 *Ziziphora capitata* **ZIZIPHORA.** Low to short, erect, densely hairy, aromatic annual; stems simple or much-branched. Leaves lanceolate to oval, pointed, mid-green, dotted with glands beneath, untoothed or minutely toothed, stalked. Flowers pink, 10-15mm long, borne in a terminal *globose head*, with broad oval bracts; calyx 2-lipped, 13-veined, somewhat bristly. Rocky places in garrigue, dry stream beds, margins of cultivated fields. Mar-June. Balkans eastwards, including Cyprus. Plants can be very small and unbranched when found on thin poor soils.

1504 *Micromeria juliana* **MICROMERIA.** Dwarf shrub to 40cm tall, often less, hairy; stems many, erect, generally unbranched. Leaves oval to linear-lanceolate, with *revolute* margins, untoothed. Flowers unstalked, purplish, small, 5mm long, in rather congested whorls; calyx hairless in the throat, straight, somewhat 2-lipped. Dry rocky places in garrigue, open scrub. Apr-July. Portugal eastwards to Turkey – not Balearic Is., Corsica, Sardinia or Cyprus.

calyx

1505 *Micromeria nervosa*. Similar, but upper leaves oval to triangular (not linear-lanceolate) and calyx *bearded* in the throat, often purplish. Similar habitats. Feb-May. Balearic Is., Italy, Sicily, Greece, Crete and the E Med, including Cyprus.

1506 *Micromeria graeca [Satureja graeca]*. Like *M. juliana*, but flowers distinctly *stalked*, 6-8mm long and calyx hairy in the throat. Similar habitats and flowering time. T – not Cyprus.

1507 *Micromeria myrtifolia.* Like *M. juliana*, but calyx hairy in the throat, the teeth only one quater as long as the tube (not half as long). Rocky hillslopes, open pine forest. May-July. Greece and Crete eastwards, including Cyprus.

Thymus **THYMES.** Dwarf undershrubs, woody at least at the base. Flowers in heads, often slightly interrupted below; calyx 2-lipped; corolla 2-lipped, with protruding stamens.

1508 *Thymus vulgaris* **THYME.** Small, deep grey-green, densely branched evergreen shrub, to 30cm tall, strongly aromatic; stems erect to spreading, woody. Leaves linear to elliptical, with leaf-clusters in the axils, hairy but not ciliate; margins revolute. Flowers whitish to pale purple, 5-6mm long, borne in rounded or oblong heads, sometimes interrupted below; calyx 10-13-veined, stiffly hairy. Garrigue, dry rocky places. Apr-July. Spain, S France and Italy; naturalised in a number of places, especially in the Balearic Is. and Greece. Important in flavouring food, but also grown medicinally and for perfumery.

1509 *Thymus zygis.* Similar, but leaves *fringed* with hairs at the base; flowers whitish. Similar habitats and flowering time. Iberian Peninsula. Also used as a culinary and medicinal herb.

1510 *Thymus longicaulis.* Low plant with *long*, creeping, woody branches, bearing erect flowering branches, up to 10cm long, in rows, each with a basal cluster of leaves. Leaves linear-lanceolate to elliptical, hairy, the margin ciliate at the base. Flowers purple, 3-4mm, borne in terminal clusters; calyx bell-shaped, the tube shorter than the upper lip. Dry rocky habitats, sandy places, banks, lowland and in the mountains. Apr-July. S France eastwards to Turkey – not on the islands, except Sicily.

1511 *Thymus comptus.* Similar, but without vegetative, non-flowering shoots; flowering stems generally more than 10cm long and leaves with margin ciliate to the middle. Similar habitats and flowering time, often near the coast. Greece and Turkey.

1512 *Thymus longiflorus* **LONG-FLOWERED THYME.** An aromatic dwarf shrub to 30cm tall; stems erect to ascending. Leaves linear, grey-felted, with revolute margins, scarcely stalked. Flowers purple, *long*, 13-15mm, borne in small terminal heads with conspicuous overlapping, purple, oval bracts; calyx 2-lipped. Garrigue and stony pastures, rocky places, sunny and exposed. Apr-May. S Spain – endemic.

1513 *Thymus membranaceus.* Very similar, but with *whitish* membranous bracts and white flowers. Similar habitats and flowering time. SE Spain.

1514 *Thymus capitatus* [*Coridothymus capitatus*]. Dwarf, somewhat aromatic shrub, to 50cm, densely branched with erect or ascending stems with axillary leaf-clusters. Leaves linear, rather fleshy, gland-dotted, with a *flat margin*. Flowers purplish-pink or pink, 7-10mm long, borne in terminal, rather oblong, clusters; bracts green, often red-tinged, oval, closely overlapping to form a *cone-like* head; calyx with 20-22 veins (10-13 in other thymes). Dry hills, heaths, rocky places, roadsides, occasionally on waste ground or sand-dunes. May-Oct. T.

Origanum **MARJORAMS.** Dwarf shrubs or perennial herbs with flowers arranged in panicles or heads, with crowded whorls (verticillasters) and often with conspicuous bracts; calyx regular or distinctly 2-lipped; corolla 2-lipped with protruding stamens.

1515 *Origanum vulgare* **MARJORAM.** Very variable, medium to tall, tufted, hairy perennial, aromatic; stems erect, often purplish. Leaves oval, untoothed or slightly toothed, short-stalked or unstalked, often with leaf-tufts in the axils. Flowers purplish-red, pinkish or whitish, often darker in bud, 4-7mm long, *borne in* broad, branched, panicle-like clusters; bracts leaf-like, 4-5mm long, often purplish; calyx scarcely 2-lipped. Rough grassy and stony or rocky habitats, in dry sunny places, banks, hedgerows, roadsides. June-Oct. T – not Balearic Is. or Crete. A common culinary herb.

1516 *Origanum heracleoticum [O. hirtum].* Similar, but a more densely hairy plant with smaller (2-3mm long), greenish bracts and smaller whitish flowers. Rocky habitats, stony ground, open scrub, often near sea-level. July-Sept. Italy eastwards, including Crete and Cyprus. Sometimes treated as a subspecies of *O. vulgare.*

1517 *Origanum virens.* Like *O. heracleoticum,* but bracts pale green, twice as long as the calyx, *membranous,* hairless; flowers white; calyx hairless. Rocky habitats, field boundaries, roadsides, hedgerows. June-Sept. Iberian Peninsula, generally close to the coast, and Balearic Is.

1518 *Origanum onites* **POT MARJORAM.** Dwarf shrub to 60cm, erect and rather hairy; stems covered with minute pimples. Leaves oval to rounded, sometimes with a heart-shaped base, untoothed or slightly toothed, the upper unstalked. Flowers white, 4-5.5mm, borne in dense broad clusters (corumbs); bracts oval to orbicular, closely overlapping; calyx one-lipped, *split* deeply along one side. Garrigue and dry rocky habitats, bushy places. May-Sept. Sicily and the Balkans, including Crete.

1519 *Origanum marjorana [Marjorana hortensis]* **GARDEN** or **SWEET MARJORAM.** Similar, but stems without tiny pimples and flowers borne in *panicles,* with long branches, the flowers extending far down the stems. Garrigue, in dry rocky and stony places, occasionally in open pine forests. May-Oct. N Africa, Turkey and Cyprus. A culinary herb, naturalised in many parts of the Med.

1520 *Origanum dictamnus [Amaracus dictamnus]* **DITTANY.** A densely *white-woolly,* tufted dwarf shrub; stems branched at the base, to 20cm long. Leaves rounded to oval, untoothed, short-stalked, greyish or whitish, with conspicuous raised veins. Flowers pink, 8-11mm long, borne in pendent, oblong spikelets, in opposite, stalked pairs, with closely overlapping purple bracts; corolla long-tubed. Rocky places, particularly cliff crevices, generally shaded or semi-shaded. June-Sept. Crete – endemic. The leaves and stems are gathered and used as a herb to flavour food, especially meat.

bract

Mentha **MINTS.** Stoloniferous perennial herbs with scented, often strongly aromatic foliage. Flowers hermaphrodite, or female, on the same or separate plants, borne in dense whorls, forming spikes or heads; calyx weakly 2-lipped; corolla also weakly 2-lipped, with 4 subequal lobes and a short tube.

1521 *Mentha spicata [M. viridis, M. crispa, M. sylvestris]* **SPEAR MINT.** Variable medium to tall, green or greyish perennial, strongly and sweetly aromatic, sometimes very musty. Leaves lanceolate to narrowly ovate, hairless or somewhat hairy, sharply toothed. Flowers pink or white, 2-3.5mm long, borne in a dense spike, sometimes branched. Damp habitats, streams, ditches, waste ground, cultivated land and gardens. July-Nov. S Italy and the Balkans eastwards, including Cyprus.

1522 *Mentha longifolia [M. incana]* **HORSE MINT.** Very variable, hairy, medium to tall perennial, to 1.2m; stems usually *white-downy.* Leaves oblong-elliptical, 5-9cm long, green or grey, usually whitish beneath, short-stalked or unstalked, the margins with sharp spreading teeth. Flowers lilac or white, 3-4.5mm long, borne in dense terminal, branched spikes. Damp habitats, streams, ditches, cultivated and waste

land. June-Oct. T – but absent from some of the islands, including the Balearics and Cyprus.

1523 *Mentha suaveolens [M. rotundifolia, M. insularis]* **APPLE MINT.** Similar, but leaves oval to sub-orbicular, *not* more than 4.5cm long. Damp places, ditches, streams, road-sides, cultivated and waste land. July-Sept. T – not Cyprus. A widely cultivated culinary herb.

1524 *Mentha pulegium [M. vulgaris]* **PENNYROYAL.** A short, usually hairy, prostrate creeping perennial with erect flowering stems, strongly pungent. Leaves small, narrowly elliptical to oval, short-stalked, untoothed or with a few distant teeth, hairy at least below; bracts leaf-like. Flowers lilac, 4.5-6mm long, borne in dense whorls, forming interrupted spikes, *without* a terminal head of flowers; calyx ribbed, hairy in the throat. Damp meadows, pool and stream margins. June-Sept. T – but scarce in the N Med area.

1525 *Mentha aquatica [M. hirsuta]* **WATER MINT.** A variable short to tall perennial, hairy or almost hairless, often purplish, with a strong aromatic scent when crushed. Leaves oval to lanceolate, pointed, toothed and stalked. Flowers lilac-pink, 4-6mm long, borne in dense oblong heads, often with 1-2 distinct whorls of flowers below; calyx hairy and distinctly veined. Swampy habitats, marshy ground, pool and stream margins. June-Sept. T.

1526 *Rosmarinus officinalis* **ROSEMARY.** An evergreen shrub to 2m, sometimes more, strongly aromatic; branches brown, erect to spreading. Leaves linear, leathery, sharply pointed, deep green, with revolute margins, whitish beneath. Flowers pale to mid-blue, occasionally pink or white, 10-12mm long, borne in small lateral clusters; corolla with 2 protruding stamens; calyx bell-shaped. Maquis, garrigue, dry scrub and open woodland, maritime rocks and fixed dunes. Jan-May (inter-mittently to Dec.). Iberian Peninsula eastwards, including Cyprus and the Lebanon. A widely cultivated ornamental and culinary plant, including many forms, some prostrate, others erect. Medicinally, the ethereal oils extracted from the leaves are used in embrocations and bath mixtures to improve the blood cir-culation. Widely used to flavour meat, especially lamb, also medicinally.

1527 *Rosmarinus eriocalyx.* Similar, but a prostrate plant with grey branches and shorter leaves to 15mm long. The inflorescence has long glandular hairs. Calcareous rocks, sandy places. S Spain and NW Africa.

Lavandula **LAVENDERS.** Small, aromatic, semi-evergreen shrubs, often with narrow leaves; bracts very different from the leaves. Flowers in crowded, often long-stalked, terminal spikes; calyx with small teeth, 13-veined; corolla 2-lipped.

1528 *Lavandula stoechas* **FRENCH LAVENDER.** Greyish-hairy shrub to 1m, though often less; stems much-branched. Leaves linear to lanceolate, untoothed. Flowers dark purple, 6-8mm long, borne in rather stubby spikes, topped by *conspicuous* large purple, oblong bracts, 10-50mm long, very occasionally white; stalk shorter than the spike. Garrigue, open maquis, rocky places, open pine forests, roadsides. Mar-June. Spain and NW Africa eastwards to the Balkans and the E Med, includ-ing Cyprus. Long a medicinal and garden plant. As a crop plant, its oil is distilled for the perfume industry.

　　1528a Subsp. *cariensis [Lavandula cariensis]*. Like the type, but spike distinctly shorter than its stalk and the calyx appendage (located on the upper tooth) lobed. W Turkey, including Thrace.

　　1528b Subsp. *lusitanica*. Like subsp. *cariensis*, but calyx appendage *not* lobed. Sandy soils. Portugal.

1529 *Lavandula viridis*. Similar, but bracts above the spike *green*, 8-20mm long; flowers white. SW Spain and Portugal.

1530 *Lavandula dentata* **TOOTHED LAVENDER**. Grey-hairy shrub to 1m, though often less. Leaves oblong to linear-lanceolate, deeply *toothed*, grey-green. Flowers dark purple, 7-8mm long, in a long-stalked spike, 25-50mm long; bracts small; calyx 13-veined. Garrigue, open woodland and scrub, rocky places. Mar-June. Iberian Peninsula, Balearic Is. and NW Africa; naturalised in Italy and Sicily.

1531 *Lavandula multifida* **CUT-LEAVED LAVENDER**. Similar, but faintly aromatic, with green, *2-pinnately-lobed* leaves. Flowers violet-blue, 12mm long, in spikes up to 70mm long; calyx 15-veined. Garrigue, stony places, waste and fallow land. Mar-June. Iberian Peninsula, NW Africa, Italy and Sicily.

1532 *Lavandula angustifolia* **COMMON LAVENDER**. Strongly aromatic, grey-hairy shrub to 1m; stems much-branched, spreading to erect. Leaves linear to lanceolate, *un-toothed*, grey-hairy, often whitish when young. Flowers bluish-purple, 10-12mm long, borne in long-stalked spikes, 20-80mm long, often interrupted below. Maquis, garrigue, stony pastures, rocky places, roadsides, cultivated land. June-Aug. Spain eastwards to the Balkans – not Balearic Is. Widely cultivated for its oil used in perfumery. The common lavender of gardens. A wide variety of forms include those with a dwarf habit as well as pink or white, blue or purplish flowers.

1533 *Lavandula latifolia [L. spica]*. Similar, but leaves grey-green, more densely hairy, and flowers smaller, 8-10mm long; bracts linear or lanceolate (not oval). The whole plant has a camphor-like smell. Iberian Peninsula eastwards to Yugoslavia – not the islands except for Sicily.

1534 *Lavandula lanata*. Like *L. angustifolia*, but a densely *white-felted* plant with oblong-lanceolate leaves and lilac flowers; calyx 8-veined (not 13). Mountain rocks and screes. S Spain – endemic.

Salvia **SALVIAS**. Herbs with distinct whorls of flowers forming a lax, bracteate spike or raceme. Both calyx and corolla are 2-lipped, the upper lip of the corolla forming a hood, the lower lip 3-lobed; stamens only 2, hinged in the middle and located beneath the corolla-hood.

1535 *Salvia officinalis* **SAGE**. Strongly aromatic, rather greyish shrub to 60cm; branches spreading to erect, becoming woody below. Leaves oblong to elliptical, rough, greenish above but white-felted beneath; margin finely toothed. Flowers violet-blue, pink or white, 20-35mm long; calyx often flushed with purple; bracts oval, hairy and gland-dotted. Garrigue, stony pastures, scrub, rocky places. May-July. Spain, S France and the Balkans, but widely grown and naturalised elsewhere. An important culinary herb, with selected strains, particularly in France – *grande sauge* and *petite sauge de Provence*.

1536 *Salvia grandiflora*. Similar, but leaves with a rounded or heart-shaped base. Balkans eastwards – not Cyprus.

1537 *Salvia fruticosa* [S. triloba, S. libanotica] **THREE-LEAVED SAGE**. Similar, but a taller shrub, to 1.2m with white-felted stems. Leaves often with 1-2 pairs of small lobes below the main one. Flowers lilac, pink or sometimes white, 16-25mm long. Maquis and garrigue, in rocky places and gullies, roadsides. Mar-June. Italy, Sicily and the Balkans eastwards, including Cyprus. The leaves are used for flavouring and also for a herbal tea in some regions, especially the E Med – called 'faskomelo' in Greek. Like other sages, an important plant for bees, and high altitude forms may be smaller in all their parts and more compact.

1538 *Salvia pomifera [S. calycina].* Like *S. officinalis,* but rather taller; leaves oval and flowers violet-blue; calyx much-enlarged in fruit. S Greece and Aegean Is.

1539 *Salvia lavandulifolia.* An aromatic subshrub to 50cm; stems erect to ascending. Leaves crowded below, *rather narrow,* oval to elliptical, whitish-grey when young, hairy. Flowers pale blue-purple, 20-25mm long, borne in rather distant whorls on a hairless stem, the individual flowers scarcely stalked; calyx often reddish-purple, hairy. Rocky and stony places, primarily in the mountains. June-Aug. Spain, S France, NW Africa.

1540 *Salvia verticillata [S. peloponnesiaca]* **WHORLED CLARY.** Medium to tall, rather foetid perennial, with erect, usually unbranched stems, often purplish. Leaves oval to lyre-shaped, with a square or heart-shaped base, the lower stalked and often with 1-2 pairs of basal lobes, toothed; upper leaves unstalked, usually purplish. Flowers lilac-blue to purplish, 8-15mm long, in *dense whorls* of 15-30, the upper lip more or less straight. Dry grassy, waste, bare and stony places, banks and roadsides. May-July. Spain eastwards to Turkey – absent from the islands except Sicily.

1541 *Salvia sclarea* **CLARY.** An unpleasant smelling medium to tall, hairy biennial or perennial; stems erect, much-branched, glandular above. Leaves broadly oval with a heart-shaped base, toothed, the lower long-stalked. Flowers lilac or pale blue, 20-30mm long, the upper lip strongly curved; bracts *conspicuous,* oval to heart-shaped, lilac or whitish, longer than the calyces. Rocky and grassy habitats, scrub, roadsides. May-July. T – not Cyprus or parts of N Africa. Grown in gardens and used in perfumery.

1542 *Salvia aethiopis.* Similar, but stems and young leaves *white-felted* and bracts shorter than the calyces, green or violet; flowers white, 10-15mm long. Dry rocky, stony and bushy places, open pine forests. May-July. S France eastwards to Turkey and Cyprus.

1543 *Salvia argentea* **SILVER SAGE.** Like *S. sclarea,* but bracts *shorter* than the calyces, usually green. Flowers white tinged with pink or yellow, 15-35mm long. Dry rocky habitats and bushy places. May-Aug. Iberian Peninsula, Italy, Sicily and the Balkans.

1544 *Salvia amplexicaulis.* Medium to tall, shaggily-hairy perennial; stems erect, branched. Leaves oblong with a heart-shaped base, toothed, densely *glandular-hairy,* short-stalked or unstalked; bracts equalling the calyces, with a heart-shaped base. Flowers violet, 8.5-12mm long, borne in rather lax whorls; calyx with spreading hairs. Bushy places, roadsides. May-July. Balkan Peninsula and Turkey.

1545 *Salvia verbenaca* **WILD CLARY** *[S. clandestina, S. multifida].* A very variable short to tall perennial; stems erect, simple or branched, glandular-hairy in the upper part. Basal leaves in a rosette, *pinnately-lobed,* with oblong lobes, wrinkled above, toothed, long-stalked; upper leaves short-stalked or unstalked. Flowers pale blue, lilac or violet, 6-10mm long, borne in lax to rather dense whorls, forming a spike; corolla sometimes remaining closed; calyx bell-shaped, prominently veined, en-larging somewhat in fruit. Fallow, cultivated and waste places, paths, roadsides, vineyards, olive groves, sometimes in open pine forest or coastal garrigue. Flowering almost throughout the year, but mainly Jan-May. T.

1546 *Salvia hierosolymitana.* Similar, but leaves irregularly toothed but not lobed and flowers *larger,* 20-25mm long, dark pink to rosy purple. Grassy and bushy places, banks, meadows. Apr-June. Cyprus and the extreme E Med.

bract

(1544)

1547 *Salvia viridis [S. horminum]* **RED-TOPPED SAGE**. Short to medium, hairy annual; stems simple or branched above. Leaves rather pale green, oval to oblong, with a rounded or heart-shaped base, finely toothed, long-stalked. Flowers pink or violet, 14-18mm long, borne in lax whorls; bracts *conspicuous*, deep green, pink or violet, rounded and pointed, the uppermost often forming a terminal tuft at the apex of the flowering shoots, up to 9mm long. Dry habitats, grassy and waste places, fields, roadsides, pathways, usually on limestone. Feb-June. T. Grown in gardens.

POTATO FAMILY Solanaceae

Herbs or shrubs with simple or pinnate leaves, usually alternate. Flowers regular or irregular, hermaphrodite, generally 5-parted, the corolla bell-shaped or star-shaped with the petals fused together below. Stamens 5, attached to the corolla-tube. Ovary superior, usually with 2 compartments. Fruit a capsule or a berry.

1548 *Lycium europaeum* **TEA TREE**. Deciduous shrub, 1-4m tall; branches rigid, *very spiny*, the spines stout. Leaves elliptical, generally broadest above the middle, 20-50mm long. Flowers pink or white, narrow funnel-shaped, 11-13mm long, solitary or in groups of 2-3; stamens usually protruding. Fruit a reddish berry. Hedges, thickets and roadsides. Apr-Sept. T, but absent from most of the islands except the Balearic Is., Sardinia and Sicily.

1549 *Lycium intricatum*. Similar, but leaves *smaller*, 3-15mm long. Flowers bluish-violet, lilac, pink or white, 13-18mm long; stamens not protruding. Fruit orange-red or black when ripe. Sandy seashores and dunes, occasionally inland. Jan-July. Iberian Peninsula and NW Africa – perhaps further east.

1550 *Lycium schweinfurthii*. Very similar to *L. intricatum*, but leaves mostly 10-50mm long and flowers usually mauve, 15-20mm long. Fruit usually *black* (orange in Cyprus apparently). Similar habitats and flowering time. Sicily, Crete and the Aegean and parts of N Africa eastwards, including Cyprus.

1551 *Lycium ferocissimum*. Like *L. europaeum*, but flowers *smaller*, only 7-9mm long, white with purple marks at the base of the corolla-lobes. Fruit at first red, then purplish-black. Naturalised in coastal habitats, roadsides and gardens. Jan-Dec. Cyprus, perhaps elsewhere in the E Med. (South Africa).

1552 *Lycium barbarum [L. halimifolium, L. vulgare]* **DUKE OF ARGYLL'S TEAPLANT**. Deciduous shrub to 2.5m, with curved branches bearing a few slender spines. Leaves alternate or in small clusters, narrow-elliptical, broadest at the middle, untoothed. Flowers purple, becoming brownish, trumpet-shaped, only 8-9mm long, solitary or several together; stamens long-protuding. Fruit orange-red when ripe. Cultivated for ornament, particularly as a hedge and occasionally naturalised. May-Sept. T – particularly in the European Med and Turkey. (China).

1553 *Lycium chinense [L. rhombifolium]* **CHINA TEAPLANT**. Similar, but leaves oval to lanceolate, broadest below the middle and flowers larger, 10-15mm long, with the corolla lobes 5-8mm long (not 4mm). Similar habitats and flowering time. Portugal, France and Italy. (China). Far less often seen than *L. barbarum*; sometimes considered an extreme form of that species.

Hyoscyamus **HENBANES**. Annual or perennial herbs, often with sticky glandular stems and leaves. Calyx tubular, 5-toothed, often persistent. Corolla 2-lipped, generally with protruding stamens. Very poisonous.

1554 *Hyoscyamus aureus* **YELLOW HENBANE**. Very *sticky*, glandular-hairy biennial or perennial; stems spreading to pendent, rather weak and brittle. Leaves oval to rounded with a wedge-shaped or heart-shaped base, stalked, irregularly lobed and toothed. Flowers golden-yellow with a purplish throat and tube, 35-45mm long, borne in lax, many-flowered racemes with leaf-like bracts and long-protuding stamens; calyx funnel-shaped, to 30mm long in fruit, with triangular teeth. Rocky places, cliffs and old walls, sea-level and in the lower mountains. Feb-July. Crete and the Aegean Is. eastwards, including Cyprus.

1555 *Hyoscyamus albus* **WHITE HENBANE**. Similar, but the flowers greenish- or yellowish-white, with a greenish or purplish throat; *stamens* not or only slightly protruding. Waste ground, old walls, around habitations, roadsides. Jan-Sept. T.

1556 *Hyoscyamus niger* **HENBANE**. Medium to tall, stickily hairy, foetid annual or biennial, erect, branched or not. Leaves oval to oblong, generally coarsely toothed or lobed, the basal stalked and forming a lax rosette; stem leaves unstalked and clasping the stem. Flowers pale yellow, *netted* with purple veins, irregularly trumpet-shaped, 20-30mm long, borne in one-sided, branched spikes; calyx tubular, flared at the mouth and with 5 short lobes. Bare, waste and disturbed ground, often near the sea or by farm buildings. Apr-Sept. T – not Balearic Is., Crete or Cyprus. As in the other species the fruit opens by means of a circular lid. All the species are extremely poisonous, containing various alkaloids such as Atropine, Hyoscyamine and Scopolamine. Used in the past to alleviate toothache.

1557 *Hyoscyamus reticulatus.* Similar, but stem leaves *not* clasping and flowers purple with darker net-veins; calyx tubular in fruit. Similar habitats and flowering time. Turkey (including European part) and parts of the E Med – not Cyprus.

1558 *Withania somnifera [Physalis somnifera]* **WITHANIA**. An erect subshrub to 1.5m tall, woody at least in the lower part; stems sparsely branched. Leaves oval to oblong, with a wedge-shaped base and a short stalk, untoothed, covered in star-shaped hairs. Flowers greenish or yellowish, 5mm, *bell-shaped*, usually in lateral clusters of 4-6. Fruit a shiny red berry, 5-8mm, surrounded by the persistent calyx. Waste places, roadsides and gardens, generally at low altitudes. Jan-Dec. T – except Portugal, France, Corsica, Sardinia, Italy and Yugoslavia. Poisonous.

1559 *Withania frutescens.* Similar, but leaves with a *heart-shaped* base, hairless or only slightly hairy. Flowers larger, 8-15mm. Similar habitats and flowering time. S and E Spain, Balearic Is. and N Africa.

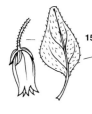

1560 *Physalis alkekengi* **CAPE GOOSEBERRY**. Medium, slightly hairy, rhizomatous perennial; stems erect, branched or not. Leaves oval, stalked, with a few coarse teeth, or untoothed. Flowers dirty-white, more or less star-shaped, 15-25mm, solitary and half-nodding in the branch forks or in the axils of the upper leaves. Fruit an orange berry, 12-17mm, completely surrounded by a greatly expanded, *lantern-shaped* calyx, orange-red and papery when ripe. Cultivated, waste ground and scrub, sometimes forming large patches. July-Aug. Italy, the Balkans and Turkey. Widely cultivated ornamental plant, both for the garden and for dried winter decoration.

1561 *Physalis peruviana* **CHINESE LANTERN**. Similar, but flowers *yellow*, with greyish, purple or brownish marks. Berry yellow, 12-20mm, surrounded by a green or yellowish green calyx. Cultivated for its edible fruits and locally naturalised in Spain and Italy, perhaps elsewhere.

1562 *Salpichroa origanifolia* **SALPICHROA**. Medium, much-branched, *scrambling,* hairy perennial; stems flexuous, becoming somewhat woody below. Leaves oval to almost rounded, short-stalked, untoothed. Flowers whitish, bell-shaped, 6-10mm long, solitary in the axils of the upper leaves. Fruit a small creamy-white berry.

Coastal habitats, especially shingle, waste places. July-Oct. Locally naturalised in the Iberian Peninsula, S France, Corsica and Italy. (South America). Naturalised in several places in southern Britain.

Solanum **NIGHTSHADES.** Herbs or shrubs with alternate, sometimes opposite, leaves. Flowers in one-sided cymes or in umbels, at the leaf-axils or opposite the leaves (leaf-opposed). Corolla star-shaped, with spreading or deflexed lobes; stamens protruding and forming a close cone around the stigma. Fruit a dryish or succulent berry. Generally poisonous.

1563 *Solanum nigrum* **BLACK NIGHTSHADE.** A variable, low to medium, hairless or some-what hairy annual; stems spreading to erect, often *blackish*. Leaves oval to lan-ceolate, untoothed to toothed or slightly lobed, stalked. Flowers white with yellow anthers, 10-14mm, in clusters of 5-10. Berry dull black when ripe, green at first and pea-like, 6-10mm. Cultivated, bare, waste and disturbed ground. Jan-Dec. T. A cosmopolitan weed. Fruit poisonous with the alkaloid Solanine.

    1563a Subsp. *schultesii.* Like the type, but a densely *glandular-hairy* plant. Scat-tered localities in the central and eastern Med.

1564 *Solanum villosum [S. luteum]* **HAIRY NIGHTSHADE.** Similar, but stems white-hairy above, flowers in clusters of 3-5 and *fruit* red, orange or yellow when ripe. Similar habitats and flowering time. T.

1565 *Solanum sodomeum* **APPLE OF SODOM.** Shrubby perennial, to 3m, though often less; stems stout and much-branched, armed with yellow prickles, somewhat hairy. Leaves oval, pinnately-lobed, *prickly*, stalked; lobes blunt. Flowers pale violet, 25-30mm, pentagonal in outline, few in a cluster or solitary, the upper often smaller and male. Berry globose, 20-30mm, at first mottled green and whitish, later yellow or brown, shiny. Coastal habitats, roadsides, stony places, waste ground, especially near the sea. May-Sept. Naturalised widely in the Med – not Cyprus. (Africa).

1566 *Solanum cornutum [Solanum rostratum]* **YELLOW NIGHTSHADE.** Low to short, much-branched annual, often rather woody at the base; stems spreading to prostrate, hairy and with recurved yellow prickles. Leaves pinnately-lobed, stalked, the lobes blunt and somewhat wavy. Flowers *yellow*, 20-40mm, borne in clusters of 3-10. Fruit a globose dry berry, 10mm, surrounded by the prickly persistent calyx. Dry, waste and sandy ground. May-Sept. Locally naturalised from France eastwards to Turkey. (S USA and Mexico).

1567 *Solanum bonariense.* Shrub with erect stems to 2m; stems stout, somewhat hairy, with a few prickles when young. Leaves oblong to lanceolate, pointed, slightly lobed or, unlobed, stalked, covered with star-shaped hairs. Flowers white or pale blue, 25-35mm, more or less pentagonal in outline, borne in clusters of 2-4. Berry globose, yellow, 7-10mm. May-Sept. Cultivated for ornament and locally naturalised in Spain and the Balearic Is., perhaps elsewhere. (Temperate South America).

1568 *Solanum elaeagnifolium.* Similar, but herbaceous or shrubby only to 1m tall, with linear or oblong leaves. Flowers purple, deeply lobed. Cultivated for ornament and occasionally naturalised in the E Med, including Cyprus. (Central and South America).

    The family also includes the **Tomato,** *Lycopersicon esculentum* (1569), the **Pepper** and **Chilli,** *Capsicum annuum* (1570), **Potato,** *Solanum tuberosum* (1571), and **Aubergine,** *S. melongena* (1572). All these are of course widely cultivated.

1573 *Mandragora autumnalis* **MANDRAKE.** Low, stemless, hairless or slightly hairy peren-nial with a thick fleshy, often branched rootstock. Leaves forming a large, rather

flat rosette, up to 60cm across, though often less, oval to oblong, stalked, wavy-margined, stalked, often rather shiny. Flowers violet or purple, 30-40mm, with 5 triangular lobes and a short tube, borne in the centre of the leaf-rosette. Fruit an orange or yellow berry, egg-shaped, 25-30mm long; calyx persistent, equalling or longer than the fruit. Cultivated and fallow land, stony and waste places, olive groves. Sept-Dec, occasionally in the spring. T – not Balearic Is., S France, Yugoslavia or Albania. Since early times the roots, which contain mildly poisonous alkaloids, were used in relieving pain and inducing sleep. They were also accorded magical and aphrodisiac properties because of their resemblance to a human figure. The plant was said to shriek if pulled from the soil!

1574 *Mandragora officinarum* **SPRING MANDRAKE**. Very similar, but flowers rather smaller and greenish-white, with narrow triangular lobes. Fruit globose, yellow, with a much shorter calyx. Similar habitats. Feb-May. Italy and Yugoslavia. The relationship between these two species is very unclear; some believe that they represent a single variable species.

1575 *Datura stramonium [D. tatula]* **THORNAPPLE**. A medium to tall, erect, foetid annual, often reaching 1.5m in height, sometimes more, generally hairless. Leaves oval to elliptical, usually lobed and with jagged teeth. Flowers white to purplish, erect funnel-shaped, 50-100mm long, solitary at the axils of the upper leaves, sometimes in the forks of branches; calyx large, half the length of the corolla, sharply angled. Fruit an *erect*, spiny, egg-shaped capsule, 10-15mm long. Waste and bare ground, field margins, cultivated land, roadsides. May-Sept. Naturalised T – not Balearic Is. (Central and South America). An extremely poisonous weed, often casual and spasmodic in appearance.

1576 *Datura ferox*. Similar, but capsule larger, 10-30mm long, covered by stout *uneven* spines, the upper longer than the lower. Cultivated for ornament and locally naturalised. Spain, S France, Italy and Sicily. (E Asia).

1577 *Datura innoxia*. An erect, hairy annual to 2m tall, though often only 30-50cm. Leaves oval with a wedge-shaped or truncated base, untoothed or somewhat lobed. Flowers white, occasionally flushed with violet, tubular, with 10 lobes. Fruit-capsule egg-shaped, 55-65mm long, *nodding*, with long slender spines. Locally naturalised in the Med – Iberian Peninsula, S France and Italy, perhaps elsewhere. (Central America). June-Oct.

1578 *Datura metel*. Similar, but plant more or less *hairless* and capsule with short spines. Locally naturalised in the Med, especially Europe, but many reports are in fact referable to the previous species. Grown in gardens where double-flowered forms are known as well as others with yellow or purple flowers.

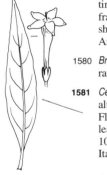

1579 *Brugmansia suaveolens [Datura suaveolens]* **ANGEL'S TRUMPET**. Large tree-like shrub to 5m tall, with thick stiff stems. Leaves oval to oblong, stalked, untoothed, sometimes downy beneath. Flowers white, pendulous trumpets, *large*, to 22cm long, fragrant, solitary at the upper leaf-axils; calyx inflated, angled. Fruit large, egg-shaped, not spiny. A widely cultivated ornamental plant. June-Oct. (Central America). A double-flowered form is often grown. Poisonous.

1580 *Brugmansia sanguinea [Datura sanguinea]*. Similar, but not more than 3m tall and with rather smaller *orange-red* flowers. Also widely cultivated. (Peru).

1581 *Cestrum parqui* **CESTRUM**. *Foetid* semi-deciduous shrub to 3m, branched. Leaves alternate, linear to lanceolate, pointed, untoothed, hairless and with a short stalk. Flowers greenish-yellow to yellow, 18-25mm long, borne in lateral or terminal leafy racemes; corolla tubular with 5 short spreading lobes. Fruit a berry, 7-10mm, blackish. Widely cultivated and locally naturalised. May-July. Spain, Italy, Sicily and Greece, perhaps elsewhere. (South America).

1582 *Nicotiana glauca* **SHRUB TOBACCO**. Hairless soft-wooded shrub or small tree, to 6m tall; stems laxly branched, greyish. Leaves alternate, elliptical to lanceolate or oval, pointed, bluish- or greyish-green, stalked. Flowers greenish-yellow, 30-40mm long, many borne in a lax panicle; corolla tubular with a short-lobed limb. Fruit an egg-shaped capsule, 7-10mm long, slightly longer than the persistent papery calyx. Gardens, roadsides, waste ground, rocky hill slopes. Jan-Dec. (South America). Naturalised in many parts of the Med.

1583 *Nicotiana tabacum [N. latissima]* **TOBACCO**. A very variable, tall, *stickily-hairy*, strong-smelling annual, to 2m. Leaves large, elliptical to lanceolate, untoothed, with a winged base that runs onto the stem. Flowers pale green or creamish, often with a pink tinge, trumpet-shaped, 35-55mm long, many borne in a broad terminal panicle. Fruit a green capsule. Cultivated land, waste places, occasionally on arable land. June-Aug. Cultivated for tobacco in many parts of the Med. (Argentine and Bolivia). Poisonous.

1584 *Nicotiana rustica* **SMALL TOBACCO**. Similar, but the leaves *not winged* onto the stem at their base. Flowers smaller, greenish-yellow, 12-17mm long. Cultivated land and waste places. July-Sept. Formerly widely cultivated for tobacco but now largely replaced by the previous species. (North America).

FIGWORT FAMILY Scrophulariaceae

Herbs, rarely shrubs or trees. Leaves opposite or alternate. Flowers irregular (zygomorphic), in spikes or racemes, sometimes solitary; bracts usually present; calyx 4-5-lobed, occasionally 2-lipped; corolla 5-lobed, or clearly 2-lipped; stamens 2 or 4. Fruit a capsule, generally 2-parted.

seed

1585 *Paulownia tomentosa* **FOXGLOVE TREE**. Deciduous tree, with a rounded top, to 16m high; branches thick, stiff, rather open. Leaves opposite, *large*, oval to 3-5-lobed (especially in young plants or those recently pruned), long-stalked, downy. Flowers bluish-purple, paler in the throat, funnel-shaped, 2-lipped, 38-50mm long, like a large foxglove flower, borne in terminal panicles. Fruit a large, 2-parted, egg-shaped, but pointed, capsule, somewhat woody, 35-50mm long. Parks, gardens and roadsides. May-June. Occasionally planted in the Med, especially in Europe. (China).

Scrophularia **FIGWORTS** Biennial or perennial herbs, often with square stems. Leaves usually opposite. Flowers in cymes, forming a lax raceme or panicle; calyx with equal lobes; corolla pouched, generally more or less 2-lipped; stamens 4, the fifth stamen usually replaced by a scale-like staminode.

1586 *Scrophularia peregrina* **NETTLE-LEAVED FIGWORT**. Short to tall, hairless or slightly glandular-hairy annual. Leaves oval with a heart-shaped or rather truncated base, irregularly toothed, *not* lobed; bracts mostly leaf-like. Flowers dark red to purple-brown, 6-9mm long. Cultivated and waste ground, path and roadsides, rocky places and old walls, stream gravels. Mar-June. T.

1587 *Scrophularia lucida*. Short to tall hairless biennial, to 1m; stem *usually solitary*. Leaves oblong, pinnately-lobed, the oblong lobes often further lobed; bracts not leaf-like. Flowers greenish-brown, 4-9mm long. Shaded rocks. Feb-May. SE France to Italy, Greece, Crete and the Aegean Is.

1588 *Scrophularia trifoliata*. Similar, but a taller perennial to 2m; bracts variable in size. Flowers purple, often glandular outside, *large*, 12-18mm long. Streamsides and other damp, shaded or semi-shaded places. Apr-July. Corsica, Sardinia and Sicily.

1589 *Scrophularia canina* **FRENCH FIGWORT**. Medium, hairless perennial; stems much-branched. Lower leaves pinnately-lobed, with narrow lobes, generally toothed; upper leaves elliptical to oblong, sometimes unlobed, the uppermost *usually alternate*; bracts small, not leaf-like. Flowers dark purplish-red, 4-5mm long, numerous; calyx-lobes with broad membranous margins. Dry hills, rocky places and screes, waste places, generally in the hills and mountains. May-Aug. T – not Cyprus.

1590 *Scrophularia ramosissima*. Similar, but much-branched with smaller, less cut leaves. Flowers in *small* 1-3-flowered cymes (not 3-11-flowered); flower-stalks (pedicels) becoming woody, persistent and spine-like. Maritime sands and other dry lowland habitats. Mar-June. S France, Corsica and Sardinia; possible Balearic Is.

1591 *Scrophularia peyronii*. Like *S. canina*, but plant to 1.5m tall and leaves more dissected. Flowers very small, 3-4mm, whitish with a maroon-red upper lip. Dry hillslopes among garrigue, dry, fallow and waste ground, roadsides. Apr-July. Cyprus, Turkey, Syria and Lebanon.

1592 *Scrophularia scopolii*. More or less hairy, medium to tall perennial, to 1m. Leaves oval to lanceolate, *doubly toothed* (bidentate), with a rounded or heart-shaped base; bracts mostly not leaf-like. Flowers greenish with a purple-brown upper lip, 7-12mm long, borne in 4-7-flowered cymes; stalks usually glandular-hairy. Woods and damp shaded or semi-shaded habitats, generally in the mountains. Italy to Turkey. Apr-July.

Verbascum **MULLEINS**. Herbs, generally biennial or perennial, often with large basal leaf-rosettes; leaves alternate, usually toothed or variously lobed. Flowers borne in spikes or panicles; calyx with 5 equal lobes; corolla yellow, white, orange or occasionally violet, with a short tube and 5 widely spreading lobes; stamens 4-5, with hairy stalks (filaments). Fruit a globose capsule. A large and complicated genus with almost 90 species in Europe alone; only the principal species are included here.

1593 *Verbascum spinosum* **SPINY MULLEIN**. Small *spiny* shrub to 50cm tall, forming rather dense hummocks; branches spine-tipped; young shoots hairy. Leaves small, to 5cm long, oblong-lanceolate, toothed or lobed, white-downy. Flowers yellow, 10-18mm, solitary at each bract. Rocky and stony habitats in hills and mountains. Apr-June. Crete – endemic.

1594 *Verbascum phoeniceum [Celsia rechingeri]* **PURPLE MULLEIN**. Medium to tall perennial; stems erect, hairy, glandular-hairy above. Basal leaves oval, slightly toothed or untoothed, rather wavy, the upper leaves unstalked. Flowers *violet*, 20-30mm, solitary at each bract, borne in lax racemes; stamens equal, the filaments with purple hairs. Grassy places, scrub, waste places and banks. May-July. Italy, the Balkans and Turkey. Widely cultivated for ornament.

1595 *Verbascum phlomoides* **ORANGE MULLEIN**. Medium to tall, whitish- or greyish-woolly biennial, to 1.2m. Basal leaves oblong-elliptical, toothed or not; stem leaves narrower and pointed, the base not or only shortly running down the stem. Flowers bright orange-yellow, 20-55mm, borne in dense woolly, spike-like racemes, the corolla hairy outside; stamens 5, the lower 2 with hairless filaments, the upper 3 with white or yellowish hairs. Waste and bare ground, banks and waysides, scrub and dry stony habitats. June-Sept. T – not Balearic Is., Crete, most of the Aegean Is. or Cyprus.

1596 *Verbascum densiflorum [V. thapsiforme]*. Similar, but base of stem-leaves running down the stem, almost to the leaf below and bracts *longer*, 15-40mm long (not

9-15mm). Similar habitats and flowering time. S France eastwards to Turkey – not on the islands, except Sicily.

1597 *Verbascum thapsus* **GREAT MULLEIN, AARON'S ROD.** Medium to tall, soft, greyish- or whitish-woolly biennial, to 2m, though often less. Basal leaves elliptical to oblong, blunt, toothed or not, with a narrow winged stalk, the stem leaves smaller with the winged base running down the stem *almost* to the leaf below. Flowers yellow, 12-35mm, borne in dense woolly, spike-like racemes; stamens 5 with white-hairy filaments, the lower 2 often hairless. Hedgebanks, scrub, roadsides, rough grassland, stony places, waste places. May-Aug. T – but scarce in the Balkans and much of the E Med. Important in mediaeval herbalism; today used only occasionally.

1598 *Verbascum boerhavii.* Similar, but the leaf-bases not running down the stem and filament hairs *violet*. Spain, Balearic Is., S France, Corsica and Italy.

1599 *Verbascum lychnitis* **WHITE MULLEIN.** Medium to tall, grey-downy biennial, to 1.5m; stems angled, erect. Basal leaves oval to oblong, toothed or almost untoothed, green above but white-mealy beneath, short-stalked, the upper leaves small, pointed and unstalked. Flowers white, occasionally yellow, 12-20mm, borne in a freely branched pyramidal panicle; stamens 5, all with whitish or yellowish hairs. Waste places, banks, roadsides. rocky places, scrub. June-Aug. Spain, S France, Corsica, Italy and the Balkans. Uncommon in the Med.

1600 *Verbascum chaixii.* Similar, but leaves often slightly lobed at the base. Flowers 15-22mm; filament hairs *violet*. NE Spain eastwards to Greece – absent from the islands except for Sicily.

1601 *Verbascum sinuatum.* Medium to tall, densely grey- or yellow-woolly biennial, to 1m; glandular-hairy in the inflorescence. Basal leaves in large *distinctive* rosettes, oblong, pinnately-lobed and undulate; bracts 3-8mm long, triangular-heart-shaped. Flowers yellow, 15-30mm, borne in clusters on a twiggy, widely branching inflorescence; stamens 5, the filaments with violet hairs. Rocky places, sandy coastal habitats, roadsides, banks, dry fields and gardens. Apr-July. T.

1602 *Verbascum undulatum.* Similar, but basal leaves unlobed to pinnately-lobed, markedly undulate. Flowers 25-50mm, borne in simple, or slightly branched, spike-like clusters; filament hairs *white*. Similar habitats and flowering time. S and W Balkan Peninsula, including many of the island.

1603 *Verbascum pinnatifidum.* Short biennial, hairy at first but becoming hairless, with several stems branched from near the base. Basal leaves oblong, deeply toothed to lobed, the lobes sometimes further lobed. Flowers yellow, 25-30mm, borne in spike-like clusters, the flowers unstalked; stamens 5, the filaments with white or yellow hairs. Coastal rocks and sands, occasionally inland. Mar-May. Aegean Is. and Turkey.

1604 *Verbascum orientale.* Similar, but annual, glandular-hairy above, with the basal leaves often withered by flowering time. Flowers solitary, not in small clusters along the spike, yellow, often with a few brownish spots; *stamens* 4, the filaments with yellow hairs. Rocky slopes and cliffs, often limestone. Feb-May. Balkans and the E Med, including Cyprus.

1605 *Verbascum rotundifolium* **ROUND-LEAVED MULLEIN.** White-downy, tall biennial, woolly above, to 1.5m tall. *Basal leaves* oval to rounded, blunt-toothed or untoothed, stalked. Flowers yellow, 15-40mm, generally borne in a simple raceme, occasionally with a few branches; stamens 5, the lower 2 much longer, all with violet filament hairs. Rocky habitats, banks, roadsides. May-July. Spain, Corsica, Sardinia, Italy and Sicily.

stamen

stamen

1606 *Verbascum arcturus [Celsia arcturus]*. Woody-based perennial, with simple, spreading to erect stems to 70cm. Basal leaves with a *large* terminal lobe and with several smaller lobes below, softly and densely white-hairy beneath, sparsely hairy above. Flowers yellow, 25-30mm, in spike-like glandular-hairy racemes; stamens 4, with violet filament hairs. Rocky places and cliffs, often in gorges. Mar-May. Crete – endemic.

1607 *Verbascum creticum [Celsia cretica]*. Similar, but leaves toothed to lobed but without an obvious terminal lobe. Flowers *larger*, 40-50mm, the upper 2 petals with brownish-purple spots; bracts 12-25mm long (not 5-8mm). Rocky habitats. Apr-June. Spain, Balearic Is., Sardinia, Italy and Sicily.

Antirrhinum **SNAPDRAGONS**. Annual or perennial herbs. Leaves generally opposite below but alternate towards the top of the plant, untoothed. Flowers in terminal racemes; bracts present, often leaf-like; calyx 5-lobed; corolla 2-lipped, with a conspicuous palate closing the mouth, not spurred but pouched at the base of the corolla; stamens 4. Capsule opening by 2 apical pores.

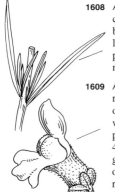

1608 *Antirrhinum siculum* **SICILIAN SNAPDRAGON**. Short to medium perennial, hairless except for the glandular-hairy inflorescence; stems erect to ascending, freely branched, often with *leaf-tufts* in the main leaf-axils. Leaves linear to narrow-elliptical. Flowers pale yellow, sometimes with red veins, 17-25mm long. Rocky places and walls. Apr-July, occasionally later. SW Italy, Sicily and Malta; naturalised in Spain and S France.

1609 *Antirrhinum majus* **SNAPDRAGON**. Variable medium to tall perennial, to 1.5m in robust specimens; stems ascending to erect, branched, especially below, hairless or sometimes glandular-hairy in the inflorescence. Leaves linear to oval with a wedge-shaped base, opposite, alternate or sometimes in threes. Flowers pink or purple, with a yellow or occasionally white palate, or all pale yellow, *large*, 30-45mm long, fragrant. Rocky places, cliffs, old walls and old buildings, cultivated ground. Mar-Nov. Widespread in the Med, but probably only naturalised in much of the east. Forms with narrow, linear, leaves and opposite flowers are often referred to var. *angustifolia* (1609a). An old garden plant with a wide range of colour forms.

1610 *Antirrhinum latifolium*. Similar, but plants glandular-hairy *throughout* and leaves oval and rather blunt-tipped. Flowers pale yellow, 33-48mm long. Rocky and stony habitats. Apr-Aug. NE Spain, S France to C Italy; absent from the islands.

1611 *Misopates orontium [Antirrhinum orontium]* **LESSER SNAPDRAGON**. Short to medium, slightly branched annual, sometimes hairy below but glandular-hairy above. Leaves linear to elliptical, untoothed, the lower opposite, the upper alternate. Flowers pink, rarely white, 10-15mm, pouched at the base, the rather unequal sepals *almost the same length* as the corolla, borne in leafy racemes. Capsule glandular-hairy, usually opening by 3 pores. Arable, waste and cultivated land, roadsides, bare places, sandy places, dry hillslopes and openings in pine forest. Mar-Sept. T. A weed in many parts of the world.

1612 *Chaenorhinum rubrifolium [Linaria rubrifolia]* **RED-LEAVED TOADFLAX**. Slender, erect, low to short annual, sparsely glandular-hairy; stems branched or not. Leaves oval, sometimes broadest above the middle, the lower opposite and short-stalked, often *red-purple beneath*, the upper alternate and unstalked. Flowers blue, violet or lilac with a yellow palate, 10-20mm long, borne in a lax terminal raceme; corolla 2-lipped and with a short, pointed spur up to 6.5mm long. Capsule with 2-3 apical pores when ripe. Dry habitats, stony fields, walls and cliffs, often on limestone.

Mar-June. W Med eastwards to Greece, occasionally further east, especially Cyprus.

1613 *Chaenorhinum minus [Linaria minor]* **SMALL TOADFLAX**. Similar, but the basal leaves not in a rosette and flowers pale yellow or lilac, *small*, 5-9mm long. Arable, cultivated and disturbed land, waste places and embankments. Apr-Aug. T, but absent from parts of the E Med, including Cyprus.

Linaria **TOADFLAXES**. Annual or perennial herbs with simple unstalked leaves, the lower opposite or whorled, the upper usually alternate. Flowers in spikes or racemes; bracts present; calyx unequally 5-lobed, generally short; corolla 2-lipped, with a palate closing the mouth, distinctly spurred at the base. Fruit capsule opening unevenly by longitudinal slits.

1614 *Linaria reflexa*. Hairless, somewhat greyish-green, low to medium annual, the stems spreading to prostrate, branched or not. Leaves elliptical, *mostly alternate* but the lowermost usually whorled. Flowers pale yellow, lilac or white, 20-30mm long, borne in lax, leafy racemes; spur 12-16mm long. Dry open, stony and rocky habitats. Apr-June. S France, Corsica, Sardinia, Italy and Sicily.

1615 *Linaria pedunculata*. Similar, but more robust, the leaves rather fleshy and the flowers *smaller*, 11-16mm long, cream, often with violet veins; spur 6-7mm long, violet. Coastal sands. Mar-June. SW Spain and S Portugal.

1616 *Linaria flava*. Like *L. pedunculata*, but flowers yellow, 10-14mm long, borne in *heads* of 1-5; spur 5-7mm long. Similar habitats and flowering time. Corsica and Sardinia.

1617 *Linaria triphylla* **THREE-LEAVED TOADFLAX**. Hairless, greyish-green, short to medium annual, often with a solitary, rather stout, stem which may be branched above. Leaves elliptical to oblong, sometimes broadest above the middle, mostly whorled, occasionally opposite or alternate on the same plant. Flowers white with an orange palate and a violet spur, sometimes pale yellow or all violet, 20-30mm long, borne in rather dense terminal racemes; spur 8-11mm long. Cultivated ground, fields, vineyards, generally at low altitudes. Feb-June. T, except for Cyprus and parts of the E Med.

1618 *Linaria hirta*. Similar, but densely *glandular-hairy*, to 80cm tall and with oblong-lanceolate leaves. Flowers pale yellow 18-30mm long; spur reddish, 10-16mm long. Cultivated and waste ground, coastal sands. Mar-June. S Spain and Portugal.

1619 *Linaria chalepensis*. Hairless, short, rather delicate annual; stems erect, simple or somewhat branched. Leaves mostly alternate, the lowermost paired or in threes, linear. Flowers white or cream, 12-16mm long, borne in long, lax racemes; spur 8-11mm long, downcurved. Dry habitats, cultivated and fallow ground, waste places, occasionally in openings in pine forest. Jan-July. T.

1620 *Linaria albifrons*. Similar, but with *small* flowers, less than 10mm long, whitish or blue, with a yellow palate; spur 2-2.5mm long, almost at right angles to the tube. Cultivated ground, field margins. Feb-Apr. E Med from Rhodes eastwards, including Cyprus.

1621 *Linaria pelisseriana* **JERSEY TOADFLAX**. Greyish green, short to medium, rather delicate annual; stems erect, few and generally unbranched. Leaves linear, *erect*, pointed, the lowermost whorled, the upper alternate. Flowers purplish-violet with a paler or whitish palate, 15-20mm long, borne in short, crowded racemes; spur 5-9mm long, more or less straight; corolla with the upper lip longer than the lower. Fields, dry and waste places. Open garrigue, cultivated ground. Mar-July. T.

1622 *Linaria vulgaris* **COMMON TOADFLAX.** Medium to tall, tufted perennial, with erect to ascending stems and a creeping rhizomatous rootstock; stems usually branched in the upper half, hairless or glandular-hairy above. Leaves linear to narrow elliptical, crowded, 1-veined, mostly alternate. Flowers pale to bright yellow, 25-33mm long, borne in long dense racemes; spur 10-13mm long, straight. Grassy habitats, waste ground, roadsides, hedgebanks and cultivated ground. June-Oct. Balearic Is., Sardinia and Crete. Rare close to the Med, but widespread in many parts of Europe.

1623 *Linaria arvensis.* Greyish, short to medium annual, hairless except for the glandular-hairy inflorescence; stems erect. Leaves linear, the lower whorled, the upper alternate. Flowers pale bluish-lilac, *small*, 4-7mm long, borne in rather dense racemes which elongate in fruit; spur 1.5-3mm long, strongly curved. Open habitats, hillslopes, garrigue, cultivated ground. Mar-June. W and C Med eastwards to Greece – not Crete.

1624 *Linaria simplex [L. parviflora].* Similar, but flowers pale yellow, usually with violet veins, 5-9mm long; spur 2-3.5mm long, straight. Similar habitats and flowering times. T.

1625 *Linaria micrantha.* Like *L. arvensis*, but flowers only 4-7mm long, the corolla scarcely longer than the calyx; spur only 1mm long. Cultivated, fallow and waste ground, rocky coastal habitats. Feb-June. T.

1626 *Linaria aeruginea [L. melanantha].* Low to short perennial, glandular-hairy, sometimes hairless below; stems spreading to ascending. Leaves linear, with *margins* rolled under (revolute), the lower whorled, the upper alternate. Flowers yellow, often tinged purple-brown or all purple-brown, violet, yellowish or whitish, with prominent veins, 15-27mm long, the spur 5-11mm long. Dry rocky habitats in hills and mountains. Apr-July. S and E Spain and Balearic Is.

Cymbalaria **IVY-LEAVED TOADFLAXES.** Trailing or scrambling herbs with delicate, thread-like stems. Leaves alternate, rarely opposite, rounded to kidney-shaped, lobed and stalked. Flowers small, solitary, borne at the leaf-axils; corolla 2-lipped, with the mouth closed by a palate, with a short blunt spur at the base, occasionally spurless. Fruit capsule dehiscing at the apex into irregular teeth.

1627 *Cymbalaria pallida.* Low trailing, somewhat hairy perennial, often with long internodes. Leaves mostly *opposite*, rounded to triangular in outline, unlobed to 5-lobed, long-stalked. Flowers pale lilac-blue, 15-25mm long; spur 6-9mm long. Rocks and rock crevices. Apr-June. Italy.

1628 *Cymbalaria muelleri.* Similar, but a more tufted plant, with leaves unlobed to obscurely 3-lobed. Flowers *smaller*, 9-10mm long, dull violet with a 2mm long reddish spur. Rocks and walls. Sardinia – endemic.

1629 *Cymbalaria longipes [Linaria longipes].* Low, slender trailing perennial, hairless apart from the fruit. Leaves alternate, semicircular to kidney-shaped, with 5-9 blunt lobes. Flowers lilac or violet, with a yellow palate, 9-15mm long; spur 4-5mm long. *Capsule* glandular-hairy. Rocky and stony coastal habitats, more rarely inland. Mar-May. S Greece, Crete, S Aegean Is. and the E Med, including Cyprus.

1630 *Cymbalaria microcalyx.* Similar, but *plant* shaggily hairy and leaves unlobed to 3-5-lobed. Flowers violet with a yellow palate; spur 1-3mm long. Capsule downy. Rocky habitats, mainly in the mountains. Apr-July. Balkans and Crete.

1631 *Cymbalaria aequitriloba.* Like *C. microcalyx,* but flowers violet to pale blue or whitish, 8-13mm long; spur 2-3mm long. Capsule *hairless.* Damp, generally shaded, habitats. Mar-June. Balearic Is., Corsica, Sardinia and Italy.

1632 *Cymbalaria muralis [Linaria cymbalaria]* **IVY-LEAVED TOADFLAX.** Trailing, often purplish, tufted, hairless perennial. Leaves alternate, kidney-shaped to almost round, 5-9-lobed, long-stalked. Flowers lilac to violet with a yellowish palate, 9-15mm long, borne on long slender stalks; spur 1.5-3mm long. Capsule *hairless.* Shady rocks, woodland, old walls. Apr-Sept. S and W Balkans, Aegean Is., Crete; widely naturalised in parts of the Med, especially Europe.

Kickxia **FLUELLENS.** Similar to *Cymbalaria,* but leaves with pinnately rather than palmately arranged veins. Fruit capsule dehiscing by apical pores.

1633 *Kickxia commutata [Linaria commutata].* Low to short spreading annual or perennial; stems slender, sometimes rooting at the nodes, glandular-hairy. Leaves oval to arrow-shaped, shaggily hairy, short-stalked. Flowers whitish tinged mauve, or with a violet-blue upper lip, a yellow lower lip and a purple-spotted palate, 11-15mm long; spur strongly curved; flower-stalks *hairless.* Cultivated, fallow and waste ground, field margins, roadsides, hillslopes. Apr-July. T.

1634 *Kickxia cirrhosa [Linaria cirrhosa].* Similar, but leaves somewhat twisted and flowers *smaller,* 4-6mm long, white, tinged and veined with violet. Damp and shady habitats, especially sandy coastal places. Mar-July. W Med eastwards to Italy and Sicily.

1635 *Kickxia elatine [Linaria elatine]* **SHARP-LEAVED FLUELLEN.** Like *K. commutata,* but a glandular-hairy plant. Flowers yellowish or bluish with a violet upper lip, 7-15mm long; spur more or less *straight;* flower-stalks long, hairy. Cultivated, fallow and waste ground, moist places. May-Nov. T.

1636 *Kickxia lanigera [Linaria lanigera].* Like *K. commutata,* but a shaggily-hairy annual with whitish, ridged stems and *heart-shaped* leaves. Flowers whitish with a violet upper lip and blue-spotted palate, 8-11mm long; spur curved; flower-stalks short, hairy. Cultivated and waste ground, roadsides. Jan-Oct. Scattered localities in Portugal, Spain, the Balearic Is., N Africa and the E Med, including Cyprus.

Digitalis **FOXGLOVES.** Perennial herbs with basal leaf-rosettes as well as alternate stem leaves. Flowers borne in a bracteate spike-like raceme, often one-sided; calyx 5-lobed; corolla funnel-shaped, weakly to strongly 2-lipped, often with prominent hairs in the throat; stamens 4. Fruit a capsule opening by terminal pores.

1637 *Digitalis viridiflora* **GREEN-FLOWERED FOXGLOVE.** Medium to tall erect, hairy perennial. Leaves oblong-lanceolate to elliptical, finely toothed. Flowers dull yellowish-green, conspicuously veined within, narrowly cylindrical, 11-20mm long, borne in a dense spike; upper and lower lips almost equal in size. Wooded habitats. May-July. Balkan Peninsula and Turkey.

1638 *Digitalis ferruginea* **RUSTY FOXGLOVE.** Medium to tall, erect perennial to 1.2m, though often less; stems *hairless.* Leaves oblong to lanceolate, hairless or more or less hairy beneath, dark green. Flowers yellowish or reddish-brown, heavily netted with darker veins, globular, 15-35mm long, borne in long tapered spikes; lip, prominent and protruding; bracts longer than the flowers usually; calyx lobes broad and blunt, with a wide papery margin. Wooded habitats and scrub, roadsides. May-Aug. Italy eastwards to Turkey – absent from most of the islands.

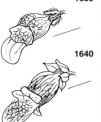

1639 *Digitalis lanata*. Similar, but the inflorescence axis often purplish and *shaggily hairy*. Flowers whitish or yellowish with brown or violet veins, 20-30mm long, with a pale, curved lip; bracts mostly shorter than the flowers. Similar habitats and flowering times. Balkans and Turkey; absent from the islands.

1640 *Digitalis laevigata*. Tall, hairless perennial, to 1m. Leaves oblong-lanceolate to lanceolate, finely toothed or untoothed. Flowers yellowish with purple-brown veins or marks and a pale protruding, scarcely curved, lip, 15-35mm long, borne in lax spikes; calyx lobes *narrow* and pointed, often with narrow papery margins; only lower bracts longer than the flowers. Woodland and scrub, occasionally along roadsides or in more exposed positions. May-July. Balkan Peninsula.

1641 *Digitalis obscura* **SPANISH RUSTY FOXGLOVE**. Hairless subshrub to 1.2m tall, though often less; stems branched near the base, leafy towards the apex. Leaves leathery, *shiny* deep green, linear-oblong to lanceolate, curved, toothed or not. Flowers orange-yellow to brown, with darker netted veins and spots within, funnel-shaped, 20-30mm long, with a protruding subacute lip. Rocky habitats, mainly in the mountains. June-Aug. Spain, except the N.

Veronica **SPEEDWELLS**. Annual or perennial herbs, generally with opposite leaves. Flowers solitary or in terminal or lateral racemes; calyx 4-lobed, the lobes fused only at the base; corolla flat or cupped, with 4, often unequal, lobes; stamens 2. Fruit capsule generally heart- or kidney-shaped.

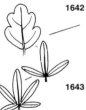

1642 *Veronica acinifolia* **FRENCH SPEEDWELL**. Low to short, glandular-hairy, erect annual, often branched from the base. Leaves oval, untoothed or slightly toothed, short-stalked. Flowers blue, *small*, 2-3mm, borne in terminal racemes. Capsule kidney-shaped, almost 2-lobed, glandular-hairy. Cultivated ground, grassy places, generally on rather damp ground. Mar-July. T – not Balearic Is., Sardinia or Cyprus.

1643 *Veronica triphyllos* **FINGERED SPEEDWELL**. Similar, but leaves and bracts divided into finger-like lobes. Flowers bright blue, 5-6mm. Cultivated and waste ground, stony slopes, gravels. Mar-May. T – local.

1644 *Veronica glauca*. Like *V. acinifolia*, but leaves shallowly lobed and flowers *larger*, 10-15mm, deep blue. Cultivated land, dry grassland. Albania and Greece.

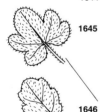

1645 *Veronica hederifolia* **IVY-LEAVED SPEEDWELL**. Low sprawling, hairy annual; stems branched at the base. Leaves kidney-shaped, 3-7-lobed, the end lobe the largest, 3-veined, all but the lowermost alternate, stalked. Flowers pale lilac or pale blue, 4-9mm, *solitary* on stalks shorter than the leaves; sepals heart-shaped at the base. Capsule rounded, very shallowly notched, hairless. Cultivated, waste and disturbed land, often abundant, roadsides and old walls. Mar-July. T.

1646 *Veronica cymbalaria* **CYMBALARIA-LEAVED SPEEDWELL**. Similar, but leaves 7-9-lobed and flowers *white*, borne on stalks as long as, or longer than, the leaves. Similar habitats. Dec-July. T.

1647 *Veronica polita* **GREY FIELD SPEEDWELL**. Like *V. hederifolia*, but leaves toothed rather than lobed and flowers *bright blue*, 6-7mm. Similar habitats, often in damper places. Dec-July. T.

1648 *Veronica anagallis-aquatica* **BLUE WATER SPEEDWELL**. Medium, hairless, occasionally glandular-hairy perennial; stems erect, unbranched or much-branched. Leaves opposite, pale green, oval to lanceolate, scarcely toothed, the lower stalked but the upper unstalked and half-clasping the stem. Flowers blue with violet lines, 5-10mm, borne in long, slender, paired racemes. Capsules rounded to elliptical, slightly notched, hairless. Wet habitats, marshes, streams and irrigation ditches. Feb-July. T.

1649 *Odontites verna [O. rubra]* **RED BARTSIA**. Very variable, short to medium, hairy, often purplish, semi-parasitic annual; stems erect to ascending, slightly square, generally branched below. Leaves opposite, lanceolate, usually toothed; bracts similar to the leaves, generally longer than the flowers. Flowers *reddish-pink*, 2-lipped, open-mouthed, the lower lip somewhat deflexed; anthers slightly protruding. Capsule hairy. Meadows, grassy places, scrub, roadsides, pathways, field margins and waste places. June-Sept. T – except the Balearic Is., Sardinia, Crete and Cyprus.

1650 *Odontites cypria*. Similar, but leaves linear, untoothed, sometimes alternate and flowers *yellow*, 6-7mm long. Rocky places in garrigue or beneath conifers. July-Dec. Cyprus – endemic.

leaf

1651 *Parentucellia viscosa [Bartsia viscosa]* **YELLOW BARTSIA**. Short to medium, glandular-hairy, semi-parasitic annual; stems erect, generally unbranched. Leaves opposite, oblong to lanceolate, pointed, coarsely toothed, unstalked; bracts similar to the leaves, decreasing in size up the stem. Flowers yellow, occasionally white, 15-24mm long, borne in spikes up to 25cm long, the corolla 2-lipped, open-mouthed, the lower lip 3-lobed, the upper forming a small hood. Capsule hairy. Damp rough grassland, often close to the coast, stream margins and irrigation channels. Apr-July. T.

1652 *Parentucellia latifolia [Bartsia latifolia]*. Similar, but flowers *smaller*, 10-12mm long, pale yellow, purple or white, borne in a much shorter spike – usually not more than 8cm long. Dry grassy habitats, pastures, roadsides, often in shady and stony places. Mar-June. T.

1653 *Bellardia trixago [Bartsia trixago, Rhinanthus trixago]* **BELLARDIA**. A short to medium, glandular-hairy, semi-parasitic annual; stems erect, usually unbranched. Leaves opposite, linear-lanceolate, toothed, unstalked; bracts like the leaves, decreasing in size up the stem, the uppermost heart-shaped and untoothed. Flowers whitish with one or both lips flushed with pink or sometimes yellow, 20-25mm long, borne in a *4-sided*, dense spike. Cultivated, fallow and waste ground, stony and waste places, roadsides, olive groves, garrigue. Mar-June. T.

BROOMRAPE FAMILY Orobanchaceae

Parasitic perennial herbs without chlorophyll. Stems erect, mostly unbranched, bearing alternate scale-like leaves. Flowers borne in dense bracteate spikes; calyx 4-5-lobed; corolla 5-lobed, 2-lipped, often glandular-hairy on the outside; stamens 4, included within the persistent calyx and corolla.

1654 *Cistanche phelypaea [C. lutea, C. tinctoria, Orobanche tinctoria, Phelypaea lutea]* **CISTANCHE**. A stout, erect, short to tall, hairless perennial; stem thick. Scale-leaves oval-lanceolate, finely toothed, membranous. Flowers bright, *shiny yellow*, 30-40mm long, borne in a dense cone-like spike; calyx 5-lobed; corolla with 5, more or less equal, lobes. Parasitic on woody members of the Chenopodiaceae at low altitudes, local. S Portugal, S Spain, N Africa, Crete, Turkey, Cyprus and parts of the extreme E Med.

Orobanche **BROOMRAPES**. Differs from *Cistanche* in having a 4-lobed calyx and in the corolla which is clearly 2-lipped. Identifying the host plant can be a useful guide to correct identification.

1655 *Orobanche ramosa [Phelypaea ramosa]* **BRANCHED BROOMRAPE**. A very variable, low to short, glandular-hairy perennial; stems usually *branched*, swollen at the base. Scale-leaves oval, pointed; bracts and bracteoles present, appearing as 3 bracts to each flower. Flowers violet, blue or cream, with a white patch at the somewhat swollen base, 10-22mm long; stigma white, cream or pale blue. Parasitic on a wide range of hosts, but especially *Cannabis, Nicotiana* and *Solanum* species and legumes (Leguminosae). Cultivated land, field margins, roadsides. Feb-Sept. T.

1656 *Orobanche aegyptiaca [Phelypaea aegyptiaca]* **EGYPTIAN BROOMRAPE**. Similar, but flowers *larger*, 20-35mm long, blue or purple with white patches in the mouth; anthers densely hairy (not hairless or only slightly hairy). Parastic on various crop plants, potatoes, tomatoes, maize, peas, beans and cucumbers in particular, sometimes in large numbers. Jan-Dec. N Africa, European Turkey and S Aegean eastwards, including Cyprus.

1657 *Orobanche lavandulacea [Phelypaea lavandulaceae]*. A short to medium, glandular-hairy perennial; stem simple or branched, somewhat swollen at the base. Scale-leaves oval-lanceolate, pointed; bracts and bracteoles *present*, linear-lanceolate, appearing as 3 bracts to each flower. Flowers usually blue with a whitish base, 16-22mm long, borne in a dense to lax spike; stigma white or yellowish. Parasitic on various herbs, but especially *Psoralea bituminosa*. Mar-June. Spain and NW Africa eastwards to Greece.

1658 *Orobanche schultzii [Phelypaea schultzii]*. Similar, but with *long* calyx-teeth, 2-3 times longer than the calyx-tube, and with pointed lobes to the lower lip of the corolla (not blunt lobes). Parasitic on umbels, Umbelliferae. Spain, Sardinia and Sicily.

style

1659 *Orobanche purpurea [Phelypaea caerulea]* **YARROW or PURPLE BROOMRAPE**. A short to medium, finely glandular-hairy perennial; stem usually unbranched, slightly swollen at the base, often grey-tinged. Scale-leaves linear-lanceolate; bracts and bracteoles present as in *O. lavandulacea*. Flowers bluish-violet with deep violet veins, whitish towards the base, 18-25mm long, narrow-bell-shaped; stigma white or blue. Parasitic on various composites, especially *Achillea*. May-July. Scattered localities T, but absent from the the islands, except Corsica.

1660 *Orobanche orientalis*. Similar, but bracts 15-20mm long (not 8-15mm), far *overtopping* the buds at the top of the spike; flowers reddish-purple, pink or mauve. Parasitic on *Astragalus, Medicago* and various other plants. Apr-June. Cyprus and the extreme E Med.

1661 *Orobanche cernua*. Short to medium, glandular-hairy perennial; stem yellowish, unbranched. Scale-leaves oval-lanceolate; bracts present, but not bracteoles, there being only one apparent bract to each flower (this applies to all the following species). Flowers violet-blue, with a *shiny white* base; stigma whitish. Parasitic primarily on *Artemisia*, occasionally on sunflowers, *Helianthus annuus*. May-Sept. T – not Portugal, Balearic Is., Sardinia or Cyprus.

style

1662 *Orobanche alba [O. epithymum]* **THYME BROOMRAPE**. Short, reddish-purple perennial, glandular-hairy; stems unbranched, slightly swollen at the base. Scale-leaves lanceolate; bracts lanceolate, pointed. Flowers purplish-red, yellowish or whitish, 15-28mm long, *fragrant*, borne in a fairly dense spike, the lower lip with a hairy margin; stamens with densely hairy filaments; stigma red or purple. Parasitic on *Thymus* and other labiates, on rock slopes and in garrigue. Mar-June. Spain eastwards to Turkey, including Sicily, Crete and Cyprus.

style

1663 *Orobanche reticulata* **THISTLE BROOMRAPE**. Similar, but more robust, the flowers scarcely fragrant with the lower lip evenly lobed (without a large central lobe), *not* hairy-margined. Parasitic on thistles, *Carduus* and *Cirsium*, and on *Knautia* and related genera. May-July. W Med, including N Africa, eastwards to Greece and Turkey.

1664 *Orobanche minor* **COMMON BROOMRAPE**. Very variable, short to medium, glandular-hairy to downy perennial, tinged with yellow, brown or purple; stems un-branched, swollen at the base. Scale-leaves oval to lanceolate; bracts oval, pointed. Flowers *pale yellow*, often tinged with dull violet distally, 10-6mm long, borne in a rather lax spike; corolla curved, the lower lip evenly lobed, without a hairy margin; stigma purple, rarely yellowish. Parasitic on a variety of hosts, particularly legumes, composites, and umbellifers; seashore and inland. Mar-July, occasionally later. T – not Balearic Is. or Crete.

1665 *Orobanche loricata [O. picridis]* **OXTONGUE BROOMRAPE**. Similar, but bracts larger, 12-20mm long (not 7-15mm) and flowers white or pale yellow tinged and veined violet, 14-22mm long; stigma purple. Parasitic on composites, particularly *Artemisia* and *Picris* and various umbellifers; rocky habitats and grassland. May-July. T – not Cyprus or parts of the east Med.

1666 *Orobanche canescens*. Like *O. minor*, but corolla yellow tinged with red and stigma *yellow*. Parasitic primarily on composites, Compositae. Apr-July. Corsica and Sardinia eastwards to Greece and Turkey, including Crete.

1667 *Orobanche amethystea*. Like *O. minor*, but flowers white or cream, *always* tinged with purple or violet throughout, 12-22mm long. Parasitic on a variety of hosts, especially umbellifers. May-July. T – except the Balearic Is., Crete, Cyprus and parts of the extreme east Med.

1668 *Orobanche grisebachii*. Like *O. loricata*, but flowers white, tinged with violet in the upper half, only 12-15mm long. Parasitic on legumes, and composites. May-July. Greece, Crete and the Aegean Is.

1669 *Orobanche pubescens [O. minor subsp. pubescens, O. versicolor]*. Short to medium, glandular-hairy perennial, pale yellow tinged with pink. Scale-leaves oblong to linear-lanceolate, 10-25mm long. Flowers pale yellow tinged with violet above, 10-20mm long, borne in a lax raceme, densely, somewhat matted, *white-hairy* on the outside; stigma violet. Parasitic on various composites, legumes and umbellifers; mainly in garrigue and on cultivated land. Mar-July. SE France eastwards, including Crete and Cyprus.

1670 *Orobanche rapum-genistae* **GREATER BROOMRAPE**. Short to tall, glandular-hairy perennial; stem pale yellow, sometimes flushed with red, strongly swollen at the base. Scale-leaves oval to linear-lanceolate; bracts linear-lanceolate, longer than the flowers. Flowers yellow tinged with purple, 20-25mm long, slightly curved, fetid, the lower lip with a *hairy margin*; stigma yellow. Parasitic on various shrubby legumes; rough grassland and scrub mainly. Apr-July. Spain eastwards to Italy and Sicily.

style

1671 *Orobanche caryophyllacea [O. vulgaris]* **BEDSTRAW BROOMRAPE**. Short to medium, glandular-hairy perennial, tinged with yellow or purple; stem scarcely swollen at the base. Scale-leaves narrow-triangular-lanceolate, pointed; bracts lanceolate, short. Flowers pink or pale yellow tinged with dull purple, 20-32mm long, *clove-scented*, borne in a rather dense spike, the lower lip of the corolla unequally 3-lobed, hairy-margined; filaments hairy; stigma purple. Parasitic on members of the Rubiaceae, *Galium* and *Rubia* in particular; garrigue, open woodland and rough grassy and scrubby places. May-July. W and C Med, but absent from most of the islands except Sicily; rare in the E Med.

1672 *Orobanche gracilis [O. cruenta]* **SLENDER BROOMRAPE**. *Slender*, short to medium, glandular-hairy perennial, yellowish or reddish. Scale-leaves oval to lanceolate;

bracts triangular, pointed, shorter than the flowers. Flowers yellowish with a red-veined lip, *shiny dark red* inside, 15-25mm long, fragrant, borne in a slender spike that is lax below; stigma yellow. Parasitic primarily on legumes, occasionally on *Cistus*; grassy and rocky habitats. Apr-July.

1673 *Orobanche variegata*. Similar, but lower lip of corolla with a large central lobe, about *twice* the size of the other two (not equally lobed); flowers sometimes brownish-red outside. Parasitic on legumes, Leguminosae. Apr-July. S France, Corsica, Sardinia, Italy and Sicily.

1674 *Orobanche foetida*. Like *O. gracilis*, but flowers *foetid*, dark purplish-red, 12-23mm long, the lower lip not fringed with hairs; stigma sometimes purple. Parasitic on various legumes, Leguminosae. Iberian Peninsula and Balearic Is.

1675 *Orobanche crenata*. Short to medium, sparsely hairy, yellowish perennial; stem slightly swollen at the base. Leaves linear-lanceolate, dense below; bracts linear to lanceolate, long-pointed. Flowers *white*, the lip often with violet veins, 20-30mm long, fragrant, borne in a rather dense spike; corolla straight, the lower lip not fringed with hairs; stigma white, yellow or pinkish. A common parasite of leguminous crops, especially beans and peas; often present in large numbers. Mar-July. T.

MYOPORUM FAMILY Myoporaceae

A small family of trees and shrubs from Australia and eastern Asia, with 5-parted flowers; fruit a drupe.

1676 *Myoporum laetum* **NGAIO**. An evergreen shrub or small tree to 15m, though often less, with sticky shoot-tips. Leaves alternate, lanceolate to oval, slightly toothed towards the tip, rather fleshy, hairless but *dotted* with oil glands. Flowers borne in lateral clusters of 2-6, white with purple dots, 8-12mm; stamens usually 4. Fruit reddish-purple and juicy when ripe, 5-7mm. Roadsides; generally planted for shelter or hedging. Apr-July. (New Zealand).

GLOBULARIA FAMILY Globulariaceae

Perennial herbs with alternate, toothed or untoothed leaves. Flowers irregular (zygomorphic), 5-parted, 2-lipped, borne in dense rounded heads, surrounded by a ruff of bracts; stamens 4. Fruit dry, surrounded by a persistent calyx.

1677 *Globularia alypum* **SHRUBBY GLOBULARIA**. An evergreen, much-branched shrub to 1m, though often less; young stems and leaves producing limy secretions. Leaves alternate, leathery, spine-tipped, sometimes 3-toothed at the apex, short-stalked. Flowers lilac-blue, borne in *globose* heads, 10-25mm diam., mostly terminal, fragrant; corolla with a single 3-lobed lip; bracts oval, overlapping and forming a ruff below the flower-heads. Dry rocky and bushy habitats, maquis, occasionally on cliffs. Nov-May. T – not Cyprus.

1678 *Globularia cambessedesii* **MAJORCAN GLOBULARIA**. Short evergreen perennial. Leaves oval, broadest above the middle, usually *3-toothed* at the apex, short-stalked; margin flat, usually toothed. Flowers blue, in terminal heads 30-35mm diam. Rocky habitats. Majorca – endemic.

PASSION FLOWER FAMILY Passifloracaeae

A large family of exotic climbers mostly from Central and South America, but a few from the Old World tropics and subtropics. The complex blooms have a tubular calyx with 5 sepals and 5 petals, within which there is a corona of thread-like filaments; 5 conspicuous stamens are carried on a column that supports the ovary and three stigmas. The fruits of some species are edible – passion fruits and granadillas.

1679 *Passiflora caerulea* **COMMON PASSION FLOWER.** Vigorous, more or less evergreen climber to 5m, sometimes more; stems slender, climbing by means of *coiled tendrils*. Leaves alternate, palmate, with 5-7 blunt, oblong lobes, untoothed, deep green, but bluish-green beneath. Flowers solitary, 7-10mm, opening during the daytime, with greenish-white sepals and petals, a corona of numerous threads banded with purple, white and blue. The egg-shaped fruits are tough-skinned, 4-8cm long, orange when ripe. Widely cultivated in parks and gardens. May-Sept. (S Brazil). A form with white flowers is sometimes seen.

1680 *Passiflora racemosa* **RED PASSION FLOWER.** Similar, but leaves 3-lobed and flowers *vivid scarlet*, borne in pendulous racemes. Occasionally grown in the mildest parts of the Med, although not reliably hardy even there. (Brazil). A hybrid between these two species, *P. caerulea-racemosa* (1681), has greenish flowers flushed with deep violet, with a violet-purple corona.

BIGNONIA FAMILY Bignoniaceae

A large family of tropical and subtropical trees and climbers with opposite leaves and large, tubular, often 2-lipped, flowers with 4 stamens (in 2 pairs). Fruit a pod-like capsule, splitting lengthwise into 2 equal halves and containing numerous, often winged, seeds.

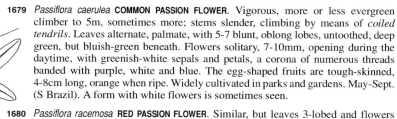

1682 *Campsis radicans* **TRUMPET VINE.** Vigorous deciduous climber, sometimes reaching 12m; stems becoming thick and woody with age, clinging by short stem roots. Leaves pinnate, with 7-11 oval, toothed leaflets, downy beneath. Flowers rich scarlet and orange, *trumpet-shaped* but 2-lipped, 60-80mm long, borne in terminal clusters. Pod spindle-shaped, to 12cm long. Widely cultivated in parks and gardens. July-Sept. (SE USA).

1683 *Campsis grandiflora.* Very similar, but with *twining* stems and deep orange and red flowers, borne in rather pendulous clusters. (China). The hybrid between these two species, *C. × tagliabuana* (1684), is the most frequently seen in many parks and gardens and often sold under the cultivar name of 'Madame Galen'.

1685 *Catalpa bignonioides* **INDIAN BEAN TREE.** Deciduous tree to 16m, with a spreading crown. Leaves large, *heart-shaped*, long-stalked, untoothed, to 30cm long, larger in young trees. Flowers white, with two rows of yellow spots within and numerous purple dots, bell-shaped, 2-lipped, 30-35mm long, borne in large terminal panicles. Pod linear, slender, dark brown, to 40cm long, pendent, persisting on the tree long after the leaves have fallen. Widely grown in parks and large gardens, occasionally as a street tree. June-Aug. (E USA). A yellow-leaved form, Aurea, is also cultivated.

1686 *Jacaranda ovalifolia* **JACARANDA.** Shrub or small tree to 8m. Leaves 2-pinnate with numerous opposite, oval to diamond-shaped, downy leaflets. Flowers *blue*, trumpet-shaped, 50-60mm long, 2-lipped, borne in large terminal panicles, often before the leaves have developed, silkily-hairy. Pod oval, brown when ripe, 60-

fruit

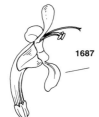

80mm long. Often grown as a pot plant, occasionally in parks and gardens, but not reliably hardy and rarely flowers as a young plant. (Brazil).

1687 *Tecomaria capensis* **CAPE HONEYSUCKLE**. Moderately vigorous *evergreen climber*, self-clinging. Leaves pinnate, with 5-9 leaflets, toothed. Flowers bright scarlet, trumpet-shaped, 45-50mm long, the corolla incurved and with 5 rounded lobes, borne in terminal racemes; stamens protruding. Grown on walls and fences in sheltered places. (Aug-Oct).

1688 *Pyrostegia venusta* **FLAME VINE**. Vigorous evergreen climber; stem woody, the young stems climbing by means of leaf-tendrils. Leaves with 2-3 oblong to oval leaflets. Flowers glowing golden-orange, tubular to club-shaped, 50-75mm long, borne in drooping panicles; corolla lobes oval, reflexed; stamens protruding. Grown in parks and gardens in mild sheltered areas. Aug-Nov. (Brazil).

1689 *Phaedranthus buccinatorius* **PHAEDRANTHUS**. Vigorous evergreen climber. Leaves with 2 elliptical to oval leaflets, terminating in a 3-lobed tendril, shiny bright green above, hairy beneath, especially when young. Flowers blood-red with yellow at the base, trumpet-shaped, 45-55mm long, drooping, borne in a terminal racemes. occasionally grown in parks and gardens. July-Sept. (Mexico).

ACANTHUS FAMILY Acanthaceae

Herbs with simple, opposite leaves and erect stems; bracts conspicuous and usually spiny. Flowers borne in dense spikes, sometimes branched; calyx 4-lobed, 2-lipped; corolla irregular (zygomorphic), 1-2-lipped, the lower 3-lobed; stamens usually 4, not protruding. Fruit a capsule, often explosive when ripe.

1690 *Acanthus mollis* **BEAR'S BREECH**. Stout, medium to tall perennial, to 1m, occasionally taller. Leaves large, the basal oval, pinnately-lobed almost to the midrib, soft and *not spiny*, hairless or minutely hairy, long-stalked, the upper leaves smaller and few; bracts purple-tinged, sharply spiny. Flowers white with purple veins, 35-50mm long, borne in dense spikes, the corolla with a distinct 3-lobed lip; calyx hairless. Rocky places and scrub, field boundaries, roadsides; mainly in the hills and often in shady, cool places. May-July. West and central Med, eastwards as far as Greece, including N Africa. Frequently grown in gardens and sometimes used for dried arrangements. The attractive leaf-shape was used in the motifs on the capitals of Corinthian columns in ancient Greece.

1691 *Acanthus balcanicus*. Similar, but the leaf-lobes clearly narrowed at the base and the lower lip of the calyx with a hairy margin. Woodland, scrub and stony hillsides. Balkans – not on the islands.

1692 *Acanthus spinosus* [*A. spinosissimus*] **SPINY BEAR'S BREECH**. Like *A. mollis*, but the basal leaves stiff with *spiny* lobes; spines whitish; whole plant often hairy. Meadows, roadsides, woodland margins, abandoned cultivation, sometimes forming large colonies. May-July. Italy, the Balkans, Crete and Turkey.

PLANTAIN FAMILY Plantaginaceae

Annual or perennial herbs, generally with basal rosettes of leaves, or opposite or alternate up the stem. Flowers small, borne in dense heads or spikes, 4-parted; calyx with lobes fused near the base; corolla papery, insignificant; stamens 4, prominent and protruding. Fruit a capsule, splitting transversely.

1693 *Plantago major* **GREATER PLANTAIN.** Low to short, hairy or hairless perennial, with a solitary or several leaf-rosettes. Leaves *broad* oval to elliptical, sometimes with a heart-shaped base, 5-9-veined, irregularly toothed or untoothed. Flowers greenish yellow, 3mm, in long slender spikes more or less equalling the unridged stalks, rarely much longer than the leaves; anthers pale purplish, turning yellowish-brown. Grassy and waste places, roadsides, irrigation channels. Mar-Oct. T. The common, broad-leaved plantain; a cosmopolitan weed of cultivated land and grassy places.

1694 *Plantago media* **HOARY PLANTAIN.** Similar, but leaves elliptical, 7-9-veined, *covered* with dense crisped hairs. Flower-spikes much longer than the leaves. Dry grassy habitats. European Med – absent from most of the islands.

1695 *Plantago cornuti.* Like *P. major*, but leaves always *entire* and bracts not more than half as long as the sepals. Damp, generally saline habitats. Apr-July. Spain, France, Italy and Yugoslavia.

1696 *Plantago coronopus* **BUCK'S-HORN PLANTAIN.** Low biennial or perennial, sometimes annual, with a solitary or several leaf-rosettes. Leaves linear to lanceolate, often pinnately-lobed, occasionally unlobed, not fleshy, toothed, hairless or finely hairy. Flowers yellowish-brown, 3mm, borne in long spikes on unridged *curved* stems; the stems longer than the leaves; anthers pale yellow. Coastal habitats, sandy or gravelly soils, occasionally inland on dry hillslopes or on fallow or waste ground. Feb-Oct. T.
    1696a Subsp. *commutata* is usually annual, with the scapes shorter than, or equalling, the leaves. Coastal and inland. C and E Med.
    1696b Subsp. *purpurascens* is like the type, but leaves toothed, not lobed, and spikes equalling the leaves, reddish. Majorca.

1697 *Plantago seraria.* Similar, but leaves regularly toothed, not lobed, and scapes equal to or longer than the leaves; spike 6-10cm long (not 1.5-5cm). Coastal and rocky habitats. Mar-Sept. Spain eastwards to Greece, including NW Africa.

1698 *Plantago macrorhiza.* Like *P. coronopus*, but always perennial and with a branched stock and several leaf-rosettes. Leaves *fleshy* and rigid. Scapes few and exceeding the leaves; spikes 2-7cm long. Coastal habitats. Mar-Sept. SW Spain to Corsica, Italy and Sicily – not Balearic Is.

1699 *Plantago maritima* **SEA PLANTAIN.** Low to short perennial with several or many leaf-rosettes. Leaves thick and rather fleshy, rigid, linear, untoothed, 3-5-veined. Flowers brownish, 3mm, borne in long greenish spikes, 3-7cm long, on unridged stalks, generally longer than the leaves; anthers yellow. Coastal habitats, especially salt marshes, sandy places, occasionally inland in saline areas. Mar-Oct. T.
    1699a Subsp. *crassifolia* [*Plantago crassifolia*] has slightly *toothed* leaves and spikes 2-5cm long; bracts much shorter than the calyx (not equalling). T.

1700 *Plantago subulata.* Similar, but the stock *much-branched* and leaves narrower, 1-2mm (not 2-15mm). Scapes not exceeding the leaves. Coastal habitats, occasionally inland. Mar-Sept. T – not Balearic Is. or Cyprus.

1701 *Plantago lanceolata* **RIBWORT PLANTAIN.** Very variable low to medium, hairy or hairless perennial, usually with several leaf-rosettes. Leaves linear-lanceolate to lanceolate, slightly toothed or untoothed, 3-5-veined, *strongly-ribbed*, stalked. Flowers brown, 4mm, borne in short blackish spikes, on ridged stalks greatly exceeding the leaves; anthers pale yellow. Cultivated, fallow and waste ground, rocky and grassy places, roadsides, open woodland. Mar-Oct. T. A cosmopolitan weed found in most parts of the world.

(1697)

(1699)

1702 *Plantago lagopus.* Similar, but a smaller, generally hairier plant; bracts *hairy* (not hairless). Similar habitats as well as sandy coastal flats. Feb-June. T.

1703 *Plantago bellardii.* Low hairy annual, with one or several leaf-rosettes. Leaves linear-lanceolate, untoothed or faintly toothed, 3-veined, often densely hairy. Flowers brownish, in short 1-3cm long, oblong or cylindrical, spikes, *not longer* than the leaves; bracts hairy. Dry sandy ground, waste and fallow habitats, rocky slopes, open garrigue, Feb-June. T.

1704 *Plantago cretica.* Similar, but stalks of spikes becoming thickened, woody and *recurved* in fruit so that the whole plant forms a small ball. Flowers borne in a globose cluster. Dry sandy and stony ground. Crete, S Aegean Is. and the E Med, including Cyprus. When dried the plant becomes a wind-dispersed ball that scatters its seeds as it rolls about.

1705 *Plantago arenaria [P. ramosa, P. psyllium, P. indica]* **BRANCHED PLANTAIN.** Short to medium, hairy annual; *stems* much-branched. Leaves linear to linear-lanceolate, opposite or whorled, not fleshy, generally untoothed. Flowers brownish-white, 4mm, borne in rounded or egg-shaped clusters; anthers pale yellow. Dry habitats, generally on sandy soils. Mar-Aug. T – not Balearic Is. or Cyprus.

1706 *Plantago afra.* Similar, but plants markedly glandular-hairy and sticky above; bracts all similar. Roadsides, waste and fallow land, grassy places in garrigue, hillsides. Feb-July. T.

1707 *Plantago squarrosa.* Like *P. arenaria,* but branches spreading (not erect) and with downturned hairs; lower bracts *leaf-like.* Dry, generally sandy places, sand-dunes, usually close to the sea. Feb-June. Greece, Crete and the Aegean Is. eastwards, including Cyprus.

1708 *Plantago albicans* **SILVERY PLANTAIN.** Low to short, tufted, *silver-hairy* perennial, with a woody stock; stems present. Leaves alternate, linear to linear-lanceolate, obscurely 3-veined, whitish or silvery hairy. untoothed. Flowers greenish or purplish, 3-4mm, borne in an egg-shaped or oblong spike, 1-6cm long, on long stems, generally only one from each leaf-rosette; stamens only slightly protruding. Dry habitats, sandy coastal places as well as inland. Mar-June. T, often local.

1709 *Plantago amplexicaulis.* Similar, but a greenish annual, only *sparsely hairy*, with elliptical leaves, often broadest above the middle, faintly 3-5-veined. Rocky habitats from coast to the hills, fallow and waste ground, roadsides. Feb-May. Spain and N Africa, S Italy, Aegean Is. eastwards, including Cyprus.

HONEYSUCKLE FAMILY Caprifoliaceae

Woody shrubs and climbers, occasionally herbs, with opposite leaves. Flowers 5-parted, hermaphrodite, solitary, paired, or borne in clusters or panicles; calyx usually small; corolla regular or 2-lipped, the lobes fused below into a short or long tube; stamens usually 5, fused to the corolla-tube; ovary inferior. Fruit a berry or nutlet.

1710 *Sambucus ebulus* **DWARF ELDER, DANEWORT.** Spreading, tall, hairless perennial, with creeping rhizomes, to 2m tall; stems erect. Leaves pinnate with 5-13, oblong to lanceolate, sharply toothed leaflets; stipules conspicuous, oval. Flowers white, occasionally pink outside, with purple anthers, borne in dense *flat-topped* clusters 5-16cm across. Berry globose, 6-7mm, purple-black and shiny when ripe. Scrub, roadsides, stream and ditch margins, field boundaries. June-Aug. T – generally inland.

(1709)

1711 *Viburnum tinus* **LAURUSTINUS.** An evergreen shrub to 7m, though often less; twigs more or less hairless. Leaves opposite, leathery, oval to oval-lanceolate, untoothed, dull deep green, sparsely hairy beneath, short-stalked. Flowers white, pinkish on the outside and in bud, 5-9mm, borne in dense rather flattened heads up to 9cm across. Fruit a berry, subglobose, 7-8mm, dark *blue* when ripe. Open woods, scrub, in the hills. T – except parts of the E Med, including Cyprus. Widely grown in gardens. The fruits are poisonous.

1712 *Lonicera etrusca* **ETRUSCAN HONEYSUCKLE.** Climbing, deciduous shrub to 5m, sometimes more, or scrambling over the ground; stems twining. Leaves broadly elliptical, bluish- or whitish-green, generally finely hairy beneath, mostly stalked, but those next to the flowers *fused* in pairs, to form a cup. Flowers yellow-white, generally tinged with purple, 35-45mm long, 2-lipped, very fragrant, borne in stalked clusters. Berries red when ripe, 8-10mm. Maquis, garrigue, scrub, open woodland, hedgerows, banks and roadsides. Apr-July. T – not Balearic Is. Widely cultivated in Med gardens. The common honeysuckle of the Med region.

1713 *Lonicera implexa.* Similar, but evergreen with smaller, *stemless* flower-heads. Similar habitats and flowering times. T – not Crete or Cyprus.

VALERIAN FAMILY Valerianaceae

Annual or perennial herbs with opposite leaves, sometimes whorled or all basal. Flowers borne in cymose heads, often dense, sometimes panicle-like; calyx usually inconspicuous, toothed; corolla funnel-shaped, sometimes spurred at the base, the limb generally 5-lobed; stamens 1-4. Fruit dry and indehiscent, with a persistent calyx.

Valerianella **CORN SALADS.** Regularly branched annuals with narrow leaves and tiny flowers; calyx with a toothed or funnel-shaped rim; corolla funnel-shaped, with 5 more or less equal lobes; stamens 3. A genus of very similar looking species that require careful analysis and a hand lens to examine the fine details of the flowers and fruits.

1714 *Valerianella discoidea.* Short annual, usually hairy; stem simple or branched from the base. Lower leaves oval to narrow spatula-shaped, blunt, untoothed to toothed; middle leaves more markedly toothed; upper leaves narrower, lobed towards the base. Bracts oval, with a wide membranous and hairy margin. Flowers pale mauve to bluish or white. Fruit 1.5-2mm long, with up to 12 well developed calyx-lobes; calyx-cup *hairy* within. Cultivated and fallow land, field margins, pastures, open stony places, rocky hillslopes, coastal maquis, garrigue. Feb-Apr. T.

1715 *Valerianella obtusiloba.* Similar, but calyx twice as large as the fruit, each tooth with 3 *hooked* spines. Similar habitats and flowering time. S Greece, Crete and the Aegean Is.

1716 *Valerianella pumila [V. tridentata].* Like *V. discoidea,* but fruiting calyx reduced to an inconspicuous *rim*; fruit almost globose, 1.5mm. Fields, cultivated and fallow land. Mar-May. T – not Balearic Is. or Sardinia.

1717 *Valerianella coronata.* Like *V. discoidea,* but inflorescence often globose and calyx regularly and obviously *6-lobed*; calyx-cup hairless within. Rocky and stony places, dry grassy slopes, garrigue. Mar-May. T.

1718 *Valerianella vesicaria.* Distinguished from all the above species by its inflated *bladder-like* fruits, 4-5mm, contracted at the mouth and with 6 refexed lobes; flowers

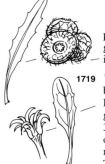

purple to lavender. Fields, margins of cultivation, rocky and stony habitats, olive groves, sandy places. Feb-May. From Sardinia, Italy and Sicily eastwards, including Crete and Cyprus.

1719 *Valerianella echinata.* Low to short, minutely hairy annual; stems generally branched. Lower leaves spatula-shaped, blunt, toothed or not; middle and upper leaves oblong to almost linear, the uppermost narrowly lobed at the base. Bracts green, with ear-like lobes at the base. Flowers bluish, mauve or lavender; calyx 3-lobed, the lobes (one long and two short) *clearly perceptible*, even in bud. Fruit of two kinds, the lower longer and narrower, the others broader, somewhat asymmetrical, 4-6mm long. Fields, rocky habitats, often shaded, gregarious. Mar-May. T.

1720 *Fedia cornucopiae* **FEDIA**. Low to short, regularly branched, hairless, slightly succulent annual. Leaves spatula-shaped to elliptical, the lower stalked and usually untoothed, the upper smaller, unstalked and toothed. Flowers purple with pink markings on the limb, 8-16mm long, borne in stalkless clusters; corolla with a slender tube and 5 lobes, somewhat 2-lipped; calyx inconspicuous; *stamens* 2, or 3 with 2 fused together. Cultivated, fallow and waste land, pastures and rocky or stony places, roadsides, olive groves, sandy habitats. Mar-June. W and C Med eastwards to Greece and Crete. A very diverse species: some authorities claim several closely allied species, including *F. caput-bovis* (1720a) from NW Africa, distinguished by its 2-horned calyx, and *F. scorpioides* (1720b) from NW Africa and perhaps Portugal with indistinct calyx-teeth.

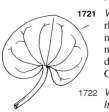

1721 *Valeriana asarifolia* **CRETAN VALERIAN**. Medium, hairless perennial, with a shortly rhizomatous stock; stems erect, unbranched. Basal leaves large, rounded to kidney-shaped, often with a heart-shaped base, toothed, long-stalked, the stem leaves narrow and irregularly lobed. Flowers pale pink or white, 6-8mm long, borne in dense *subglobose* heads; corolla slightly pouched at the base, 5-lobed; stamens 3. Calcareous rocks, often in shaded damp places. Mar-May. Crete and Karpathos.

1722 *Valeriana tripteris.* Similar, but a shorter plant, without tuberous rhizomes; stems *hairy* at the nodes. Flowers smaller, 3-5mm. Woods, scrub and rocky places. May-July. N Spain eastwards to the Balkans – absent from the islands.

Centranthus **VALERIANS**. Like *Valeriana*, but corolla distinctly spurred at the base and stamens only 1 per flower.

1723 *Centranthus ruber [Valeriana ruber]* **RED VALERIAN**. Tufted, medium to tall, greyish, somewhat *fleshy and waxy* perennial. Leaves lanceolate to oval, pointed or blunt, the uppermost slightly toothed at the base and clasping the stem. Flowers red, pink or white, funnel-shaped, 8-12mm long, borne in large panicles, fragrant, long-spurred at the base, the spur 4-7mm long. Fruit 1-seeded, with a feathery persistent calyx. Rocky places, old walls, generally coastal. Apr-Aug. T. Often on garden walls.

1723a Subsp. *sibthorpii* is distinguished by its lanceolate leaves which are untoothed and *do not* clasp the stem. S Balkans, Aegean Is. and Cyprus.

1724 *Centranthus angustifolius* **NARROW-LEAVED VALERIAN**. Similar, but leaves very narrow, *linear*; spur 2-4mm long. Rocky habitats and screes. S France, N and C Italy.

1725 *Centranthus calcitrapa.* Low to short, hairless annual; stems simple or branched. Leaves rounded to oval, pale green often flushed with purple, toothed or not, stalked, the upper leaves smaller, unstalked and often lobed. Flowers white or purple, 2mm long, borne in small terminal clusters; corolla pouched or short-spurred at the base. Fruit with a feathery persistent calyx. Rocky and stony habitats, screes, pine woodland, waste places. Mar-June. T.

1726 *Centranthus macrosiphon.* Similar, but flowers *larger*, 7-9mm long, spurred, pink with a red mouth. Rocky and waste places. S and SE Spain.

TEASEL FAMILY Dipsacaceae

Annual or perennial herbs with opposite or whorled leaves. Flowers small, but borne in dense heads surrounded by a ruff (involucre) of bracts; calyx small, generally reduced to 4-5 or 10 bristles; corolla 4-5-lobed or 2-lipped; stamens 4, occasionally 2. Fruit a dry achene, often with a persistent, papery calyx, which aids in the wind dispersal of the seeds.

Cephalaria **CEPHALARIA**. Annuals, biennials or occasionally shrubs. Flower-heads subglobose, with the marginal and central florets almost equal in size; calyx cup-like; corolla 4-lobed; receptacle-scales membranous.

1727 *Cephalaria squamiflora. Shrub* to 90cm. Leaves oval-lanceolate to elliptical, some-times broadest above the middle, untoothed, toothed or somewhat lobed, leathery, tapered to a short stalk. Flower-heads yellow or white, 9-12mm; flower-bracts oval, hairy. Rock crevices, generally limestone. May-July. Balearic Is., Corsica, Sardinia and Crete.

1728 *Cephalaria leucantha [C. boetica].* Tall perennial herb to 1m, with a woody stock; stems erect, branched. Leaves *pinnately-lobed*, with narrow segments, hairless or occasionally hairy. Flower-heads white or yellowish, 10-15mm; flower-bracts oval, hairy. Dry stony habitats, grassy pastures, roadsides. July-Sept. European Med and NW Africa – not Balearic Is. or Crete.

1729 *Cephalaria syriaca.* Similar, but leaves unlobed or only weakly lobed and flowers blue or lilac, 8-14mm. Cultivated and waste places, field margins, roadsides. Apr-June. E Med, including Cyprus; naturalised in parts of the European Med.

1730 *Cephalaria transsylvanica.* Tall, somewhat hairy annual, to 1.2m; stems erect, branched. Leaves lyre-shaped to pinnately-lobed, with elliptical to linear seg-ments, toothed or not. Flower-heads blue or yellow, 10-12mm; flower-bracts, lan-ceolate, *pointed*. Fields, fallow and waste land, roadsides, vineyards and olive groves. June-Aug. S France eastwards to Turkey – absent from most of the is-lands.

1731 *Cephalaria joppica.* Similar, but flower-heads white to pink, the corolla *smaller*, 8-9mm long (not 10-12mm) and receptacle scales 4.5-6mm long (not 7-15mm). Roadsides, waste ground. S Italy, Sicily and Turkey.

1732 *Dipsacus fullonum [D. sylvestris]* **WILD TEASEL**. Tall biennial, to 2m; stems stiffly erect, prickly on the angles. Basal leaves in a large rosette, oblong-elliptical, untoothed, prickly, withering early in the second season; stem leaves linear-lanceolate, the pairs *fused together around the stem*. Flower-heads pinkish-purple, large, oblong-cylindrical, 3-8cm long, spiny, with some long, curved bracts at the base. Waste and fallow ground, roadsides, Woods, riverbanks, gardens, often in damp places. July-Sept. T – not Crete or Cyprus or the extreme E Med. Water often collects in the cup-like bases of the fused stem leaves.

1733 *Dipsacus laciniatus* **CUT-LEAVED TEASEL**. Similar, but leaves *pinnately-lobed*. Meadows, streamsides and waste places. France eastwards to Turkey – absent from the islands.

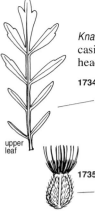

Knautia **KNAUTIA**. Scabious-like plants distinguished by a calyx with 8-10, occasionally more, teeth and a hairy receptacle. The marginal florets in the flower-head are often larger than the central ones.

1734 *Knautia purpurea* **PURPLE KNAUTIA**. Short to medium, hairy perennial, without underground stolons; stems erect, branched above. Leaves oblong-lanceolate, often rather thick, the lower often undivided and in a basal rosette, the upper 1-2-pinnate with oblong or linear-lanceolate, toothed segments. Flower-heads purple or violet, 18-25mm, solitary, somewhat domed; calyx cup-like, with 8-10 awns. Rocky and grassy habitats, hillslopes, meadows and roadsides. May-Aug. Spain, S France and Italy.

upper
leaf

1735 *Knautia arvensis* **FIELD SCABIOUS**. Similar, but plants often stoloniferous and *stems* purple-spotted; leaves thinner. Flower-heads bluish-violet to lilac, 20-40mm; calyx generally 8-awned. Meadows, open woodland, roadsides; generally inland. June-Sept. Scattered localities from the Iberian Peninsula to Yugoslavia – absent from the islands.

1736 *Knautia integrifolia*. Variable, short to tall, erect annual, hairy below but often hairless above. Leaves pinnately-lobed or the upper undivided, the lower in a basal rosette and with broader, often oval, segments; upper leaves usually linear-lanceolate, unstalked and clasping the stem. Flower-heads violet, 25-35mm, solitary, almost flat, the bracts shorter than the flowers; calyx not awned but with 12-24 teeth. Grassy and rocky places, fields, roadsides, hillslopes. June-Oct. T – not Cyprus.

1737 *Knautia degenii*. Similar, but flower-heads with *fewer* florets, only 5-15 (not 20-40) and involucre of bracts more elongated, the bracts with prominent veins. Disturbed and fallow ground, scrub. May-July. W Turkey, including the European part (Thrace).

1738 *Knautia orientalis*. Like *K. degenii*, but the flower-heads purplish-red, with only 5-10 florets, the tube of the outer 7-12mm long (not 5-6mm). Similar habitats and flowering time. SE Greece, N Aegean Is. and Turkey.

Pterocephalus **PTEROCEPHALUS**. Like *Knautia* and *Scabiosa*, but calyx with feathery bristles.

1739 *Pterocephalus plumosus [Knautia plumosa, Scabiosa papposa, S. plumosa]* **ANNUAL PTEROCEPHALUS**. Short to medium, erect, glandular-hairy annual. Leaves oblong to pinnately-lobed, toothed. Flower-heads pink, mauve or purplish, 18-30mm, the outer florets somewhat larger than the inner; calyx with 11-12 *feathery awns*. Fruit-heads semi-globose, feathery; achenes grooved. Dry habitats, hillslopes, roadsides, olive groves. Apr-July. E Med from the Balkans and Crete eastwards – probably not in Cyprus.

1740 *Pterocephalus brevis [P. involucratus, Scabiosa involucata]*. Similar, but a low to short annual with whitish florets tipped with purple; achene with a distinct cup-like corona as well as awns. Dry grassy and rocky places, garrigue. Mar-June. Crete and Karpathos eastwards, including Cyprus.

1741 *Pterocephalus multiflorus*. Distinguished from the previous two species by its shrubby, multi-stemmed, habit, unlobed, but toothed, leaves and pinkish-mauve flower-heads, 12-30mm. Dry rocky slopes, garrigue, open pine woods. Apr-Nov. Cyprus – endemic.

1742 *Pterocephalus perennis [P. parnassi]*. Low, *mat-forming* greyish, softly hairy perennial. Leaves lyre-shaped or unlobed, toothed, short-stalked. Flower-heads pink or pale purple, 25-30mm, solitary on short stalks, the outer florets larger than the inner; calyx with 13-16 awns. Rocky habitats, mainly in the mountains. June-Sept. Albania and Greece.

Scabiosa **SCABIOUS**. Annual or perennial herbs with simple or pinnate leaves, the lower often in a basal rosette. Florets borne in flattish or domed, long-stalked flower-heads, the outer often larger than the inner; calyx with 5 awns; corolla with 5 unequal lobes.

1743 *Scabiosa cretica*. Short, tufted perennial, woody at the base; stems spreading, *white-downy*. Leaves lanceolate to oval, silvery-hairy, untoothed, short-stalked. Flower-heads lilac, 35-50mm, the outer florets about twice the size of the inner; involucral bracts hairy like the leaves. Rocky habitats, slopes and cliffs. May-June. Balearic Is., Italy and Sicily.

1744 *Scabiosa albocincta*. Similar, but leaves broad-elliptical, with straight (not curved and straight) hairs. Similar habitats and flowering time. W Crete – endemic.

1745 *Scabiosa minoana*. Like *S. albocincta*, but leaves not more than 3 times longer than broad. E Crete – endemic.

1746 *Scabiosa variifolia*. Like *S. cretica*, but leaves clearly broadest above the middle, silvery-hairy when young, but *becoming* hairless; stem leaves pinnately-lobed. Rocky habitats. May-July. Crete, Karpathos and Rhodes.

1747 *Scabiosa crenata*. Variable, low to short tufted or cushion-forming perennial, woody at the base, hairy or hairless. Leaves oblong to oval, the lower toothed the upper 1-2-pinnately-lobed. Flower-heads pinkish-lilac, 20-40mm, generally solitary, the outer florets longer than the inner. Rocky habitats. June-Aug. Italy, Sicily and the Balkans – not Crete.

1748 *Scabiosa sicula*. Low to short, erect or sprawling, hairy annual. Leaves spatula-shaped to oblong, the lower toothed or not, the upper pinnately-lobed, with rather narrow segments. Flower-heads mauve or reddish, 10-15mm, becoming globose or egg-shaped in fruit, the outer florets slightly larger than the inner; involucral bracts *much longer* than the florets. Dry stony habitats, field margins, roadsides, olive groves. Mar-June. Spain, Sicily, N Africa and the E Med from Yugoslavia eastwards, including Cyprus.

1749 *Scabiosa atropurpurea* [*S. maritima*] **MOURNFUL WIDOW**. Short to medium, hairy annual or biennial; stems erect, branched above. Leaves oblong to spatula-shaped, the lower untoothed and long-stalked, the upper pinnately-lobed. Flower-heads lilac to dark purple, 20-30mm, becoming oblong in fruit, the outer florets about twice the size of the inner; involucral bracts *not longer* than the florets. Dry habitats, fallow and waste ground, sandy coastal places. June-Oct. T. Grown in gardens where white, pink, lavender and purple variants are found.

1750 *Scabiosa prolifera* **CARMEL DAISY**. Rather robust short to medium, hairy annual; stems erect, branched above, often purplish. Leaves oval to spatula-shaped, thin and pale green, the lower generally withered by flowering time, the upper smaller and narrower. Flower-heads pale yellow or whitish, 30-40mm, often unstalked, the outer florets much larger than the inner. Fruit-heads globose, 15mm, rusty-brown and papery when ripe. Waste and fallow ground, cultivated fields, roadsides. Feb-May. SE Turkey and the extreme E Med, including Cyprus.

1751 *Scabiosa brachiata* [*Knautia palaestina, Pterocephalus palaestinus, Tremastelma palaestinum*] **TREMASTELMA**. A low to short, erect, hairy annual; stems usually branched above, regularly forked. Leaves oval, pinnately-lobed or the lowermost unlobed, short-stalked. Flower-heads violet or pale mauve, 15-25mm, borne on long slender stalks, the outer florets slightly longer than the inner; involucral bracts about the

same length as the florets. Fruit-head globose, papery and brown when ripe; achenes with *ten* awns (not 5 as in all the other species). Rocky places, garrigue, hillslopes. Apr-June. Balkans, Crete, Aegean Is. and the E Med, including Cyprus.

1752 *Pycnocomon rutifolium [Scabiosa rutifolia]* **PYCNOCOMON**. A rather robust, tall, hairy or hairless perennial to 1.75m; stems erect, usually branched. Leaves rather fleshy, lobed to 1-2-pinnate, the lowermost sometimes unlobed, the uppermost small and bract-like. Flower-heads pink, yellowish or white, 5-20mm, globose, the outer florets slightly larger than the inner; involucral bracts *fused* together in the lower half to form a cup around the florets. Outer achenes without awns, the inner with 5. Coastal sands. May-July. Iberian Peninsula and NW Africa eastwards to Italy and Sicily – not Balearic Is.

BELLFLOWER FAMILY Campanulaceae

Annual or perennial herbs, usually with white latex when cut. Leaves generally alternate. Flowers often large and showy, borne in heads, racemes or panicles, occasionally solitary; calyx with 5 teeth; corolla frequently bell- or saucer-shaped, shallowly to deeply lobed, with a short or long tube; stamens 5, fused or free; style solitary. Fruit a capsule, dehiscing by slits or pores.

Campanula **BELLFLOWERS**. Flowers generally large and showy with a bell-shaped corolla; stamens free; fruit capsule dehiscing by lateral pores.

1753 *Campanula sparsa*. Thin-stemmed, short to medium, hairy annual; stems erect, branched above. Leaves oblong-lanceolate, the upper linear and more pointed; all bluntly toothed and unstalked. Flowers violet-blue, bell-shaped with deep spreading lobes, 18-23mm long; calyx-teeth spreading, very slender, 1-veined, about as long as the corolla. Capsule top-shaped, with sub-apical pores when ripe. Woods, thickets and grassy places. Apr-July. Balkans and Turkey – absent from the islands.

    1753a Subsp. *frivaldskyi* has more or less erect calyx-teeth and flowers about 30mm long. Mainland Balkans.

1754 *Campanula phrygia*. Similar, but a small plant not more than 20cm tall; calyx-teeth lanceolate, *3-veined*, and flowers only 6-7mm long; capsule grooved. Mainland Balkans.

1755 *Campanula ramosissima*. Like *C. sparsa*, but calyx-teeth broader and *3-veined*; corolla broadly bell-shaped, with the calyx teeth showing between the lobes. Capsule *bristly* along the distinct grooves. Grassy, rocky and stony habitats, olive groves, mainly in the hills and mountains. Apr-May. Balkans and Italy, Palestine – absent from the islands.

1756 *Campanula spatulata* subsp. *spruneriana*. Like *C. sparsa*, but perennial, often taller, to 50cm. Flowers blue, larger, the corolla more funnel-shaped; calyx-teeth *with* 2-4 glandular teeth. Scrub and open woodland, especially in the lowlands. Apr-June. Balkans, including some of the islands.

1757 *Campanula patula* **SPREADING BELLFLOWER**. Medium, hairy or hairless, rather rough biennial or perennial; stems erect or ascending, rather slender. Leaves slightly hairy, the basal ones oval, broadest above the middle, toothed; upper leaves few, linear-lanceolate, unstaked. Flowers violet to pale blue, rarely white, 20-25mm long, *erect* wide bells, a few to many in a lax, long-branched inflorescence; buds pendent. Capsules erect, with 10, prominent veins. Grassy habitats, open woodland, scrub, hedgerows, banks and waste places. June-Sept. Spain eastwards to Yugoslavia – not Balearic Is., Corsica or Sicily.

1758 *Campanula persicifolia* **PEACH-LEAVED BELLFLOWER**. A medium to tall, hairless perennial; stems erect, *unbranched*. Basal leaves lanceolate to oval, blunt-toothed, stalked; upper leaves linear-lanceolate, toothed. Flowers blue or white, 30-40mm long, horizontal to ascending, broad bell-shaped, not nodding, borne in a lax raceme; calyx-teeth half the length of the corolla. Meadows and open woods, cultivated land, roadsides, waste places. June-Aug. Spain eastwards to Turkey – absent from the islands except Sardinia.

1758a Subsp. *sessiliflora* has almost stalkless flowers and a bristly ovary. Balkan Peninsula. The species is widely grown in gardens.

1759 *Campanula rapunculus* **RAMPION BELLFLOWER**. Similar, but the inflorescence branched and the flowers *smaller*, 10-20mm, pale blue or white and more funnel-shaped. Similar habitats and flowering time. Spain eastwards to Turkey – absent from the islands except for Corsica.

1760 *Campanula trachelium* **NETTLE-LEAVED BELLFLOWER**. Medium to tall, hairy perennial, to 1m; stems erect, branched or unbranched, bristly, sharply angled, often reddish. Leaves rough, paler beneath, broad-lanceolate, long-pointed, irregularly toothed, the lower stalked and often slightly heart-shaped at the base, the upper similar but unstalked. Flowers violet-blue or pale blue, 30-50mm long, ascending to horizontal bells, borne in leafy racemes, *uppermost* flowers opening first; calyx about half their length of the corolla. Scrub, woodland margins, hedgerows. Spain eastwards to Turkey – absent from most of the islands.

1760a Subsp. *athoa* has smaller flowers, 15-20mm long, almost stalkless. Balkan Peninsula.

1761 *Campanula rapunculoides* **CREEPING BELLFLOWER**. Similar, but less stout and with long spike-like racemes, generally one-sided, the flowers bluish-violet, 20-30mm long, the lowermost opening first. Woodlands margins, meadows and rocky places, cultivated ground. June-Sept. Spain eastwards to Yugoslavia – absent from the islands, but sometimes grown in gardens.

1762 *Campanula peregrina*. Somewhat like *C. rapunculoides*, but a more bristly perennial with stem leaves narrower, *broadest* above the middle; corolla broadly funnel-shaped, hairless (not slightly hairy along the edge). Damp habitats in pine forest and along the margins of streams. July-Oct. E Med including Cyprus and Rhodes.

1763 *Campanula versicolor*. Medium, hairless perennial; stem stout, ascending to erect, branching into a broad panicle above. Leaves leathery, the basal oval, often with a heart-shaped base, stalked, the upper unstalked and narrowed at the base. Flowers pale lilac or pale blue, with a deeper violet centre inside, 15-25mm long, but 25-30mm across, *salver-shaped*, borne in clusters along the spike-like branches; corolla with rather pointed lobes. Rocky places, especially cliffs. July-Oct. SE Italy and the Balkan Peninsula.

1764 *Campanula pyramidalis*. Rather like the previous species, but a much taller plant to 1.5m, the leaves with *gland-tipped* teeth. Flowers borne in a broad pyramidal inflorescence, pale lilac-blue. Similar habitats and flowering time. N Italy, S Yugoslavia and Albania.

1765 *Campanula rupestris*. Softly hairy, greyish biennial forming a leaf-*rosette* in the first year, with radiating flowering stems in the second. Leaves lyre-shaped with a large end-lobe, the basal leaves stalked, the stem leaves oval, unstalked and somewhat toothed. Flowers blue or lilac-blue, narrow bell-shaped, 13-15mm long, finely hairy on the outside; calyx shorter than the corolla, with short broad

teeth; stigmas 3. Limestone rock crevices. Apr-July. SC Greece (Levadhia region).

A complex of similar species occur, mostly in Greece: the following 6 are very similar and difficult to tell apart, although their distribution helps.

1766 *Campanula andrewsii.* Similar, but stems with long branches and flowers more tubular, violet, 14-23mm long; *stigmas* 5 (not 3). Capsule 5-parted. S Greece (E Peloponnese).

1767 *Campanula topaliana.* Like *C. rupestris*, but basal leaves *heart-shaped* and flowers 8-15mm long. Stigmas 5. S Greece (Delphi, S of Delphi).

1768 *Campanula celsii.* Like *C. rupestris*, but basal leaves irregularly lobed and flowers *larger*, 18-30mm long; stigmas 5. SE Greece (from Mt Parnes to Euboia).

1769 *Campanula lyrata.* Like *C. rupestris*, but a *rough-hairy* plant; leaf-stalks with small pointed lobes; flowers tubular, 12-25mm long blue; stigmas 5. Dry hillsides. Turkey (European and Asian).

1770 *Campanula hagielia [C. sporadum].* Like *C. rupestris*, but basal leaves oval to heart-shaped, often with a small pair of leaflets below, occasionally lyre-shaped. Flowers large, tubular-bell-shaped, 20-30mm long; stigmas 5. Rock crevices. Turkey. (W Anatolia and adjacent Aegean Is.).

(1768)

1771 *Campanula tubulosa.* Like *C. lyrata*, but the basal leaf-stalks without lobes and the flowers lilac-blue. Damp rock crevices. W Crete – endemic.

1772 *Campanula lingulata.* Bristly, short biennial; stems solitary or many, unbranched. Basal leaves oblong-spatula-shaped, toothed, narrowed at the base; upper leaves oblong to lanceolate, unstalked. Flowers violet-blue, 20-25mm long, tubular-funnel-shaped, stalkless, borne in terminal *heads*, occasionally with a few lateral clusters below. Scrub, grassy places and banks. June-Aug. Italy, the Balkans and Turkey – absent from the islands.

1773 *Campanula dichotoma.* Short, bristly annual, not more than 15cm tall; stem erect, regularly branched. Leaves oblong to oval, slightly toothed or untoothed, un-stalked, the upper half-clasping the stem, all softly hairy. Flowers lilac-blue, tubular-bells, 20-30mm long, *solitary* in the leaf-axils on short stalks, the whole forming a wide pyramidal inflorescence; calyx half the length of the corolla, with small alternating lobes. Stony and sandy places in the lowlands and lower mountains. May-July. Spain, Balearic Is., Italy and Sicily.

1774 *Campanula erinus.* Low, rather delicate, bristly annual; stems regularly branched, slightly angular. Leaves alternate or opposite, oval, usually broadest above the middle, toothed, sometimes slightly lobed, unstalked. Flowers pale blue, 3-5mm long, *small* and rather inconspicuous, unstalked; calyx without appendages, the teeth erect, scarcely shorter than the corolla. Capsule pendent. Dry habitats, cliffs, banks, rocky hillslopes, old walls. Mar-June. T.

1775 *Campanula drabifolia.* Similar, but flowers short-stalked, larger, 7-16mm long, at least *twice* as long as the calyx. Ovary bristly. Similar habitats. Apr-June. S Greece, Aegean Is., SW Turkey and Cyprus. A very variable species – several subspecies are sometimes recognised.

1776 *Campanula delicatula.* Like *C. erinus*, but a weak and rather spreading plant with stalked flowers, pale lavender-blue, 5-6mm long, the corolla bristly, clearly longer than the calyx. Limestone rocks and cliffs. Apr-June. Crete, NE Greece, Turkey and Cyprus.

1777 *Symphyandra cretica* **SYMPHYANDRA**. Short to medium, hairless perennial. Leaves large, *heart-shaped*, the lower stalked, the upper unstalked, toothed. Flowers blue or occasionally white, 28-30mm long, bell-shaped, borne in one-sided racemes; calyx lobes usually serrated, half the length of the corolla. Capsule with 3 valves close to the base. Rocky habitats and walls. May-July. Greece (Samothrace, Sporades) and Crete. Often confused with *Campanula*, but the anthers are fused together, forming a tube around the style.

Legousia **VENUS'S LOOKING GLASSES.** Annual herbs with flowers in panicles or racemes, occasionally spike-like; calyx 5-lobed, from the top of an elongated ovary; corolla flattish, 5-lobed, the lobes fused together near the base; anthers 5; stigmas 3. Fruit cylindrical, many times longer than broad, with 3 upward curving valves when ripe.

1778 *Legousia speculum-veneris [Specularia speculum-veneris]* **LARGE VENUS'S LOOKING GLASS.** Short to medium, often rather hairy annual; stems generally much-branched, ascending to erect. Leaves alternate, oblong, scarcely wavy, unstalked or occasionally the lowermost short-stalked. Flowers violet or violet-purple, occasionally blue or white, 15-23mm, opening widely to form a blunt 5-pointed star, borne in large, generally lax, panicles; calyx teeth almost as long as the petals; filaments hairless. Capsule 10-15mm. long. Cultivated, fallow and waste land, roadsides, occasionally on open stony hillsides or in garrigue. Mar-June. T. Declining in many places with modern farming practices.

1779 *Legousia hybrida [Specularia hybrida]* **VENUS'S LOOKING GLASS.** Similar, but with markedly *wavy* leaves and flowers few, borne in a terminal cluster, small, 8-15mm, reddish-purple to violet; the petals about half as long as the calyx teeth. Capsule 15-30mm long. Cultivated and fallow fields, waste places. Mar-June. T. A scarce plant in the British Is.les.

1780 *Legousia pentagonica [Campanula pentagonica]*. Similar to *L. speculum-veneris*, but flowers *larger*, 20-30mm, flowers borne in a less dense racemose or paniculate inflorescence; filaments hairy at the base. Capsule 20-30mm long, not narrowed at the apex. Similar habitats and flowering times. Greece and Crete eastwards – not Cyprus.

1781 *Legousia falcata [Specularia falcata]* **SPICATE VENUS'S LOOKING GLASS.** Low to short, erect to spreading annual; stems hairless or somewhat bristly, often tinged with purple. Leaves oval, often broadest above the middle, slightly wavy, the lowermost usually short-stalked. Flowers violet to purple or lavender, 5-8mm, solitary or paired, but forming a *spike-like* inflorescence; calyx teeth linear, spreading, often curved to one side, longer than the petals; corolla occasionally absent (in cleistogamous flowers). Capsule 15-20mm long, narrowed at the top. Garrigue, stony pastures and hillslopes, occasionally by road or stream sides. Apr-June. T.

1782 *Legousia castellana*. Similar, but calyx and corolla *equal* and calyx teeth not curved. Similar habitats and flowering times. Iberian Peninsula, NW Africa, S France and Corsica.

Trachelium **THROATWORTS.** Perennials with alternate leaves. Flowers borne in dense clusters; corolla with a slender tube and 5 small spreading lobes; stigmas 2-3. Capsule opening by basal pores.

1783 *Trachelium caeruleum* **THROATWORT.** Medium to tall, almost hairless perennial, woody at the base. Leaves oval to lanceolate, toothed, often hairy on the margin, mostly stalked. Flowers blue, rarely white, 5-7mm, numerous borne in almost flat-topped clusters; corolla slender and long-tubed (4-6mm), with 5 tiny spreading lobes much shorter than the tube. Capsule pear-shaped. Damp and shady

habitats, old walls and rocks. May-Sept. Iberian Peninsula, Italy and Sicily. This and the other species are very attractive to butterflies.

1784 *Trachelium jacquinii [T. rumeliana, Diosphaera jacquinii].* Similar to the previous species but a short perennial with a stout stock, hairy or hairless; only the lower leaves stalked. Flowers bluish-lilac, the corolla tube 4-5mm long, *equalling* the lobes. Capsule shaped like a top. Rocky habitats and cliffs, often in partial shade. June-Oct. Greece, Sporades, Crete.

1785 *Trachelium asperuloides.* Cushion-forming perennial with stems up to 5cm long. Leaves oval to rounded, small, shiny deep green, stalkless. Flowers pink, solitary or up to 5 in the axils of the upper leaves; corolla tube 5-6mm long, the lobes about half as long as the tube. Rock crevices. S Greece – endemic.

1786 *Petromarula pinnata* PETROMARULA. Robust, medium to tall perennial, minutely hairy above. Leaves mostly in a large basal rosette, pinnate to pinnately-lobed, the lower long-stalked; leaflets oval to oblong, coarsely toothed. Flowers pale blue, 9-10mm, borne in large, rather narrow panicles; corolla with 5, spreading to recurved, linear lobes. Capsule opening by 3 pores in the middle. Rock crevices – cliffs and old walls. Apr-May. Crete – endemic.

1787 *Wahlenbergia nutabunda* WAHLENBERGIA. Short to medium, erect annual, much-branched. Leaves oblong, sometimes broadest above the middle, toothed or not, the base narrowed into a winged stalk. Flowers pale blue, pink or white, funnel-shaped, 4-5mm long, borne in large spreading panicles; corolla-lobes longer than the tube. Capsule erect, with 3-5 apical slits when ripe. Dry habitats, always local. Mar-June. Spain, Sardinia, S Italy and Sicily.

1788 *Jasione corymbosa* CORYMBOSE SHEEP'S BIT. Rather stout, short, somewhat bristly annual; stems erect with short stiff branches in the upper part, leafy almost to the top. Leaves linear-lanceolate, wavy and with a somewhat thickened margin; bracts as long as, or longer than, the flowers. Flowers blue, borne in *dense heads*; corolla 5-lobed, almost to the base, the lobes linear. Sandy and stony habitats at low altitudes. May-July. Spain and S Portugal.

fruit

1789 *Jasiona lusitanica* PORTUGUESE SHEEP'S BIT. Similar, but a short to medium perennial, hairy or hairless, with *numerous* leafy stems, the leaves often broadest above the middle; outer bracts shorter than the flowers. Coastal sands. NW Portugal – endemic.

1790 *Laurentia gasparrinii [L. michelii]* LAURENTIA. A slender, low to short, hairless or finely hairy annual or perennial. Leaves oblong to spatula-shaped, slightly toothed to untoothed (in basal rosettes in perennial plants). Flowers blue, lilac or white, 4-11mm long, *2-lipped* and lobelia-like, solitary, long-stalked; corolla with upper lip 2-lobed and lower 3-lobed; stigmas 2. Capsule opening by 2 apical pores. Damp habitats; marshes, woods and springs. May-July. T – not Cyprus. The annual form is commoner in the W Med, the perennial in the east.

fruit

DAISY FAMILY Compositae

Herbs or shrubs with alternate, opposite or rosetted leaves. Flower-heads with an involucre of closely overlapping bracts (flower-bracts) around the base, some-times spine-tipped. Flowers (florets) small, borne in congested heads (capitula), often with receptacle scales at the base of each floret. Florets variable, all the same in the flowerhead or those in the centre (the disc) different from the outer (rays), giving the typical daisy flowerhead; three main types occur – tubular and 4-5-toothed, tubular and 2-lipped, or ligulate with a one-sided, strap-like appendage (ray). Stamens 5, fused together around the style. Ovary inferior. Fruit an achene, often with a feathery appendage (pappus).

Bellis **DAISIES**. Small annuals or perennials, generally with basal leaf-rosettes. Flower-heads solitary, with ray florets and a central disc – the typical daisy head. Achenes without a pappus.

1791 *Bellis annua* **ANNUAL DAISY**. Low, hairless or somewhat bristly annual with short, ascending to erect *stems*. Leaves oval to spatula-shaped, toothed or not, the lowermost stalked. Flower-heads white with a yellow disc, 5-15mm, the rays often tinged with purple or red beneath. Grassy and damp habitats, moist sands and depressions subject to winter flooding. Feb-June. T.

1792 *Bellis perennis* **DAISY**. Similar, but stemless, the leaves in a dense basal rosette and the flower-heads larger, 15-30mm. Grassy habitats and cultivated areas. Flowering throughout the year in favoured areas. T. The common lawn daisy throughout Europe and much of the Med region.

1793 *Bellis sylvestris* **SOUTHERN DAISY**. Low to short perennial with fleshy roots, usually stemless. Leaves in a basal rosette, oblong, often broadest above the middle, dark green, *3-veined*, narrowed to the base. Flower-heads white with a yellow disc, the rays often tinged with reddish-purple, especially beneath, 20-40mm, borne on long slender stalks. Woods, thickets, grassy places, roadsides, garrigue, hillsides. Sept-May. T.

1794 *Bellis rotundifolia [B. cordifolia]*. Similar, but leaves kidney-shaped to heart-shaped, long-stalked. Damp or shaded habitats. SW Spain and NW Africa.

Bellium. Like *Bellis*, but flowerheads with a single row of involucral bracts (not two).

1795 *Bellium bellidioides*. Low to short, hairy to almost hairless perennial, with thread-like spreading *stolons*. Leaves in a basal rosette, elliptical, untoothed, narrowed into a long stalk. Flower-heads white or pinkish, with a yellow disc, 9-15mm, solitary on long slender stalks, the rays often reddish beneath; involucral bracts hairy. Stony places, often close to the sea. Mar-June. E Spain, Balearic Is. and Sardinia.

1796 *Bellium minutum*. Similar, but leaves with a shorter stalk (about equal in length to the blade) and flower-heads numerous, *smaller*, 6-7mm, with 7-10 (not 11-14) rays. Coastal rocks, very local. Sicily, Greece and Crete.

1797 *Bellium crassifolium*. Like *B. bellidioides*, but *without* stolons and generally with a short stem. Rocky habitats. Sardinia.

1798 *Erigeron acer* **BLUE FLEABANE**. Very variable, densely grey-hairy, short to medium annual or biennial; stems erect. Basal leaves narrow-elliptical to oval, toothed or not, stalked, the upper leaves lanceolate and unstalked. Flower-heads 10-15mm, with purple or lilac, rather erect rays and a yellow disc, borne in panicles, often flat-topped; rays linear, borne in 2 rows, *scarcely longer* than the disk florets; involucral bracts usually purplish. Achene with a hairy pappus. Dry grassy habitats. June-Aug. T – not Balearic Is., Sardinia, Sicily, Crete or Cyprus.

Aster **ASTERS**. Herbs, mostly perennial, with simple alternate leaves. Flower-heads solitary or in panicles or clusters, each with a single row of rays surrounding a central disc, usually blue or pink, occasionally yellow. Achenes with a hairy pappus.

chene

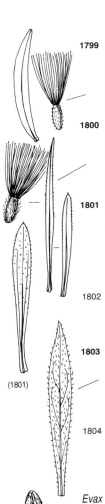

1799 *Aster tripolium [Tripolium vulgare]* **SEA ASTER**. Short to medium, hairless annual or short-lived perennial; stems often reddish, erect or ascending from a branched base. Leaves *fleshy*, linear to lanceolate, rounded in section, half-clasping the stem, the upper unstalked. Flower-heads with bright blue or purple rays surrounding a yellow disc, 8-20mm, borne in large, often flat-topped, panicles. Coastal, habitats, sometimes in saline places inland. June-Oct. T – not Cyprus.

1800 *Aster linosyris [Linosyris vulgaris]* **GOLDILOCKS ASTER**. Short to medium, hairless perennial; stems spreading to erect, slightly roughened, densely leafy. Leaves linear, pointed, unstalked, rough-edged, 1-veined, gland-dotted. Flower-heads small, 12-18mm, *bright yellow*, without rays, borne in dense flat-topped clusters. Rocky places, cliffs, open grassland, generally at low altitudes. July-Sept. European Med and Turkey – absent from most of the islands.

1801 *Aster sedifolius [A. punctatus]*. Medium to tall rather rough perennial, occasionally an annual; stems erect, rough. Leaves linear to elliptical, rough, untoothed, *gland-dotted*, unstalked, often grey-downy, the lower 3-veined. Flower-heads 12-16mm, blue to pinkish-lilac, borne in panicles, often rather flat-topped; rays usually 5-10; involucral bracts in 3-5 rows, shiny and sticky. Dry habitats, and waste places, mainly in the hills. June-Aug. Spain eastwards to Albania – absent from the islands.

1802 *Aster squamatus*. Similar, but annual or biennial with linear or linear-lanceolate leaves; rays violet-blue. Flower-heads borne in symmetrical panicles. Naturalised on saline soils, generally close to the sea. June-Sept. Scattered localities from Spain to Greece. (South America).

(1801)

1803 *Conyza canadensis [Erigeron canadensis]* **CANADIAN FLEABANE**. Short to tall, hairy annual, to 1.5m. Leaves alternate, narrow-oblong, often broadest above the middle, stalked, the lower often deciduous before flowering. Flower-heads 2-5mm, with white, rarely pinkish, borne in branched clusters; rays florets scarcely longer than the yellow disk florets, flower-bracts usually hairless. Naturalised on cultivated, waste and fallow land, old walls and dunes. June-Sept. T. (North America).

1804 *Conyza bonariensis [Erigeron bonariensis, E. crispus]*. Similar, but taller, to 2.5m, and more densely hairy; inflorescence often with long branches *overtopping* the main axis. Flower-heads larger, 7-10mm. Similar habitats and flowering times. T. (Tropical America).

Evax **EVAX**. Annuals with alternate leaves. Flower-heads usually in clusters, without ray florets, generally forming a domed cushion; involucral bracts generally numerous.

1805 *Evax pygmaea*. Tiny *grey-felted* annual, to 4cm only, often branched at the base. Leaves in a rosette, oblong, blunt, sometimes broadest above the middle, 5-15mm long. Flower-heads brownish-yellow, borne in compact clusters 5-35mm across. Dry open habitats, often in garrigue, stony and grassy places, hillslopes, pathways. Apr-May. T.

1806 *Evax astericifolia*. Similar, but stem *well developed*, 3-13cm long, rigid and leaves pointed; flower-heads numerous, in clusters 12-28mm wide. Similar habitats and flowering time. Spain and NW Africa, eastwards to Italy and Sicily – not Balearic Is.

1807 *Evax contracta*. Like *E. astericifolia*, but less robust, the flower-heads forming a dense dome-shape, 6-20mm. Dry habitats, pathways, fallow and waste land, hillsides. Mar-May. E Med including Cyprus.

1808 *Evax rotundata.* Like *E. pygmaea*, but plants with *radiating* lateral branches and broad, almost round, rosette leaves. Flower-head clusters only 2-8mm across. Coastal sands. Corsica and Sardinia.

1809 *Evax lusitanica.* Like *E. pygmaea*, but rosette leaves *broader*, 7-8mm wide (not 2-5mm) and flower-head clusters 8-16mm across. Dry habitats, mainly near the coast. S Spain and SE Portugal.

1810 *Evax eriosphaera.* Dwarf, white-woolly annual forming *mats* up to 12cm across by numerous spreading branches, each terminating in a leaf-rosette. Leaves narrow spatula-shaped, up to 3mm wide, pointed to blunt. Flower-heads densely white-woolly, 5-15mm across. Bare, often trampled ground, roadsides, coastal and inland. Mar-June. Aegean Is., Turkey, Cyprus and the Lebanon.

Filago **CUDWEEDS.** Downy and woolly annuals with alternate, untoothed leaves. Flower-heads small, in lateral or terminal clusters; florets all tubular, the outer usually female, the inner hermaphrodite. Pappus usually present. A difficult group of often rather similar looking species.

1811 *Filago eriocephalus.* Short, greyish-white woolly annual; stems erect to spreading. Leaves oblong-lanceolate, 8-24mm long; bracts broadly lanceolate. Flower-heads yellowish, each 3-4mm long, but borne in dense *oblong clusters* of 30-50, not overtopped by the uppermost leaves; flower-bracts 3mm long. Garrigue, maquis, in dry places, hillslopes, vineyards, olive groves, rock crevices, cypress plantations. Apr-June. T – not Iberian Peninsula or Balearic Is.

1812 *Filago vulgaris [F. canescens, F. germanica]* **COMMON CUDWEED.** Similar, but generally more robust, to 35cm tall, and flower-heads in *globose* clusters of 20-35; flower-bracts linear-lanceolate, 4-4.5mm long, with a transparent apex. Similar habitats, and disturbed ground, dry grassy places, generally on light sandy soils. Late May-Aug. T.

1813 *Filago lutescens [F. apiculata]* **RED-TIPPED CUDWEED.** Short yellowish-green plant covered in *yellow* wool; stems erect, rather irregularly branched. Leaves oblong-lanceolate, to spatula-shaped, 15-20mm long. Flower-heads yellowish, 5mm long, borne in lax clusters of 10-25, overtopped by 1-2 narrow subtending leaves; flower-bracts yellowish 4-4.5mm long, tipped with red or purple. Dry fields, fallow and waste places, roadsides, stony or gravelly areas, generally on light sandy soils. Apr-July. Iberian Peninsula eastwards to Italy and Sicily – not Balearic Is., Corsica or Sardinia.

1814 *Filago fuscescens.* Similar, but flower-heads in *smaller* groups of 3-8; flower-bracts brownish. SE Spain and NW Africa.

1815 *Filago pyramidata* **BROAD-LEAVED CUDWEED.** Like *F. lutescens*, but a greyish-white plant, often almost prostrate, and with narrower leaves. Flower-heads in clusters of 5-20, generally overtopped by the subtending leaves; flower-bracts curved, yellow-tipped. Arable fields, fallow and waste land, disturbed habitats, roadsides, generally on light sandy soils. Mar-July. T.

1816 *Filago congesta.* Short greyish-woolly annual with prostrate or ascending stems. Leaves lanceolate to narrow spatula-shaped, 8-16mm long. Flower-heads yellowish, 5-6mm, in clusters of 3-6 usually (plant with many clusters); flower-bracts 4-5mm long, hairy only along the margin, borne in 5 *very distinct* rows, finely pointed. Sandy and rocky places, fields. Apr-July. W Med east as far as Italy and Sicily.

1817 *Filago mareotica*. Similar, but flower-heads *solitary*, forming one-sided spikes, not in heads or clusters. Sandy margins of salt lakes or depressions, close to the sea. Mar-May. SE Spain, N Africa, Cyprus (rare) and Egypt.

1818 *Filago arvensis [Gnaphalium arvensis, Logfia arvensis]*. Low to short, white-woolly annual; stems erect, with *short* lateral branches above. Leaves oblong to linear-lanceolate, 10-20mm long. Flower-heads yellowish, 2.5-6mm long, borne in small clusters of 2-7, generally overtopped by the uppermost leaves, borne in raceme-like inflorescences or panicles; flower-bracts with a transparent apex. Arable land, dry fields, garrigue, olive groves, stony and rocky places, sandy habitats. May-July. T – not Balearic Is. or Crete.

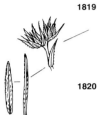

1819 *Filago minima [Logfia minima]* **SMALL CUDWEED**. Low to short, grey-silky annual with very slender stems, branched above the middle. Leaves oblong-linear to linear, 4-10mm long. Flower-heads 2.5-3.5mm long, not overtopped by the uppermost leaves, terminal or in the branch forks; flower-bracts pale, hairless in the upper part. Fields, waste and fallow land, sandy and gravelly or stony places. June-Sept. T – not Balearic Is., Crete, Cyprus or parts of the extreme E Med.

1820 *Filago gallica [Logfia gallica]* **NARROW-LEAVED CUDWEED**. Similar, but leaves linear and thread-like, *longer*, 15-25mm long, and flower-heads overtopped by the uppermost leaves; flower-bracts woolly and somewhat swollen below, with a yellowish tip. Dry stony places, gravels and thin grassland, garrigue, vineyards and olive groves. Apr-July. T.

1821 *Bombycilaena discolor [Micropus discolor, M. bombicinus]* **BOMBYCILAENA**. A whitish-woolly, low to short annual; stems erect to spreading. Leaves linear to oblong, often broadest above the middle, 5-20mm long. Flower-heads brownish, in clusters 10-16mm across, globose, not overtopped by the uppermost (subtending) leaves; flower-heads *without* a pappus. Dry stony and sandy habitats, hillsides, cultivated, fallow and waste ground, roadsides. Mar-June. T – not Portugal, Balearic Is., Corsica, Sardinia, Sicily, Crete or Yugoslavia.

1822 *Bombycilaena erecta [Micropus erectus]*. Similar, but clusters of flower-heads smaller, only 7-10mm across, *overtopped* by the subtending leaves. Dry sandy and stony habitats. T – absent from most of the islands and the extreme E Med.

1823 *Pseudognaphalium luteo-album [Gnaphalium luteo-album]* **JERSEY CUDWEED**. Short to medium, white-woolly annual; stems branched near the base, erect to spreading. Leaves alternate, linear to oblong with slightly inrolled or wavy margins, 0.8-8cm long. Flower-heads yellowish to reddish, without rays, borne in egg-shaped, leafless clusters of up to 40; flower-bracts yellowish, membranous, oval to lanceolate, *hairless*; corollas tinged with purple. Rocky or sandy habitats, often close to water. Apr-July. T.

Helichrysum **HELICHRYSUMS**. Dwarf shrubs or herbs with alternate, untoothed leaves. Flower-heads often aggregated into clusters; florets all tubular; flower-bracts thin and papery, persistent, often shiny. Pappus present.

1824 *Helichrysum stoechas*. Dwarf shrub to 50cm tall, with rather upright growth. Leaves white-felted, linear, *strongly aromatic* when crushed, untoothed, sometimes becoming almost hairless above, mostly 20-30mm long, with revolute margins. Flower-heads yellow, borne in dense clusters 15-30mm across; involucre of flower-bracts bright glossy yellow, globular to egg-shaped, the outer flower-bracts shorter, hairless or slightly hairy at the base. Garrigue, sandy and rocky habitats, including sand-dunes. Mar-July. Iberian Peninsula and NW Africa eastwards to Turkey – not Cyprus.

1825 *Helichrysum conglobatum* [*H. siculum, H. stoechas* subsp. *barrelieri, Gnaphalium barrelieri, G. conglobatum*]. Similar, but *scarcely aromatic*, with broader linear to spatula-shaped leaves and clusters of flower-heads 25-64mm across. Similar habitats. Mar-June. N Africa and S Italy and Sicily eastwards, including Cyprus. In both this and the previous species, dwarf forms, often less than 20cm tall, can be found in exposed coastal habitats.

1826 *Helichrysum rupestre*. Like *H. stoechas*, but leaves larger, 30-80mm long, not aromatic, and clusters of flower-heads 30-70mm across. Rocky habitats, cliffs and old walls. Apr-June. Spain, eastwards to Italy and Sicily – not S France or Corsica.

1827 *Helichrysum ambiguum*. Like *H. rupestre*, but lower leaves wider, 6-7mm (not 2-3mm). Limestone cliffs. Balearic Is.

1828 *Helichrysum italicum*. Very aromatic subshrub to 50cm tall, grey-felted when young. Leaves greenish, linear, with revolute margins, becoming hairless above. Flower-heads yellow, in clusters 15-80mm across; involucre of bracts *dull-yellow*, oblong to narrow bell-shaped (globose in *H. stoechas*). Garrigue, stony pastures and cliffs, dry mountain sides. June-Sept. T, including Cyprus but not much of the extreme E Med.

    1828a Subsp. *microphyllum* is a smaller plant to 30cm, the lower leaves only 5-10mm long; non-flowering shoots with lateral leaf-clusters. Coastal rocks and cliffs. Balearic Is., Corsica, Sardinia, Sicily and Crete.

1829 *Helichrysum saxatile*. Similar, but lower leaves generally 30-70mm long (not less than 30mm), narrow spatula-shaped, and the involucre more bell-shaped. Limestone rocks and cliffs. Sardinia and Sicily.

1830 *Helichrysum orientale*. Short, white-woolly perennial. Leaves flat, oblong-spatula-shaped, the basal crowded and short-stalked, the upper fewer and smaller. Flower-heads yellow, in clusters 20-80mm across; involucre of bracts semi-globose, bright shiny yellow. Cliffs at low altitudes. Apr-June. Greece, Aegean Is. and Crete.

Phagnalon **PHAGNALONS**. Dwarf shrubs with alternate leaves. Flower-heads solitary at the branch-tips; florets yellowish, all tubular; flower-bracts closely overlapping, with up to 5 rows. Pappus present.

1831 *Phagnalon rupestre* [*Phagnalon graecum*]. A small subshrub to 50cm tall, often less; stems erect to ascending, white-felted. Leaves oval to oblong, broadest above the middle, 10-40mm long, usually hairless above, but white-felted beneath, slightly toothed on the somewhat recurved (revolute) margin. Flower-heads solitary, *long-stalked*, yellowish, oblong to bell-shaped, 8-15mm; flower-bracts brownish, membranous, somewhat hairy and closely overlapping, oval to lanceolate. Garrigue, maquis, on dry rocky ground, banks, roadsides. Mar-May. T.

    1831a Subsp. *graecum* is distinguished by its more prominently toothed leaf-margins that are sometimes hairy above and narrower and more pointed flower-bracts, often tipped reddish-brown. Similar habitats and flowering time. Italy and Sicily eastwards, including Crete and Cyprus.

1832 *Phagnalon sordidum*. Like *P. rupestre*, but rarely more than 30cm tall and with linear leaves, white-felted on both surfaces, with a strongly recurved margin. Flower-heads *clustered*, short-stalked or stalkless; flower-bracts oval, brownish. Rocky habitats and walls. Spain eastwards to Italy, not Sicily.

1833 *Phagnalon saxatile* [*P. methanaeum*]. Like *P. rupestre*, but often taller and with leaves linear, often broadest above the middle, 25-60mm long, greenish, the margin

sometimes recurved; middle flower-bracts with *wavy* (not flat) margins. Rocky habitats and walls. Iberian Peninsula and NW africa eastwards to the Balkans – not Crete.

Inula **INULAS.** Annual or perennial herbs, occasionally subshrubs with simple alternate leaves, sometimes toothed. Flower-heads usually yellow, generally with ray as well as disk florets, occasionally rayless; flower-bracts several rows. Pappus present.

1834 *Inula salicina* **IRISH FLEABANE.** Medium to tall, hairy to sparsely hairy perennial; stems erect, often somewhat bristly at the base. Leaves linear-lanceolate to oval, stalked, stiff, hairless above, the upper leaves narrow heart-shaped, *half-clasping* the stem; all leaves prominently net-veined above. Flower-heads yellow, 25-45mm, with long, slender rays; flower-bracts hairy only along the margin, lanceolate to linear. Rocky and wooded places, marshes, stony shores, often in moist habitats. May-July. Iberian Peninsula eastwards to Turkey; absent from most of the islands, except for Corsica and Sardinia.

1835 *Inula hirta.* Very similar, but a lower more hairy plant, the upper leaves scarcely clasping the stem; flower-bracts all linear, *densely hairy.* Grassy habitats. June-Aug. Spain, France, Italy and Yugoslavia.

1836 *Inula oculus-christi.* Short to medium, silkily-hairy, tufted perennial; stems erect, branched above. Leaves oblong to elliptical, finely toothed or not, the upper clasping the stem with a heart-shaped base; all leaves *without* a prominent net-vein above. Flower-heads yellow, 25-30mm, with numerous linear rays; flower-bracts lanceolate to linear, silkily-hairy. Grassy habitats and scrub, woodland margins, hedgerows, meadows. May-July. Balkans and Turkey.

1837 *Inula crithmoides* **GOLDEN SAMPHIRE.** Sprawling, medium perennial or subshrub, generally with a woody base; stems branched below. Leaves *fleshy*, crowded, linear to linear-lanceolate, untoothed or with a 3-toothed apex. Flower-heads yellow with a golden disk, 20-28mm, borne in branched, rather flat-topped clusters; flower-bracts linear, erect, hairless and with membranous margins. Coastal habitats, sandy and rocky, salt marshes and the margins of salt lakes. June-Sept. T.

1838 *Inula conyza* [*I. squarrosa, Conyza squarrosa*] **PLOUGHMAN'S-SPIKENARD.** A medium to tall, hairy perennial; stems erect, purplish, to 1.2m. Leaves elliptical to lanceolate, finely toothed, the uppermost unstalked, not clasping the stem. Flower-heads small, 9-11mm, dull yellow, the outer florets *with or without* a very short and inconspicuous ray, many flower-heads borne in a flat-topped cluster; inner flower-bracts purplish. Dry generally rocky habitats, open woods, scrub, grassy places. July-Sept. T – absent from Crete and most of N Africa.

1839 *Inula candida* [*I. limonifolia*]. Similar, but a short *white-downy* perennial with un-toothed leaves with inconspicuous veins. Flower-heads somewhat smaller. Rocky habitats, especially cliffs. July-Aug. C and S Greece and Crete.

1840 *Inula verbascifolia* [*I. candida* susbp. *verbascifolia*]. Like *I. candida*, but taller, to 50cm, with *toothed* leaves which have prominent veins beneath. Rocky habitats. S Italy, Balkans and Crete.

1841 *Dittrichia graveolens* [*Inula graveolens*] **STINK ASTER.** A medium, densely glandular, slender annual, smelling of *camphor*; stems erect. Leaves lanceolate to oblong, untoothed or slightly toothed. Flower-heads yellow, small, 5-12mm, borne in spike-like panicles; rays 3-4mm long. Roadsides, waste and fallow ground, stony hillslopes, damp habitats. Aug-Nov. T – not Cyprus.

1842 *Dittrichia viscosa [Inula viscosa]*. Similar, but a stouter perennial, the upper leaves half-clasping the stem and flower-heads 10-20mm, with *longer* rays, 6-8mm long, clearly longer than the flower-bracts. Similar habitats and flowering times. July-Nov. T – not Cyprus.

1843 *Pulicaria dysenterica* **COMMON FLEABANE**. Medium, *softly-hairy*, stoloniferous perennial; stems erect, branched above. Basal leaves oblong, narrowed at the base, withered by flowering time; stem leaves heart- or arrow-shaped, clasping the stem with unstalked bases; all leaves green above, softly grey-downy beneath, toothed or untoothed. Flower-heads daisy-like, golden yellow, 15-30mm, borne in lax-topped clusters; rays numerous, linear; flower-bracts linear, downy. Damp habitats, marshes, stream margins, irrigation ditches, roadsides. Aug-Nov. T. Very like *Inula* but differing in the pappus which has an outer row of closely fused scales.

1844 *Pulicaria sicula*. Similar, but an annual, not more than 50cm tall, the leaves with strongly recurved margins; flower-heads with short rays; rays not exceeding the flower-bracts. Seasonally damp habitats, brackish marshes. July-Oct. T – absent from parts of N Africa.

1845 *Pulicaria odora*. Like *P. dysenterica*, but plant *without* stolons but with basal leaves at flowering time. T – not Cyprus.

1846 *Pulicaria arabica*. Like *P. sicula*, but a low to short annual with flattish leaves and terminal or lateral flower-heads (not only terminal). Fallow and waste ground, pastures, hollows subjected to winter flooding. May-July. E Med, including Cyprus.

1847 *Pallenis spinosa*. Short to medium, softly-hairy annual or biennial; stems woody at the base, branched, the branches generally overtopping the main stem. Leaves lanceolate to elliptical, blunt, the basal stalked, but the stem leaves unstalked and half-clasping the stem. Flower-heads daisy-like, deep yellow with a yellow disk, 18-20mm, surrounded by spreading *spine-tipped* flower-bracts, twice as long as the rays; inner flower-bracts tough and papery, not spine-tipped. Rocky places, garrigue, waste and fallow ground, fields, olive groves, roadsides. Mar-July. T – not Cyprus.

1848 *Asteriscus maritimus [Odontospermum maritimus]* **YELLOW SEA ASTER**. Short, hairy perennial or subshrub, with spreading, often *mat-forming* stems, woody towards the base, much-branched. Leaves oblong to spatula-shaped, grooved and short-stalked, untoothed. Flower-heads deep yellow, daisy-like, 30-40mm, terminal, surrounded by leafy flower-bracts, not spine-tipped; rays numerous, linear, 3-toothed at apex. Coastal rocks, occasionally inland. Mar-June. European Med and N Africa.

1849 *Asteriscus aquaticus [A. citriodorus, Odontospermum aquaticum]*. Similar, but a short to medium *aromatic* annual with erect stems; flower-heads 13-18mm, the outer flower-bracts much longer than the rays. Damp and sandy places, garrigue, cultivated and waste ground, roadsides, coastal and inland. Apr-June. T.

1850 *Bidens aurea* **BIDENS**. An almost hairless, medium to tall, slender perennial, to 1.8m, though often less. Leaves linear-lanceolate to lanceolate, or cut into into narrow pointed lobes, toothed. Flower-heads erect, yellow, 30-60mm, daisy-like, with only 5-6 broad, *purple-lined* rays; flower-bracts all similar, much shorter than the rays. Naturalised in damp places. July-Sept. Iberian Peninsula, S France, Italy. (Central America).

1851 *Bidens bipinnata*. Similar, but not more than 1m tall, often far less, the leaves *pinnate*, lobed almost to the middle, with the lobes lanceolate to diamond-shaped.

chene

lower
bract

lower
bract

Flower-heads smaller, 5-10mm. Naturalised in fields, waste places and roadsides. July-Sept. S France, Italy and Yugoslavia. (South America). Grown in gardens.

1852 *Xanthium strumarium* **ROUGH COCKLEBUR**. Medium to tall, stiffly branched annual, to 1.2m, not spiny. Leaves alternate, oval to triangular, with a heart-shaped base, unlobed or with 3-5 toothed lobes, bristly. Flower-heads greenish, male and female separate but borne on the same plant, 5-6mm, in *lateral clusters*, occasionally terminal, the globular male borne above the egg-shaped female; flower-bracts with straight or hooked spines, the heads enlarging in fruit to 14-18mm. Naturalised in damp places, especially along streams and rivers, wet pastures and marshes, on disturbed ground, occasionally along roadsides and seashores. July-Oct. T. (Probably North America). A cosmopolitan weed.

1853 *Xanthium spinosum* **SPINY COCKLEBUR**. Similar, but plants with simple or 3-forked yellowish *spines* at the base of each leaf. Fruit-heads 8-12mm, covered with dense, hooked spines. Cultivated, fallow and waste ground, roadsides. June-Sept. T. (South America). A cosmopolitan weed.

1854 *Helianthus annuus* **SUNFLOWER**, with its huge and familiar flowerheads is widely cultivated on a field-scale in many parts of the Med, occasionally also in gardens. It is cultivated primarily for its seeds that are rich in oil and as a fodder crop.

1855 *Santolina chamaecyparissus* **LAVENDER COTTON**. Dwarf, aromatic, greyish- or whitish-hairy, evergreen shrub, to 70cm. Leaves alternate, small, narrow-oblong, toothed to pinnately-lobed, crowded on the non-flowering stems, *almost round* in cross-section. Flower-heads deep yellow or cream, 6-10mm, terminal on stems leafless towards the top; all florets tubular; flower-bracts lanceolate to oval, hairy. Dry rocky habitats, lowland and in the mountains. June-Aug. Spain eastwards to Yugoslavia. Widely grown in gardens, where a number of different forms exist.

1855a Subsp. *squarrosa* has pale yellow flower-heads and hairless flower-bracts. Spain, Balearic Is. and S France.

1855b Subsp. *insularis* is a taller plant than the type with the leaf-lobes at least 2.5mm long (not up to 2mm) and flower-bracts densely hairy. Corsica and Sardinia eastwards to Yugoslavia.

1856 *Santolina rosmarinifolia [S. viridis]*. Similar, but leaf-lobes few and distant. Flower-heads bright yellow, borne on stalks *thickened* towards the top. Similar habitats and flowering times. Iberian Peninsula and S France.

Anthemis **CHAMOMILES**. Herbs or occasionally dwarf shrubs with alternate, often finely divided, leaves. Flower-heads solitary, often on long stalks, usually daisy-like with the outer florets rayed, occasionally rays absent and all the florets tubular, all borne on a prominent conical receptacle; flower-bracts generally in several rows. Some of the species are very aromatic and are used for herbal teas, pot pourris etc.

1857 *Anthemis maritimus*. Dwarf, hairless or somewhat hairy subshrub to 70cm tall, though often less; stems rather stout, rooting at the base, densely leafy in the upper part. Leaves usually pinnately-lobed, *fleshy* and gland-dotted. Flower-heads 24-40mm, with white rays and a yellow disk, borne on slender stalks up to 10cm long. Coastal sands. Apr-June. Iberian Peninsula and NW Africa eastwards to Italy, including the islands.

1858 *Anthemis arvensis* **CORN CHAMOMILE**. Very variable, short to medium, hairy, aromatic annual, often overwintering; stems much-branched from the base, the side branches longer than the main stem. Leaves oblong, 1-3-pinnately-lobed, with linear, pointed segments, woolly beneath, especially when young. Flower-heads 20-40mm, with white rays and a yellow disk; flower-bracts often with brown,

achene

papery margins. Cultivated, fallow and waste ground, roadsides, pathways. Apr-July. T – not Cyprus.

1859 *Anthemis auriculata*. Similar, but flower-heads 15-35mm; achenes with distinct *auricles*. Dry hillslopes, open pine woods. S Yugoslavia, Greece, Aegean Is. and Turkey.

1860 *Anthemis flexicaulis*. Like *A. arvensis*, but leaves rather fleshier, almost *palmately-divided*; flower-heads with distinctly deflexed rays and a disk 6-10mm diam. Coastal rocks. W Aegean Is.

1861 *Anthemis tomentosa* **WOOLLY CHAMOMILE**. Low to short, *woolly-haired* annual, with spreading to prostrate stems. Leaves 1-2-pinnately-lobed, with oval lobes. Flower-heads 15-37mm, with white rays and a yellow disk, the rays rather short, rarely absent, spreading; flower-bracts woolly. Rocky and sandy coastal habitats, dry hillslopes. Mar-June. Italy and Sicily eastwards to Turkey, not Cyprus.

1862 *Anthemis securidiramea*. Similar, but less hairy, often somewhat *shiny* and with red-dish stems; flower-heads 17-25mm. Coastal habitats, both sandy and grassy. S France to Italy and Sicily, including Corsica and Sardinia.

1863 *Anthemis tricolor*. Like *A. tomentosa*, but generally less hairy and with the flower-heads with a *pink or purple* centre. Rocky and stony habitats, lowlands and moun-tains. Feb-May. Cyprus – endemic.

1864 *Anthemis plutonia*. Like *A. tricolor*, but leaves 2-pinnately-lobed (not 1) and achenes with a well developed corona. Igneous rocks in the mountains. Mar-July. Cyprus – endemic.

1865 *Anthemis amblyolepis*. Short, thinly hairy annual, usually branched from the base. Leaves numerous, 1-2-pinnately-lobed, with small pointed, oblong lobes. Flower-heads *rather large*, 25-40mm, with white rays and a yellow disk; flower-bracts with a pale membranous margin; flower-stalks thickened at the top in fruit. Cultivated, fallow and waste land, coastal garrigue, roadsides. Feb-May. E Med, including Cyprus.

1866 *Anthemis palaestina [A. melanolepis]*. Similar, but stem commonly more branched, especially above, often purplish, less thickened below the flower-heads in fruit, the receptacle-scales becoming dark *bronze-purple* in fruit (not brownish). Stony habitats, coasts and along rivers, cultivated fields, hillslopes. Mar-June. Rhodes, Cyprus and the E Med – not Turkey.

1867 *Anthemis cotula* **STINKING MAYWEED**. Short to medium, *stinking*, slightly hairy annual; stems erect or ascending, branched above to give a flat-topped inflorescence. Leaves slightly fleshy, irregularly 2-3-pinnately-lobed, the lobes linear, pointed. Flower-heads 12-30mm, with white rays and a yellow disk; receptacle scales linear; flower-bracts oblong, with a pale brown membranous margin. Cultivated, fallow and waste ground, sometimes in garrigue, roadsides, salt marsh margins. Apr-Sept. T.

achene

1868 *Anthemis pseudocotula*. Similar, but plant often prostrate, with radiating branches and flower-stalks becoming greatly *thickened* in fruit. Similar habitats. Mar-July. Aegean Is. and E Med, including Cyprus.

1869 *Anthemis chia*. Low to medium, almost hairless annual; stems erect, simple or few-branched, erect or ascending. Leaves 1-2-pinnately-lobed, with oval or triangular lobes. Flower-heads 20-45mm, with white rays and a yellow disk, borne on long stems, the disk florets expanded in the middle of the tube; receptacle scales blunt; flower-bracts triangular-lanceolate, pointed, with *brown or blackish* papery mar-gins. Cultivated, fallow and waste ground, olive groves, orchards, roadsides.

Mar-June. Italy and Sicily eastwards, including Cyprus. The common spring-time white daisy in much of the E Med, often occurring in large colonies.

1870 *Anthemis rigida* **RAYLESS CHAMOMILE**. Low, slightly hairy annual, with spreading stems which become gradually thickened and rigid. Leaves 1-2-pinnately-lobed, the lobes lanceolate to linear. Flower-heads 3-9mm, yellow, sometimes suffused with pink, usually *without* ray florets, borne on thickened, often curved, stalks. Sandy and stony coastal habitats, occasionally inland. Feb-May. Crete and Greece eastwards, including Cyprus.

1871 *Anthemis tinctoria [Cota tinctoria]* **YELLOW CHAMOMILE**. Very variable, slightly to dense-ly hairy, medium perennial; stems usually branched. Leaves 2-pinnately-lobed, green above, white-woolly beneath. Flower-heads 25-45mm, rays and disk *all yellow*, borne in branched, flat-topped clusters; ray florets rarely absent. Cul-tivated and waste land, roadsides, scrub, generally at low altitudes and in dry habitats. July-Sept. France eastwards to Turkey – absent from most of the islands. Once the source of a yellow dye (*tinctoria* = used in dyeing).

Achillea **SNEEZEWORTS**. Perennial herbs with pinnately-divided or undivided, alter-nate leaves. Flower-heads small, generally congested into dense, flat-topped clusters; ray florets present, often short and 3-toothed at the apex; disk florets present.

achene

1872 *Achillea millefolium* **YARROW, MILFOIL**. Variable, short to medium, hairy, stoloniferous perennial, generally patch-forming, strong-smelling; stems erect, unbranched. Leaves *feathery*, lanceolate, finely 2-pinnately-lobed, 5-12mm wide, with small, narrow segments. Flower-heads small, 4-6mm, white, occasionally pink or red-dish, with a white or cream disk, borne in broad flat-topped heads; rays short; flower-bracts usually hairless, with a brown margin. Grassy and waste habitats, open scrub, roadsides, banks and hedgerows. T – not Balearic Is., Sicily, Crete, Cyprus and parts of the E Med. Grown in gardens, mostly as red-flowered cul-tivars. This is the common yarrow in many parts of Europe and western Asia, sometimes becoming a garden weed.

1873 *Achillea setacea*. Similar, but not more than 30cm tall and with leaves 3-pinnately-divided, 4-6mm wide; flowers always white; flower-bracts *hairy*. Dry grassy and rocky places. Italy, Yugoslavia and Greece.

1874 *Achillea pannonica*. Like *A. setacea*, but leaves usually 2-pinnatetely-lobed (not 3) and flower-bracts hairy only close to the margins. Dry grassy habitats. Mainland Balkans.

1875 *Achillea ligustica*. Medium to tall tufted, hairy perennial, *not stoloniferous*; stems erect, unbranched. Leaves 1-2-pinnately-lobed, 12-15mm wide, with up to 10, rather broad, lanceolate primary segments. Flower-heads 5-7mm, with white rays; flower-bracts hairy. Dry grassy habitats, open scrub. May-July. Spain eastwards to the Balkans – not Balearic Is.

1876 *Achillea tomentosa*. Similar, but the stem leaves rounded (not flat) in cross-section, with the segments in several planes; flower-heads with *yellow* rays. Similar habitats and flowering times. Spain, S France, Italy.

1877 *Achillea clypeolata*. Like *A. tomentosa*, but stem-leaves *flat* in cross-section; rays 1mm long (not 2). Balkan mainland.

1878 *Achillea biebersteinii*. Like *A. tomentosa*, but stem-leaves flat in cross-section and rays orange-yellow, 1.5-2mm long. Waste and fallow ground, roadsides. Apr-June. Greece eastwards, including Cyprus.

1879 *Achillea ageratum*. Like *A. ligustica*, but most leaves flat and toothed, *not* pinnately-divided; flower-heads with yellow rays about 1mm long. Damp habitats. Iberian Peninsula, NW Africa, eastwards to Italy – not Sicily.

1880 *Achillea santolina* **SANTOLINA-LEAVED SNEEZEWORT.** An erect, much-branched sub-shrub, to 30cm; stem generally white-woolly, becoming woody below. Leaves *pinnately-lobed*, with numerous overlapping segments, rather like those of *Santolina*. Flower-heads yellow, 2-3mm, borne in dense, slightly domed heads, the rays very short (not more than 1mm), with 3 rounded lobes; flower-bracts hairy, with narrow membranous margins. Dry fields, rocky places, roadsides. Mar-May. Turkey eastwards, including Cyprus.

1881 *Achillea cretica*. Like *A. santolina*, but forming a more compact small shrub to 30cm with *white* flower-heads, 5-6mm, with the rays strongly recurved. Rocky habitats, generally close to the sea. Apr-July. Crete, Aegean Is., SW Turkey, including Rhodes and Cyprus.

1882 *Chamaemelum mixtum [Anthemis mixta, Osmenis mixta]*. Short to medium, somewhat hairy annual; stems usually much-branched. Leaves oblong in outline, the lower 1-2-pinnately-divided, the upper pinnate or toothed, unstalked; leaf-lobes linear-lanceolate, toothed or not. Flower-heads 18-25mm, daisy like, with spreading white rays and a yellow disk; rays 3-toothed at the apex; flower-bracts erect in fruit, greenish with a brownish membranous margin. Cultivated, fallow and waste ground, coastal sands, roadsides. Apr-July. Iberian Penisula and NW Africa, eastwards to Greece – not Balearic Is.

1883 *Chamaemelum fuscatum [Anthemis fuscata]*. Similar, but a shorter hairless annual, less densely branched and with rather erect, rather than spreading, branches. Flower-heads *arched* in bud, with reflexed rays; flower-bracts black-margined, reflexed in fruit. Iberian Peninsula and NW Africa, eastwards to Italy and Sicily – not Balearic Is.

1884 *Chamaemelum nobile [Anthemis nobilis]* **CHAMOMILE.** A low to short, hairy, creeping and rooting perennial with spreading stems, *aromatic* when crushed. Leaves alternate, oblong, 2-3-pinnately-lobed, feathery, with slender segments, hairless beneath. Flower-heads 18-25mm, white with a yellow disk, solitary, long-stalked; rays occasionally absent; flower-bracts thin, shiny and white-margined. Grassy, cultivated and sandy habitats, coastal and inland. May-July. Iberian Peninsula; naturalised elsewhere. Widely cultivated in some areas for ornament, aromatic lawns and herbal infusions.

1885 *Matricaria perforata [M. inodora, Tripleurospermum inodorum]* **SCENTLESS MAYWEED.** Short to tall, scarcely scented annual, hairless or slightly hairy; stems erect to ascending. Leaves alternate, not fleshy, irregularly 2-3-pinnately-lobed, with narrow, pointed, segments. Flower-heads *large*, 30-45mm, with white rays and a yellow disk; flower-bracts oblong, with a brownish or colourless margin. Cultivated, fallow and waste land, roadsides, salty soils. June-Sept. T – but absent from most of the islands. Very common in some areas.

1886 *Matricaria trichophylla [Tripleurospermum tenuifolium]*. Similar, but plant usually biennial and *glandular*, often taller, to 1.5m; flower-heads 30-50mm. Similar habitats and flowering times. Mainland Balkans and Turkey.

1887 *Matricaria recutita [M. chamomilla, Chamomilla recutita]* **SCENTED MAYWEED.** An aromatic, short to medium, hairless annual; stems ascending to erect, branched. Leaves alternate, 2-3-pinnately-divided, with finely pointed divisions. Flower-heads 10-25mm, with white rays and a yellow, conical, hollow, *disk*, the rays downturned soon after the flowers open; flower-bracts greenish with a brown membranous margin. Cultivated, fallow and waste ground, roadsides, on salty, sandy or loamy

achene

443

soils. Mar-July, occasionally later. T. Sometimes cultivated as a medicinal plant. Very common in some areas and often forming large scattered colonies.

1888 *Matricaria aurea [Chamomilla aurea, Cotula aurea, Anthemis complanata]* **RAYLESS MAYWEED**. Similar, but rarely more than 20cm tall, the flower-heads bright yellow, 5-8mm, *without rays*; florets 4-lobed (not 5). Cultivated and waste ground, roadsides, old walls, often close to the sea. Feb-May. S Portugal, Spain, N Africa, Malta and Lampedusa, Sicily and E Med, including Cyprus.

1889 *Anacyclus clavatus [A. tomentosus]* **ANACYCLUS**. A short to medium, widely branched, hairy annual. Leaves alternate, 2-3-pinnately-lobed, with linear segments. Flower-heads 15-20mm, with white, erect or recurved rays and a yellow disk, solitary; flower-stalks becoming *conspicuously* thickened below the fruiting head; flower-bracts lanceolate to oval, greenish with a narrow white or purplish margin; achenes without a pappus. Waste and fallow ground, coastal rocks. May-July. T – not Cyprus or parts of the E Med.

1890 *Anacyclus radiatus*. Similar, but often taller, the rays *yellow*, often purplish beneath. Coastal sands and gravels. T – not Cyprus or the extreme E Med.

flower
bract

1891 *Anacyclus pyrethrum*. Like *A. clavatus*, but perennial with longer rays, white, *purplish* beneath. SE Spain and N Africa.

1892 *Otanthus maritimus [Diotis maritima]* **COTTONWEED**. A short, *white-woolly* spreading perennial; stems ascending, stout, branched above. Leaves alternate, oblong to lanceolate, untoothed to blunt-toothed, fleshy, unstalked. Flower-heads yellow, 7-10mm, globose, button-like, without rays, borne in close, flat-topped clusters; flower-bracts white-woolly. Coastal habitats, stabilised shingle and sand-dunes. June-Aug. T. Often growing on the seaward side of sand-dunes.

achene

1893 *Cladanthus arabicus* **CLADANTHUS**. Strong-smelling, minutely hairy annual. Leaves alternate, 1-2-pinnately-lobed, with linear segments, the uppermost in a *whorl* close below the flower-heads, with radiating branches at the same whorl. Flower-heads yellow, 30-50mm, semi-spherical; flower-bracts oval with a wide membranous appendage. Cultivated and fallow ground and open sunny sites. May-July. S Spain and N Africa.

1894 *Chrysanthemum segetum* **CORN MARIGOLD**. Short to tall, greyish, hairless annual, somewhat fleshy; stems erect to ascending, branched or unbranched. Leaves alternate, oblong, deeply and sharply toothed, the uppermost sometimes untoothed. Flower-heads yellow, daisy-like, 35-55mm, with strap-shaped rays and a flat disk. Cultivated and fallow ground, disturbed places, roadsides, banks, open garrigue, seashores. Feb-June. T – probably only native in Asia Minor. A common plant of cornfields, declining in some areas with modern farming practices.

1895 *Chrysanthemum coronarium* **CROWN DAISY**. Similar, but sometimes slightly hairy and leaves 2-pinnately-lobed. Flower-heads somewhat larger, 30-60mm, pale yellow or the rays white in the upper half (var. *discolor*) (**1895a**). Similar habitats. Jan-Sept. T. Often associated with the previous species. Both are grown in gardens.

1896 *Chrysanthemum carinatum* **ANNUAL CHRYSANTHEMUM**. Like *C. coronarium*, but shorter, usually not more than 60cm. Flower-heads variable, the rays white with a yellow base, variously banded with red, purple or maroon; disk dark purple. Cultivated and disturbed ground, in dry sunny places. Mar-June. NW Africa, especially Morocco. Grown in gardens.

1897 *Coleostephus myconis [Chrysanthemum myconis]*. Short to medium, sparingly branched annual, usually hairless. Leaves oval, regularly toothed, not lobed, the lower narrowed below into a stalk, the upper unstalked and half-clasping the stem. Flower-heads 18-22mm, with yellow or whitish rays, occasionally bicolored, and a yellow disk. Cultivated, fallow and waste ground. Mar-June. T – not Balearic Is. or Cyprus.

1898 *Coleostephus clausonis [C. hybridus]*. Similar, but *stems* spreading to prostrate and leaves irregularly toothed. Iberian Peninsula eastwards to Italy and Sicily – not Balearic Is.

Tanacetum **TANSIES.** Annual or perennial herbs, often aromatic when crushed, with alternate, pinnately-divided leaves. Flower-heads usually rayed, daisy-like, borne in flat-topped clusters or solitary; pappus usually forming a cup.

1899 *Tanacetum vulgare [Chrysanthemum vulgare, C. tanacetum]* **TANSY.** A medium to tall, strongly aromatic, patch-forming, almost hairless perennial, to 1.5m. Leaves pinnately-lobed, with lanceolate, toothed segments, deep green; uppermost leaves unstalked. Flower-heads yellow, 7-12mm, *button-like*, rayless, borne in large rather flat-topped clusters. Grassy and waste land, scrub, roadsides, river gravels. July-Sept. T – not Balearic Is., Crete or much of the E Med. An old culinary and medicinal herb. The form in Corsica, Sardinia and Sicily has more finely divided leaves than elsewhere.

achene

1900 *Tanacetum parthenium [Chrysanthemum parthenium, Leucanthemum parthenium]* **FEVER-FEW.** A short to medium, *strongly aromatic* biennial or short-lived perennial; stems erect, branched above. Leaves rather yellowish-green, 1-2-pinnately-divided, mostly stalked. Flower-heads 10-25mm, with white rays and a yellow disk, many borne in lax, flat-topped clusters; rays spreading. Cultivated and waste ground, roadsides, rocky places, old walls. June-Sept. Balkans, but widely naturalised in the Med. Formerly widely cultivated as a medicinal herb and today used in the treatment of migraine and other disorders. Some garden forms have yellow leaves or double flowers.

achene

1901 *Tanacetum corymbosum [Chrysanthemum corymbosum, Leucanthemum corymbosum]*. Similar, but stem leaves *unstalked* and flower-heads larger, 25-40mm. Open woodland, scrub and grassy habitats. June-Sept. T – not Balearic Is., Crete, Cyprus and much of the extreme E Med.

1902 *Prolongoa pectinata* **PROLONGOA.** Short, somewhat hairy annual; stems erect, simple or branched, leafless above. Leaves alternate, pinnately-lobed with a few pairs of narrow pointed lobes. Flower-heads 20-25mm, with yellow rays and disk, *nodding* before and after flowering; rays with neatly truncated tips; flower-bracts with wide membranous margins. Rocky and sandy habitats, cultivated and fallow fields. Mar-June. C and S Spain.

1903 *Leucanthemum vulgare [Chrysanthemum leucanthemum]* **OX-EYE DAISY.** Short to tall, hairless or slightly hairy, patch-forming perennial, with short leafy stolons; stems erect to ascending, ridged, often branched. Leaves alternate, dark green, oblong, toothed, the basal stalked, the stem leaves unstalked and *clasping* the stem. Flower-heads large daisies, 25-50mm, with white rays and a rather flat yellow disk; rays long and strap-shaped. Rough grassy places, meadows, roadsides, embankments, occasionally along the seashore or in open woodland. May-Sept. T – not Balearic Is., Crete or Cyprus. One of the commonest summer 'white daisies' throughout much of Europe and western Asia.

achene

1904 *Leucanthemum paludosum [Chrysanthemum paludosum]*. Similar, but rays shorter, pale yellow or whitish with a yellow base; flower-heads 20-30mm. Iberian Peninsula and Balearic Is.

1905 *Nananthea perpusilla* **NANANTHEA.** Slender, low, hairless annual, not more than 6cm tall. Leaves rather succulent, oblong with 3-5 oval lobes, long-stalked. Flower-heads *small*, 2-5mm, with white rays and a yellow disk. Coastal rocks and sands. Apr-June. Corsica and Sardinia.

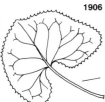

1906 *Petasites fragrans* **WINTER HELIOTROPE**. Short to medium, patch-forming, hairy perennial. Leaves appearing with the flowers, kidney-shaped or heart-shaped, slightly hairy beneath, hairless and rather shiny above, regularly toothed. Flower-heads pinkish-white, *vanilla fragrant*, 14-18mm, few borne in a broad raceme with bract-like leaves below, male or female borne on separate plants, with few to many short rays; flower-bracts pale green or purplish, more or less hairless. Damp, generally shaded habitats. Sardinia, Italy and Sicily; naturalised in the Iberian Peninsula, Balearic Is. and Corsica, perhaps elsewhere in the Med.

Calendula **MARIGOLDS**. Annual or perennial herbs, usually aromatic, with alternate, undivided leaves. Flower-heads daisy-like, with yellow or orange rays; flower-bracts in 1-2 rows. Achenes with a narrow beak, often strongly curved, the inner often smaller; pappus absent.

1907 *Calendula suffruticosa*. A short to medium perennial, *woody* below. Leaves linear-lanceolate to oblong, somewhat fleshy, pointed, few-toothed, glandular-hairy. Flower-heads large, 30-40mm, yellow, the rays sometimes tipped with red; rays up to 20mm long. Fruit-heads with an outer row of narrow-beaked, spreading achenes. Rocky habitats, coastal sands and other dry places, occasionally inland. Mar-July. Iberian Peninsula and NW Africa eastwards to Greece – absent from the islands, except Sicily.

    1907a Subsp. *tomentosa [C. tomentosa]* is distinguished by its white-woolly leaves and stems. S Portugal and S Spain.

1908 *Calendula arvensis* **FIELD MARIGOLD**. Short, generally thinly hairy, erect or spreading annual. Leaves oblong to oval, finely toothed. Flower-heads *small*, 10-27mm, yellow or orange, the disk a similar colour or brown or violet-purple. Fruit-head with the outer row of achenes beaked and strongly incurved. Cultivated, fallow and waste ground, roadsides, olive groves and vineyards, open garrigue. Mar-June, occasionally later. T.

1909 *Calendula officinalis* **GARDEN or POT MARIGOLD**. Similar, but flowers much larger, 40-70mm, yellow or orange with a yellow, orange or brownish disk. A larger plant altogether. Cultivated, fallow and waste ground, rocky places. Apr-Sept. Naturalised T. (Origin unknown). A widely cultivated ornamental plant and pot herb – the petals can be eaten in salads and have been used as a source of yellow dye for colouring food. Cultivated forms include those with double flowers in which all the florets are rayed.

1910 *Calendula stellata*. Like *C. arvensis*, but rays with a violet *tip*; disk violet-purple. Cultivated and waste ground. Sicily and N Africa.

Senecio **RAGWORTS**. Herbs or dwarf shrubs with alternate leaves. Flower-heads often numerous, borne in flat-topped clusters; outer florets generally rayed; disk florets tubular; flower-bracts (involucre) mostly in only one row. Pappus present, white or greyish.

1911 *Senecio bicolor [S. cineraria]* **CINERARIA**. A *white-felted*, dwarf shrub to 50cm tall, much-branched at the base, with leaves crowded at the base of the flowering shoots. Leaves oval to lanceolate, toothed to pinnately-lobed, with rather narrow segments, white beneath, whitish, greyish or greenish above. Flower-heads 12-15mm, yellow, borne in dense terminal clusters; rays present. Coastal habitats, sandy and rocky. May-Aug. W and C Med, eastwards to Greece – not Crete. Widely grown in gardens, where a number of different forms exist.

1912 *Senecio ambiguus*. Similar, but with fewer, thinner, basal branches which are leafy throughout. Flower-heads smaller, 10-12mm. Rocky and sandy habitats. S Italy, Sicily, S Greece and N Africa.

1913 *Senecio gallicus [S. coronopifolius]*. Short to medium, hairless or somewhat hairy annual, usually with several branches from the base. Leaves rather thick, pinnately-lobed, with untoothed or lobed segments, only the basal leaves stalked; the upper unstalked and *clasping* the stem. Flower-heads 15-22mm, yellow, borne in few-headed clusters; rays about 8mm long. Cultivated and fallow land, stony slopes, coastal sands. Mar-Sept. T – not Corsica, Sardinia or Cyprus and parts of the E Med.

1914 *Senecio leucanthemifolius*. Similar, but plant very fleshy, hairless or white-hairy; flower-bracts often *black-tipped*. Coastal habitats, rocky and sandy. Feb-June. T.

1915 *Senecio lividus*. Like *S. gallicus*, but stems often simple (unbranched) and leaves hairless or somewhat glandular; flower-heads *smaller*, 6-10mm, with the flower-bracts black-tipped; rays 5mm, recurved. W and C Med eastwards to Greece – not Crete.

1916 *Senecio vulgaris* GROUNDSEL. Rather like *S. lividus*, but without rays in the flower-head. Cultivated, fallow and waste ground, stony places, seashores. Jan-Dec. T. A very well known plant which has become a widespread weed in many temperate regions of the world.

1917 *Senecio glaucus*. Like *S. leucanthemifolius*, but plant hairless, the flower-bracts *without* a black tip. Coastal habitats. Jan-Apr. E Med, including Cyprus.

1918 *Senecio vernalis* SPRING GROUNDSEL. Like *S. gallicus*, but branches *erect* (not spreading), leaves variably dissected, often with rather broad segments and flower-heads larger, 20-25mm. Similar habitats and flowering times. Balkans and Turkey.

1919 *Gundelia tournefortii* SILIFA. Hairless or slightly hairy, leafy, thistle-like perennial; stems stout, unbranched. Leaves elliptical, pinnately-lobed, the basal stalked, the upper unstalked, the leaf-blade often running down the stem as a thin wing; all leaves conspicuously veined, the midrib often purplish, the margin with small *yellowish spines*. Flower-heads white, yellow, pink, purple or red, aggregated into spiny sea-holly-like heads, 4-5cm across; florets all tubular, few to each flower-head; flower-bracts fused, spine-tipped. Coastal habitats, roadsides, scrub. May-June. Turkey, Cyprus and the E Med. A tumbleweed; the fruiting heads eventually break up to disperse the seeds. In Turkey the flowerheads are eaten like those of the Globe Artichoke, *Cynara scolymus*.

Carlina CARLINE THISTLES. Spiny annuals and perennials, often with pinnately-lobed leaves. Flower-heads solitary or aggregated, with only tubular florets; flower-(involucral) bracts radiating, linear, pointed and often shiny, much longer than the florets and resembling ray-florets at a casual glance.

1920 *Carlina corymbosa [C. thracica]* FLAT-TOPPED CARLINE THISTLE. Vary variable, somewhat white-felted, short to tall perennial; stems solitary or several. Leaves oblong-lanceolate, toothed to pinnately-lobed, wavy, spiny-margined. Flower-heads small, 12-20mm, with yellow florets and yellow or brownish flower-bracts; flower-heads solitary at branch-tips, but forming a flat-topped inflorescence. Dry stony habitats. June-Sept. T – except Cyprus and the E Med where it is replaced by the very similar looking *C. involucrata* (1921).

flower bracts

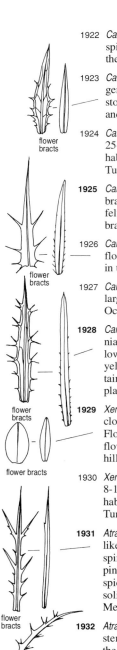

flower
bracts

flower
bracts

flower
bracts

flower
bracts

flower bracts

flower
bracts

flower
bracts

1922 *Carlina diae [Lyrolepis diae]*. Similar, but plant densely white-felted and *without* spines; flower-heads 15-20mm. Similar habitats and flowering times. Is.lands off the N coast of Crete – endemic.

1923 *Carlina racemosa*. Like *C. corymbosa*, but flower-heads 8-15mm, unstalked and generally *overtopped* by branches supporting other flower-heads. Grassy and stony habitats, often forming large colonies. Aug-Oct. Iberian Peninsula, Sardinia and NW Africa.

1924 *Carlina sicula*. Like *C. corymbosa*, but almost hairless and with *larger* flower-heads, 25-35mm, the flower-bracts silvery-white, often purplish beneath. Similar habitats and flowering times. SE Italy, Sicily and surrounding small islands, Turkey.

1925 *Carlina lanata* **PURPLE CARLINE THISTLE.** Low to short, partly hairy annual; stems un-branched or branched. Leaves oblong, pinnately-lobed, wavy, spine-toothed, felted beneath. Flower-heads 20-40mm, with *reddish-purple* florets and flower-bracts. Dry rocky slopes generally in scrub or garrigue. June-Aug. T.

1926 *Carlina macrophylla*. Similar, but usually biennial, the leaves lanceolate in outline; flower-bracts whitish *above*, but purplish beneath. Open woods and scrub, mainly in the mountains. July-Aug. Corsica, Sardinia, Italy and Sicily.

1927 *Carlina pygmaea [C. lanata var. pygmaea]*. Like *C. lanata*, but perennial with rather larger flower-heads with purple florets. Dry pastures and rocky hillslopes. June-Oct. Cyprus – endemic.

1928 *Carlina acanthifolia* **ACANTHUS-LEAVED CARLINE THISTLE.** *Stemless* monocarpic peren-nial. Leaves oval, pinnately-lobed, spine-margined, white-felted beneath, the lower leaves stalked. Flower-heads large, 30-70mm, with pink or lilac florets and yellowish flower-bracts. Dry grassy habitats, stony pastures, in hills and moun-tains. July-Sept. Spain eastwards to Greece – absent from the islands. In some places, especially in Spain, the fruiting heads are nailed to doors for good luck.

1929 *Xeranthemum inapterum* **XERANTHEMUM.** An erect, short to medium annual, branched close to the base. Leaves linear to oblong, untoothed, white-felted beneath. Flower-heads *papery and everlasting*, 10-20mm, with pink, purplish or lilac flower-bracts; florets all tubular, purplish. Pappus scaly. Dry habitats, fields and hillsides. Feb-May. T.

1930 *Xeranthemum cylindraceum [X. foetidum]*. Similar, but taller and flower-heads smaller, 8-15mm; outer flower-bracts with a whitish *patch* of hairs; inner pink. Similar habitats as well as cultivated and fallow ground. Iberian Peninsula eastwards to Turkey – absent from the islands.

1931 *Atractylis gummifera [Carlina gummifera]* **ATRACTYLIS.** A low, stout but *stemless*, thistle-like plant, hairy in part. Leaves oblong in outlines, pinnately-divided into many spine-tipped segments; stalks sheathing at the base. Flower-heads purple or pinkish, 30-70mm, solitary, with only tubular florets; flower-bracts not con-spicuous as in *Carlina*, the middle ones with 3 apical spines, the inner with a solitary brown spine. Dry habitats, fields, banks, roadsides. June-Sept. W and C Med, including NW Africa, eastwards to Greece – not Balearic Is.

1932 *Atractylis humilis*. Slender, low to short, downy or hairless perennial, with erect stems. Leaves linear-oblong in outline, spiny-margined, the lower short-stalked, the upper unstalked and more obviously pinnately-lobed; outer flower-bracts *leaf-like*, encircling the base of the flower-heads, the inner notched at the spine-tipped apex. Flower-heads purple, 15-25mm, solitary, with all florets tubular. Stony habitats, dry grassy places, garrigue. July-Sept. Spain, S France, Balearic Is., NW Africa.

1933 *Atractylis cancellata.* Similar, but annual, with the outer flower-bracts divided and *comb-like* around the flower-head. Similar habitats as well as field margins, roadsides. Mar-July. T.

1934 *Cardopatium corymbosum [Echinops corymbosus, Carthamus corymbosus]* **CARDOPATIUM.** A short, much-branched, very spiny perennial as broad as high. Leaves oblong in outline, pinnately-divided into many spine-tipped segments, hairless. Flower-heads *small*, bright blue, 5-10mm, congested into broad clusters, each flower-head with up to 10 tubular florets; flower-bracts mostly spiny. Dry open habitats, grassy places, waste ground, garrigue, rocky slopes, often close to the sea. May-Sept. Italy eastwards, including Crete and Cyprus.

Echinops **GLOBE THISTLES.** Distinctive spiny thistly-like plants with flower-heads small but congested into tight symmetrical balls; florets solitary to each flower-head. Pappus consisting of bristles or scales.

1935 *Echinops sphaerocephalus.* Medium to tall, felted, occasionally glandular-hairy perennial, to 1.5m. Leaves oblong to oval, 1-2-pinnately-lobed into spine-tipped, narrow-triangular, segments, white with hairs beneath; spines short and slender. Flower-heads 30-60mm, *greyish-blue or whitish*; flower-bracts long-pointed, hairy-margined, glandular on the outside. Dry pastures, fallow and waste land, rocky places, coastal and inland. June-Sept. Spain eastwards to Turkey – not the islands.

1936 *Echinops spinosissimus [E. viscosus].* Similar, but usually with more deeply cut leaves and white or pale blue flower-heads; inner flower-bracts *fused* to form a membranous tube. Rocky habitats, garrigue, roadsides, waste ground. July-Oct. Sicily and Greece eastwards, including Crete and Cyprus.

1937 *Echinops ritro* **GLOBE THISTLE.** Medium to tall, stiffly erect, white-felted to almost hairless perennial, often with glandular hairs. Leaves elliptical in outline, 1-2-pinnately-divided into spine-tipped segments, with recurved margins, generally white-felted beneath, spines long and slender. Flower-heads 35-45mm, *blue*; inner flower-bracts not fused, hairy-margined. Dry grassy habitats, stony pastures, coastal and inland. July-Sept. Spain eastwards to Turkey, but absent from the islands except for Sicily. The common Globe Thistle of gardens, whose flowers attract many butterflies and bees.

1938 *Echinops graecus.* Similar, but flower-heads smaller, 30-40mm, shiny silvery-white with blue florets; inner flower-bracts *fused* to form a membranous tube. Dry rocky habitats. July-Sept. E Greece and the Cyclades.

1939 *Arctium lappa [A. majus, Lappa officinalis]* **GREATER BURDOCK.** Tall biennial to 1.5m; stems hairy or almost hairless. Basal leaves large, to 50cm, heart-shaped, stalked. Flower-heads globose, 20-25mm, larger in fruit (35-42mm), shiny golden-green and almost hairless on the outside, the florets reddish-purple, rarely white; flower-bracts with *hooked* tips. Open woodland, hedgerows, roadsides, rough grassy places, streamsides, mostly in the mountains in the region. July-Oct. T – scarcer in the E Med and N Africa. The hooked flower-heads aid in the dispersal of seeds, closely adhering to clothes, animal fur etc.

1940 *Arctium tomentosum [Lappa tomentosa].* Very similar, but flower-heads smaller, 12-20mm, not more than 25mm in fruit, densely *white-cottony*. Similar habitats and flowering time. T – not Portugal, or parts of N Africa and the E Med.

1941 *Jurinea mollis* subsp. *anatolica [J. anatolica]* **JURINEA.** A medium perennial, leafy at least at the base; stems unbranched white-felted. Leaves pinnately-lobed, the *lobes* lanceolate to oval with undulate and recurved margins, grey-felted beneath.

449

Flower-heads globular, 20-50mm, purple; flower-bracts lanceolate, with recurved purple tips, felted. Dry grassy and rocky habitats. June-Sept. Greece and the Aegean region.

1942 *Jurinea albicaulis* subsp. *kilaea*. Similar, but the lower leaves linear, *scarcely lobed*, grey-hairy above and the flower-heads longer than wide, 18-25mm long. Coastal habitats, sandy and grassy. June-Sept. Greece (Thrace) and Turkey.

1943 *Staehelina dubia* **STAEHELINA**. Small rounded subshrub, to 40cm, densely branched, with white-felted stems. Leaves alternate, crowded, narrow-lanceolate, with a somewhat recurved and slightly toothed margin, white-felted beneath. Flower-heads purple, 20-30mm long, *narrow-cylindrical*, solitary or 2-4 together; flower-bracts green with a reddish apex or all red. Rocky and stony habitats, garrigue. June-Aug. W Med eastwards as far as Italy.

1944 *Staehelina uniflosculosa*. Similar, but leaves oval and flower-heads half the size, pink, in clusters at the stem tips. Rocky mountain habitats. June-Aug. Balkans.

1945 *Staehelina fruticosa*. Similar, but a *robust* tufted shrub, often more than 1m, with lanceolate, pointed leaves and whitish, clustered flower-heads. Limestone cliffs. June-Sept. Crete and S Aegean.

1946 *Staehelina arborea*. Similar, but stems silvery-felted; leaves oval, silvery beneath, *crowded* near stem tips. Flower-heads *larger*, 25-35mm, pink. Limestone cliffs. May-Sept. Crete – endemic.

Carduus **THISTLES**. Annual, biennial or perennial herbs with spiny-winged stems. Leaves alternate, often spine-toothed. Flower-heads globose to cylindrical, typically shaving-brush shaped; florets all tubular, often purple or pink; flower-bracts in many rows, spine-tipped; pappus consisting of simple hairs.

1947 *Carduus macrocephalus*. Stout, grey-felted biennial, to 1.5m; stems with spiny wings to 5mm wide. Leaves pinnately-lobed, the lobes 6-10 pairs, each with an apical spine to 12mm long. Flower-heads large, 40-80mm, bright reddish-purple, subglobose, long-stalked, *half-nodding*; flower-bracts with a prominent midvein, the outer recurved and spine-tipped. Roadsides and waste places. May-Aug. Sardinia, Italy, Sicily and the Balkans. Closely related to the Nodding or Musk Thistle, *C. nutans* (1948), which is widespread in central and western Europe.

flower
bract

1949 *Carduus thoermeri*. Similar, but flower-bracts *velvety* with a distinct flattened appendage, 4-8mm wide. Similar habitats and flowering time. Balkans and Turkey.

1950 *Carduus acicularis [C. bicolor]*. Medium to tall, white-felted annual; stems rather slender, *narrowly winged* (not more than 4mm wide), leafless above. Leaves oval to lanceolate, with 2-5 pairs of spine-tipped lobes (spines 1-3mm long), felted with hairs beneath, sparsely so above. Flower-heads oblong, 15-20mm, rose-purple; flower-bracts narrow, spine-tipped, with a thickened margin, erect to spreading. Fallow and waste places, roadsides. Mar-July. S France eastwards, but absent from many of the islands with the exception of Sicily and Cyprus. Treated by R.D. Meikle in *Flora of Cyprus* as a subspecies of *C. argentatus*.

(1948)
flower
bract

flower
bract

1951 *Carduus argentatus*. Very similar, but leaves with white blotches and flower-bracts distinctly *constricted* in the middle and without a thickened margin; flower-stalks often longer, more than 3cm. Similar habitats and flowering time. Crete, Karpathos and Turkey.

1952 *Carduus pycnocephalus*. Very variable tall, grey- or whitish-felted annual; stems erect, with wings to 5mm wide. Leaves oblong, with 2-5 pairs of palm-like lobes, spine-tipped, the *apical spines* to 12mm long. Flower-heads oblong-cylindrical,

flower bracts

15-20mm long, rosy-purple, generally borne in clusters of 2-3 at the end of leafy branches; flower-bracts erect or slightly recurved, with thickened margins, widened in the lower third, tapered above to the spine-tip. Cultivated, fallow and waste ground, garrigue, roadsides, stony hillslopes. Mar-June. T. In Cyprus all the material is referable to subsp. *albidus* (1952a) which has smaller, white-felted, flower-heads.

1953 *Carduus australis.* Similar, but stems with wider wings, 7-8mm, and apical spines of leaf-lobes to 30mm. Flower-heads narrower, in clusters of 2-5. Similar habitats and flowering time. Corsica eastwards to Turkey – not Crete.

1954 *Carduus cephalanthus.* Like *C. pycnocephalus,* but an annual or biennial to 1m tall, with the leaves almost hairless beneath and with the veins raised beneath; flower-heads in clusters of 5-20. Rocky habitats, generally close to the sea. Spain, Corsica, Sardinia, Italy and Sicily.

1955 *Carduus fasciculiflorus.* Like *C. cephalanthus,* but leaf-veins raised beneath only in the distal third (not throughout) and flower-bracts with a narrow membranous margin. Waste places and scrub. Corsica, Sardinia and S Italy.

lower
ract

Cirsium **THISTLES.** Very like *Carduus* and distinguished primarily by a pappus of feathered hairs.

1956 *Cirsium eriophorum [C. chatenieri, C. vandasii]* **WOOLLY THISTLE.** Very variable. medium to tall, stout biennial to 1.5m; stems *unwinged,* white-cottony, branched above. Leaves pinnately-lobed with long rigid spines, white-cottony beneath. Flower-heads large, 25-50mm, reddish-purple, usually solitary, erect; flower-bracts interspersed with cobwebby hairs, the outer recurved, spine-tipped. Rough grassland, roadsides and scrub, generally in open habitats. July-Sept. Spain eastwards to the Balkans – absent from the islands.

1957 *Cirsium echinatum.* Similar, but a smaller plant not more than 40cm tall, usually perennial; flower-heads 25-40mm, slightly *overtopped* by the uppermost leaves. Dry habitats, grassy places, roadsides, banks. June-Sept. S and E Spain, Balearic Is., S France, Sicily and N Africa.

flower
bract

1958 *Cirsium vulgare [C. lanceolatum]* **SPEAR THISTLE.** Very variable, tall biennial, to 1.5m; stems with spiny wings *to the top.* Leaves lanceolate, pinnately-lobed, sharply spine-margined, dull green, prickly-hairy on the upper surface. Flower-heads purple, 20-40mm, borne in a panicle or flat-topped cluster; flower-bracts straight, with a yellow spine-tip. Grassy and waste places, disturbed ground, roadsides, orchards and olive groves. July-Oct. T – not Crete. A widespread weed of cultivation.

lower
bract

1959 *Cirsium italicum.* Similar, but an annual or biennial with leaves immediately *below* the flower-heads; flower-heads smaller, 8-15mm; florets 12-14mm long (not 26-36mm). Similar habitats and flowering time. Corsica and Sardinia eastwards to Turkey – not Crete.

1960 *Cirsium scabrum [C. giganteum].* Like *C. vulgare,* but a tall plant to 2m or more, *without* winged stems; flower-heads pink, 18-26mm; florets 22-28mm long. Scrub and hedgerows, roadsides. June-Sept. S Spain, Sardinia, S Italy and Sicily.

flower
bracts

1961 *Cirsium creticum [C. polyanthemum].* Medium to tall perennial; stems spiny-winged and leafy to the top, much-branched above the middle. Leaves leathery, strongly undulate, with stoutly-spined lobes, the spines to 15mm long, without bristles above and sparsely woolly beneath. Flower-heads 7-12mm, purple, solitary or clustered; florets 14-17mm long; flower-bracts erect with spreading spines. Wet

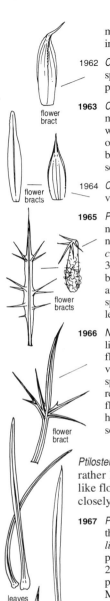

flower
bract

flower
bracts

flower
bracts

flower
bract

leaves

leaf

leaf

meadows, marshes and riversides. Apr-July. Corsica eastwards to Turkey, including many of the islands, not Cyprus.

1962 *Cirsium flavispina.* Similar, but a biennial, the stems *not* winged near the top, the spines yellow; flower-heads clustered, purple occasionally white. Sandy damp places, generally close to water. Iberian Peninsula.

1963 *Cirsium candelabrum* **CANDELABRA THISTLE.** Tall *pyramidal*, hairless biennial, to 2m, much-branched. Leaves leathery, undulate, lanceolate to oblong, pinnately-lobed, with stout marginal spines; spines 10-15mm long. Flower-heads 7-13mm, white or whitish-yellow, in stalkless slightly nodding clusters at the stem tops; flower-bracts striped, erect, with a short spine-tip. Grassy and stony habitats, screes and scrub, mainly in the mountains. May-Aug. Balkan Peninsula.

1964 *Cirsium arvense* **CREEPING THISTLE,** a widespread weed of cultivation, with its vigorous creeping underground stolons, occurs in various parts of the Med.

1965 *Picnomon acarna [Cirsium acarna]* **PICNOMON.** Short to medium, very spiny, erect annual, grey with cobwebby hairs; stems much-branched, with somewhat spiny, narrow wings. Leaves alternate, narrow-oblong to lanceolate with *marginal clusters* of long slender, marginal, gold spines. Flower-heads cylindrical, 22-30mm long, purple, in clusters surrounded by the uppermost leaves; flower-bracts terminated by a branched recurved spine. Dry rocky habitats, cultivated and waste ground, road and track sides. July-Sept. T. Readily recognised in the spring, before flowering, by its clusters of narrow, greyish or almost silvery leaves. Often gregarious.

1966 *Notobasis syriaca [Carduus syriacus, Cirsium syriacum]* **SYRIAN THISTLE.** Medium, thistle-like annual; stems stiff, sometimes branched above, not spiny-winged, often flushed with bluish-purple. Leaves alternate, deep green with pale or whitish veins, narrow-elliptical, mostly pinnately-lobed, with narrow triangular lobes, spine-tipped, the uppermost leaves *clustered* around the stalkless flower-heads, reduced to stout stiff spines. Flower-heads 15-23mm, purple, occasionally white; flower-bracts with a short spine-tip. Cultivated, fallow and waste ground, stony hillsides, garrigue, roadsides. Feb-June. T. Particularly common in the lowlands; sometimes gregarious.

Ptilostemon **PTILOSTEMONS.** Shrubs or herbs, sometimes spiny, with alternate, often rather leathery, leaves. Inflorescence often branched and paniculate with thistle-like flowers; florets all tubular, often with somewhat unequal lobes; flower-bracts closely overlapping, spine-tipped. Pappus present, feathery.

1967 *Ptilostemon chamaepeuce* **SHRUBBY PTILOSTEMON.** Spineless evergreen shrub to 1m, though often less; stems often white-downy, especially when young. Leaves *linear*, white-downy beneath, with recurved (revolute) margins. Flower-heads purple, 14-24mm, in lax spreading, few-flowered, clusters or solitary; florets 20-25mm long; flower-bracts oval to lanceolate, not or only slightly spreading, pointed but without a rigid spine-tip. Rocky habitats, cliffs, on various rock types. May-July. Greece, Crete and the E Med, including Cyprus (var. *cyprius* 1967a).

1968 *Ptilostemon gnaphaloides.* Similar, but leaves with a short *bristle-tip* and with 1-2 narrow, often short, lobes on each side near the base. Similar habitats and flowering time. S Italy, Greece and Crete.

1969 *Ptilostemon stellatus* **ANNUAL PTILOSTEMON.** Short to medium annual, seldom more than 40cm tall. Leaves linear to lanceolate, untoothed, with a short spine-tip and with several stout *basal* marginal spines, each up to 20mm in length. Flower-heads generally few, borne in spreading clusters or racemes, purple, short-stalked, 14-20mm long; flower-bracts with a spreading spine-tip and with a whitish swelling on the side. Bare and waste habitats, stony ground. Apr-June. S Italy and Sicily eastwards to the Balkans, including Crete.

1970 *Ptilostemon hispanicus [Chamaepeuce hispanica]*. Like *P. stellatus*, but a stout perennial to 1m, becoming woody at the base. Leaves oblong to oval, *lobed or toothed*, with stout marginal spines. Flower-heads larger, to 36mm; flower-bracts spine-tipped. Rocky, stony or sandy habitats. May-July. S Spain.

1971 *Galactites tomentosa* **GALACTITES**. White-downy, short to tall annual, to 1m, though often less. Leaves alternate, oblong, pinnately-lobed, with spiny lobes or teeth, with *white veins or variegations* above, white with down beneath. Flower-heads purple to lilac, occasionally white, 15-20mm, solitary or in branched clusters; outer florets larger than the inner and spreading; flower-bracts narrowed suddenly into a spine, white-downy. Dry habitats, stony and sandy ground, fallow and waste places. Apr-July. T – except the E Med.

1972 *Tyrimnus leucographus* **TYRIMNUS**. Slender, greyish- or whitish-downy, short to medium annual or biennial. Leaves alternate, elliptical, toothed and lobed, with a very spiny margin, the leaf-base running down the stem *as a wing*. Flower-heads pink or violet, 14-16mm, solitary on long leafless stalks; florets all tubular; flower-bracts closely overlapping, with a short spine-tip. Dry habitats, bare, waste and fallow land, sandy and stony habitats, roadsides, vineyards and olive groves. Apr-June. T.

Onopordum **SCOTCH THISTLES**. Stout biennials, generally with spiny-winged stems and often covered with cobwebby hairs. Leaves spiny margined. Flower-heads large, often reddish-purple or purple, occasionally pink or white; florets all tubular, deeply 5-lobed; flower-bracts thick and leathery, in several rows, spine-tipped, hairy or hairless.

1973 *Onopordum illyricum* **ILLYRIAN SCOTCH THISTLE**. Stout tall biennial, to 1.3m, with *yellowish*, densely spiny stems, hairy and winged. Leaves oblong, pinnately-lobed, with triangular-wedge-shaped lobes, densely white with hairs. Flower-heads purple, 40-60mm; flower-bracts 5-7mm wide, the outer and middle ones strongly recurved. Rocky and stony habitats, waste and fallow ground, field boundaries, roadsides. June-July. Iberian Peninsula eastwards to the Balkans. A variable species; forms with almost hairless stems from the C Med region are often assigned to subsp. *horridum* (1973a).

1974 *Onopordum cyprium* **CYPRUS SCOTCH THISTLE**. Similar, but with narrowly winged stems and more deeply dissected leaves with oblong lobes; flower-heads smaller, 30-40mm, purple or occasionally whitish. Similar habitats. Apr-July. Cyprus – endemic.

1975 *Onopordum acanthium* **SCOTCH THISTLE**. Like *O. illyricum*, but plant more cobwebby with hairs and flower-bracts *linear*, not recurved; flower-heads purple or white. Similar habitats plus cultivated ground. May-July. Iberian Peninsula eastwards to Turkey, but widely naturalised in the Med region as a whole. Often grown in gardens for ornament.

1976 *Onopordum bracteatum*. Like *O. illyricum*, but stems yellowish or white, to 1.8m; flower-heads larger, 50-70mm, *hairless* (not hairy below). Rocky and stony habitats, roadsides, mainly in the hills and mountains. S Balkans and Crete.

1977 *Onopordum argolicum*. Like *O. illyricum*, but stem *brownish*, scarcely hairy and leaves dark green. Sardinia, Malta, Sicily, S Greece.

upper leaf

lower bracts

flower bracts

flower bracts

stem portion

flower bract

1978 *Onopordum tauricum.* Like *O. argolicum*, but leaves with 6-8 pairs of lobes (not 10-12). Greece eastwards to Turkey, including Crete, not Cyprus.

1979 *Cynara cardunculus* **CARDOON**. Stout, medium to tall perennial, to 1m; stem ridged, *unwinged*. Leaves rather thick, pinnately-lobed and toothed, edged with rigid yellow spines, bright green above but white-downy beneath. Flower-heads blue, or violet-purple, occasionally whitish, 40-55mm, solitary or several on branched stems; florets all tubular; flower-bracts oval to elliptical, greyish-green or purplish, terminating in a stout erect or spreading spine. Waste, fallow and cultivated land, stony places, roadsides, field margins. May-July. Iberian Peninsula eastwards to Turkey – not Cyprus. Occasionally cultivated as a vegetable – the young shoots and leaves are blanched before being eaten. Also grown as an ornamental flower in gardens.

flower bracts

1980 *Cynara scolymus* **GLOBE ARTICHOKE**. Very similar, but to 2m, the leaves not spiny and flower-heads generally larger; flower-bracts with or without a spine-tip. Unknown in the wild and possibly derived from *C. cardunculus*. Widely grown as a vegetable in the Med region. The young flower-heads are cooked and eaten, especially the 'hearts'.

1981 *Cynara cornigera.* Like *C. cardunculus*, but plant not more than 30cm tall, the leaves with solitary (not clustered) spines and the flower-heads *yellowish-white*. Rocky and stony habitats, poor pastures, often coastal. Apr-May. S Greece, Crete, Aegean Is., Cyprus, Libya, Egypt.

1982 *Silybum marianum* **MILK THISTLE**. Robust, short to tall, weakly spiny (except for the the very spiny flower-heads) biennial, to 1.5m. Basal leaves oblong, pinnately-lobed, large, white-veined, often with large *white blotches*, hairless or almost so, stalked; stem leaves smaller and less deeply lobed, clasping the stem with a lobed base. Flower-heads purple, 25-40mm, solitary at the end of a branched stem; florets all tubular; flower-bracts oblong, terminating in a stout spine up to 70mm long. Waste and fallow ground, open woodland, roadsides, olive groves, field margins. Mar-June. T. Widely cultivated, primarily for its ornamental leaves.

flower bract

1983 *Silybum eburneum.* Similar, but stems *whitish* (not green) and leaves with stouter spines; outer flower-bracts spineless. Field margins, roadsides. Apr-July. N Spain and NW Africa.

1984 *Serratula cichoracea* **SERRATULA**. Short to medium perennial; stems finely hairy, leafless above. Leaves oblong to elliptical, usually toothed, not spiny; stem leaves linear-lanceolate, the base usually forming a narrow wing down the stem. Flower-heads purple, 30-40mm; florets all tubular; flower-bracts *shiny*, with a rigid spine-tip, usually recurved. SE Spain, N Africa, S Italy, Sicily and Crete. The Cretan form, which has slightly ciliated flower-bracts with a short apical spine, is referable to subsp. *cretica* (1984a).

flower bract

1985 *Serratula cerinthifolia.* Similar, but leaves sometimes pinnately-lobed, with oblong lobes and stems leafy above. Flower-heads rather smaller, *yellow*. Dry stony and rocky habitats, at low altitudes and in the mountains. June-Aug. Turkey, Cyprus and Palestine.

1986 *Leuzia conifera [Centaurea conifera]* **LEUZIA**. A low to short, hairy, tufted perennial; stems leafy to the top. Leaves oval to lanceolate, the lower undivided or pinnately-lobed and lyre-shaped, the upper divided with narrow segments, all green above but white-felted beneath. Flower-heads 40-50mm, solitary, purple or whitish, the flowers small and rather insignificant but the involucre of flower-bracts large and *cone-like*, with broad, closely overlapping, shiny-brown, rather papery bracts. Achene black, warted, with a white feathery pappus. Garrigue,

flower bracts

open pine woodland, rocky and stony places, poor grassland, uncultivated land. May-July. Iberian Peninsula and NW Africa eastwards to Italy and Sicily.

flower
bract

1987 *Volutaria lippii [Centaurea lippii]* **VOLUTARIA**. A short to medium hairy annual; stems erect, branched, leafy to the top. Basal leaves lyre-shaped to pinnately-lobed, with oblong, toothed segments, the lower leaves long-stalked, generally in a basal rosette, the upper with a short winged stalk that runs slightly down the stem. Flower-heads bright pink, *small*, 12-14mm long, solitary or paired at the branch-tips. Achenes hairy; pappus present. Cultivated, fallow and waste ground. Apr-July. N Africa, Turkey and the extreme E Med, not Cyprus; naturalised in the Iberian Peninsula and S France.

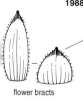

flower bracts

1988 *Mantisalca salmantica [Centaurea salmantica]* **MANTISALCA**. A short to tall, somewhat hairy perennial; stems erect, slender, usually branched. Basal leaves in a crowded rosette, oval in outline, lyre-shaped and pinnately-lobed, hairy, usually stalked; stem leaves rather few, linear to oblong, toothed, occasionally lobed. Flower-heads pink or mauve, 15-20mm, solitary on branches; flower-bracts oval, yellowish-green with a blackish apex, *without* an appendage but with a short apical spine. Achenes dark brown with a whitish or brownish pappus. Coastal sands, cultivated and waste ground, roadsides, dry stony habitats. May-Aug. T – not Corsica or Crete.

Centaurea **CORNFLOWERS and KNAPWEEDS**. Annual to perennial herbs, occasionally shrubby. Leaves alternate, divided or undivided. Flower-heads solitary or clustered in 2-3s; florets tubular, the outermost often larger, sterile and spreading, the inner hermaphrodite; flower-bracts forming a globose to cylindrical involucre, each bract with a characteristic cut or spiny apical appendage. Pappus usually present, feathery.

flower
bract

1989 *Centaurea spinosa*. Dwarf shrub, much-branched, not more than 20cm tall; *stems* thick and spiny. Leaves pinnately-lobed or unlobed, grey-hairy, the lobes spiny. Flower-heads pale pink, small, 5-8mm, solitary; flower-bracts terminating in a spine-tipped appendage. Pappus absent. Coastal sands, rarely inland. May-July. S Greece, Crete and the Aegean Is.
    1989a Subsp. *cycladum* has cream-coloured flowers. Cyclades.

flower
bracts

1990 *Centaurea calcitrapa* **RED STAR-THISTLE**. Short to tall, much-branched, almost hairless, spreading perennial, with grooved stems. Leaves pinnately-lobed, the lobes bristle-pointed, the lower generally withered by flowering time, the upper smaller and narrower. Flower-heads purple, 8-10mm, the florets equal, surrounded by conspicuous spreading, long-spined flower-bracts, yellowish and forming a *star*, often with shorter spines towards the base. Pappus absent. Cultivated, fallow and waste ground, dry bare and grassy habitats, sandy places, roadsides. June-Aug. T. Represented in Cyprus by subsp. *angusticeps* (1990a), which is endemic and has smaller flower-heads and slenderer spines. The seed is often introduced into northern Europe as an impurity in Lucerne and Clover seed which is used for agricultural purposes.

flower bract

1991 *Centaurea cineraria*. Very variable *white- to grey-woolly*, medium to tall perennial; stems erect. Leaves pinnately-lobed, with oval, toothed segments. Flower-heads purple, 15-32mm, solitary; flower-bracts oval with a dark brown pointed, not spiny, appendage. Pappus present. Coastal rocks. May-Aug. Italy and Sicily. Grown in gardens, especially forms with striking white foliage; several subspecies are recognised.

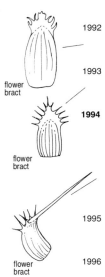

flower bract

flower bract

flower bract

flower bract

flower bract

flower bract

flower bract

1992 *Centaurea kilaea*. Similar, but flower-heads in flat-topped clusters, pale pink; flower-bracts with a very short apical spine, pale brown. Coastal sands. Turkey – including European part.

1993 *Centaurea cuneifolia*. Like *C. kilaea*, but a biennial; flower-bracts with prominent veins, with or without an apical spine. Rocky and stony habitats, hillslopes. Balkans and Turkey.

1994 *Centaurea solstitialis* **ST BARNABY'S THISTLE, YELLOW STAR-THISTLE.** Medium to tall, greyish-downy biennial; stems erect, branched and winged. Lower leaves pinnately-lobed, stalked, the upper linear-lanceolate, unstalked and untoothed. Flower-heads pale yellow, 10-12mm, solitary, the florets all the same length; flower-bracts terminating in a long straw-coloured spine, generally with short spines at the base of the bract. Garrigue, dry habitats, fields, stony ground, roadsides, embankments, grassy and rocky habitats. May-Aug. T – not Portugal or parts of N Africa.

1995 *Centaurea nicaeensis*. Similar, but stems *unwinged* and flower-heads larger, surrounded by the upper leaves. Cultivated, fallow and waste ground. Spain, Sardinia, Italy, Sicily and Malta.

1996 *Centaurea melitensis* **MALTESE STAR-THISTLE.** Like *C. solstitialis*, but stem less branched, leaves greener and rough-hairy; flower-heads solitary or clustered in 2-3s; flower-bracts with a *shorter* spine, 5-8mm long. Dry habitats, disturbed and waste ground. Iberian Peninsula and NW Africa eastwards to the Balkans, including Crete.

1997 *Centaurea aegialophila [Aegialophila cretica]*. Low almost stemless perennial, occasionally up to 20cm tall. Leaves with cobwebby hairs, in a spreading rosette, oval to lyre-shaped, often with a heart-shaped base, occasionally with a few small basal lobes, stalked. Flower-heads purple, 15-30mm, solitary or clustered; flower-bracts oval, with a thin membranous, slightly toothed margin and a short apical spine, 1-3mm long. Coastal sands, including sand-dunes. Mar-July. Crete, S Turkey and Cyprus.

1998 *Centaurea pumilio*. Very similar, but spines of flower-bracts *longer*, 5-9mm. Similar habitats. Apr-May. Crete and NE Africa.

1999 *Centaurea raphanina*. Like *C. aegialophila*, but leaves narrower, oblong-lanceolate, unlobed to pinnately-lobed or lyre-shaped. Flower-heads pink or purple; flower-bracts usually with a terminal spine 2-9mm long. Rocky and sandy habitats, coastal and in the lower mountains. Apr-June. Crete, Cassos and Karpathos.

1999a Subsp. *mixta [Centaurea mixta]* is distinguished by its shiny, *hairless* leaves, toothed leaf-lobes and flower-bracts with a 9-25mm long apical spine. S and E Greece, Cyclades.

2000 *Centaurea diffusa*. Short to medium annual or biennial; stems erect, regularly and much-branched. Leaves green, the lower 2-pinnately-lobed, sparsely cobwebby-hairy. Flower-heads pink, 8-12mm, solitary, but numerous; flower-bracts with a spine-tipped appendage, the spine 2-3mm long, erect or spreading. Coastal sands, rocky and waste places. May-July. Balkans and Turkey; naturalised in France and Italy.

2001 *Centaurea sonchifolia*. Medium, minutely hairy perennial; stems erect, branching into a broad flat-topped inflorescence, with wide, toothed, *wings*. Leaves oval to lyre-shaped, stalked, with spiny-toothed margins; upper leaves lanceolate to lyre-shaped. Flower-heads purple, 28-26mm; flower-bracts with 5-7 reflexed apical spines; florets all similar, the outer scarcely spreading. Coastal sands. Apr-July. Spain, Italy, Sicily and Greece.

flower bract

wer
.ct

2002 *Centaurea sphaerocephala.* Similar, but stems *unwinged* and leaves cobweb-hairy, the upper leaves often clasping the stem with small basal lobes. Flower-heads often larger; flower-bracts with 5-9 yellowish apical spines. Coastal sands, occasionally inland. Apr-June. Iberian Peninsula eastwards to Italy and Sicily, NW Africa – not S France or the Balearic Is.; possibly in Greece. A rather variable species; several subspecies are recognised in Spain and Portugal.

2003 *Centaurea weldeniana.* Medium, tufted perennial; stems moderately branched, long and *rod-like.* Leaves rough, grey-hairy, unlobed, the lower lanceolate, pointed, the upper similar but smaller. Flower-heads pinkish-orange, 14-18mm, solitary, the outer florets larger than the inner, spreading; flower-bracts with papery, white to yellowish or brownish, rounded appendages, covering the bracts, the margin finely toothed or untoothed. Pappus absent. Stony and grassy habitats. May-July. Italy and the Balkans – not Crete.

flower
bract

2004 *Centaurea jacea* **BROWN-RAYED KNAPWEED.** Medium to tall perennial; stems unbranched or few-branched, rough, erect to ascending, to 1.2m, thickened below the flower-heads. Leaves green, the basal oval to lanceolate, untoothed, toothed to pinnately-lobed, hairy; stem leaves often narrower, unlobed. Flower-heads purple, occasionally white, 18-24mm, borne in a *flat-topped* cluster, the outer florets larger and spreading; flower-bracts with rounded, papery, pale brown, often toothed appendages, concealing the bracts. Grassy habitats, meadows, open woodland and thickets. Spain eastwards to Turkey – absent from the islands, except Sicily.

er bract

2005 *Centaurea alba.* Similar, but very variable, the *lower leaves* 1-2-pinnately-lobed. Flower-heads pink, purple or white; flower-bracts concolorous or with a pale or dark centre. Dry stony and grassy habitats. Spain, Italy, Sicily and the Balkans.

2006 *Centaurea pullata.* Low to medium annual; stem branched or unbranched. Leaves rough and hairy, the lower in a basal rosette, lyre-shaped to shallowly-lobed, the upper leaves pinnately-lobed, rarely unlobed. Flower-heads bluish-purple, occasionally white, *large*, 30-50mm, solitary, often surrounded by the uppermost leaves; outer florets much longer than the inner, widely spreading; flower-bracts hairless, pale green, with a conspicuous black margin with a comb-like apex. Dry grassy, stony or rocky habitats in open situations in the lowlands and mountains. Apr-July. Iberian Peninsula, NW Africa; naturalised in France and occasionally casual elsewhere.

r

2007 *Centaurea triumfetti.* Very variable short to tall perennial, sometimes rhizomatous; stems generally erect, unbranched or few-branched, rarely more than 70cm tall. Leaves *unlobed*, oblong to lanceolate or linear, white-cottony when young, the lower stalked. Flower-heads blue to violet-blue or purple, 40-60mm, solitary, the outer florets much larger than the inner and spreading; flower-bracts with a papery, blackish-brown margin fringed usually by whitish or silvery bristles. Grassy, stony and rocky habitats, scrub. May-July. Iberian Peninsula and NW Africa eastwards to Turkey – absent from the islands, except for Sicily.

er
t

2008 *Centaurea cyanus* **CORNFLOWER.** Medium to tall annual; stems slender, erect, usually branched above, grey-cottony. Leaves lanceolate, untoothed or slightly toothed, the lower sometimes with a few narrow lobes. Flower-heads violet-blue or dark blue, rarely white or purple, 15-30mm, solitary, the outer florets spreading, much longer than the inner; flower-bracts narrowly fringed with brown or silver. Cereal fields, disturbed, waste and cultivated ground, roadsides. Apr-June. Sicily, the Balkans and Turkey; widely naturalised elsewhere in the Med, particularly in cereal fields. Widely grown in gardens and as a cut flower, where white, pink, purple, blue and red forms are known.

flower bracts

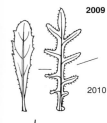

2009 *Crupina crupinastrum* **CRUPINA**. Short to medium, soft annual, not spiny; stems thinly-branched, naked above – leafy only in the lower half. Basal leaves generally pinnately-lobed, the upper oblong, toothed, slightly hairy beneath. Flower-heads purple, egg-shaped, 17-22mm long; florets 9-15, not spreading; flower-bracts pale green, oblong-lanceolate, pointed. Garrigue, dry habitats, waste and fallow ground, stony places, hillslopes, coastal pastures, open pine forest. Apr-June. T.

2010 *Crupina vulgaris*. Similar, but stem leafy up to the branches, the basal leaves never lobed; flower-heads with only 3-5 florets. Dry grassy and stony habitats. T – not Sicily, Crete, most Aegean Is. or Cyprus.

2011 *Cnicus benedictus [Centaurea benedictus]* **BLESSED THISTLE**. Softly-hairy, short to medium annual; stem branched usually only at the base, reddish-purple. Leaves alternate, oblong, pale green, with prominent white veins beneath, the basal often rosetted, pinnately-lobed, stalked, the upper smaller, half-clasping the stem, spine-tipped. Flower-heads yellow and pale green, 25-40mm long, solitary, the florets small, all tubular, *surrounded by a ruff* of small upper leaves; flower-bracts variable, the outer spine-tipped, the inner with a stouter, pinnately-divided, spine. Garrigue, Cultivated, fallow and waste ground, dry hillslopes, vineyards, olive groves. Feb-July. T – not Balearic Is., Corsica, Sicily. A medicinal plant.

flower bracts

Carthamus **CARTHAMUS**. Thistle-like annuals or perennials, often spiny and glandular. Leaves usually pinnately-lobed, with a spiny margin. Flower-heads solitary, surrounded by an involucre of spiny bracts, the outer often leaf-like; florets all tubular, deeply lobed. Pappus present (as scales) only on the inner achenes.

2012 *Carthamus lanatus [Kentrophyllum lanatum]*. A medium to tall glandular annual; stems straw-coloured, branched above, covered with white woolly hairs to begin with. Leaves lanceolate to oval, pinnately-lobed, with a spiny margin, the basal leaves withered by flowering time, the upper half-clasping the stem. Flower-heads yellow, 20-30mm; flower-bracts with a spine-toothed appendage, the inner ones much shorter and rather inconspicuous; anthers yellow. Cultivated, fallow and waste ground, roadsides, vineyards, olive groves, tracksides. Apr-Aug. T – rarer in the east of its range and often replaced by the following subspecies.

    2012a Subsp. *baeticus [Carthamus baeticus]* is distinguished by its less hairy habit and whitish stems, pale yellow flower-heads and white anthers *with* violet lines. S Spain, S Greece and the E Med, including Cyprus.

flower bract

2013 *Carthamus arborescens*. Similar, but a stout, *woody-base* perennial, to 2.5m; flower-heads usually 30-50mm. Rocky and sandy coastal habitats, occasionally inland. Apr-Aug. S Spain, NW Africa.

2014 *Carthamus dentatus*. Thistle-like, glandular, short to medium annual, cobwebby-hairy. Stem leaves greyish, lanceolate to oval, pinnately-lobed with a spiny margin; basal leaves generally withered by flowering time. Flower-heads egg-shaped, violet to pinkish-purple, 20-30mm long; flower-bracts variable, the outer leaf-like, the inner smaller, with an oval to lanceolate, toothed appendage. Fallow and waste ground, dry pastures, vineyards, olive groves. July-Sept. Balkans, including Crete, Turkey.

    2014a Subsp. *ruber* is distinguished by its less hairy habit and flower-bracts with long spreading or reflexed spines, the outer much longer than the inner. S Greece, Aegean Is., Crete, Turkey and Cyprus.

flower bracts

2015 *Carthamus boissieri*. Similar, but the middle and inner flower-bracts *without* an apical appendage, but spine-tipped; flower-heads smaller. Similar habitats. June-Aug. Crete, S Aegean Is., Cyprus.

2016 *Carthamus leucocaulos.* Like *C. boissieri*, but plant scarcely hairy, with an unspotted (not spotted) whitish or purplish stem and leaves *shiny*, often pinnate. Crete and the Aegean Is.

2017 *Carthamus tenuis.* Like *C. boissieri*, but middle and inner flower-bracts gradually (not abruptly) tapered to a spine tip; plant often taller, to 80cm. Dry habitats, cultivated and fallow fields, waste ground. July-Sept. Cyprus, Palestine and Egypt.

2018 *Carduncellus caeruleus [Carthamus caeruleus, Kentrophyllum caeruleum]* **CARDUNCELLUS.** A medium, hairy perennial; stems generally *unbranched*, erect, becoming hairless. Leaves shiny, variable from simple to toothed or pinnately-lobed and lyre-shaped, the teeth terminating in a whitish bristle; upper leaves half-clasping the stem. Flower-heads blue, solitary, 20-30mm, surrounded by leaf-like outer flower-bracts; inner flower-bracts often shorter, with a membranous, rounded appendage; florets all tubular, deeply 5-lobed. Garrigue, cultivated and fallow fields, pastures. May-July. T – rarer in the E.

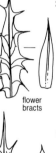

flower
bracts

2019 *Carduncellus monspelliensium.* Similar, but stem often short, only 2-20cm tall, occasionally stemless; stem leaves 2-6 (not 10 or more), pinnately-lobed. Flower-heads often stalkless, 30-40mm; outer flower-bracts spreading, leaf-like. Dry habitats, rocky and stony places, open scrub, in hills and mountains. Spain, Balearic Is., S France, Italy.

2020 *Scolymus hispanicus* **SPANISH OYSTER PLANT.** Medium to tall, usually hairy biennial or perennial, with latex when cut; stems with interrupted *spiny wings*. Lower leaves oblong, broadest above the middle, soft, pinnately-lobed, with a few spines, long-stalked; upper leaves more rigid and more spiny. Flower-heads golden-yellow, thistle-like, 20-30mm, borne in a narrow panicle; florets all rayed; flower-bracts lanceolate, narrowed to a sharp point, with a membranous margin. Pappus absent or reduced to a few small bristles. Cultivated, fallow and waste ground, fields, roadsides, olive groves, sandy soils. May-Sept. T. Sometimes confused with *Carthamus lanatus* which has unwinged stems and all-tubular florets which are deeply 5-lobed.

flower
bracts

2021 *Scolymus maculatus.* Similar, but annual, the leaves and stem-wings with a thick white *margin* and veins; corolla brown-hairy (not white-hairy) in the lower half. Similar habitats. Apr-Aug. T – not Crete.

2022 *Scolymus grandiflorus.* Like *S. hispanicus*, but flower-bracts *very hairy* (not hairless or only slightly hairy), oval to linear-oblong, rather abruptly constricted to the spiny apex. W Med from S France to Italy and Sicily.

flower
bracts

Cichorium **CHICORIES.** Annual or perennial herbs with white latex when cut. Leaves variable, simply toothed to pinnately-lobed. Flower-heads numerous, terminal and axillary; florets all rayed, the rays strap-like and spreading, toothed at the tip; flower-bracts in 2 rows, the outer shorter. Pappus consisting of short scales.

2023 *Cichorium intybus* **CHICORY.** Hairless, or somewhat stiffly-hairy, medium to tall perennial; stems branched, erect. Basal leaves pinnately-lobed to deeply toothed, short-stalked; upper leaves lanceolate, toothed or not, clasping the stem. Flower-heads clear *bright blue*, rarely pink or white, 25-40mm, borne in leafy branched spikes; outer flower-bracts only a half the length of the inner. Garrigue, grassy habitats, fields, cultivated and fallow ground, roadsides, occasionally along the seashore. May-Aug. T – rarer in the extreme E Med. A widely cultivated crop plant; cultivated forms are generally larger with bigger flowers and these sometimes become naturalised. Chicory has long been used as a salad crop; the young leaves are eaten or the shoots forced and blanched. The roots when dried and

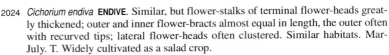

powdered yield chicory which is often added to coffee. The true distribution of
the wild plant is unclear on account of its long association with cultivation.

2024 *Cichorium endiva* **ENDIVE.** Similar, but flower-stalks of terminal flower-heads greatly thickened; outer and inner flower-bracts almost equal in length, the outer often with recurved tips; lateral flower-heads often clustered. Similar habitats. Mar-July. T. Widely cultivated as a salad crop.

2025 *Cichorium spinosum* **SPINY CHICORY.** Densely and intricately branched subshrub, forming *mounds* to 20cm tall, occasionally more; stems branched from the base, the upper non-flowering and spine-like. Leaves fleshy, elliptical, broadest above the middle, toothed or somewhat lobed, mostly in the lower part of the plant. Flower-heads blue, 10-15mm, almost stalkless, solitary or in clusters of 2-4; outer flower-bracts oval, one third the length of the inner lanceolate bracts; florets few, 5-6 to a flower-head. Rock crevices, sandy places, generally coastal. June-Oct. S Spain, Balearic Is., Italy, Sicily, S Greece, Aegean Is., Crete and Cyprus.

2026 *Catananche caerulea* **CUPIDONE.** Thin-stemmed short to tall perennial, covered with short appressed hairs; stems stiff, somewhat branched. Leaves mostly basal, linear, unlobed and untoothed, or with 2-4 teeth; stem leaves few and distant. Flower-heads blue, 25-35mm, solitary; florets all rayed, toothed at the tip; flower-bracts oval, abruptly pointed, papery, closely overlapping to form a shiny, *silvery* involucre, each bract with a dark central stripe. Garrigue, dry pastures, bushy places, roadsides, open woodland. May-Sept. Spain, Balearic Is., S France and Italy. Widely grown in gardens.

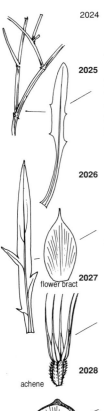

flower bract

2027 *Catananche lutea* **YELLOW CUPIDONE.** Similar, but flower-heads *yellow*; flower-bracts variable, the outer oval, abruptly pointed, the inner longer and narrower, gradually tapered to the pointed apex. Plant rarely more then 30cm tall. Grassy places, hillslopes, sand-dunes, dry rocky places. Mar-June. Sardinia, Italy and Sicily eastwards.

2027a Subsp. *carpholepis* has a larger involucre, 20-30mm long (not 15-20mm). S Spain and N Africa.

achene

2028 *Hymenonema laconicum* **HYMENONEMA.** Short to tall perennial, pale-hairy; stems solitary or few, usually branched, rarely more than 70cm tall. Leaves pinnately-lobed, with toothed segments, the terminal one larger than the lateral. Flower-heads yellow, *large*, 38-46mm, solitary or 2-3 together; florets all rayed, rather narrow; flower-bracts in several closely overlapping rows, oval to oblong, with membranous, sometimes toothed, margins. Achenes 5-angled, appressed-hairy; pappus feathery and scaly. Dry grassy habitats. S Greece – Peloponnese.

2029 *Hymenonema graecum.* Similar, but leaves with a narrow terminal lobe, only up to 10mm (not 15-30mm) wide and rays yellow, sometimes with a purple spot at the base. Stony and rocky habitats, roadsides. Crete and the S Aegean Is. – Cyclades in particular.

flower
bracts

2030 *Tolpis barbata* **TOLPIS.** Low to tall, somewhat hairy annual; stems slender, spreading, usually branched. Leaves oval to linear-lanceolate, untoothed to toothed or slightly lobed. Flower-heads yellow with a dark reddish-purple *centre*, 15-30mm, solitary or several borne on thickened stalks; florets all rayed; flower-bracts numerous, slender, pointed and spreading, often longer than the rays; leaf-like bracts as long as the flower-bracts and forming a ruff beneath the involucre. Pappus present, of rigid hairs. Garrigue, dry habitats, grassy and sandy places, uncultivated ground. Apr-July. T – not Sardinia, Sicily or Yugoslavia.

achene

2031 *Tolpis virgata.* Similar, but a stouter biennial or perennial with a woody stock; upper leaf-like bracts small, *not forming* a ruff beneath the involucre. Similar habitats. May-July. SE France eastwards – not Yugoslavia.

achene

2032 *Hyoseris radiata.* Short to medium perennial, hairy or almost hairless. Leaves all basal, pinnately-divided with *backward* pointing, triangular, toothed lobes. Flower-heads yellow, dandelion-like, 25-35mm, solitary on somewhat roughened, leafless stalks; florets all rayed, overlapping, the outermost somewhat longer than the inner; flower-bracts linear to oblong, pale to dark, in two rows, the outer much shorter than the inner, all shorter than the florets. Pappus of rigid hairs and scales. Grassy and stony pastures, roadsides, olive groves. Jan-Dec. Spain eastwards to Greece and N Africa.

2033 *Hyoseris scabra.* Similar, but a low annual, with flower-stems (scapes) up to 7cm long (not 6-36cm), often *swollen* at or above the middle, prostrate or ascending rather than erect. Inner flower-bracts erect rather than spreading at fruiting time, as long as the florets. Cultivated, fallow and waste ground, roadsides, sometimes in garrigue. Mar-July. T – rarer in the N Med than elsewhere.

2034 *Hedypnois rhagadioloides* [*H. cretica, H. polymorpha*] **HEDYPNOIS.** A variable low to short, somewhat hairy annual; stems slender, spreading to ascending, branched. Leaves elliptical, often broadest above the middle. untoothed to toothed or lobed, the lower often with winged stalks, the upper unstalked. Flower-heads dull golden-yellow, 13-16mm, solitary to numerous, borne on thickened stalks, especially just below the flower-heads; florets all rayed; flower-bracts linear-lanceolate, becoming *strongly incurved* in fruit. Achenes cylindrical, sometimes incurved, 5-7.5mm long; pappus consisting of narrow scales. Dry habitats, cultivated, fallow and waste ground, sand-dunes, roadsides, garrigue. Feb-July. T. An introduced weed in parts of the Southern Hemisphere and North America.

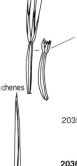

chenes

2035 *Hedypnois arenaria.* Similar, but flower-stalks *not* much thickened and outer flower-bracts scarcely incurved in fruit. Pappus of hairs as well as scales. Coastal habitats, especially sands. S Portugal and SW Spain.

2036 *Koelpinia linearis* **KOELPINIA.** Low to short annual; stems generally branched, sprawling to erect. Leaves grass-like, linear, 3-veined, greyish-green. Flower-heads yellow to whitish-yellow (drying purplish), 6-8mm, solitary or 2-3 together; florets all rayed, few; flower-bracts few, lanceolate to linear, equalling the florets. Achenes linear-cylindrical, hooked and *strongly incurved*, 12-16mm long. Field margins, stony slopes, streamsides, roadsides, sandy places, semi-deserts. Mar-May. SE Spain, N Africa and the E Med, including Cyprus.

achene

2037 *Rhagadiolus stellatus* **STAR HAWKBIT.** Low to medium, coarsely hairy annual; stems usually branched, erect to spreading. Leaves oblong, often broadest above the middle, toothed to pinnately-lobed or lyre-shaped, indistinctly stalked, the upper leaves sometimes oval or lanceolate. Flower-heads yellow, 7-10mm, long-stalked, borne in a lax spreading panicle, occasionally with few flowers; flower-bracts with an outer row of small scales, the inner row of 5-8 linear-lanceolate bracts, as long as the florets. Achenes linear, pointed, 10-16mm long, slightly curved and forming a 7-8-pointed *star.* Cultivated, fallow and waste ground, open garrigue, hillslopes, stony ground. Mar-June. T.

hene

2038 *Rhagadiolus edulis.* Similar, but leaves with a large terminal lobe, stalked; *achenes* 5-6, short, 10-13mm long, spindle-shaped, straight. Similar habitats and flowering time. T. Often confused with the previous species and apparently less common.

2039 *Urospermum dalechampii* **UROSPERMUM.** Low to short, hairy perennial. Basal leaves pinnately-lobed, with backward pointing lobes; stem leaves oval to lanceolate, toothed or not, clasping the stem, the upper opposite. Flower-heads sulphur-yellow, often with a black centre, 35-50mm, solitary; florets all rayed, the outer flushed with reddish-brown on the reverse; flower-bracts lanceolate, softly hairy. Achenes long-beaked, 13-19mm long overall; pappus of red-brown

hene

hairs. Cultivated, fallow and waste ground, roadsides, olive groves. Apr-Aug. Spain eastwards to Yugoslavia. Sometimes grown in gardens.

2040 *Urospermum picroides*. Similar, but flower-bracts oval-lanceolate, often with a dark violet margin, *long-pointed* and bristle-hairy. Flower-heads somewhat smaller, pale yellow. Achenes 11-15mm long; pappus white. Similar habitats. Mar-June. T.

2041 *Hypochoeris achyrophorus [H. aethnensis]* **MEDITERRANEAN CAT'S-EAR**. Rough-hairy, low to short annual; stems generally branched, often thickened below the flower-heads. Leaves forming a *basal rosette*, spatula-shaped to oval, generally broadest above the middle, lobed or unlobed; stem leaves absent or few. Flower-heads golden-yellow to orange-yellow, 12-15mm, solitary; florets all rayed; flower-bracts linear, bristly. Achenes 5-7mm long, beaked; pappus feathery. Garrigue, dry sandy habitats, grassy places, rocky slopes. Mar-June. T – rarer in the E.

2042 *Hypochoeris glabra* **SMOOTH CAT'S-EAR**. Low to short, hairless or rarely slightly bristly annual; stems slightly to strongly thickened above, usually branched. Leaves oblong, broadest above the middle, pale *shiny green*, pinnately-lobed or toothed. Flower-heads pale to bright yellow, small, 10-15mm; flower-bracts lanceolate, with dark tips, unequal, the longest as long as the rays, hairless. Achenes to 8.5mm long, beaked or unbeaked. Garrigue, stony places, seashores, roadsides, grassy places. Mar-June. T.

2043 *Hypochoeris cretensis*. Similar, but often taller, the stems with at least one large leaf and flower-heads larger, 15-22mm. Rocky and grassy habitats, heaths. Apr-June. Sardinia eastwards to the Balkans, including Sicily and Crete.

2044 *Leontodon tuberosus [Thrincia tuberosa]* **TUBEROUS HAWKBIT**. Tuberous-rooted, low to short, hairy perennial. Leaves borne in a basal rosette, oval to oblong, generally widest above the middle, toothed to pinnately-lobed, the lobes generally pointing somewhat backwards. Flower-heads golden-yellow, 20-28mm, solitary on long, *unbranched*, hairy stalks; florets all rayed, the outer often green on the reverse; flower-bracts oblong, hairy or not. Achenes 3-7mm long, usually beaked, two kinds, the outer curved, the inner straight; pappus feathery. Garrigue, grassy places, open scrub, roadsides, lowland and in the mountains. Feb-June. T.

2045 *Leontodon crispus*. Similar, but not tuberous and flower-heads often larger. Achenes all similar, 7-12mm long. Rocky and grassy habitats, mainly in the hills and mountains. Spain eastwards to Turkey – not Portugal, Balearic Is., Sardinia, Crete or Cyprus.

Picris **OXTONGUES**. Annual to perennial herbs, rough-hairy, often with hooked basal branches; stems solitary, branched. Leaves often pinnately-lobed. Flower-heads with rayed florets, yellow, the outer often with a reddish stripe on the reverse; flower-bracts in several closely overlapping rows. Achenes pointed or beaked, ridged; pappus of simple and feathery hairs.

2046 *Picris echioides [Helmintia echioides, Helminthotheca echioides]* **BRISTLY OXTONGUE**. Medium to tall, bristly annual or biennial, each bristle arising from a *pimple*; stems branched. Leaves elliptical to oblong, wavy-edged, pimply, the lower with winged stalks, the upper unstalked, oval and clasping the stem. Flower-heads yellow, 20-25mm, numerous; flower-bracts with bristly margins, the outer heart-shaped. Pappus white. Grassy and waste places, cultivated fields, brackish marshes, roadsides, olive groves, streamsides. Apr-July. T – not Cyprus or parts of the E Med.

achenes

(2041)

achenes

achene

achenes

2047 *Picris pauciflora*. Similar, but the leaves untoothed to toothed and the flower-heads fewer and smaller; flower-bracts *all* linear-lanceolate, pointed. Bare stony places and poor pastures, roadsides, lowland and in the mountains. Apr-July. S France eastwards to Turkey, including Cyprus and Crete, not Italy and Sicily.

2048 *Picris altissima [P. sprengeriana]*. Like *P. echioides*, but bristles on flower-stalks and flower-bracts 2-4-barbed and stem-leaves with small clasping lobes at the base; flower-bracts all linear-lanceolate. Achenes only 2.5-3mm (not 5-7)mm long. Cultivated, fallow and waste ground, stony slopes, roadsides, olive groves. SE France, Italy, the Balkans, Crete and the E Med, including Cyprus.

2049 *Picris hieracioides* **HAWKWEED OXTONGUE.** Short to tall, bristly biennial or short-lived perennial; stems usually branched. Leaves lanceolate to oblong, toothed or not, stalked, the upper small and unstalked, clasping the stem. Flower-heads yellow, 20-35mm, stalked, in a cluster; flower-bracts lanceolate, with *blackish hairs*, the outer shorter and spreading. Pappus creamy. Grassy habitats, roadsides, scrub. Apr-July. T – not Balearic Is., Crete and most of the E Med.

achene

Scorzonera **VIPER'S-GRASSES.** Perennial herbs; stem solitary or several. Leaves often narrow, unlobed to pinnately-lobed. Flower-heads solitary to many, yellow, pink or purple, occasionally white; flower-bracts several closely overlapping rows; florets all rayed, toothed at the tip. Achenes cylindrical; pappus feathery. The cultivated Scorzonera, whose roots are eaten as a vegetable is the Common Viper's-grass, *S. hispanica*, a native of S Europe.

2050 *Scorzonera laciniata [Podospermum laciniatum]* **CUT-LEAVED VIPER'S-GRASS** . A very variable, short to medium annual or biennial, occasionally a monocarpic perennial (dying after flowering). *Basal leaves* 1-2-pinnately-lobed, with slender segments; upper leaves less divided, clasping the stem. Flower-heads plain yellow, 15-25mm, solitary on stout stalks; flower-bracts lanceolate to oval, the inner equalling or slightly shorter than the rays. Cultivated and waste ground, rocky habitats, roadsides. Mar-June. T.

2051 *Scorzonera jacquiniana [S. cana, Podospermum canum]*. Similar, but a hairy perennial, the stems often branched up to the middle. Flower-heads yellow, but greenish, reddish or purplish on the *reverse*; flower-bracts much shorter than the rays. Grassy and rocky places, salty soils. Mar-June. Sardinia and Italy eastwards – not Crete. Represented in Cyprus and parts of the E Med by subsp. *subintegra*, which has less cut leaves.

2052 *Scorzonera villosa* **VILLOUS VIPER'S-GRASS.** Low to short, hairy, tufted perennial, sometimes with cobwebby hairs, especially at the stem-and leaf-bases; stems solitary or few. Leaves linear, *untoothed*, with whitish basal sheaths. Flower-heads yellow, reddish on the reverse, 20-35mm. Achenes hairless; pappus pale reddish-brown. Grassy habitats. Apr-July. Sardinia, Italy, Sicily and Yugoslavia.

flower
bracts

2053 *Scorzonera hirsuta*. Similar, but stems sometimes branched in the middle and leaves with prominent veins. Flower-heads often plain yellow. Achenes *densely hairy*. Dry rocky and grassy habitats. NE Spain, S France, Italy and Sicily.

2054 *Scorzonera cretica* **CRETAN VIPER'S-GRASS.** Like *S. hirsuta*, but a more leafy plant, the leaves 1-10mm wide (not 1-4mm) and the flower-heads often reddish on the reverse. Rocky and dry grassy habitats, old walls and cliffs, roadsides. Apr-May. Crete and S Aegean Is. A very variable species.

flower
bract

Tragopogon **GOAT'S-BEARDS.** Annual to perennial herbs, with latex when cut; stem usually solitary, branched or not. Leaves linear-lanceolate to linear, with parallel

leaf

veins, those on the stem sheathing at the base. Flower-heads solitary or several; florets all rayed; flower-bracts in a single row, long. Fruit a large 'clock'; achenes beaked. The flowers generally open in the mornings only.

2055 *Tragopogon porrifolius* **SALSIFY.** Medium to tall, hairless biennial; stem erect, usually branched, to 1.2m, though often less, broadening below the flower-heads. Leaves broad-linear, widened at the base. Flower-heads *lilac to dull reddish-purple*, 25-48mm; flower-bracts often 8, equalling or slightly longer than the rays. Grassy habitats, roadsides, cultivated and waste ground. Apr-June. T – not Portugal, Cyprus and parts of the extreme E Med. The swollen fleshy rootstock, White Salsify, can be cooked and the young green shoots can be added to salads.

2056 *Tragopogon hybridum [Geropogon hybridus].* Similar, but a smaller and more delicate annual, rarely more than 50cm tall. Flower-heads pinkish-lilac, smaller, with few, often only, 5 florets (not many), much exceeded by the narrow, pointed flower-bracts. Pastures, waste and fallow land, grassy and stony places. Mar-May. T – not Cyprus.

achene

2057 *Tragopogon crocifolius.* Like *T. porrifolius*, but leaves scarcely widening at the base and the flower-heads violet with the central florets *yellow*. Grassy and stony habitats, waste places. Apr-June. Iberian Peninsula eastwards to the Balkans – absent from the islands except Corsica.

2058 *Tragopogon sinuatus [T. australis, T. longiostris, T. porrifolius* subsp. *australis].* Like *T. porrifolius*, but often minutely hairy, the stem rarely more than 50cm tall, often less. Flower-heads mauve to deep violet, the rays *half as long* as the flower-bracts. Similar habitats. Mar-June. T.

2059 *Tragopogon pratensis* **GOAT'S-BEARD.** Variable medium to tall annual to perennial, hairless or slightly hairy; stems often unbranched, rarely more than 70cm tall. Leaves linear-lanceolate, channelled, the stem leaves half-clasping, tapered to a fine point. Flower-heads *pale yellow*, 18-40mm, solitary; flower-bracts usually 8-10, longer than the rays; flower-stalks not inflated. Fruit a large 'clock' to 12cm diam. Cultivated, waste and fallow ground, garrigue, roadsides, scrub, occasionally on sand-dunes. Apr-June. T – not Portugal and most of the islands.

achene

2060 *Tragopogon dubius [T. major, T. dubius* subsp. *campestris].* Similar, but a shorter plant with the flower-stalks *strongly inflated* below the flower-heads; flower-bracts 8-12. Dry woodland, scrub, plantations, rough grassy places. T – absent from the islands.

flower bracts

2061 *Reichardia tingitana [Picridium tingitanum]* **REICHARDIA.** A low to short, hairless annual to perennial, like a Hawkbit. Leaves oblong, toothed to pinnately-lobed, smooth or with tiny white pimples, the basal with a broad-winged stalk; stem leaves few, similar or linear, half-clasping. Flower-heads yellow, 18-24mm, solitary; rays *purplish* at the base, the outer with a red stripe on the reverse; flower-bracts oval, with wide membranous margins, hairless. Dry rocky and grassy places, pathsides, gravelly seashores. Mar-May. S. Spain, Balearic Is., N Africa, Sicily, Greece, Crete, Cyprus and parts of the E Med.

leaf

2062 *Reichardia gaditana.* Similar, but leaves without white pimples and flower-bracts longer, 15-22mm long (not 10-15mm). Sandy and rocky coastal habitats. W Spain and Portugal.

2063 *Reichardia picroides.* Like *R. tingitana*, but rays yellow at the base, *not* purple; flower-stalks not thickened towards the top. Fallow and waste ground, bare places, cultivation. Mar-May. T.

2064 *Reichardia intermedia.* Like *R. picroides*, but annual (not perennial) and the flower-bracts with a wide membranous margin, to 1.25mm (not 0.5mm); outer flower-

flower
bracts

bracts 4-7mm long (not 3-5mm). Rocky and stony habitats, fallow fields and scrub. T – France, Corsica, Sardinia or Yugoslavia.

2065 *Launaea resedifolia* **LAUNAEA**. Short, hairless biennial or perennial; stem branched or unbranched. Leaves mostly in the lower half of the stem, oblong, pinnately-lobed with narrow segments, the upper often grading into the bracts. Flower-heads yellow, 20-26mm, solitary; florets all rayed. Achenes not beaked; pappus consisting of *simple* hairs. Coastal sands and dry hillslopes. Spain, Sicily, N Africa, Cyprus and parts of the E Med.

2066 *Launaea nudicaulis*. Similar, but leaf-margins with tiny *white* spines; achenes 3-4mm long (not 5-7mm). Dry saline or gypsaceous soils. SE Spain, N Africa, Turkey.

Crepis **HAWKSBEARDS**. Annual or perennial herbs with spirally arranged leaves, often lobed and with the lobes pointing backwards; stems normally branched. Flower-heads, often yellow, occasionally orange, pink or white; florets all rayed; flower-bracts in 2 rows, the outer shorter. Pappus usually white, of simple, often brittle, hairs. A large and complicated genus with 70 species in Europe alone.

ene

2067 *Crepis nicaeensis* **FRENCH HAWKSBEARD**. Hairy, short to tall annual or perennial; stems branched from the middle upwards, reddish and ribbed below. Leaves oblong, toothed or pinnately-lobed, narrowed into a stalk, the uppermost leaves lanceolate, unstalked often clasping the stem with a pair of pointed lobes; all leaves with yellowish hairs. Flower-heads yellow, often reddish on the reverse or at the tip, 20-25mm, borne in *branched*, flat-topped clusters; flower-bracts linear-lanceolate, downy. Meadows and grassy places, arable fields, roadsides. Apr-July. Spain eastwards to Yugoslavia; absent from the islands but sometimes casual, especially in forage crops.

2068 *Crepis zacintha [Zacintha verrucosa]*. Short, hairy annual; stem branched from the base. Leaves oblong, pinnately-lobed to lyre-shaped with a large end lobe, stalked, the lowermost withered by flowering time, the uppermost lanceolate or bract-like, with a pair of pointed lobes clasping the stem. Flower-heads yellow, *small*, 12-15mm; rays with a purple stripe on the reverse; flower-bracts lanceolate to almost linear, usually hairless. Rocky and grassy habitats, cultivated, waste and fallow ground. Mar-May. T – not Portugal, Balearic Is. or Sicily.

2069 *Crepis sancta [Lagoseris sancta]*. Similar, but hairy or hairless and with few stem leaves, linear or bract-like. Flower-heads larger, 15-20mm; flower-bracts hairy, the outer with a *conspicuous* pale margin, much shorter than the inner. Fields, grassy and heathy places, cultivated, fallow and waste land, coastal garrigue, roadsides. Dec-May. Balkans, Crete and the E Med, including Cyprus.

2070 *Crepis rubra* **PINK HAWKSBEARD**. Low to medium, hairy annual, not more than 40cm tall, often less. Leaves mostly basal, oblong, broadest above the middle, deeply toothed to pinnately-lobed, with triangular to lanceolate lobes; stem leaves few, mostly bract-like. Flower-heads *pink or white*, 25-32mm, on branched or un-branched stems; flower-bracts in 2 rows, the outer half the length of the inner and often hairless, the inner glandular-hairy. Achenes dark brown, ribbed and with tiny spines. Grassy habitats, olive groves, roadsides, cultivated land. Apr-June. S Italy, Balkans and Crete.

hene

Sonchus **SOW-THISTLES**. Annual or perennial herbs, usually with a solitary, branched stem, producing copious latex when cut. Leaves alternate, toothed to pinnately-lobed, often rather bristly; stem leaves clasping. Flower-heads yellow; florets all rayed; flower-bracts numerous, usually in three rows. Pappus present; fruit-head a 'clock'.

2071 *Sonchus asper* **PRICKLY SOW-THISTLE**. A short to tall, greyish annual, to 1.2m, though often less, hairless except for glandular-hairs on the upper part of the angled stem. Leaves elliptical to lanceolate, thin, pinnately-lobed or unlobed, with a soft-spiny margin, the upper leaves clasping the stem with *rounded* basal lobes. Flower-heads golden-yellow, 20-25mm, borne in lax clusters; flower-bracts 35-45. Cultivated, waste and fallow ground, field margins, meadows, roadsides, olive groves, vineyards, ditches. Feb-Oct. T – not Cyprus and parts of the E Med.

   2071a Subsp. *glaucescens* is distinguished by its biennial habit, and its thicker leaves which form a distinctive basal rosette, often with more strongly prickly margins. T – including Cyprus.

2072 *Sonchus oleraceus* **SMOOTH SOW-THISTLE**. Similar, but the leaves generally more deeply lobed and clasping the stem with *pointed*, triangular leaf-bases. Flower-bracts up to 35 and achenes smooth (not rough). Similar habitats and flowering time. T – a cosmopolitan weed. Occasionally hybridises with *S. asper*.

2073 *Sonchus tenerrimus*. Short to tall annual, biennial or often perennial; stem usually branched, hairless or glandular towards the top. Leaves oblong in outline, pinnately-lobed, the lobes clearly *narrowed* at the base, linear-lanceolate, occasionally linear, toothed or not, the lower often withered by flowering time, the upper clasping the stem with rounded or pointed lobes; lower leaves hairless, the upper often with white hairs. Flower-heads 20-30mm; flower-bracts 27-35, and flower-stalks white-hairy. Achenes rough. Grassy habitats, field margins, open woodland, dune-slacks, stream-beds, disturbed ground. Feb-June. T – often local.

2074 *Sonchus maritimus*. Similar, but a *rhizomatous* perennial. Leaves narrower, linear to oblong, undivided or occasionally somewhat pinnately-lobed, toothed, the upper clasping the stem with rounded lobes. Damp saline soils, especially close to the coast. Iberian Peninsula and NW Africa eastwards to Yugoslavia, not Crete.

achene

Lactuca **LETTUCES**. Annual, biennial or perennial herbs with copious milky latex when cut. Leaves unlobed or variously lobed and toothed, often bristly. Flowers yellow or blue; florets all rayed; flower-bracts several rows, generally rather narrow. Pappus present; achenes beaked.

2075 *Lactuca viminea [Scariola viminea]* **PLIANT LETTUCE**. Medium to tall, hairless biennial or perennial; stems erect, generally numerous, slender, branched above. Leaves dark grey-green, the lower pinnately-lobed, with linear-lanceolate, usually toothed, lobes; upper leaves lanceolate, unlobed except for two basal lobes that extend *down the stem*. Flower-heads pale yellow, borne in a much-branched spike-like panicle; florets often 5 per head, sometimes up to 8, the rays broad with a toothed apex. Achenes blackish, ribbed, 12-15mm long. Dry habitats, rocky and stony ground, open scrub, grassy places. June-Sept. T – not Corsica and Cyprus.

   2075a Subsp. *chondrilliflora* is very similar, but the stems are branched throughout, not only in the upper part; achenes smaller, 7-9mm long. W and C Med, east to the W Balkans.

   2075b Subsp. *ramosissima* is a lower plant, not more than 30cm tall and branched from the base; achenes 9-11mm long. T – not Cyprus.

2076 *Lactuca serriola [L. scariola]* **PRICKLY LETTUCE**. A tall greyish annual or biennial to 1.8m, though often less; stems stiff and erect, hairless or rather bristly. Leaves oblong, pinnately-lobed, *prickly* along the margins and on the midrib beneath; upper leaves smaller, more or less vertical, clasping the stem with a lobed base. Flower-heads pale yellow, 11-13, borne in a narrow pyramidal panicle; flower-

achene

achene

heads with 7-15 rays. Achenes greyish, 6-8mm long. Cultivated, fallow and waste ground, stony and rocky slopes, occasionally on sand-dunes. July-Oct. T.

2077 *Lactuca saligna* **LEAST LETTUCE**. Similar, but with *whitish stems*, to 1m, though often less; leaves greyish, not prickly, the lower pinnately-lobed, the upper unlobed, oblong to linear, clasping the stem with an arrow-shaped base. Flower-heads with 7-17 rays, slightly smaller. Bare and grassy places, field margins, ditches, poor pastures, waste ground. July-Oct. T.

2078 *Lactuca perennis* **MOUNTAIN** or **BLUE LETTUCE**. Medium to tall, hairless perennial with erect stems that are branched above. Leaves greyish-green, pinnately-lobed, with narrow segments, short-stalked, the upper leaves usually unstalked and half-clasping the stem. Flower-heads *pale blue to lilac*, 30-40mm, borne in a broad, rather flat-topped, panicle, each flower-head with 12-20 rays. Achenes 10-14mm long, black. Dry habitats, rocks, stony ground, grassy places, usually on limestone. Apr-July. Iberian Peninsula eastwards to Yugoslavia – absent from the islands.

2079 *Chondrilla juncea [C. canescens, C. latifolia]* **CHONDRILLA**. A medium to tall, greyish biennial or perennial, hairless or stiffly hairy, especially in the lower part; stems usually solitary, to 1m, stiff and broom-like, few-leaved. Leaves oblong, lobed to deeply toothed, the lower soon withering, the upper linear, unlobed, often untoothed. Flower-heads unstalked, yellow, 9-10mm, in small clusters on branched stems; florets all rayed; flower-bracts linear-lanceolate, erect, hairy or not. Garrigue, dry open habitats, hillslopes, on sandy or stony ground. June-Sept. T. The seeds are poisonous.

2080 *Lapsana communis* **NIPPLEWORT**. Short to tall annual, sometimes overwintering; stems erect, to 1.5m though often less, *without* milky latex when cut, branched or unbranched. Leaves oval, toothed, often lobed at the base, the lower stalked, the uppermost smaller and often unstalked. Flower-heads yellow, 10-20mm, borne in a lax-branched panicle; florets all rayed; flower-bracts lanceolate, erect. Fallow, waste and disturbed ground, cultivated places, hedgerows, roadsides, olive groves, woodland margins and scrub, in sunny or shaded places. May-Oct. T – not Crete or Cyprus. A widespread, fast-growing weed of cultivation.

2081 *Andryala integrifolia [A. arenaria, A. dentata, A. sinuata]* **ANDRYALA**. Short to tall, whitish-yellow, hairy annual to perennial; stems leafy, moderately to densely branched. Leaves oval to lanceolate, unlobed to pinnately-lobed, the uppermost often half-clasping the stem, densely covered with yellowish glandular and star-shaped hairs. Flower-heads pale to mid-yellow, 10-20mm, borne in *flat-topped* clusters; flower-bracts linear-lanceolate, hairy like the leaves. Sandy and rocky habitats, heathy places, tracksides. Apr-July. Iberian Peninsula and NW Africa eastwards to Italy and Sicily, Greece – not Crete. A very variable species that some authorities split into several species.

achene

2082 *Andryala laxiflora*. Similar, but the flower-heads larger; involucre of bracts 12-15mm wide (not 5-10mm). Similar habitats and flowering time. Iberian Peninsula.

2083 *Andryala ragusina*. Like *A. integrifolia*, but a more white-felted, tufted plant with rather larger flowers; involucre white-felted, *without* glandular hairs. Similar habitats and flowering time. Iberian Peninsula, S France, Balearic Is. and Corsica.

Order – Monocotyledons

The other major grouping of the flowering plants, but a minority of the families in this book. Monocotyledons ('monocots') have a single seed-leaf (cotyledon). The stem vessels consists of a distinct series of bundles or are scattered. The leaves nearly always have parallel veins. Flowers are typically 3-parted, or multiples thereof. Although relatively few families belong here, they are important in the region. The Amaryllidaceae, Liliaceae, Iridaceae, Orchidaceae and Gramineae are important monocot families.

FROGBIT FAMILY Hydrocharitaceae

A family of aquatic plants with floating or submerged leaves. Flowers enclosed in bract-like spathes; sepals and petals 3; stamens 2-15. Fruit a capsule, splitting lengthwise.

2084 *Halophila stipulacea* **HALOPHILA**. Submerged marine plant, with a creeping rhizome. Leaves linear to oblong, finely toothed, 3-veined, to 6cm long, *paired* on short shoots. Flowers tiny, greenish, without petals, unisexual, the male stalked the female unstalked, with 3 styles. Fruit elliptical, 5mm, with an equally long beak. Submerged mud or sand. Coasts of Sicily, Crete, Greece and the Extreme E Med. Has spread west along the Med from the Red Sea, via the Suez Canal, since it was opened in 1869.

POSIDONIA FAMILY Posidoniaceae

A small family of submerged marine perennial herbs with creeping rhizomes. Inflorescence spike-like or several spikes, with leaf-like bracts below; flowers usually hermaphrodite, without a perianth; stamens 3. Fruit a berry.

2085 *Posidonia oceanica* **POSIDONIA**. Rhizomatous perennial, with the base densely clothed in fibrous scale and sheath remains. Leaves basal, alternate, linear, untoothed, blunt or notched at the apex, to 55cm long, with 13 or more veins; leaf-base sheathing. Spikes 3-5-flowered, borne on stout stalks, with leaf-like bracts. Sandy and muddy coastal habitats, in deep water, often 5m or more. T. Often found on beaches and shorelines as characteristic tangled balls of leaves and debris; brought ashore during storms.

fruit

ARROW-GRASS FAMILY Juncaginaceae

A small family of annual or perennial plants of marshy and aquatic habitats, with basal and alternate leaves. Flowers borne in a terminal spike or raceme, small and greenish; perianth segments 6, sepal-like; stamens 3-6. Fruit often 3-parted.

2086 *Triglochin bulbosa* subsp. *barrelieri* **BULBOUS ARROW-GRASS**. A low to short perennial with a bulbous rootstock. Leaves few, linear, tapered to a fine point, not more than 4mm wide. Flowers tiny and greenish, 1.5-2.5mm, borne in slender *spikes* to 10cm long without the stalk. Fruit elliptical, spreading, 5-12mm long. Salt marshes and the margins of brackish pools and lakes, at low altitudes. Feb-May. T.

2086a Subsp. *laxiflora* is distinguished by flowering in Sept-Nov and having the fruit pressed *close* to the axis of the spike. Similar habitats and distribution. The typical plant, subsp. *bulbosa*, is confined to southern Africa.

plant base

fruit

468

LILY FAMILY Liliaceae

A large family of perennial herbs, often with a bulbous, tuberous or rhizomatous stock. Leaves often linear or lanceolate, with parallel veins, occasionally heart-shaped. Perianth generally 6-parted, often all similar and petal-like (tepals), separate or fused; stamens usually 6; style 1, occasionally 3. Fruit a 3-parted capsule or a berry. The family has recently been divided into more than twenty distinct families; this has not been followed here so as to allow for consistency with standard floras and reference-bookss on the area.

Asphodelus **ASPHODELS**. Robust, hairless, herbaceous perennials. Leaves borne in a basal tuft and the leafless stems support a raceme or panicle of star-shaped flowers, each subtended by a papery bract. Fruit a 3-parted capsule. Often seen in great numbers in areas subjected to heavy grazing as they are generally unpalatable to livestock.

2087 *Asphodelus fistulosus* **HOLLOW-LEAVED ASPHODEL**. Short to medium perennial, with numerous fleshy roots. Leaves linear, *hollow* and cylindrical, not more than 5mm wide. Flowers white or pinkish, 16-24mm, the tepals 12-14mm long, with a median brown or pink vein, carried in a branched inflorescence. Capsule 5mm diam. Dry rocky, grassy and waste places, field margins, roadsides, olive groves. Feb-June. T. A slighter and more delicate looking species than *A. aestivus*, sometimes occurring in large colonies.

2088 *Asphodelus tenuifolius* **ANNUAL ASPHODEL**. Similar, but an annual plant with fibrous roots; flowers *smaller*, the tepals only 4-7mm long. Capsule 3-4mm diam. Grassy, sandy and rocky places. Mar-May. N Africa, E Med, including Cyprus, scarcer in the European Med. Sometimes included in the previous species.

2089 *Asphodelus aestivus* [*A. microcarpus*] **COMMON ASPHODEL**. Robust, medium to tall perennial to 1m, with numerous fleshy roots. Leaves strap-shaped, *flat*, slightly keeled beneath, grey-green, 12-30mm wide. Flowers white, 20-30mm, the tepals with a pinkish-brown midvein, usually 13-16mm long, borne in a much-branched inflorescence; bracts whitish; lateral branched of the inflorescence almost as long as the central raceme. Capsule 6-8mm diam. Garrigue, rocky slopes, waste ground, roadsides, olive groves, open pine forest, occasionally on the seashore. Jan-June. T Often forms extensive colonies, sometimes with *Asphodeline lutea* below: both are unpalatable to grazing animals. The roots, which bear spindle-shaped tubers, are just edible and were formerly used as a glue.

2090 *Asphodelus ramosus* [*A. cerasiferus*]. Similar, but with the side branches of the inflorescence short and *stubby*. Similar habitats and distribution, though far less frequent; absent from the Balearic Is., Crete and Cyprus. Sometimes considered to be a hybrid between *A. albus* and *A. aestivus*.

2091 *Asphodelus albus* **WHITE ASPHODEL**. Medium to tall perennial to 1m, with swollen roots. Leaves linear, grey-green, channelled, tapered to the tip. Flowers white, 30-40mm, borne in a dense simple *spike-like* raceme; tepals with a narrow green midvein; bracts usually dark brown. Rocky ground, waste places, open woodland, meadows, at low altitudes and in the mountains. Mar-June. Spain eastwards to Greece; absent from the islands except for the Balearic Is. and Sardinia.

2092 *Asphodeline lutea* **YELLOW ASPHODEL**. Medium to tall herbaceous perennial, to 1.2m high, with fleshy roots. Leaves linear, deep green or bluish-green, 2-3mm wide, untoothed, carried the whole length of the stem, the lowermost the longest. Flowers *yellow*, 30-40mm, somewhat asymmetric, borne in a dense raceme, each tepal 18-20mm long with a green midvein; stamens 3 long and 3 short, the former with markedly curved stalks (filaments). Capsule 10-12mm diam. Rocky slopes in hills and mountains, garrigue, occasionally on cliffs or by roadsides or in scrub. Mar-May. Italy, Sicily, the Balkans and Crete eastwards, including Cyprus.

2093 *Asphodeline liburnica*. Similar, but a slighter plant, the stem leafy only in the lower two thirds. Flowers borne in a lax raceme. Similar habitats. May-July. Italy, Crete, the Balkans and Turkey.

2094 *Anthericum liliago* **ST BERNARD'S LILY.** Short to medium, hairless herbaceous perennial. Leaves grey-green, borne in a basal tuft, linear, 3-8mm wide, about half the length of the flowering stem. Flowers white, 20-40mm, flattish and star-shaped, borne in a *lax raceme*; style curved but the stamens with straight stalks (filaments). Fruit capsule 8-10mm long. Grassy habitats, woodland and stony places. Apr-June. T – but absent from most of the islands and parts of the extreme E Med. Sometimes confused with *Asphodelus*, but the anthers are attached at the base to the filaments, not in the middle.

2095 *Anthericum ramosum*. Similar, but with smaller flowers, 14-16mm, which have rather reflexed tepals when fully opened, borne in a *branched* panicle; style straight. Dry grassy places and scrub, open woodland. May-July. Spain eastwards to Turkey.

2096 *Aphyllanthes monspeliensis* **APHYLLANTHES.** Medium, tufted, *rush-like* plant, hairless; stems numerous, tough, slender, bluish-green. Leaves reduced to membranous sheaths, often reddish-brown. Flowers blue, rarely white, 25-30mm, in a head of 2-3 surrounded by overlapping papery bracts at the base; tepals with a dark midvein. Fruit a capsule containing 3 seeds. Dry grassy and rocky places; garrigue. Apr-July. Iberian Peninsula eastwards to NW Italy – including the Balearic Is.

Aloe **ALOES.** Succulent, often shrubby plants with rosettes of thick, spiny-margined leaves. Flowers in scapose racemes, often branched; corolla tubular, spreading to pendent, the tepals free at the top. Fruit a capsule, fleshy or papery; seeds numerous. An African and Madagascan genus; many species are cultivated in the Med and some have become naturalised.

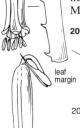

leaf
margin

2097 *Aloe vera* [*A. vulgaris*]. *Suckering* perennial to 1m tall in flower, with numerous basal leaf-rosettes. Leaves triangular-lanceolate, bluish-- or greyish-green, sometimes red-tinged or spotted, smooth, margin spiny. Inflorescence unbranched or with 1-2 lateral branches; flowers yellow, 25-30mm long, pendulous, with protruding stamens. Coastal habitats, both rocky and sandy. Apr-June. Widely naturalised in the Med. (Probably South Africa).

2098 *Aloe aristata*. Similar, but non-stoloniferous. Leaves smaller, 8-10cm long (not 35-60cm), erect or incurved, with a few whitish warts and a soft, white, *terminal spine*. Flowers orange-red, tinged with brownish-green, 30-40mm long. Naturalised in SE France, possibly elsewhere. (South Africa).

2099 *Aloe brevifolia*. Like *A. vera*, but leaves oval-lanceolate, with a few *warts* on the underside towards the apex. Inflorescence unbranched; flowers orange-red, 25-40mm long. Naturalised in SE France. (South Africa).

2100 *Aloe succotrina*. Very variable shrub, to 2m, branched or unbranched. Leaves triangular-lanceolate, 30-50cm long, grey-green, occasionally with paler spots; margin with *dark purplish* teeth. Flowers pinkish-red, 30-40mm long, borne in long, unbranched racemes; bracts purple. Naturalised in SE Spain and SE France. (South Africa).

2101 *Aloe arborescens* . B ranched shrub to 3m, sometimes more. Leaves triangular-lanceolate, 50-60cm long, crowded, spreading to deflexed, dull greyish-green, smooth and without paler spots, margin with green teeth. Inflorescence usually unbranched; flowers scarlet, 35-40mm long. Naturalised in rocky coastal habitats. May-Aug. Iberian Peninsula and S France. (Malawi southwards to South Africa).

Gagea **GAGEAS**. Small bulbous herbs with few basal leaves; stems leaves few or absent. Flowers yellow or white, bell- or star-shaped, with separate tepals. Fruit a small capsule, membranous when ripe. A difficult group with many similar looking species; the leaf type and position are important for identification.

2102 *Gagea graeca [Lloydia graeca].* Low hairless perennial. Basal leaves 2-4, linear; stem leaves alternate, linear-lanceolate, few. Flowers *white*, with purple stripes outside, bell- or funnel-shaped, 10-15mm long, nodding at first but later erect, borne in racemes of 2-5, rarely solitary. Dry grassy habitats, stony and rocky ground, old walls, cliffs, garrigue, occasionally in open pine woodland. Mar-May. S Greece, Crete eastwards, including Cyprus.

2103 *Gagea trinervia.* Similar, but flowers usually *solitary*; anthers 2-3mm long (not 0.5-1mm). Shady and rocky habitats. Sicily and N Africa.

2104 *Gagea pratensis [G. stenopetala]* **MEADOW GAGEA**. Low, slender perennial with a hairless stem. Basal leaf solitary, broad-linear, flat; stem leaves 2, *opposite*, lanceolate; leaf-margins hairy. Flowers 2-6, yellow, slightly green-tinged, 20-30mm, star-shaped; petals rather blunt. Grassy habitats, field margins. Mar-May. Iberian Peninsula eastwards to Greece – absent from most of the islands except Sicily.

2105 *Gagea fistulosa [G. liotardii].* Low to medium perennial with paired bulbs; stem hairless. Basal leaves 2, linear, cylindrical (hollow); stem leaves 2, opposite, broadly lanceolate, hairless. Flowers 3-5, yellow, star-shaped, 25-35mm; tepals broad. Rocky and grassy habitats, mainly in the mountains. May-June. Spain eastwards to Italy and Sicily – not Balearic Is. or Sardinia.

2106 *Gagea arvensis [G. dubia, G. villosa].* Low to medium, finely hairy perennial. Basal leaves 2, linear, *grooved*, 3-4mm wide; stem leaves 2, opposite, occasionally with tiny bulbils in the axils. Flowers 5-12, greenish-yellow, star-shaped, 15-20mm, the outer tepals often deflexed. Dry open habitats, stony places and fields. Spain eastwards to Turkey – absent from most of the islands, except Sicily.

2107 *Gagea granatelii.* Similar, but outer 3 tepals *densely hairy* outside, not deflexed. Grassy and stony habitats, mainly in the mountains. Spain eastwards to Greece – not Balearic Is. or Crete.

2108 *Gagea peduncularis.* Low plant; stem minutely hairy. Basal leaves 2, thread-like to linear, grooved; stem-leaves *alternate*, lanceolate to elliptical, hairless or with a hairy margin. Flowers 1-3, yellow, 10-20mm, stalks often white-hairy. Dry hillslopes and stony places, scrub, grassy habitats. Jan-Apr. Yugoslavia, Greece, Crete and Turkey.

2109 *Gagea foliosa.* Similar, but stems hairless and basal leaves *flat*, similar to the stem leaves. Flowers 1-5. Sparse woodland and scrub, mainly in the mountains. Apr-July. S France, Corsica, Sardinia, SE Italy and Sicily.

2110 *Gagea chlorantha.* Like *G. foliosa*, but flowers often solitary. Rocky and grassy places, bare ground. Jan-Mar. E Med, including Cyprus.

2111 *Gagea juliae.* Like *G. peduncularis*, but flowers 3-15, smaller, the tepals not more than 10mm long, with a broad greenish stripe on the outside. Garrigue, on damp hillslopes, moist rock crevices, roadsides. Feb-Apr. Cyprus – endemic.

2112 *Gagea fibrosa.* Like *G. peduncularis*, but stem very short, often less than 2cm, with leaves congested; basal leaves often *recurved*. Tepals finely pointed. Rocky and grassy habitats, bare places. Feb-Mar. E Med, including Cyprus.

Colchicum **AUTUMN CROCUSES**. Cormous perennials with basal clusters of leaves; leaves appearing with or after the flowers. Flowers conspicuous, goblet-shaped or somewhat star-shaped with spreading tepals; tepals 6, similar and petal-like, white, pink, mauve or purple; stamens 6; styles 3. Fruit a capsule, located in the centre of the leaf-tufts. Most species are very poisonous to livestock: many are grown in gardens.

2113 *Colchicum autumnale* **AUTUMN CROCUS, MEADOW SAFFRON**. Low to short perennial, flowering in the autumn *before* the leaves appear. Leaves broad-lanceolate, usually 4, deep shiny green. Flowers pink to lilac-purple with yellow anthers, solitary or up to 6; tepals 40-60mm long; styles whitish, curved at the tip. Damp grassy meadows, open woodland, roadsides. Aug-Oct. Iberian Peninsula eastwards to Greece. The source of the drug colchicine; formerly used medicinally for gout.

2114 *Colchicum lusitanicum.* Similar, but leaves 4-5, linear-lanceolate. Flowers slightly chequered on the outside; anthers black-purple, to pale purplish-pink, rarely yellow. Dry rocky hillslopes. Sept-Nov. Iberian Peninsula, Balearic Is., C Italy.

2115 *Colchicum neapolitanum [C. kochii, C. longifolium].* Like *C. autumnale*, but leaves usually 3-4, linear-lanceolate. Flowers *smaller*, the tepals 30-45mm long; anthers yellow. Meadows and grassy hillslopes. Sept-Nov. Iberian Peninsula eastwards to Greece – not Balearic Is. or Sicily.

2116 *Colchicum variegatum.* Low plant flowering in the autumn before the leaves appear. Leaves 3-4, greyish-green, linear-lanceolate, usually spreading on the ground and with undulate margins. Flowers flattish, 5-6cm, 1-3, pinkish-purple to reddish, *strongly chequered*; tepals pointed, 4.5-7cm long, somewhat twisted; anthers deep purple and styles curved at the top. Rocky hillslopes, scrub and open pine woodland. Sept-Dec. S Greece, Aegean Is. and SW Turkey.

2117 *Colchicum bivonae [C. sibthorpii, C. bowlesianum, C. visianii].* Low to short plant flowering in the autumn before the leaves appear. Leaves 5-9, linear-lanceolate to lanceolate, hairless, glossy green and more or less erect, 15-25cm long. Flowers *goblet-shaped*, 4-6cm, 1-5, varying from pinkish-lilac to deep rosy-purple, strongly chequered; tepals 5-6cm long, not twisted; anthers purplish to brownish. Rocky places and dryish grassy hillslopes, often in scrub. Aug-Oct. Sardinia and Italy eastwards to Turkey – not Crete.

2118 *Colchicum turcicum.* Similar, but leaves greyish- or bluish-green with a hairy margin. Flowers faintly chequered, usually deep crimson-purple. Meadows and stony places. Aug-Oct. S Yugoslavia, NE Greece and Turkey.

2119 *Colchicum boissieri.* Low to short plant, to 20cm tall in leaf. Leaves 2, green, linear, sometimes with a hairy margin, appearing after the flowers or just the tips appearing with the flowers. Flowers generally solitary, bright lilac-purple, not chequered, with spreading tepals, 20-35mm long; anthers yellow; *styles* straight or very slightly curved. Stony hillsides in scrub or beneath pines. Sept-Dec. S Greece.

2120 *Colchicum psaridis.* Low plant, rarely more than 5cm tall; corm producing horizontal stolons. Leaves usually 2, bright green, *well developed* at flowering time, linear-lanceolate to lanceolate, sometimes with a hairy margin. Flowers small, 1-6, pinkish-purple, not chequered; tepals 1-2.5cm long, rather narrow; anthers brownish or purplish-black and styles straight. Stony and rocky ground, hillslopes, olive groves. Sept-Dec. S Greece (Peloponnese).

2121 *Colchicum triphyllum [C. catacuzenium].* Low plant to 8cm tall. Leaves usually *three*, dull green, present at flowering time but rather short, lanceolate, normally 3-5cm long, later expanding to 15cm. Flowers 1-4, pinkish-lilac, not chequered, the tepals 1.5-3cm long; anthers purple-black to purplish-green; styles straight. Open stony habitats, especially hillslopes. Feb-Apr. S Spain, SE Greece and Turkey.

2122 *Colchicum cupanii.* Low plant. Leaves usually 2, linear to linear-lanceolate, sometimes the margin hairy near the base, present at flowering time but often short, variable in size, eventually up to 15cm long. Flowers 1-5, purplish-pink or pale pink, the tepals *narrow-elliptical*, 1-2.5cm long; anthers purplish-black; styles yellow. Rocky habitats. Sept-Dec. SE France eastwards to Greece – not Corsica or Yugoslavia.

2123 *Colchicum pusillum [C. cretense, C. hiemale].* Low plant seldom more then 5cm tall. Leaves 3-5, green, normally present at flowering time, but sometimes only the tips showing, thread-like to linear, to 4-8cm long. Flowers 1-4, pale mauve-pink or white, the tepals 1-2cm long, linear-elliptical; anthers purple-black to grey or pale brown, occasionally yellow. Rocky and sandy habitats, dry pastures. Oct-Dec. C and S Crete, S Aegean Is., Crete, Cyprus.

2124 *Colchicum stevenii.* Like *C. pusillum*, but tepals pink, not white, 20-30mm long (not 10-20mm); anthers *yellow*. Dry hillslopes and banks. Oct-Dec. N Cyprus, Turkey, Syria and Palestine.

2125 *Colchicum peloponnesiacum.* Like *C. pusillum*, but flowers bright purplish-pink and anthers yellow. Rocky and stony habitats. Oct-Dec. S Greece (Peloponnese).

2126 *Colchicum troodii [C. decaisnei].* Low plant with the leaves appearing *after* the flowers. Leaves 2-5, strap-shaped, suberect to spreading, dark green to hairy, to 22cm long when fully developed. Flowers 2-6, white to pale pink, the tepals narrow-oblong to lanceolate, 2.5-4.5cm long; anthers yellow; styles slightly curved at the top. Garrigue, dry rocky slopes, pine and hazel forest, lowland and in the mountains. Sept-Nov. Cyprus, SE Turkey, Syria and Palestine.

2127 *Androcymbium europaeum* **ANDROCYMBIUM**. Low cormous perennial. Leaves linear to lanceolate, flat and rosette-like, hairless, forming a *collar* around the flower cluster, borne on a short stem. Flowers 1-6, white or pink, striped with mauve, sometimes with darker speckling; tepals 2-2.5cm long, long-pointed, free from one another and with yellowish swollen glands near the base of the blade. Fruit a 3-valved capsule. Open sandy or rocky habitats, sparse grassy places. Dec-Feb. SE Spain; a rare plant, known only from the Cabo de Gata.

2128 *Androcymbium rechingeri.* Similar, but tepals blunter. Fruit not splitting, but eventually rots and breaks up. Rocky coastal habitats. W Crete (Elaphonisi Is.). Another rare species.

2129 *Androcymbium graminea.* Like *A. europaeum*, but with narrower leaves. Rocky habitats. N Africa.

Merendera **MERENDERAS**. Like *Colchicum*, but tepals separate (free) from one another and anthers fixed at the base (not in the middle).

2130 *Merendera attica.* Low cormous perennial. Leaves appearing at flowering time, linear-lanceolate, with a rather rough margin. Flowers 2-3, usually pink-purple, the tepals *spreading*, 15-25mm long, narrow-elliptical; anthers violet. Open stony places and grassy places with scrub. Oct-Jan, occasionally later. Feb. S Greece.

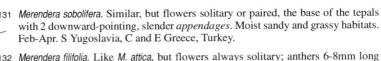

2131 *Merendera sobolifera*. Similar, but flowers solitary or paired, the base of the tepals with 2 downward-pointing, slender *appendages*. Moist sandy and grassy habitats. Feb-Apr. S Yugoslavia, C and E Greece, Turkey.

2132 *Merendera filifolia*. Like *M. attica*, but flowers always solitary; anthers 6-8mm long (not 1.5-3.5mm). Sandy and stony habitats, scrub and beneath pines. Aug-Nov. Iberian Peninsula, Balearic Is., S France.

tepal

Tulipa **TULIPS**. Bulbous perennials, with a solitary stem, sometimes branched above. Leaves few, fleshy, alternate, untoothed, with inconspicuous veins. Flowers large and showy; tepals, all petal-like, the outer often somewhat narrower and longer than the inner; stamens 6. Fruit a 3-parted capsule, containing many, flattish seeds. A number of the species associated with cultivated land have become rarer in recent years with modern farming practices.

2133 *Tulipa aegenensis [T. oculus-solis]*. Stout medium perennial; stem hairless or slightly hairy. Leaves green, linear-lanceolate, flat, hairless, the upper smaller and narrower than the lower. Flowers solitary, scarlet, the tepals 48-85mm long, each with an oblong blackish-brown, yellow-edged, blotch at the base; tepals elliptical more than three times longer than broad. Naturalised in and around cultivation, orchards, vineyards, arable fields. Mar-May. S France, Italy, Aegean Is., Turkey and Palestine. (SW Asia). Grown in gardens and occasionally sold as a cut flower.

2134 *Tulipa praecox*. Similar, but leaves greyish- or bluish-green. Flowers orange tinged green on the outside, the tepals broad, elliptic-oval, 36-82mm long, about twice as long as broad. Stamens hairless. Similar habitats and flowering time. Portugal, France, Italy, Greece and Turkey, possibly elsewhere. (SW and SC Asia). Grown in gardens.

2135 *Tulipa undulatifolia [T. boeotica]*. Short to medium perennial; stem finely hairy or hairless. Leaves greyish-green, broadly lanceolate, *wavy-edged*, the upper smaller and narrower. Flowers solitary, scarlet, the tepals with a basal black, yellow-edged, blotch, elliptical, 28-69mm long, long-pointed. Cultivated land, especially wheat fields, rocky places. Mar-May. S Yugoslavia, Greece and Turkey. The origin of this striking species is not known; plants are nearly always associated with cultivated fields.

2136 *Tulipa cypria*. Similar, but leaf margins scarcely undulate and flowers dark purple-crimson, the tepals with rounded or shortly pointed tips, sometimes without a dark basal blotch. Cereal fields and juniper forests, in the hills. Mar-Apr. W and N Cyprus – endemic.

stamen

2137 *Tulipa clusiana* **LADY TULIP**. Short to medium perennial with a slender, hairless stem. Leaves, narrow-lanceolate to linear, *channelled*. Flowers solitary, erect in bud, white, the outer tepals flushed with pinkish-crimson on the exterior, all with a basal purple zone inside; tepals oblong, 25-60mm long; stamens hairless. In and around cultivation. Naturalised in Portugal, France, S France, Italy and Greece, perhaps elsewhere. (Iran eastwards to Pakistan). Grown in gardens for several centuries.

2138 *Tulipa sylvestris* **WILD TULIP**. Short to medium, hairless perennial. Leaves usually 2-3, linear-lanceolate to linear, channelled. Flowers solitary, *nodding* in bud, yellow, the outer 3 tepals tinged with green or red on the outside, becoming recurved often; tepals elliptical to oblong, 33-70mm long; stamens hairy at the base of the filaments. Fruit rarely produced. Fields, scrub, open woodland, roadsides, generally at low altitudes. Apr-May. Scattered localities throughout the European Med and probably naturalised in some. This plant seems to be sterile and often forms patches by underground stolons. It is generally believed to have been derived from the following species.

2139 *Tulipa australis [T. sylvestris* subsp. *australis].* Similar, but a smaller plant, the tepals 20-35mm long, the outer 3 usually tinged with pink or crimson on the exterior; anthers only 2.5-4mm long (not 9-14mm). Fruit often formed. Mountain meadows, rocky places. Apr-June. Similar distribution. The flowers are sometimes sold in bunches, especially in Spain.

2140 *Tulipa celsiana.* Like *T. australis,* but a dwarfer plant with the leaves often *coiling* close on the ground. Similar habitats. May-June. S Spain and NW Africa.

2141 *Tulipa orphanidea [T. hageri, T. thracica]* **ORANGE WILD TULIP.** Short perennial, the stems finely hairy above the uppermost leaf or hairless. Leaves 2-5, linear-lanceolate to linear, channelled, hairless. Flowers solitary, occasionally paired, *orange to orange-red,* the outer 3 tepals usually tinged with green on the outside, all tepals with a darker zone at the base inside; tepals elliptical to oval, 30-47mm long, pointed; stamens hairy at the base of the filaments. Damp meadows, margins of cultivation and rocky mountain slopes. Mar-May. Balkan Peninsula. Very like an orange-flowered form of *T. sylvestris,* and pale orange-yellow-flowered plants sometimes found in Greece may be hybrids between the two species.

2142 *Tulipa whittalii.* Very like the previous species and possibly synonymous, but generally a squatter plant with larger flowers. Similar habitats and flowering time. W Turkey.

2143 *Tulipa doerfleri.* Like *T. orphanidea,* but flowers crimson-red. Grassy meadows and arable fields. Apr-May. W and C Crete – endemic.

2144 *Tulipa goulimyi.* Like *T. orphanidea,* but with 5-7 wavy-edged leaves. Sandy fields, stony habitats and low scrub. Apr-May. SE Greece (especially Kythira Is.), W Crete. The bulb is very distinctive with layers of soft felted hairs between the tunic layers; this is a very rare plant, however, and should not be dug up under any circumstances.

2145 *Tulipa saxatilis* **ROCK TULIP.** Short hairless perennial, patch-forming by means of underground stolons. Leaves generally 2-3, oblong-lanceolate to linear-lanceolate, *shiny* deep green above. Flowers solitary or up to 4 on a branching stem, pink to lilac-purple, the tepals 38-55mm long with a white-edged, yellow basal blotch inside; stamens hairy at the base of the filaments. Fruit rarely formed. Cultivated fields, fields margins, rock crevices, screes, lowland and in the mountains. Mar-Apr. Crete and SW Turkey; naturalised in S Italy. Often forming large patches of solitary leaves with few flowers, but flowering more profusely in some seasons.

2146 *Tulipa bakeri.* Very similar to *T. saxatilis* and sometimes considered synonymous, but has rather smaller flowers of a deep royal purple. Generally produces fruits. Rocky places and scrub in the mountains. Apr-May. W Crete – endemic.

2147 *Tulipa cretica* **CRETAN TULIP.** Low to short, hairless perennial. Leaves usually 2-3, greyish-green, narrow-lanceolate, flat or somewhat channelled. Flowers 1-2, occasionally up to 4, *white,* sometimes very pale pink, the outer 3 tepals tinged with pink or purple and green on the outside, all stained with yellow inside at the base; tepals elliptical, 15-32mm long; stamens hairy at the base of the filaments. Rocky and stony habitats, screes, lowland and in the mountains. Mar-May. Crete – endemic. Sometimes forming large colonies in the wild.

2148 *Lilium candidum* **MADONNA LILY.** Tall, hairless bulbous perennial; stems erect, greenish. Basal leaves appearing in the autumn, larger than the stem leaves, elliptical to lanceolate; stem leaves alternate, lanceolate; all leaves shiny green and untoothed. Flowers large white *trumpets,* 8-12cm long, borne in 3-6 flowered

nen

en

tamen

racemes, occasionally more, very fragrant; tepals recurved towards the apex; anthers yellow. Rocky slopes and scrub, generally in hot, rather dry places. May-June. Greece, Yugoslavia and the Lebanon; naturalised in various parts of the European Med. Widely grown in gardens. The white flowers have long represented purity, hence the common name.

Fritillaria **FRITILLARIAS**. Bulbous perennials with a solitary, unbranched stem. Leaves alternate, opposite or sometimes whorled, untoothed, rather fleshy, mostly on the stem. Flowers solitary or in lax racemes, tubular or bell-shaped, nodding on arched stalks; tepals 6, all petal-like, often somberly coloured in yellows, browns, greens, or purples, sometimes faintly chequered, inside with a basal nectary; stamens 6; style 3-lobed. Fruit an erect, 3-parted capsule, containing many flattish seeds. The flowers often smell rather unpleasant and attract a variety of insects including wasps and various kinds of bee.

2149 *Fritillaria persica [F. libanotica]*. Erect, tall, hairless perennial. Leaves numerous, crowded below, alternate, greyish- or bluish-green, linear-lanceolate, pointed; basal leaves, if present, often broader and a brighter green, stalked. Flowers greenish-purple or dark purplish-brown, widely bell-shaped, 18-24mm long, borne in a *terminal spike* with up to 30 flowers; tepals oblong; anthers brown or purplish. Capsule subglobose, 20-25mm, 6-grooved but not winged. Rocky and grassy habitats, cereal fields and field margins, hillslopes, open scrub. Feb-Apr. S Turkey, N Cyprus (rare, possibly extinct), to Syria and Palestine. Widely cultivated in temperate gardens and easily recognised by its racemes of flowers.

2150 *Fritillaria acmopetala*. Short to medium perennial; stems slender, often purplish. Leaves 5-9, green or bluish-green, alternate, the lowest two sometimes opposite, elliptical to linear. Flowers solitary or 2-3, greenish-yellow suffused with greyish-brown, the inner tepals *flared*, suffused, or banded, with reddish-purple, 30-40mm long. Capsule not winged. Cereal fields and grassy places or open scrub. Mar-Apr. S Turkey, N Cyprus (rare, possibly extinct), Syria and Palestine. Grown in gardens.

2151 *Fritillaria messanensis*. Short perennial; stems erect, slender, greyish, sometimes suffused with purple. Leaves 7-10, linear, opposite or alternate, the upper three often in a simple whorl. Flowers yellowish or brownish, somewhat chequered, sometimes with a green band down the middle of each tepal, broad bell-shaped, 22-32mm long, solitary; tepals not flared at the tip, with an oval green nectary inside at the base. Capsule not winged. Open woodland, scrub and grassy habitats, garrigue. Late Mar-May. S Italy, Sicily, Balkans, Crete.

2151a Subsp. *gracilis* has the upper leaves alternate and the flowers *unchequered*. W and S Yugoslavia, Albania.

2152 *Fritillaria lusitanica [F. hispanica]*. Similar, but *all leaves* alternate. Flowers greenish- or reddish-brown, flushed or chequered with green on the outside, 20-40mm long; nectaries linear. Open woods, grassy places, rocky places and screes. Apr-May. Iberian Peninsula, except the north. Closely related to *F. pyrenaica*, which is endemic to the Pyrenean mountains.

2153 *Fritillaria graeca*. Low to short perennial; stem greyish-green. Leaves 5-12, grey-green, lanceolate to elliptical, the lowest opposite, the others alternate. Flowers solitary or two, brownish-red to purplish-brown with a green stripe down the middle of each tepal, 18-28mm long, sometimes slightly chequered; nectaries lanceolate to linear. Capsule without wings. Open woods, scrub and rocky slopes and screes, generally on limestone and mainly in the mountains. May-June. S and E Greece, possibly Crete.

2153a Subsp. *thessala* *[F. ionica, F. thessalica]*. Like the type, but the lowest pair of leaves opposite and the upper three in a simple whorl; flowers larger, 28-38mm long, pale green with brownish shading, usually chequered; nectaries oval to oval-lanceolate. S Yugoslavia, Albania and NW Greece.

2154 *Fritillaria pontica*. Rather like *F. graeca* subsp. *thessala*, but flowers plain green, often with a slight bloom, the tepals suffused with purplish-brown at the tips, 24-45mm long, not chequered; nectaries round, blackish. Capsule *winged*. Open woods and scrub. May-June. Balkan Peninsula and Turkey.

2155 *Fritillaria davisii*. Like *F. graeca*, but leaves *shiny* bright green. Flowers without a green stripe down the middle of each tepal, chequered. Scrub, olive groves, cereal fields. Feb-Mar. S Greece – Mani Peninsula, endemic. A rare species, known from only a few localities.

2156 *Fritillaria conica*. Low to short perennial; stem green. Leaves 5-7, broad-lanceolate, shiny-green, the lowest pair opposite, the others alternate. Flowers solitary or two, *yellow*, small rather cone-shaped bells, 12-20mm long, not chequered; nectaries greenish-yellow. Capsule not green. Scrub and cultivated land. Feb-Mar. S Greece – W Peloponnese.

2157 *Fritillaria euboeica*. Similar, but a low plant, not more than 10cm tall, with grey-green leaves. Rocky limestone slopes. E Greece – Euboia.

2158 *Fritillaria obliqua*. Short perennial. Leaves 8-11, grey-green, lanceolate, alternate, the lowest pair sometimes opposite. Flowers solitary or two, *blackish*, cone-shaped bells, 20-30mm long, not chequered but with a greyish bloom on the outside; nectaries linear, green; style 3-lobed. Capsule not winged. Rocky hillslopes and scrub. Mar-Apr. S Greece – Attica.

2159 *Fritillaria tuntasia*. Similar, but more robust, to 35cm with 1-4 flowers. Leaves more, up to 20, *somewhat twisted*. Similar habitats and flowering time. S Greece – Cyclades. Endemic to the island of Kythnos.

2160 *Fritillaria ehrhartii*. Like *F. obliqua*, but flowers narrow-bell-shaped, dark purplish-brown, greenish-yellow inside, 14-23mm long; style *undivided*. Similar habitats. Feb-May. Aegean Is. – Euboia and Cyclades.

2161 *Fritillaria rhodocanakis*. Low to short plant, rarely more than 15cm tall. Leaves lanceolate, green, the lowest pair opposite, the others alternate. Flowers solitary, dark purple-brown, with yellow *margins*, occasionally all yellowish-green, not chequered, wide bell-shaped, 15-25mm long; tepals with a flared apex; style 3-lobed. Rocky places, scrub and vineyards. Mar-Apr. S Greece – island of Hydra, endemic.

2162 *Fritillaria orientalis* *[F. tenella]*. Short to medium perennial, to 40cm tall. Leaves 6-10, linear, the lowest opposite or 3 in a whorl, the uppermost three in a *simple whorl*. Flowers 1-3, greenish, strongly chequered with purplish-brown, 20-30mm long; nectaries linear, green. Capsule not winged. Scrub and rocky places. Apr-June. SE France eastwards to the Balkans – absent from the islands.

2163 *Urginea maritima* **SEA SQUILL**. Stout bulbous, tall perennial, to 1.5m tall; bulb very large, often on, or close to the surface, up to 15cm diam. Leaves all basal, tough, shiny-green, broadly lanceolate, *disappearing* before the flowers appear. Flowers white, 10-16mm, star-shaped, borne in a long spike-like raceme, each tepal with a median green or purplish stripe. Capsule triangular in cross-section. Dry rocky habitats, coastal sands. July-Oct. T. A very characteristic plant of the region, often occurring in large colonies across hillslopes – the tough leaf-tufts may be seen in spring and early summer. The plant is very poisonous and the dried bulb has been used medicinally for many centuries for the treatment of heart disease and in

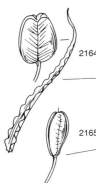

cough mixtures. In N Africa forms with red bulb-coats are the source of Red Squill, a powerful rat poison.

2164 *Urginea undulata* **UNDULATE SEA SQUILL**. Short to medium perennial; bulb to 3.5cm diam. Leaves linear-oblong, in a basal tuft, 3-10mm wide, *wavy-margined*, disappearing before the flowers appear. Flowers dull pink to greyish or greenish-purple, 20-26mm, borne in a lax raceme with up to 30 flowers; tepals with a red midvein; styles longer than the stamens. Rocky habitats. Aug-Oct. S Spain, NW Africa, S Corsica and Sardinia.

2165 *Urginea fugax* **RED SEA SQUILL**. Similar, but plant not more than 35cm tall and with thread-like leaves, only 2mm wide. Flowers pale pink with a red midvein. Dry hills and rocky places. Corsica, Sardinia, Italy N Africa and Syria.

Ornithogalum **STARS OF BETHLEHEM**. Bulbous perennials with basal leaves, solitary to several in a rosette. Flowers white to yellowish-green, generally star-shaped, occasionally bell-shaped, borne in racemes, often dense and nearly flat-topped; tepals separate, petal-like, often with a green median stripe on the outer surface; stamens 6. Fruit a 3-valved capsule, containing many seeds.

2166 *Ornithogalum narbonense*. Medium perennial. Leaves 4-6, linear with a sheathing base, pale to rather bright green. Flowers milky-white, 16-26mm, borne in a many-flowered, *slender raceme*; tepals with a green stripe on the reverse, spreading; anthers yellow. Grassy habitats, open scrub, garrigue, vineyards, olive groves, cultivated fields, waste places. May-July. T. One of the commonest and most widespread Med species, easily identified by its long, rather narrow, flower spikes.

2167 *Ornithogalum montanum*. Short perennial, not more than 20cm tall. Leaves usually 3-6, 10-20mm wide, *flat*, tapering from the base to a pointed apex, borne in a spreading rosette, hairless, green or grey-green. Flowers white, 20-30mm, carried in a wide, often flat-topped raceme; tepals with a broad green stripe on the outside; bracts shorter than the flower-stalks. Rocky ground and mountain pastures. Apr-May. Italy eastwards to Turkey – not Crete.

2168 *Ornithogalum collinum [O. gussonei, O. tenuifolium]*. Low to short plant, to 20cm. Leaves 4-15, linear, *channelled*, with a white stripe down the middle. Flowers white, 20-32mm, borne in a broad raceme *at ground level* or on a very short scape up to 4cm; tepals with a bright green median stripe on the outside; anthers pale yellow, occasionally reddish. Capsule with 3 pairs of angles. Grassy and rocky habitats, garrigue. Apr-May. Spain eastwards to the Balkan Peninsula.

2169 *Ornithogalum pedicellare*. Like *O. collinum*, but with 5-12 leaves, often spreading to recurved, only 1-3mm wide (not 3-8mm), with or without a pale median stripe. Pastures, garrigue and rocky slopes, lowland and mountains. Mar-Apr. S Greece, Aegean Is. and S Turkey.

2170 *Ornithogalum trichophyllum*. Like *O. pedicellare*, but leaves fewer, 4-8, and flowers borne in a *spike-like* inflorescence. Rocky pastures. Mar-Apr. Cyprus, Palestine and Egypt.

2171 *Ornithogalum umbellatum* **STAR OF BETHLEHEM**. Short perennial, generally with numerous offsets forming *tufts* of leaves around the parent plant. Leaves 6-9, linear, channelled, with a white central strip. Flowers glistening white, 28-40mm, borne in a broad pyramidal raceme, elongating in fruit; tepals with a broad bright green stripe on the outside; anthers yellow. Capsule with 6 equal angles. On cultivated, fallow or waste land, rocky slopes, and garrigue. Mar-May. T. Widely grown in gardens. Like most species of *Ornithogalum* the flowers open widely in bright sunshine and remain closed in dull weather.

2172 *Ornithogalum exscapum*. Similar, but flower-stalks *deflexed* in fruit (not ascending or spreading), borne on a short scape; tepals not more than 15mm long (not 15-22mm). Grassy and rocky habitats. Mar-Apr. Spain eastwards to Greece – not Balearic Is.

2173 *Ornithogalum nutans*. Short to medium perennial. Leaves 4-6, strap-like, 10-15mm wide, with a median white stripe. Flowers white, broadly bell-shaped, 30-45mm, nodding in a *one-sided* raceme; tepals recurved somewhat, with a greyish-green stripe on the outside. Open woodland and grassy habitats, pastures. Mar-May. Greece, Crete and Turkey, but widely naturalised elsewhere, especially in the European Med. Widely grown in gardens.

2174 *Ornithogalum arabicum*. Stout medium to tall perennial. Leaves 7-8, flat or somewhat channelled, plain green, without a median stripe, sheathing at the base. Flowers white or cream, 30-50mm, with a conspicuous *violet-black* ovary in the centre, borne in a lax raceme with up to 25 flowers; tepals broad, forming a bowl-shape, without a median stripe. Rocky places, cultivated and fallow ground. Apr-May. Iberian Peninsula and NW Africa eastwards to the Balkans – not Crete. Grown in some regions as a cut flower; one of the most striking species in the genus and readily identified on account of its dark ovary dominating the centre of the flower.

2175 *Ornithogalum pyrenaicum* **BATH ASPARAGUS**. Medium to tall perennial; stems slender, green, asparagus-like in young bud. Leaves 5-8, linear, slightly channelled, without a pale median stripe, generally withered by flowering time. Flowers pale *yellowish-green*, 13-17mm, star-shaped, borne in a long slender spike-like raceme with numerous flowers, faintly fragrant; tepals with a darker stripe on the back; anthers pale yellow. Meadows and scrub, open woodland, rocky places. May-July. Iberian Peninsula eastwards to Yugoslavia. The young flowering shoots can be eaten like asparagus.

2176 *Ornithogalum sphaerocarpum*. Similar, but tepals very pale greenish-white, *transparent*. Meadows and scrub. France eastwards to Turkey – not Crete.

2177 *Ornithogalum visianicum*. Like *O. pyrenaicum*, but lower bracts oval (not lanceolate) and flowers greenish-yellow, *whitish* on the outside. W Yugoslavia – Palagruza Is.

2178 *Dipcadi serotinum [Uropetalum serotium]* **DIPCADI**. A hairless, bulbous perennial. Leaves all basal, linear, few, spreading, usually greyish-green. Flowers greenish to brownish-yellow to orange-red, borne in a one-sided raceme; tepals 12-15mm long, linear-oblong, the outer three curving outwards, the inner three straight, all fused together in the basal third. Fruit a small capsule. Rocky, stony and sandy places, in dry sandy habitats. May-July. Iberian Peninsula, NW Africa, Balearic Is., S France (rare) and Italy (rare). A curious plant, rather difficult to spot because of its rather sombre appearance.

2179 *Hyacinthus orientalis* **HYACINTH**. Hairless, low to medium, hairless bulbous perennial. leaves all basal, 4-6, linear to linear-lanceolate, suberect, almost flat, encircling the base of the scape, deep green. Flowers blue, pink or white, 10-25mm, *sweetly scented*, half-nodding, borne in a 5-15-flowered raceme, the tepals fused into a tube in the lower half, spreading widely above; anthers dark blue. Rocky and grassy places, gardens. Mar-May. Turkey and the E Med, but naturalised from cultivation in parts of the European Med and Cyprus. Cultivated since early times and probably the 'Lily-of-the-valleys' referred to in the Bible. Cultivated forms have larger and denser flower scapes in a variety of bright colours from blue, pink and red to purple, yellow and white.

2180 *Brimeura fastigiata [Hyacinthus fastigiatus]* **BRIMEURA**. A low, hairless, bulbous perennial, rarely more than 5cm tall. Leaves several, linear, all basal, dark green. Flowers white or pale pinkish-lilac, 5-7mm long, bell-shaped, horizontal to slightly erect, 1-10 borne in a short dense raceme; tepal-lobes longer than the tube and flared outwards so that the flowers appear to be star-shaped. Loamy pockets in scrub or among rocks. Apr-June. Balearic Is., Corsica and Sardinia, S Greece – Taiyetos. A rather insignificant little plant, easily overlooked.

Scilla **SQUILLS**. A genus of bulbous perennials with basal leaves and leafless scapes. Flowers borne in racemes, sometimes spike-like, occasionally solitary, each with a solitary bract at the base of the flower stalks (pedicels); tepals 6, separate, spreading, star-shaped, often blue, occasionally pink or white; stamens 6, spreading. Fruit a small 3-parted capsule.

2181 *Scilla bifolia* **ALPINE SQUILL**. Low to short perennial, to 15cm. Leaves usually *two*, linear, becoming wider towards the tip, 5-10mm wide, dark green. Flowers deep purple-blue to bright blue or pale lilac, rarely white, 10-15mm, starry, 1-7 borne in a rather loose one-sided raceme; anthers dark blue; bracts minute. Short grassy places, meadows and open woodland. Jan-May. Spain eastwards to Turkey – not Balearic Is., Crete or Cyprus. Widely grown in gardens.

2182 *Scilla hyacinthoides*. Rather robust, medium to tall perennial; *scape* erect, to 80cm, often flushed with violet-blue towards the top. Leaves 8-12, linear-oblong, 13-30mm wide, rather tough, shiny deep green, finely hairy along the margin. Flowers mid-violet-blue, starry, 8-12mm, up to 150 borne in a long tapered spike-like raceme; tepals narrow; bracts 1-1.5mm long. Rocky habitats, hedgerows and dry fields, generally at low altitudes. Apr-May. Iberian Peninsula eastwards to Turkey – not Balearic Is., Crete or Cyprus.

2183 *Scilla peruviana*. Rather variable short to medium perennial. Leaves 6-10, strap-shaped, tapered to a pointed end, spreading, 10-35mm wide, sometimes with a hairy margin. Flowers bright deep blue, violet-blue, very occasionally paler blue cream or white, starry, 10-20mm, numerous borne in a broad *cone-shaped* raceme, with the lower flower-stalks much longer than the upper, the raceme lengthening in fruit; bracts papery-white, 20-40mm long. Damp and sandy habitats, scrub, roadsides, woodland fringes, often near the coast and at low altitudes. Mar-May. Iberian Peninsula and N Africa, eastwards to Italy and Sicily – not Balearic Is. or Corsica. Despite its specific name this is an entirely western Med species, not at all connected to Peru where it was first thought to have originated. It is a very striking species and, for this reason, is widely grown in gardens. Forms from N Africa have been reported with yellowish or brownish flowers.

2184 *Scilla litardierei [S. amethystina, S. pratensis]* **MEADOW SQUILL**. Short perennial. Leaves 3-6, linear to lanceolate, tapering very gradually to a pointed tip, 3-8mm wide, about as long as the scape. Flowers blue, occasionally violet-pink or white, *small*, 5-7mm, starry, borne in a fairly dense raceme of up to 30; bracts 1-1.5mm long. Rocky habitats, cliffs, open scrub, grassy and stony slopes. Apr-June. W Yugoslavia – endemic.

2185 *Scilla messeniaca* **MESSENIAN SQUILL**. Similar, but leaves 6-15mm wide and flowers *larger*, 10-14mm, borne in a laxer raceme. Shady habitats, rocks and grassy places. Feb-Apr. SW Greece – Peloponnese, (Kalamata region).

2186 *Scilla ramburei.* Like *S. litardierei,* but a *taller* plant, to 50cm, with grey-green leaves and larger violet-blue flowers, 16-20mm; bracts very narrow, 5mm long or more. Sandy habitats, often slightly shaded and close to the sea. Feb-Apr. Portugal and S Spain.

2187 *Scilla monophyllos.* Like *S. messeniaca,* but bulbs with only *one* leaf each. Flowers bright blue, 7-9mm, subtended by bluish bracts. Sandy and stony habitats, bushy places. Mar-May. Portugal, S Spain and Morocco.

2188 *Scilla cilicica.* Short perennial; scape often flushed with purple. Leaves 2-4, bright green, linear, channelled, often partly withered at flowering time. Flowers purplish-blue, 22-28mm, *few* borne in a 2-6-flowered raceme; tepals spreading or slightly cupped; bracts membranous, 2-4mm long and wide. Shaded limestone rock crevices. Jan-Mar. S Turkey, Cyprus, Syria and Lebanon.

2189 *Scilla autumnalis* **AUTUMN SQUILL.** Low to short perennial. Leaves 3-12, linear, 0.5-3mm wide, channelled, hairless, *absent* at flowering time. Flowers pale to deep lilac, blue or pinkish-purple, starry, 5-7mm, borne in a 6-20-flowered raceme; bracts absent. Dry grassy and rocky places, open scrub, fields, roadsides, often gregarious. Sept-Nov. T. The only widespread autumn-flowering *Scilla* in the region.

2190 *Scilla obtusifolia [S. intermedia].* Similar, but a shorter plant with only 2-5 leaves, linear-lanceolate, spreading to recurved with a minutely hairy *margin.* Dry grassy habitats and scrub. Aug-Sept. NE Spain, Balearic Is., Corsica, Sardinia and Sicily.

2191 *Scilla hispanica [Endymion hispanicus, E. campanulatus, Hyacinthoides hispanicus]* **SPANISH BLUEBELL.** Rather robust short to medium perennial. Leaves 4-8, linear-lanceolate to lanceolate, bright green, up to 25mm wide. Flowers pale to mid-blue, occasionally pink or white, *broad bell-shaped,* 12-20mm long, borne in lax racemes; tepals recurved at the tip; anthers blue; bracts 2 to each flower. Meadows and rocky scrub, roadsides, cultivated land. Apr-May. Iberian Peninsula; naturalised in France, Italy and Yugoslavia, perhaps elsewhere. Although primarily a mountain species, this plant is so widely grown in gardens that it is likely to turn up anywhere as an alien.

2192 *Hyacinthella millingenii [Bellevalia millingenii, Hyacinthus nervosus, Hyacinthella nervosa* subsp. *millingenii]* **HYACINTHELLA.** A low to short bulbous perennial, not more than 15cm tall. Leaves 2, linear, grey-green, erect to recurved, hairless. Flowers pale blue, bell-shaped, 4-6mm long, 3-15 borne in a short *spike,* the individual flowers stalkless; tepals free only in the top third; bracts minute. Rocky hillslopes, often on limestone. Nov-Feb. S Turkey and Cyprus.

2193 *Hyacinthella dalmatica.* Similar, but generally with more flowers which have a very short stalk, 1mm long (to 5mm in fruit). Similar habitats. Mar-Apr. W Yugoslavia.

2194 *Hyacinthella leucophaea [H. rumelica].* Like *H. dalmatica,* but leaves always erect (not recurved) and flowers pale blue or whitish. Rocky and grassy places, mainly in light woodland. Mar-May. N Greece and SE Yugoslavia.

2195 *Hyacinthella atchleyi.* Like *H. dalmatica,* but flowers deep blue, borne on *stalks* (pedicels) 2-4mm long. Stony and grassy habitats. Feb-Mar. Greece – region of Halkis and Thebes.

Bellevalia **BELLEVALIAS.** Very like *Muscari* in general appearance, but usually with rather dull flowers; corolla small, not constricted at the mouth, tubular or funnel-shaped and with the anthers in the throat. Fruit a 3-parted capsule.

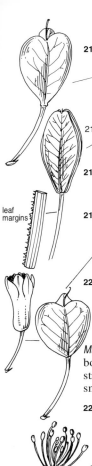

leaf margins

2196 *Bellevalia dubia.* Medium bulbous perennial, to 40cm tall. Leaves 2-5, narrow-lanceolate, with a long tapering apex, spreading. Flowers brilliant steely-blue or violet *in bud*, but changing soon to a dingy brown, with whitish teeth, 5-7mm long, tubular, 20-30 borne in a cylindrical raceme; flower-stalks 5-7mm long and held at right angles to the main stem. Grassy habitats, cultivated land, olive groves. Mar-May. Italy, Sicily, SW Yugoslavia and Greece.

2197 *Bellevalia ciliata.* Similar, but leaf margins with *long hairs*. Racemes conical, 30-50-flowered; flowers 9-11mm long, lilac with greenish teeth. Cultivated land and fields, at low altitudes. Mar-Apr. S Italy, Greece and Turkey.

2198 *Bellevalia trifoliata.* Like *B. ciliata*, but racemes *cylindrical*, the flowers violet at first but becoming brownish, 8-16mm long. Similar habitats. Feb-May. S Turkey, Cyprus and the E Med.

2199 *Bellevalia romana.* Short bulbous perennial. Leaves 3-6, linear, erect to recurved. Flowers *whitish*, sometimes tinged with blue, becoming dingy brown, bell-shaped with the lobes flared outwards, 8-10mm long, borne in an oblong raceme, 20-30-flowered. Cultivated land and grassy places. Apr-May. S France eastwards to the Balkans – not Sardinia or Crete.

2200 *Bellevalia nivalis.* Similar, but the flowers borne in a *spike-like* raceme, the individual flowers more tubular, tinged with mauve or pink in bud, with very short stalks, 0.5-4mm long (not 8-20mm). Coastal garrigue, cultivated land and rocky hillslopes. Jan-Apr. S Turkey, Cyprus and Syria.

Muscari **GRAPE HYACINTHS**. Bulbous perennials with basal leaves. Flowers small, borne in spike-like racemes on leafless stalks; perianth tubular to bell-shaped, constricted at the mouth into 6 small teeth; stamens hidden below the mouth. Fruit a small 3-parted capsule.

2201 *Muscari comosum [Leopoldia comosa]* **TASSEL HYACINTH**. Short to medium, rather slender, bulbous perennial. Leaves 3-6, linear or tapered gradually to the tip, 5-20mm long. Flowers brownish with cream or pale yellowish-brown teeth, 5-10mm long, urn-shaped, carried on stalks up to 15mm long, the uppermost flowers sterile, *blue or violet*, occasionally white, on slender violet-blue stalks; flowers in lax racemes. Dry grassy habitats, open scrub, roadsides, olive groves and vineyards. Mar-June. T. One of the commonest and easily identified species. In some regions, especially Greece and Crete, the bulbs are collected and eaten and can sometimes be see in local markets. Often grown in gardens.

2202 *Muscari gussonei.* Similar, but fertile flowers with yellowish teeth, on stalks *less* than 5mm long; sterile (uppermost) flowers short, 0.5mm (not 4-10mm), stalkless. Sandy coastal habitats. Italy and Sicily.

2203 *Muscari cycladicum.* Like *M. comosum*, but fertile flowers with yellowish teeth, stalkless or stalks to 1mm only; sterile flowers on very short stalks, *not* erect. Rocky hillslopes and cliffs, generally on limestone. Crete and the Cyclades.

2204 *Muscari weissii.* Like *M. comosum*, but the fertile flowers with yellowish teeth; sterile flowers *many*, not erect, on stalks 5-10mm long. Sandy coastal habitats or low scrub. Mar-Apr. Greece and Crete.

2205 *Muscari spreitzenhoferi.* Like *M. comosum*, but fertile flowers with yellowish teeth, carried on stalks more than 5mm long; sterile flowers *very small* and few, occasionally absent. Rocky places in scrub. Mar-July. Crete.

2206 *Muscari neglectum [M. atlanticum]* **COMMON GRAPE HYACINTH**. A low to short bulbous perennial. Leaves 3-6, linear to linear-lanceolate, channelled, bright green.

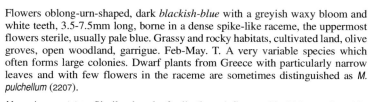

Flowers oblong-urn-shaped, dark *blackish-blue* with a greyish waxy bloom and white teeth, 3.5-7.5mm long, borne in a dense spike-like raceme, the uppermost flowers sterile, usually pale blue. Grassy and rocky habitats, cultivated land, olive groves, open woodland, garrigue. Feb-May. T. A very variable species which often forms large colonies. Dwarf plants from Greece with particularly narrow leaves and with few flowers in the raceme are sometimes distinguished as *M. pulchellum* (2207).

2208 *Muscari commutatum.* Similar, but the fertile (lower) flowers blackish-purple, *without* white teeth; sterile flowers paler. Grassy and rocky habitats. Apr-May. Italy, Sicily and the Balkans.

2209 *Muscari inconstrictum.* Like *M. commutatum*, but flowers dark indigo or violet, *not* constricted at the mouth. Garrigue and dry rocky habitats. Dec-Mar. S Turkey, Cyprus, Syria and Palestine.

2210 *Muscari armeniacum* **ARMENIAN GRAPE HYACINTH.** Like *M. neglectum*, but flowers *bright blue*, occasionally tinged with purple, the teeth pale or white. Grassy and rocky habitats. Mar-May. S Yugoslavia and Greece eastwards to Turkey. Widely grown in gardens and sometimes sold as a cut flower.

2211 *Muscari parviflorum* **AUTUMN GRAPE HYACINTH.** Short, slender, bulbous perennial. Leaves 3-5 linear to thread-like, less than 3mm wide, shorter than the scape. Flowers pale sky-blue, oblong-bell-shaped, 3-5mm long, borne in a sparse raceme; sterile flowers few or absent, very small. Grassy and rocky habitats, garrigue and cultivated fields, often close to the sea. Oct-Dec. Spain eastwards to the east Med – not France, Corsica or Sardinia. The only autumn-winter flowering species of *Muscari* in the region.

Asparagus **ASPARAGUS.** Hairless rhizomatous perennials with tough stems, sometimes becoming woody, often with a rather ferny appearance. Leaves replaced by green leaf-like cladodes (slender reduced stems), borne usually in clusters; true leaves reduced to small papery, bract-like structures. Flowers small, whitish or greenish, bell-shaped, each with 6 tepals fused together at the base; flower-stalks often jointed in the middle, either male or female and borne on separate plants in all the species except *A. albus*. Fruit a small globose berry.

2212 *Asparagus acutifolius.* Tall plant, sometimes reaching 2m; stems woody, much-branched, whitish or grey. Cladodes in clusters of 10-30, 2-8mm long, subequal, *spine-tipped*. Flowers in groups of 2-4, 3-4mm long, yellowish-green, sweetly scented, mixed with the leaves. Berry black when ripe, 4.5-7.5mm. Dry rocky habitats, maquis, garrigue, scrub and hedgerows, occasionally in pine woodland. Apr-June. T. The young shoots are eaten as a vegetable in some areas, although the species is not cultivated.

2213 *Asparagus stipularis.* Similar, but cladodes solitary or in groups of 2-3, 15-30mm long. Flowers in clusters of 2-6, 3.5-4mm long. Berry 5.5-8mm. Rocky or sandy habitats, often close to the sea. Mar-June. T – not Corsica or Yugoslavia.

2214 *Asparagus albus.* Like *A. acutifolius*, but cladodes 5-25mm long, soon falling to leave bare spiny stems. Flowers 2-3mm long, white, sweetly scented. Hedgerows and scrub. Apr-June. Iberian Peninsula and NW Africa eastwards to the Balkans and Crete – not France.

2215 *Asparagus aphyllus.* Like *A. acutifolius*, but not more than 1m tall with smooth green stems. Cladodes unequal, in clusters of 3-7, 10-20mm long. Flowers in groups of 3-6. Berry black when ripe, 7-8mm. Rocky habitats and scrub. Apr-June. T – not France, Corsica, Yugoslavia, Crete or parts of the extreme E Med.

2216 *Asparagus maritimus* **MARITIME ASPARAGUS.** Medium to tall erect perennial, to 1m; stems herbaceous, green, ridged. Cladodes in clusters of 4-7, erect or spreading, somewhat flattened, 10-30mm long. Flowers greenish-white, bell-shaped, 4-6mm long, usually in pairs, not mixed with the cladodes. Berry red when ripe, 6-12mm. Coastal sands, occasionally on rocks. May-July. Spain and N Africa, eastwards to the Balkans.

2217 *Asparagus tenuifolius.* Similar, but stems and branches smooth and cladodes in clusters of 15-40. Flowers 6-8mm long, mixed with the cladodes. Balkans eastwards to Turkey.

2218 *Asparagus officinalis* **COMMON ASPARAGUS.** Very variable, medium to tall plant, to 2m, though often less; stems erect to arching, green, erect and smooth, *herbaceous*, branched above. Cladodes in clusters of 4-15, flattened or thread-like, 10-25mm long, scarcely spreading, soft. Flowers yellowish or greenish-white, 4.5-6.5mm long, usually in pairs, not mixed with the cladodes. Berry red when ripe, 6-10mm. Hedgerows, grassy and waste places, scrub, coastal rocks, garrigue. June-Aug. T – absent from most of the islands. Widely cultivated as a vegetable and for decorative purposes and frequently naturalised.

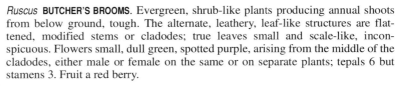

Ruscus **BUTCHER'S BROOMS.** Evergreen, shrub-like plants producing annual shoots from below ground, tough. The alternate, leathery, leaf-like structures are flattened, modified stems or cladodes; true leaves small and scale-like, inconspicuous. Flowers small, dull green, spotted purple, arising from the middle of the cladodes, either male or female on the same or on separate plants; tepals 6 but stamens 3. Fruit a red berry.

2219 *Ruscus aculeatus* **BUTCHER'S BROOM.** Tufted subshrub to 1m, though often less; stems erect, hairless. Cladodes alternate, dark green, oval 1-4cm long, *spine-tipped*. Flowers greenish-white, 3mm, solitary or in pairs, borne on the upper surface of the cladodes, the male and female on separate plants. Berry globose, 12-15mm. Woods, scrub, hedgerows, rocky slopes, garrigue, generally in shade. Feb-Apr. T. Often grown in gardens.

2220 *Ruscus hypoglossum* **LARGE BUTCHER'S BROOM.** Short to medium, shrub-like plant, to 40cm tall; stems generally unbranched, spreading to erect. Cladodes mid-green, elliptical to lanceolate, 3-10cm long, *not* spine-tipped. Flowers greenish, 3-5mm, borne in clusters of 3-5 on the upper surface of the cladodes; male and female on separate plants. Berry scarlet, 18-20mm. Deciduous woods and scrub. Jan-Apr. Italy eastwards to Turkey – not Crete or Cyprus. Occasionally grown in gardens.

2221 *Ruscus hypophyllum* **SPANISH BUTCHER'S BROOM.** Similar, but a taller plant to 70cm, the cladodes flexible, oval to lanceolate, 5-9cm long. Flowers borne on the upper or lower surface of the cladodes. Woodland. Jan-Mar. S and E Spain, SE France, NW Africa and SE Sicily.

2222 *Smilax aspera [S. mauritanica, S. nigra]* **COMMON SMILAX.** Variable, creeping or scrambling, extremely tough shrub, to 15m; stems angled, smooth or prickly. Leaves leathery, shiny deep green, oblong to triangular or heart-shaped, smooth or with prickles on the stalk or margins, with a pair of *tendrils* at the base of the leaf-stalk; leaf-stalk thickened towards the top. Flowers greenish-white to greenish-yellow, 3-5mm, borne in branched clusters, male and female on separate plants. Berry red or black when ripe, 2-4mm. Maquis and garrigue, scrub and bushy places, hedgerows. Aug-Nov. T. The young asparagus-like shoots are edible when cooked.

2223 *Smilax excelsa* **LARGER SMILAX.** Similar, but even more robust with membranous or slightly leathery, more rounded leaves, the stalk *not thickened* towards the top.

Flowers greenish, 6-9mm, borne in long-stalked umbels. Berry red. Scrub and bushy habitats. Balkans, Aegean Is. and Turkey.

Allium **ONIONS**. Bulbous perennials, smelling strongly of onion or garlic when crushed. Leaves partly sheathing the scapes, often only at the base. Spathes usually 1-2, completely enclosing the flowers in bud. Flowers borne in distinctive umbels; tepals 6, all similar, forming a star or bell-shape usually; stamens 6. Fruit a 3-parted capsule, often with many seeds.

2224 *Allium roseum* **ROSY GARLIC**. Variable, short to medium, hairless bulbous perennial. Leaves 2-4, linear, keeled, sheathing the low fifth of the scape; spathe solitary, 3-4-lobed, papery and persistent, shorter than the equal flower-stalks. Flowers usually *pink*, occasionally white, bell-shaped, 7-12mm long, borne in an umbel up to 7cm across, sometimes with bulbils (var. *bulbiferum* 2224a) mixed in the head; stamens not protruding; anthers yellow. Grassy and bushy places, cultivated ground, roadsides, dry fields. Mar-June. T. Grown in gardens.

2225 *Allium neapolitanum* **NAPLES GARLIC**. Short to medium bulbous perennial; scape *triangular* in cross-section, smooth. Leaves 2-4, linear, to linear-lanceolate, sheathing the lower quarter of the scape, keeled on the back, hairless; spathe solitary, shorter than the flower-stalks. Flowers white, cup-shaped or starry, 15-20mm, borne in an umbel 5-9cm diam. Dry grassy and stony habitats, cultivated and fallow ground, roadsides, bushy places, open pine forest. Feb-May. T – often local. Widely grown in gardens and often becoming naturalised. Occasionally sold as a cut flower.

2226 *Allium trifoliatum*. Similar, but leaves and sheaths *hairy*, at least along the margins, stem round in section and flowers white, the tepals with a pinkish or purplish midvein, sometimes flushed with pink. Garrigue, stony pastures, rocky and stony slopes, salt steppe. Mar-May. Sardinia, S Italy and Sicily eastwards, including Crete and Cyprus, but not the Balkans.

2227 *Allium subhirsutum*. Similar, but a shorter plant, not more than 30cm tall, with *pure white* flowers in umbels 3-6cm diam; anthers brown (not yellowish). Rocky and sandy habitats. Apr-June. T – not Cyprus or parts of the extreme E Med. Often grown in gardens. One of the commoner white-flowered onions in the Med region, often found close to the sea.

2228 *Allium subvillosum*. Like *A. subhirsutum*, but with denser umbels of flowers, 2.5-3.5cm diam., the individual flowers more *cup-shaped* than starry; anthers yellow. Grassy and sandy habitats, often close to the sea. Mar-May. S Portugal, S Spain, Balearic Is., Sicily and N Africa, where it is particularly common in some places.

2229 *Allium triquetrum* **THREE-CORNERED LEEK**. Short to medium bulbous perennial; scapes triangular in section. Leaves 2-3, linear. tapered, with a sharp keel. Flowers white, the tepals with a greenish midvein, bell-shaped, 10-18mm long, pendent, borne in a *one-sided* umbel, with only 5-15 flowers. Damp woodland, hedgerows, streamsides, waste places. Mar-May. Iberian Peninsula eastwards to Italy and Sicily. Grown in gardens. The one-sided umbels of flowers are very distinctive.

2230 *Allium pendulinum*. Similar, but flowers smaller, only 3-5mm long, borne in a more symmetrical umbel. Similar habitats and flowering time. Corsica, Sardinia, Italy and Sicily.

2231 *Allium chamaemoly*. Low bulbous perennial, to only 5cm tall. Leaves 2-5, *spread flat* on the ground, sheathing only the very base of the scape, linear with a hairy margin; spathes 1-valved, 2-4-lobed. Flowers white, starry, 10-16mm, borne in umbels of up to 20 flowers; tepals with a greenish or purplish midvein. Sandy and stony habitats, often close to the sea. Dec-Mar. Iberian Peninsula and NW Africa eastwards to the Balkans.

2232 *Allium cupanii.* Low to short bulbous perennial; scapes round in section. Leaves 3-5, thread-like, borne on the lower third of the scape or more, hairless. Flowers white or pink, narrow-bell-shaped, 5.5-9mm long, up to 15 borne in a *shuttlecock-shaped* umbel, 2-4cm across; tepals with a darker midvein; anthers yellow, included. Dry rocky and stony habitats. May-Oct. Balearic Is., Italy and Sicily eastwards to Turkey.

2233 *Allium circinnatum.* Similar, but leaves hairy, *tightly coiled*; flowers few and whitish. Rocky habitats. Mar-Apr. Crete – endemic.

2234 *Allium paniculatum.* Very variable medium, bulbous perennial; scape round in section. Leaves 3-5, sheathing the lower part of the stem, linear, channelled above, ribbed beneath; spathes unequally 2-valved, with a long *tail-like* appendage, much longer than the flower-stalks. Flowers whitish, lilac-pink, greenish-brown, purplish or yellowish, bell-shaped, 4.5-7mm long, borne in dense uneven umbels with the outer flowers drooping on long slender stalks; stamens equalling the tepals. Dry grassy and stony habitats, garrigue, vineyards, olive groves, occasionally beneath pine trees or on the seashore. May-Aug. T. Various subspecies are recognised, including subsp. *pallens* (2234a), which has smaller more compact umbels, the flower-stalks *not* markedly different in length; tepals whitish with a green or purplish midvein. Scrub and dry grassy places. T.

2235 *Allium flavum* **SMALL YELLOW ONION**. Low to medium, rather variable, bulbous perennial; scape round in section, green or grey. Leaves 2-3, grey-green, sheathing the lower part of the stem, cylindrical; spathes 2-valved, with a long tail-like appendage up to 11cm long. Flowers *yellow*, bell-shaped, 4.5-5mm long, borne in a many-flowered umbel with the inner flowers on erect stalks, the outer curving downwards; stamens protruding; anthers yellow to violet. Dry grassy and stony habitats. S France eastwards to Turkey – absent from the islands except Sicily. Grown in gardens. Mountain forms are often dwarf compared to their lowland counterparts; some are delicately scented.

2236 *Allium hymettium.* Similar, but with smaller flowers borne in a more compact umbel, with no flower-stalks over 15mm long. S Greece – endemic.

2237 *Allium ampeloprasum* **WILD LEEK**. Very variable medium to tall bulbous perennial, to 1.5m. Leaves 4-10, linear, V-shaped in section, usually rather greyish-green, rough on the margin, sheathing the lower part of the scape and generally withered by flowering time; spathes I-valved, *quickly falling*. Flowers white to pink, purple or dark red, bell-shaped or cup-shaped, 4-5.5mm long, borne in large very dense umbels, 5-9cm diam., with up to 500 flowers; stamens usually protruding. Cultivated. fallow and waste land, roadsides, sandy coastal habitats, scrub. May-July. T. The cultivated Leek, *Allium porrum* (2238), is generally believed to have been derived from this species.

stamen

2239 *Allium atroviolaceum.* Similar, but generally rather less robust; flowers *dark purple*, occasionally flushed green, borne in umbels 3-6cm diam. Cultivated and waste ground, dry grassy habitats. Italy, Yugoslavia, Greece and Turkey.

stamen   2240 *Allium commutatum.* Like *A. ampeloprasum*, but leaves 5-11, without a rough margin; flowers whitish-pink or dull magenta with a green or purplish keel, 4mm long; margin of inner tepals *finely toothed*. Open rock and sandy coastal habitats. May-June. Corsica and Sardinia eastwards to the Balkans.

2241 *Allium sphaerocephalon* **ROUND-HEADED LEEK**. Medium to tall bulbous perennial; scape round in section. Leaves 2-6, semi-cylindrical, with a slight groove on the

stamen

stamen

upper surface, sheathing the lower part of the stem; spathes 2-valved, short-beaked, shorter than the umbel. Flowers dark purplish-red, occasionally white with a greenish keel to each tepal, tubular to egg-shaped, borne in a *very dense globose*, many-flowered umbel, 2-4cm diam; stamens much-protruding. Sandy or rocky places in grass or scrub, garrigue, vineyards and olive groves, roadsides. May-July. T – not Crete.

2242 *Allium vineale* **CROW GARLIC**. Medium to tall bulbous perennial, to 1.2m, though often less; scape round in section. Leaves 2-4, *cylindrical*, sheathing the lower half of the scape; spathes 1-valved, beaked. Flowers pinkish, reddish or greenish, bell-shaped, 2-4.5mm long, some or sometimes most of the flowers in the umbel replaced by bulbils; stamens protruding. Dry pastures, cultivated, fallow and waste ground, roadsides, garrigue. May-Aug. T – not Crete or Cyprus or parts of the extreme E Med. Forms with many bulbils in the umbel usually have few flowers.

stamen

2243 *Allium amethystinum*. Medium to tall bulbous perennial, to 1.2m; scape round in section, often reddish above. Leaves 3-7, linear, cylindrical, sheathing the lower part of the stem and generally *withered* by flowering time. Flowers purple, tubular-bell-shaped, 3-4.5mm long, many borne in a dense globose umbel, 3-5cm diameter, the inner often on erect stalks, the outer on pendulous ones; stamens protruding. Rocky places, often in or near cultivation. May-July. Italy and Sicily eastwards to Turkey and Cyprus.

2244 *Allium margaritaceum [A. guttatum]*. Similar, but *tepals* all equal in length (the inner not longer than the outer), whitish with a greenish, or pinkish midvein or with a purple blotch; umbel 1.5-3cm diam. Dry grassy and stony habitats, garrigue, hillslopes. June-July. T – not Balearic Is., Corsica, S France or Crete. A very variable species.

2245 *Allium nigrum*. Medium to tall bulbous perennial; scapes round in section. Leaves 3-6, all basal, broadly linear, tapered to a pointed apex, much shorter than the scape; spathes 2-4 parted, with pointed tips. Flowers white or very pale lilac with a green midvein to each tepal and a dark *blackish-green* ovary, star-shaped when fully open, 12-18mm, borne in a dense semi-spherical or shuttlecock-shaped umbel; anthers yellow. In or close to cultivated land, waste ground, hillsides. Mar-June. T. Wide-leaved forms (leaves up to 9cm wide) from Cyprus are sometimes referred to *A. multibulbosum* (2246).

2247 *Allium orientale*. Like the last species, but a *smaller* plant not more than 40cm tall, with leaves not more than 2.5cm wide. Similar habitats. Feb-May. Aegean Is., Turkey and Cyprus eastwards.

2248 *Allium cyrilli*. Like *A. nigrum*, with narrower *tepals*, only 1-1.5mm wide (not 1.5-3mm) with incurved tips. S Italy and Greece.

2249 *Nectaroscordum siculum [Allium siculum]* **NECTAROSCORDUM**. A robust, medium to tall, bulbous perennial to 1.25m, with a strong onion smell; scape green, round in section, smooth. Leaves sheathing the lower third of the stem, more or less triangular in section, fleshy, strongly keeled beneath; spathes 1-valved, papery, deciduous. Flowers greenish with maroon or pink, bell-shaped, 14-16mm long, drooping on thick *stalks* that become erect in fruit; umbels lax; tepals 3-7-veined (only 1-veined in *Allium*). Fruit a many-seeded capsule. Woods or scrub, cultivated land. Apr-June. Corsica, Sardinia eastwards to Turkey – not the Balkans. Grown in gardens; the dried seedheads are excellent for floral decorations. Inside each flower can be seen three glistening oval nectaries. The form from Bulgaria, Turkey and Rumania, with greenish-white flowers, is sometimes distinguished as *N. bulgaricum* (2250).

2251 *Dracaena draco* **DRAGON TREE.** Very stout and rather sombre-looking tree to 15m, occasionally more; large specimens rare, much-branched. Leaves densely clustered at the branch-tips, linear-lanceolate, tough, dark grey-green, to 90cm long, erect to recurved, untoothed. Flowers greenish-white, small, borne in a large panicle, seldom produced. (Canary Is.). Sometimes planted in parks as young plants in summer bedding schemes. A red gum sometimes exudes from the trunk, in the past called dragon's blood and prized for its medicinal or magical properties.

2252 *Phormium tenax* **NEW ZEALAND FLAX.** Large clump forming evergreen perennial. Leaves strap-shaped, folded down the middle, borne in *broad fans*, up to 3m long, thick and leathery, overlapping one another at the base, pointed. Flowers dull red or reddish-brown, tubular, the inner segments spreading at the tip, borne in a very stout panicle to 5m tall; stamens 6, protruding. Fruit a straight, 3-parted capsule. Widely planted in parks and gardens and along roadsides, occasionally naturalised. June-Sept. (New Zealand). Many forms are grown in gardens, especially dwarfer variants and those with strikingly coloured or variegated leaves.

AGAVE FAMILY Agavaceae

A family of trees, shrubs and large scapose perennials. Leaves thick, often fibrous. Inflorescences a large terminal panicle; flowers tubular with 6 free or partly fused tepals and 6 stamens; ovary inferior in *Agave*, superior in *Yucca*.

2253 *Agave americana* **AGAVE, CENTURY PLANT.** Very robust stoloniferous perennial, to 7m tall in flower. Leaves very large, spear-shaped, forming basal rosettes close to the ground, greyish- or bluish-green, tapered gradually from a sheathing base, terminating in a sharp *black spine*, with a few spiny teeth along the margin. Scape becoming woody, very stout, with a few triangular bracts. Flowers greenish-yellow, 70-90mm long, borne in a very large panicle, tubular, erect. Fruit an oblong capsule, triangular in section. Naturalised in rocky places, along cliffs and roadsides; planted in parks; mainly coastal. June-Aug. (Mexico). The rosette dies after flowering, although generally then producing some basal side shoots; it may take 10 years or more to reach flowering size. In Mexico the drink 'pulque' is made from juice extracted from the young flower spikes. Long cultivated in the region and widely naturalised.

2254 *Agave sisalana* **SISAL.** Similar, but smaller, with stiff leaves, bright green. Inflorescence shorter; flowers bluish-green, generally mixed with *leafy bulbils* which become detached to start new plants. (Yucatan). Occasionally grown in the region and sometimes naturalised, especially in E Cyprus. The leaves produce tough fibres that are the source of Sisal Hemp, used for rope making. It is grown for this in a number of tropical and subtropical countries.

2255 *Yucca gloriosa* **YUCCA.** Tough shrub, to 1.2m; trunk thick and woody, branching with age, terminating in a large leafy rosette. Leaves dark green with reddish-brown margins, leathery and rigid, tapered gradually from the base to a spine-tip, sparsely toothed along the margin. Flowers white or cream, often flushed with purplish-red, bell-shaped, pendent, 40-60mm long, borne in large teriminal panicles on a stout stem; tepals 6, similar and separate from one another. Fruit 6-ribbed, not splitting when ripe, dry. June-Sept. (SE USA). Widely cultivated in the Med region in parks and gardens, sometimes planted along roadsides. Naturalised on sand-dunes in Italy, perhaps elsewhere in the region.

2256 *Yucca filamentosa.* Similar, but a slighter plant with narrower leaves which have numerous whitish *curly filaments* along the margin. Flowers creamy-white, 35-

50mm long. Fruit splitting when ripe. June-Sept. Naturalised in S France and NW Italy. (SE USA). Widely grown in gardens.

DAFFODIL FAMILY Amaryllidaceae

A family of bulbous perennials with scapes (leafless stems). Leaves basal, linear to strap-shaped, generally rather fleshy, with parallel veins, often only partly developed at flowering time. Flowers solitary or clustered in an umbel, subtended by one or several 'bract-like' spathes which cover and protect the flowers in bud; tepals 6, usually all petal-like, arising, like the other flower parts, from the top of the ovary, which is inferior; stamens 6. Fruit a 3-parted capsule.

2257 *Sternbergia lutea* **COMMON STERNBERGIA**. Low to short, hairless bulbous perennial. Leaves 3-9, deep green, strap-shaped, slightly channelled, 8-15mm wide, appearing with or before the flowers. Flowers golden-yellow, goblet-shaped and *crocus-like*, 40-50mm long, borne on slender scapes; tepals oblong-elliptical, 7-15mm wide, fused at the base into a short tube; spathe 1-valved. Dry scrub, rocky and grassy slopes, generally in the hills and low mountains. Aug-Oct. Spain and NW Africa (Algeria) eastwards to Turkey – not France, Corsica or Cyprus.Widely grown in gardens. The flowers look very crocus-like, but the short green scape as well as 6 (not 3) stamens make it easy to distinguish.

 2257a Subsp. *sicula [Sternbergia sicula]* is similar, but a more delicate plant, the leaves only 3-5mm wide and the flowers with narrow oblong tepals, 4-8mm wide. S Italy, Sicily, S Greece and the Aegean Is. One of the first autumn flowering bulbs to appear in the Med region.

2258 *Sternbergia colchiciflora* **SLENDER STERNBERGIA**. Low bulbous perennial, not more than 4cm high. Leaves deep green, linear, 2-5mm wide, slightly channelled, often lying flat on the ground. Flowers pale to bright yellow, rather funnel-shaped, 30-40mm long, borne at ground level *after* the leaves have withered; tepals linear, broadest above the middle; stamens 6 in contrast to *Crocus* which has 3. Dry stony and grassy places, open scrub. Spain eastwards to Turkey – absent from Balearic Is., Corsica, Sardinia, Crete and Cyprus.

Galanthus **SNOWDROPS**. Bulbous perennial, often clump-forming, with 2-3 leaves per bulb usually and solitary nodding flowers borne on slender scapes. Outer tepals large and petal-like, plain white, but the inner tepals smaller, often with green markings and notched at the apex.

2259 *Galanthus reginae-olgae [G. nivalis* subsp. *reginae-olgae, G. corcyrensis]* **AUTUMN SNOWDROP**. Low to short bulbous perennial, hairless. Leaves 2 to a bulb, greyish- or bluish-green, with a pale central stripe, usually appearing *after the flowers*, linear to strap-shaped. Flowers white, the inner tepals with a green, heart-shaped mark at the notched end, 20-35mm long. Woodland and rocky places. Oct-Dec. Sicily, SW Yugoslavia and W Greece. Very similar in appearance to the common Snowdrop, *Galanthus nivalis* (2260), save for its autumn-flowering habit. The flowers are sweetly scented.

2261 *Galanthus elwesii*. Short, often tufted bulbous perennial, to 18cm, though often less. Leaves generally 2 perennial bulb, grey-green, *folded* around each other at the base at maturity, elliptical, 12mm wide or more, ridged on the back in the lower half. Flowers white, 15-28mm long, the inner tepals with a green patch at both the base and at the notched end. Woodland and rocky habitats, banks, stony meadows. Feb-Apr. N Aegean region and W Turkey.

2262 *Galanthus ikariae*. Similar, but leaves *bright green* and shiny, the inner tepals with a green mark only at the notched apex. Aegean islands of Andros and Tinos.

Leucojum [Leucoium] **SNOWFLAKES**. Like *Galanthus*, but all the tepals similar in shape and without green markings; flowers sometimes several on each scape.

2263 *Leucojum autumnale* **AUTUMN SNOWFLAKE**. Low to short, rather delicate bulbous perennial. Leaves thread-like, deep green, generally appearing *after* the flowers. Flowers white tinged with pink at the base, occasionally all pink, bell-shaped, 9-14mm long, the outer tepals 3-toothed at the apex; scape usually with 1-3 flowers. Rocky and stony hillslopes. Aug-Sept.W Med from the Iberian Peninsula and NW Africa to Sardinia and Sicily.

2264 *Leucojum roseum* **ROSE SNOWFLAKE**. Similar, but spathes 2-valved (not 1-valved) and flowers *pink*, solitary, the tepals pointed. Rocky ground and stony pastures. Sept-Oct. Corsica and Sardinia.

2265 *Leucojum trichophyllum [L. grandiflorum]* **THREE-LEAVED SNOWFLAKE**. Short, elegant bulbous perennial. Leaves linear, often 3 to a bulb, developed at flowering time. Flowers white, sometimes tinged with pink, 12-20mm long, broad bells borne in clusters of 2-4, on longer slender *stalks* up to 60mm long, the scape up to 30cm, but often less; spathes valves 2. Dry sandy habitats, at low altitudes. Dec-Apr. Portugal and S Spain, N Africa. A very attractive species.

2266 *Leucojum longifolium*. Similar, but flowers pure white, *smaller*, 8-11mm long; style shorter (not longer) than stamens. Rocky ground and dry hillslopes. Apr-May. Corsica – endemic.

2267 *Leucojum nicaeensis [L. hiemale]* **FRENCH SNOWFLAKE**. Low to short, bulbous perennial, not more than 18cm tall, often less. Leaves linear, developed at flowering time. Flowers white, widely bell-shaped, 8-12mm long, usually *solitary*, occasionally 2-3; spathe with 2 valves; styles slightly longer than the stamens; ovary disc-like, 6-lobed. Rocky habitats. Mar-May. SE France – Maritime Alps and neighbouring Med coast.

2268 *Leucojum valentinum*. Similar, but leaves thread-like and flowers 11-14mm long, appearing *after* the leaves have withered. Rocky pastures. Aug-Sept. E Spain – Valencia, and NW Greece.

2269 *Leucojum aestivum* **SUMMER SNOWFLAKE**. Robust, clump-forming, medium bulbous perennial. Leaves bright deep green, broad-linear, 5-20mm wide, well developed at flowering time; scapes somewhat flattened, 2-winged. Flowers white, each tepal with a *green spot* towards the tip, 13-22mm long, borne in umbels of 2-5, occasionally more, all on different length stalks. Damp meadows, ditches, open woodland, stream margins. Apr-June. S France eastwards to Turkey. Widely grown in gardens.

    2269a Subsp. *pulchellum* is similar, but with *narrower* leaves, 5-12mm wide, the scape without transparent wings; flowers 8-14mm long. Late Mar-Apr. Balearic Is., Corsica and Sardinia, where it replaces the type.

2270 *Pancratium maritimum* **SEA DAFFODIL, SEA LILY**. Short to medium, rather tough, hairless, bulbous perennial, often clump-forming. Leaves fleshy, grey-green strap-shaped, 5-20mm wide. Flowers white, large, 10-15cm long, fragrant, borne in umbels of 3-15; tepals all similar, linear-lanceolate; stamens 6, borne on the rim of a distinctive cone-shaped *trumpet* (corona), toothed along the rim, two thirds the length of the tepals. Fruit a 3-valved capsule. Sandy coastal habitats, including sand-dunes. Aug-Oct. T. A very distinctive species of the Med coastline, even when not in flower.

2271 *Pancratium illyricum* **ILLYRIAN SEA LILY.** Similar, but flowers smaller, 6-9cm, with elliptical tepals and a *short* corona half the length of the tepals, deeply cleft into 12 scales. Rocky habitats, generally close to the sea. May-June. Corsica, Sardinia and S Italy – Capri.

Narcissus **NARCISSI.** Bulbous perennials with basal leaves and hollow scapes carrying one or several flowers. Tepals 6, similar and petal-like; stamens 6 surrounded by a cup- or trumpet-shaped corona. Capsule 3-parted, often many-seeded.

2272 *Narcissus serotinus [Braxireon humilis, Hermione serotina].* Short, very slender, bulbous perennial. Leaves linear, cylindrical, only 1mm wide, rather bluish-green, 1-2 to a bulb, appearing in the spring, *absent* at flowering time. Flowers white with an orange cup (corona), 20-30mm, solitary or occasionally paired; tepals oblong, pointed; corona shallow, 6-lobed. Dry habitats, stony hillslopes, rock pockets. Sept-Dec. T – not S France or Albania.

2273 *Narcissus elegans.* Similar, but leaves 2-4.5mm wide and the flowers in *clusters* of 3-7, 22-38mm, with a yellowish or orange-brown corona, fragrant. Similar habitats and flowering time. S Italy and Sicily.

2274 *Narcissus viridiflorus* **GREEN-FLOWERED NARCISSUS.** Short, rather slender and inconspicuous bulbous perennial. Leaves rush-like, hollow, 1-4mm wide, generally only one from each bulb, appearing shortly after the flowers. Flowers dull *olive-green*, 20-30mm, rather foetid, borne in clusters of 2-5; tepals narrow-oblong, pointed, often reflexed backwards; cup shallow, 6-lobed. Damp sandy habitats, at low altitudes and often close to the coast. Sept-Oct. SW Spain, including Gibraltar, and Morocco.

2275 *Narcissus cavanillesii [N. humilis, Tapeinanthus humilis]* **TAPEINANTHUS.** A short, slender bulbous perennial. Leaves rush-like, 1mm wide, generally one per bulb. Flowers yellow, 18-22mm, solitary or occasionally paired, the tepals narrow and pointed; cup very shallow, consisting of 6 small *scales*. Grassy habitats, open woods at low altitudes. SW Spain – endemic

2276 *Narcissus tazetta* **POLYANTHUS NARCISSUS, ROSE OF SHARON.** Very variable, medium, hairless, bulbous perennial. Leaves broad strap-shaped, grey-green, slightly channelled, 5-25mm wide. Flowers *bicolored*, white with a deep yellow cup, 15-40mm, borne in clusters of 2-7, very fragrant; tepals broad-oval; cup 3-6mm deep, slightly lobed. Meadows, grassy places, cultivated fields, garrigue, rock crevices. Nov-Mar. T – not Crete, Italy, Sicily or the Balkans. Widely grown as a bulb for 'forcing' indoors or as a cut-flower: large numbers are sold in markets in early spring. It also occurs eastwards, as far as China, although its native distribution is unclear after a long history of cultivation.

2277 *Narcissus aureus.* Similar, but the *whole* flower is a bright golden yellow. SE France, NW Italy and Sardinia, occasionally naturalised elsewhere. The typical plant is the 'Soleil d'Or' of gardens, much sold as a cult flower around Christmas time.

    2277a Subsp. *italicus [Narcissus italicus, N. ochroleucus]* is distinguished by its cream to pale yellow tepals. N Africa, S France, Corsica and Sardinia, S Italy, Sicily and the Balkans, including Crete.

2278 *Narcissus papyraceus* **PAPERWHITE NARCISSUS.** Like *N. tazetta*, but the whole flower is *pure white*, borne in umbels of up to 20, each flower 25-40mm, intensely fragrant; cup with shallow rounded teeth; leaves bluish-green. Dry rocky places, meadows and fields, vineyards, olive groves, cultivated ground. Oct-Apr. Iberian Peninsula, NW Africa, eastwards to the Balkans – not the Balearic Is., Corsica,

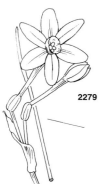

Sardinia or Crete. The species is widely cultivated as a bulb for indoors flowering as well as a cut flower.

2278a Subsp. *polyanthos* has green leaves and an untoothed cup. S France; naturalised in Spain and Italy.

2278b Subsp. *panizzianus* has smaller flowers, 20-25mm, and a markedly 2-edged scape. Portugal, SW Spain, SE France, N Italy and possibly NW Africa.

2279 *Narcissus jonquilla* **COMMON JONQUIL**. Short, often tufted, bulbous perennial. Leaves linear, *deep green*, 2-4mm wide, semi-cylindrical, slightly grooved. Flowers rich golden-yellow, 22-32mm, in clusters of 2-5, fragrant; tepals widely spreading; cup shallow, only 3-5mm deep; tepal-tube 20-30mm long. Damp meadows and other damp habitats. Mar-May. C and S Spain, Portugal and N Africa; naturalised in S France, Italy and Yugoslavia. One of the sweetest scented of any plant, much prized for its perfume which is used in perfumery – for this reason it has become naturalised in some regions of the Med.

2280 *Narcissus cantabricus* **WHITE HOOP PETTICOAT NARCISSUS**. Low to short, often tufted bulbous perennial. Leaves linear, 1-1.5mm wide, dark green, generally only one per bulb. Flowers white, solitary, horizontal on the end of the scape, with linear-lanceolate tepals and a *large* cone-shaped corona, 12-18mm long, flared and toothed at the rim. Scrub and grassy places. Jan-Mar. S Spain, Balearic Is. and NW Africa. Occasionally cultivated. The common Hoop Petticoat Narcissus, *N. bulbocodium* (**2281**), with its familiar yellow flowers, is a plant of mountain pastures, native to the Iberian Peninsula and SW France as well as NW Africa.

YAM FAMILY Dioscoreaceae

A large family of primarily tropical species that include the important yams, *Dioscorea*. The flowers are generally small and greenish, borne in spikes or racemes, or small clusters in the leaf-axils, the male and female on separate plants.

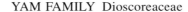

2282 *Tamus communis* **BLACK BRYONY**. Tall, twining perennial climber, to 4m, dying down in the autumn to a large underground tuber. Leaves *glossy green*, oval-heart-shaped, long-stalked, the margin untoothed, with 3-9 curved primary veins. Flowers greenish-yellow, 3-6mm, borne in lax lateral racemes, the male with 6 fairly broad lobes and 6 stamens; female with 6 minute lobes and a conspicuous ovary, in much shorter racemes, on separate plants. Fruit a globose or oval, glistening berry, bright red when ripe. Thickets, shrubberies, hedgerows and fences, roadsides, open woodland, streamsides. Mar-July. T. The berries are poisonous. Sometimes confused with *Smilax*, which has evergreen, prickly leaves.

IRIS FAMILY Iridaceae

A family of bulbous, tuberous or rhizomatous perennials, often with narrow, linear or sword-shaped leaves, all basal or alternate. Flowers 3 parted, generally enclosed in one or two spathes in bud; tepals 6, often petal-like, all similar or three different; stamens 3; styles 3 or 3-lobed, or variously divided. Ovary inferior. Fruit a 3-parted capsule.

2283 *Hermodactylus tuberosus [Iris tuberosa]* **SNAKE'S HEAD IRIS, WIDOW IRIS**. Short tuberous perennial, rather slender. Leaves greyish-green, linear, square in section, very long, 1.5-3mm wide. Flowers yellowish-green except for dark velvety brownish-violet on the lower tepals (falls), occasionally all greenish-yellow, solitary; falls 45-55mm long; standards about half as long as the falls, very narrow. Grassy and rocky habitats, banks, roadsides, garrigue and scrub. Mar-May. SE France eastwards to the Balkans and Turkey. Often sold in the late winter and early spring as a cut flower. The flowers are sweetly scented. The genus *Hermodactylus* contains only a single species, which is a typical Med plant.

Iris **IRIS**. A genus of bulbous or rhizomatous perennials. Flowers with the 3 outer tepals (falls) horizontal or downturned, sometimes bearded on the upper surface, and the 3 inner tepals (standards) which are usually erect; styles 3, broad, arching over the falls, each with a single stamen underneath.

2284 *Iris unguicularis [I. stylosa]* **ALGERIAN IRIS**. Low, densely tufted, rhizomatous perennial. Leaves tough, deep green, strap-shaped, flexuous, pointed, 7-15mm wide normally. Flowers solitary, 5-7cm, lilac or bluish-purple with white markings on the falls and darker veins, with an orange band in the centre, scented; falls oblong-elliptical, 55-80mm long; perianth tube *very long*, 10-20cm long, with ovary at or below ground level; standards almost as long as the falls, but narrower. Dry sunny habitats, rocky places, banks, open scrub, rock ledges. Dec-Apr. NW Africa – Algeria and Tunisia, Turkey, Rhodes and the extreme E Med – not Cyprus. A very variable species widely grown in gardens and noted for its flowers which appear in midwinter.

2285 *Iris cretensis*. Similar, but leaves *very narrow*, rarely more than 3mm wide. Flowers violet or deep lavender, the falls often very strikingly marked, white below with dark veining; style branches often bronzy-purple; falls narrow, not more than 15mm wide, not more than 55mm long. Similar habitats. Feb-Apr. S Greece – Peloponnese, and Crete. The seeds, as in *I. unguicularis*, are distributed by ants.

fall

2286 *Iris foetidissima* **ROAST BEEF PLANT, STINKING IRIS**. Medium, tufted, tough, rhizomatous perennial. Leaves shiny deep green, evergreen, sword-shaped, pointed, with a strong and rather unpleasant smell when crushed, 10-25mm wide. Flowers dull purple, violet tinged with yellow, or occasionally pale yellow, generally with darker veins on the falls, 5-7cm, borne on a rather flattened stem with 2-3short branches, several flowers opening in succession; spathes green and leaf-like, but much shorter. Fruit opening to reveal rows of bright orange seeds which persist through the winter months. Woods, scrub and hedgerows. May-July. Iberian Peninsula and NW Africa eastwards to Italy and Sicily – not Balearic Is. Not very striking in flower, but the boldest of all irises in fruit.

2287 *Iris orientalis [I. ochroleuca, Iris spuria* subsp. *ochroleuca]*. Robust, medium to tall, rhizomatous perennial, often forming large clumps. Leaves sword-shaped, 6-20mm wide, somewhat foetid when crushed; spathes green and leaf-like, up to 8cm long. Flowers white with a *yellow patch* in the centre of the falls, 8-10cm; falls with a rounded blade that often curls under at the end, 3-8cm long; standards erect, narrower than the falls. Wet and saline habitats, often growing in damp hollows or along irrigation ditches or on marshy ground. Apr-June. NE Greece, E Aegean Is., W Turkey. Grown in gardens.

2288 *Iris monnieri*. Similar, but flowers *lemon-yellow* all over. Similar habitats and flowering time. E Aegean Is., possibly W Turkey.

2289 *Iris spuria* subsp. *maritima*. A medium tufted rhizomatous perennial. Leaves grey-green, 6-10mm wide, sword-shaped; spathes green, like the leaves but much shorter. Flowers relatively *small*, cream with lilac-blue or purple veining on the falls merging into darker purple on the blades and with a greenish-yellow median strip; falls 3-4.5cm long. Damp habitats, salt marshes. Iberian Peninsula, Spain, S France, Corsica and NW Africa (where it is sometimes distinguished as forma *reichenbachii* 2289a).

fall

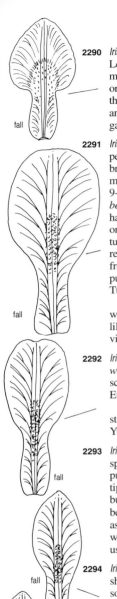

2290 *Iris pseudacorus* **YELLOW FLAG.** Robust, tall, rhizomatous perennial to 1.8m tall. Leaves greyish- or pale-green, sword-shaped, 1-3cm wide; spathes green, with membranous margins. Flowers usually 5-10, bright yellow, 7-10cm, with brown or violet marks on the broad oval blades of the falls; standards *much shorter* than the falls, 2-3cm long, narrow-oblong. In or close to water, marshy ground, stream and river margins, lakes and ditches. May-July. T – not Cyprus. Widely grown in gardens and often naturalised.

2291 *Iris germanica* **TALL BEARDED IRIS, GERMAN IRIS.** A robust medium to tall, rhizomatous perennial, to 1m; rhizome thick, spreading on the surface of the ground. Leaves broad sword-shaped, grey-green, 2-4.5cm wide; spathes green in the lower half, membranous and papery above, often tinged with purple. Flowers violet-blue, 9-11cm, the standards often somewhat paler, the falls with a distinctive *yellow beard* along the centre, fragrant; borne on a slightly branched stem. Dry rocky habitats, field margins, graveyards, cultivated land, roadsides. Apr-June. T. The origin of this plant is unknown for it has been widely cultivated for many centuries. It is an extremely variable species with a number of different 'species' recognised by some authorities in different parts of the Med; *I. belouinii* (2291a) from Morocco, *I. cypriana* (2291b), from Cyprus, *I. trojana* (2291c), with brownish-purple veining on the falls, from W Turkey and *I. mesopotamica* (2291d), from S Turkey, southwards to Syria and Israel. Many cultivars are known in gardens.

2291e Subsp. *florentina* [*Iris florentina*]. Like the type, but the flowers *pure* white with a pale yellow beard on the falls, occasionally with a slight hint of blue or lilac. Grown commercially, especially in France and Italy. Orris Root, with a violet scent, is derived from the rhizomes.

2292 *Iris pallida*. Similar, but leaves more bluish-green, thick and finely ribbed, spathes *wholly* papery, silvery, and flowers a uniform pale lilac-blue. Rocky habitats and scrub. Apr-June. N Italy and W Yugoslavia; naturalised in various parts of the European Med. Widely grown in gardens.

2292a Subsp. *cengialtii* [*Iris cengialtii*], generally a smaller plant, has green leaves, strongly ribbed; spathes brown and papery; flowers deep violet. NE Italy and NW Yugoslavia.

2293 *Iris albicans*. Very like *I. germanica*, but a shorter plant, rarely more than 60cm tall; spathes *green* at flowering time or papery only at the very tip, often flushed with purple; flowers 8-9cm, usually pure white, occasionally blue, with a white beard tipped with yellow. Cultivated ground, dry grassy places, graveyards, around old building. May-June. Naturalised T. (Arabia). It is believed that this species has been introduced to many parts of the Med by man; in the Arab world it is closely associated with graveyards. The normal white-flowered form is often confused with *I. germanica* subsp. *florentina*, but the papery brown bracts of the latter is a very useful distinguishing feature.

2294 *Iris lutescens* [*I. chamaeiris*]. Low to short, rhizomatous perennial. Leaves sword-shaped, *scarcely curved*, 5-25mm wide; spathes green, rather loosely arranged, sometimes somewhat membranous at the tip, 35-55mm long. Flowers 1-2, 6-7cm, violet, yellow or bicoloured, rarely white; falls 50-75mm long, with a yellow beard along the centre. Grassy and rocky habitats, occasionally beneath pine trees. Mar-Apr. Iberian Peninsula, S France and Italy. Widely grown in gardens.

2295 *Iris subbiflora* [*I. lutescens* subsp. *subbiflora*]. Very similar, but with deep violet flowers in which the beard is *violet or white*. Portugal and SW Spain.

2296 *Iris attica*. Very variable low rhizomatous perennial. Leaves greyish-green, strongly curved, *scimitar-shaped*, 4-7mm wide; spathes tubular, rounded on the back, 5-7cm long. Flowers blue, purple or yellow, or bicoloured, 3.5-4.5cm, the falls with a yellowish or bluish beard. Low grassy habitats, rocky places, in the hills and mountains. Mar-May. S Yugoslavia, mainland Greece, W Turkey.

2297 *Iris pseudopumila [I. panormitana]*. Similar, but leaves only slightly curved, 10-15mm wide; spathes somewhat swollen, *long*, 9-12cm. Flowers larger, 6-8cm, similarly coloured, often bicoloured. Similar habitats and flowering time. SE Italy, Sicily, Malta, Gozo, W Yugoslavia.

2298 *Iris planifolia [I. alata]*. A low to short, bulbous perennial, rarely more than 20cm tall. Leaves all basal, shiny-green, produced in a fan, channelled, not flat, tapered, 10-30mm wide, arching somewhat. Flowers 1-3, 6-7cm, bluish-violet with darker veining around the yellow crest on the falls, sometimes a paler blue or white; perianth-tube very long, 8-15cm; falls broadly winged on the hafts; standards *very small*, horizontal, 20-25mm long, usually toothed. Rocky and grassy, exposed habitats, open scrub, mainly in the hills and lower mountains. Nov-Feb. Portugal, S Spain, N Africa, Sardinia, Sicily, Crete.

2299 *Iris xiphium* **SPANISH IRIS.** Rather slender, medium, bulbous perennial. Leaves greygreen, slender, 3-5mm wide, channelled, appearing in the autumn. Flowers 1-2, blue or violet, with an orange or yellow crest on the falls, rarely all yellow or white; the falls with a narrow *unwinged* haft and an oval blade, 45-65mm long; standards erect, somewhat shorter than the falls. Grassy habitats and scrub, in sandy or rocky ground, occasionally on sand-dunes. Apr-May. Iberian Peninsula and NW Africa eastwards to Italy – not Balearic Is. or Sicily. This species has long been cultivated and is the common florist's iris. Yellow-flowered forms from Portugal are sometimes distinguished as *I. lusitanica* (2300).

2301 *Iris tingitana*. Similar, but leaves silvery-green, long and arching; flowers pale to deep blue with with sharply *pointed* standards. Morocco and Algeria.

2302 *Iris filifolia*. Like *I. xiphium*, but leaves only 0.5-3mm wide and flowers dark reddishpurple, with a conspicuous orange patch on the falls. Dry rocky habitats. May-June. S Spain, including Gibraltar, Morocco and Tunisia.

2303 *Iris juncea*. Like *I. xiphium*, but lower leaves only 1-3mm wide and flowers entirely yellow; spathes with membranous tips (not entirely green); perianth-tube 35-50mm long (not 1-3mm), long and slender. May-June. S Spain, Sicily and N Africa.

2304 *Iris boissieri*. Like *I. juncea*, but flowers deep violet-blue, with a yellow *beard* on the falls. Scrub, on rocky, acid soils. June. N Portugal and NW Spain.

2305 *Gynandriris sisyrinchium [Iris sisyrinchium]* **BARBARY NUT.** Variable, low to medium, cormous perennial. Leaves few, often 1-2, deep green, channelled, 5-8mm wide, often longer than the flower-stem; bracts up to 4 pairs, each enclosing several flowers, papery. Flowers 22-40mm, short-lived, bluish-lilac to violet, with a white or yellow patch on the falls, iris-like; falls oval to elliptical, 25-35mm long; standards slightly shorter, half the width of the falls; ovary with a slender, solid *neck*, 20-30mm long. Cultivated, waste and fallow ground, field margins, olive groves, scrub and open woodland, roadsides. Feb-May. T. A common Med plant. The small, short-lived, flowers open at midday and wither in the evening. Small plants with a solitary leaf and flowers only 20mm across (not 30-40mm) are sometimes distinguished as *G. monophylla* (2306).

Gladiolus **GLADIOLI.** A genus of cormous plants with fans of flat, sword-shaped, ribbed leaves. Flowers in long spikes, each subtended by a green bract that encloses the flower in bud; corolla forming a curved tube with an obvious lower lip, hooded above; tepals 6, not equal, fused into a short tube near the base; stamens 3; style 3-lobed at the apex.

2307 *Gladiolus italicus [G. segetum]* **FIELD GLADIOLUS.** Medium to tall cormous perennial. Leaves 3-5, 5-17mm wide, the upper narrower than the lower, irregularly veined; basal sheaths pale to dark red, often white-spotted. Flowers pinkish-purple to reddish, 40-50mm long, 6-15 in a more or less *two-sided* spike; lower 3 tepals with pinkish spear-shaped marks outlined with purple; anthers longer than the filaments. Cultivated land, particularly cereal fields, roadsides, hillslopes, occasionally in garrigue. Mar-June. T. The common gladiolus seen in many parts of the Med region. Occasionally sold as a cut flower.

corm

2308 *Gladiolus illyricus*. Similar, but plants not more than 50cm tall, often far less and flowers 3-10 per spike, 25-40mm long; anthers equal in length, or shorter than, the filaments. Grassy and heathy places, scrub or light woodland. Apr-July. Iberian Peninsula and NW Africa eastwards to the Balkans and the E Med – not Cyprus.

2309 *Gladiolus communis*. Like *G. italicus*, but flowers pink, 10-20 borne in a loose spike, often *branched* below; lower 3 tepals with red or white blotches or lines; anthers equal to, or shorter than, the filaments. Dry grassy habitats and scrub, meadows. Apr-June. Iberian Peninsula eastwards to Greece.

2310 *Gladiolus imbricatus*. A medium to tall cormous perennial. Leaves generally 3, 10-15mm wide. Flowers 4-12, pale carmine to reddish-violet or reddish-purple, 30-40mm long, borne in a *one-sided* spike; lower 3 tepals with white, spear-shaped marks outlined in deep purple; perianth-tube strongly curved near its apex; anthers equal to, or shorter than, the filaments. Damp meadows and scrub. Apr-June. Balkans and Turkey.

2311 *Gladiolus atroviolaceus*. Similar, but with narrower leaves, only 4-8mm wide and flowers dark violet, often appearing blackish; anthers longer than filaments. Cultivated and fallow ground, grassy slopes, often in cereal fields. Apr-July. Greece, Turkey to Iraq.

2312 *Gladiolus triphyllus [G. trichophyllus]*. Short to medium cormous perennial. Leaves usually 3-4, linear, only 3-4mm wide, with 3-4 strong veins, the upper leaves much shorter than the lower, all pointed. Flowers 1-7 borne in a rather lax spike, each 30-42mm long, rose-pink, the lower 3 tepals paler and with a whitish median stripe; anthers shorter than the filaments. Garrigue, maquis, open pine forests, rock hillslopes. Mar-May. Cyprus – endemic.

2313 *Gladiolus byzantinus* **BYZANTINE GLADIOLUS.** Medium to tall cormous perennial, to 1m. Leaves 4-5, 10-25mm wide. Flowers deep *reddish-purple*, 40-50mm long, borne in a two-sided spike, often with 1-2 short branches below; lower 3 tepals with narrow spear-shaped marks outlined in dark purple, the perianth-tube only slightly curved; anthers equal in length to, or shorter than, the filaments. Scrub, fields and grassy places, sometimes among *Chamaerops* palms. Mar-June. S Spain, Sicily and NW Africa. Widely grown in gardens and naturalised in some areas of the Med.

Romulea **ROMULEAS.** Low cormous plants with basal linear leaves generally 4-grooved; spathes present, usually 2, green to papery, enclosing the flowers in bud. Flowers crocus-like, but borne on a distinct green stem; tepals 6, equal, with a very short perianth-tube; stamens 3, usually yellow; style solitary, 3-branched.

2314 *Romulea bulbocodium [Romulea clusiana]*. Leaves usually 3-7, deep green, curved to straight. Flowers relatively large, white to lilac, often greenish on the outside and *striped* with violet, yellow in the throat; tepals elliptical, pointed, 20-35mm long. Rocky and grassy habitats; lowland and in the mountains. Feb-May. T – not Balearic Is., Cyprus or parts of the extreme E Med. This is the common romulea of the Med region, often forming extensive colonies.

2314a var. *clusiana* has especially large flowers, the tepals 30-35mm long. Iberian Peninsula.

2314b var. *subpalustris* has lilac flowers with no yellow in the throat. Cyclades.

2315 *Romulea requienii*. Leaves usually 3-7, generally *flat on the ground*, green, 0.75-1.25mm wide; spathes green with a papery margin or all papery, speckled with violet or brown. Flowers dark violet with darker veins but no yellow in the throat; tepals oblong with a rounded apex, 14-21mm long. Sandy coastal habitats. Feb-Mar. Corsica, Sardinia and SC Italy.

2316 *Romulea ramiflora*. Leaves usually 4-6, erect to recurved, 0.75-1.5mm wide; spathes *green* with a membranous margin. Flowers pale to deep bluish-purple, sometimes with darker veins and occasionally greenish outside, the throat with or without yellow; tepals elliptical, often broadest above the middle, 7-12mm long; styles equalling the stamens. Coastal habitats, bare sandy or grassy, marshy ground, water meadows. Feb-Mar. T.

2316a Subsp. *gaditana* [*Romulea gaditana*] has larger flowers, lilac or pink, greenish outside; tepals 16-23mm long. W and S Spain and Portugal.

2317 *Romulea linaresii*. Leaves 3-6, spreading to recurved, 0.9-1.5mm wide; lower spathe green, upper papery. Flowers deep violet-purple, *without* any yellow in the throat; tepals elliptical, broadest above the middle, blunt or pointed, 15-19mm long; stigmas below the top of the anthers. Sandy coastal habitats, occasionally inland. Feb-Mar. Sicily.

2317a Subsp. *graeca* has smaller flowers; tepals 7-15mm long, pointed. Grassy and stony habitats, lowland and in the mountains. Greece, Aegean Is., Crete and Turkey.

2318 *Romulea revelierei*. Similar, but flowers smaller with a paler or whitish throat; tepals 9-11mm long; stigmas equalling the anthers or slightly longer. Moist places or those subjected to winter flooding, usually close to the coast. Feb-Mar. Corsica, N Sardinia and Capri.

2319 *Romulea melitensis*. Like *R. linaresii*, but flowers deep violet with a yellow throat. Damp habitats near the sea. Feb-Mar. Malta and Gozo.

2320 *Romulea columnae* **SAND CROCUS**. Leaves 3-8, fairly short, deep green, 0.5-1mm wide. Flowers small, pale lilac or purplish with darker veins, sometimes greenish on the outside, with a yellow throat, occasionally whitish; tepals lanceolate, pointed, 9-19mm long. Grassy and sandy habitats, dry banks, primarily coastal. Feb-Apr. T.

2320a Subsp. *rollii* has narrower leaves, not more than 0.75mm wide, and hairy stalks to the stamens. Coastal sands. S France eastwards.

2321 *Romulea tempskyana*. Similar, but flowers deep violet, rarely pure white, with a yellow throat; tepals 14-26mm long. Garrigue, maquis, grassy places, open pine forests, hillslopes. Jan-Mar. Aegean Is., S. Turkey, Cyprus and Palestine.

2322 *Romulea ligustica*. Like *R. tempskyana*, but flowers pale to deep lilac with a yellow throat, the perianth-tube 5-7mm long (not 8-17mm) and the stigmas *below* the top of the anthers (not longer). Grassy and stony coastal habitats. Feb-Mar. Corsica, Sardinia and NW Italy.

Crocus **CROCUSES**. Cormous perennials. Leaves basal, enclosed in the lower part by several sheaths, linear, with a white stripe down the centre on the upper surface. Flowers one to several per corm, each enclosed within one or two spathes, which enclose the base of the tepal-tube when the flowers are fully developed; tepals 6, all similar or the inner somewhat smaller; stamens 3; style solitary with 3 many-branched stigmas. The position of stamens and styles and the style-branching can be valuable aids to identification. Many species are grown in gardens. The genus has a distribution from Europe eastwards to central Asia and the western Himalaya; the majority are to be found in the Med region.

stamens & styles

2323 *Crocus longiflorus.* Low to short cormous perennial. Leaves usually 4-6, green, with a very distinct white stripe, 1-3mm wide, usually partly developed at flowering time. Flowers lilac to purple, often with darker veining on the outside and a deep yellow *throat*, fragrant; tepals blunt or rather pointed, oval, broadest above the middle, 22-43mm long; stamens yellow; style with 3 orange-red branches, each flared or slightly lobed at the tip. Grassy habitats and woodland margins. Oct-Nov. SW Italy, Sicily and Malta.

2324 *Crocus nudiflorus.* Low to short cormous perennial, producing stolons and patch-forming. Leaves 3-4, green, 2-4mm wide, appearing *long after* flowering. Flowers deep purple to lilac-purple, indistinctly veined on the outside, the throat white to lilac; tepals elliptical, 30-60mm long; tepal-tube very long, 10-22cm; stamens with yellow anthers and white stalks; style with many short orange branches. Moist meadows. Sept-Oct. NE Spain; also SW France.

2325 *Crocus serotinus.* Similar, but not stoloniferous, the leaves generally *partly developed* at flowering time and flowers pale lilac to violet-blue, sometimes with darker veining on the outside and often with a *pale yellow* throat, scented; tepals not more than 38mm long; perianth-tube short, 2-5cm. Rocky and sandy habitats, rocky grassland and open pine woods. Oct-Nov. C and S Portugal.

2325a Subsp. *clusii [Crocus clusii]* has leaves often not present at flowering time, generally 4-7 (not 3-4). N and C Portugal, NW and SW Spain.

2325b Subsp. *salzmannii* has unscented flowers and 5-7 leaves; corms sometimes stoloniferous. Flowers often with darker veins on the outside, covered by a silvery wash; tepal-tube 4-11cm long. Sept-Dec. Spain, Gibraltar and NW Africa.

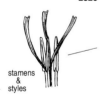

stamens & styles

2326 *Crocus cartwrightianus* **WILD SAFFRON CROCUS**. Low cormous perennial. Leaves 5-11, grey-green, generally partly developed at flowering time, 0.5-1.5mm wide. Flowers pale to deep lilac-purple, strongly darker veined on the outside, often stained darker towards the base, occasionally pure white, the tepals oval, broadest above the middle, 14-32mm long; stamens with yellow anthers and whitish or purplish stalks; style divided into 3 *very long* deep red branches, flared at the tips, each 15-27mm long. Rocky hillsides, scrub or sparse grassy places, occasionally in open pine woods. Oct-Dec. S Greece, Cyclades and Crete. The styles are sometimes gathered for saffron.

stamens & styles

2327 *Crocus sativus* **SAFFRON CROCUS**. Very like the previous species, but with larger flowers, the tepals 35-50mm long and the style branches *very long*, 25-32mm, often flopping over the side of the flower. Occasionally cultivated in the Med region; rarely naturalised. This plant, which is a sterile triploid, is almost certainly an ancient selection of *Crocus cartwrightianus*. It has been cultivated in the Med region, the Middle East, east as far as Kashmir, for many centuries. The styles, laboriously collected, are the Saffron, long used as a medicinal and dye plant and for flavouring food. Today Saffron is very expensive, but it is still produced in some parts of Greece and Crete and elsewhere. A cheaper, less effective, form sold as yellow saffron consists of the stamens rather than the styles.

2328 *Crocus thomasii.* Like *C. cartwrightianus*, but flowers generally pale lilac with slightly darker veins on the outside and a *pale yellow* throat; style branches 10-16mm long. Similar habitats. Oct-Dec. S Italy and W Yugoslavia; primarily along the Adriatic coast.

2329 *Crocus pallasii.* Like *C. cartwrightianus*, but flowers lilac, scarcely darker veined on the outside; style branches only 6-15mm long. Similar habitats. Oct-Dec. S Yugoslavia, Lesbos in the Aegean, Turkey, Lebanon and Israel.

2330 *Crocus hadriaticus.* Like *C. cartwrightianus*, but flowers *white* rarely flushed with lilac and throat yellow; tepals 20-45mm long and style branches 10-16mm long. Grassy and rocky places, fields, scrub. Sept-Dec. S and W mainland Greece, Cephalonia, Levkas and Corfu.

2331 *Crocus tournefortii.* Low cormous perennial. Leaves 3-8, 1-3mm wide, present at flowering time. Flowers lilac with a yellow throat, sometimes with darker veins on the outside; tepals blunt, 15-36mm long; stamens with white anthers and yellow, hairy stalks; style *conspicuous*, protruding, divided into many slender yellow or orange branches. Scrub, dry grassy and stony habitats, rock crevices. Sept-Dec. Crete, many Aegean Is., especially the Cyclades, Rhodes. This species is unusual in being the only one known that keeps its flowers open all night.

2332 *Crocus laevigatus.* Low cormous perennial. Leaves usually 2-4, 1-2.5mm wide, partly developed at flowering time, dark green. Flowers white or lilac, usually strongly *veined or stained* with purple on the outside, goblet-shaped, but generally opening to a wide star, sweetly scented; tepals 13-30mm long, blunt; stamens with white anthers and yellow stalks, hairless or hairy only at the very base; style orange or yellow, with many linear branches, as long as, or somewhat exceeding, the stamens. Open stony and rocky habitats, sparse scrub, rock crevices, occasionally in open pine woodland. Oct-Feb. S Greece, the Cyclades, Crete.

2333 *Crocus boryi [C. cretensis].* Similar, but flowers goblet-shaped, normally *creamy-white* with a yellow throat, very occasionally stained or veined with pale purple on the outside, unscented; tepals 15-50mm long. Leaves usually 3-7. Rocky hillslopes, sandy places, including dunes, banks, olive groves, roadsides, garrigue, scrub. Sept-Dec. W and S Crete, including the Ionian Is., SE Crete. Sometimes confused with *C. hadriaticus*, which is distinguished by its yellow anthers and 3-branched styles.

2334 *Crocus goulimyi.* Low to short cormous perennial. Leaves 4-6, green, 1-2.5mm wide, short at flowering time. Flowers pale to deep lilac, lilac-purple or pure white, sweetly scented, the throat whitish; tepals elliptical, 16-38mm long, the inner often paler and somewhat shorter than the outer; perianth-tube white, *very long*, 8-21cm; stamens with yellow anthers and white filaments; style white to yellow, 3-branched, slightly flared at the tips. Dry stony habitats, roadsides, olive groves, base of dry stone walls. Oct-Nov. S Greece – S Peloponnese, rather rare. Only discovered in the 1950s but, despite this, widely grown in gardens.

2335 *Crocus niveus.* Low to short cormous perennial. Leaves 5-8, dark green, 1-2mm wide, short at flowering time. Flowers goblet-shaped, white or very pale lilac, or the outer tepals a deeper lilac, the throat *deep yellow*; tepals oval, 15-35mm long, thick; perianth-tube yellowish or brownish, 9-18cm long. stamens yellow; style with 3 orange to red branches, somewhat flared at the tips. Rocky places, scrub, olive groves, roadsides, below old stone walls. Oct-Nov. S Greece – S and SE Peloponnese.

2336 *Crocus cancellatus.* A very variable low to short cormous perennial. Leaves 4-5, grey-green, 1-2mm wide, *absent at flowering time*. Flowers white to deep lilac-blue, often veined on the outside with violet-purple, the throat usually pale yel-

499

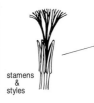

stamens
&
styles

low; tepals blunt or rather pointed, oblong to oval, 30-55mm long; perianth-tube usually whitish, up to 15cm long; stamens with yellow anthers and whitish to pale yellow stalks; style divided into many pale orange, linear branches. Rocky and stony slopes, open pine woodland, dry fields. Sept-Nov. S Turkey eastwards to the Lebanon and N Israel.

2336a Subsp. *mazziaricus* has the inner bract (at the base of the flower) visible and the style much exceeding the anthers (not equal to or slightly longer). S Yugoslavia, Greece, including the Ionian Is., Naxos, S and W Turkey.

2336b Subsp. *lycius* has smaller flowers, the tepals only 25-30mm long, white or very pale lilac, and the style equal to or shorter than the stamens. SW Turkey.

2336c Subsp. *pamphylicus* is readily distinguished from the type by its white anthers and deep yellow to orange throat. S Turkey.

stamens
&
styles

2337 *Crocus cambessedesii*. Low cormous perennial. Leaves 3-5, green, 0.5-1mm wide, short to long at flowering time. Flowers *very small*, white to cream or deep lilac, striped purple on the outside, with a white throat; tepals blunt, elliptical, 14-18mm long; stamens white; style with 3 orange to red branches which are flared or slightly lobed at the top, shorter to slightly longer than the stamens. Rocky habitats, scrub and pine woodland. Sept-Mar. Balearic Is. – endemic.

stamens
&
styles

2338 *Crocus corsicus*. Very similar, but somewhat larger, with only one (not two) spathes around the base of the perianth-tube, often brown-spotted; *tepals* 20-35mm long. Scrub and rocky hillslopes, mountain meadows. Jan-Apr, occasionally later at the higher altitudes. C and N Corsica – endemic.

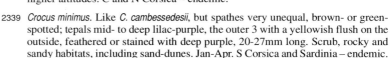

2339 *Crocus minimus*. Like *C. cambessedesii*, but spathes very unequal, brown- or green-spotted; tepals mid- to deep lilac-purple, the outer 3 with a yellowish flush on the outside, feathered or stained with deep purple, 20-27mm long. Scrub, rocky and sandy habitats, including sand-dunes. Jan-Apr. S Corsica and Sardinia – endemic.

2340 *Crocus versicolor*. Like *C. corsicus*, but leaves grey-green, *wider*, 1.5-3mm (not 1-1.5mm) and tepals 25-35mm long, white to lilac or purple, the outer usually striped with purple; throat white to pale yellow. Grassy and rocky habitats, deciduous woodland. SE France, Monaco and NW Italy.

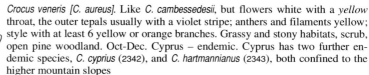

2341 *Crocus veneris [C. aureus]*. Like *C. cambessedesii*, but flowers white with a *yellow* throat, the outer tepals usually with a violet stripe; anthers and filaments yellow; style with at least 6 yellow or orange branches. Grassy and stony habitats, scrub, open pine woodland. Oct-Dec. Cyprus – endemic. Cyprus has two further endemic species, *C. cyprius* (2342), and *C. hartmannianus* (2343), both confined to the higher mountain slopes

2344 *Crocus flavus*. Low cormous perennial. Leaves 5-8, erect, green, often with a minutely hairy margin and keel, 2.5-4mm wide. Flowers pale yellow to deep golden-yellow, fragrant, occasionally suffused with brown at the base of the tepals; tepals elliptical, broadest above the middle, 15-35mm long; stamens yellow; stigma pale yellow to orange with 3 short branches, occasionally further lobed, usually shorter than the stamens. Dry grassy habitats, scrub and open woodland. Mar-Apr. S Yugoslavia, N and C Greece and NW Turkey. Commonly grown in gardens.

stamens
&
styles

2345 *Crocus olivieri* subsp. *balansae [Crocus balansae]*. Similar, but leaves spreading, not erect, only 2-4 per corm, *wider*, 4-6mm; tepals orange-yellow, sometimes flushed or striped with purplish-brown or mahogany on the outer 3 tepals; style with 12-15 slender branches. Hillslopes and scrub. Jan-Mar. W Turkey. The typical form of *C. olivieri*, distinguished by its unstriped tepals and 6-branched style, is a plant of mountains above 500m in the Balkan Peninsula and Turkey.

2346 *Crocus chrysanthus.* Like *C. flavus,* but leaves 3-7, *grey-green,* only 0.5-2.5mm wide; flowers pale to deep yellow, sometimes with a brownish or purplish tube, the tepals 15-35mm long; anthers yellow, sometimes with black basal lobes, rarely all black before dehiscence. Grassy and stony places, snow hollows, woodland and scrub, lowland and mountains. Jan-Apr. S Yugoslavia, N and C Greece, the islands of Thasos, Samothraki and Chios, Turkey, except the N.

2347 *Crocus candidus.* Like *C. olivieri,* but leaves only 1-2, deep shiny green, 2.5-4mm wide, and flowers *white,* the outer tepals spotted and flushed with grey. Scrub and open stony habitats. Feb-Mar. NW Asiatic Turkey.

2348 *Crocus biflorus.* Very variable, low to short cormous perennial. Leaves 2-5, green, 0.5-2.5mm wide, partly developed at flowering time. Flowers honey-fragrant, white to pale lilac-blue, the outer tepals usually strongly striped with brown or purple, generally as *three bands* of colour, throat yellow; tepals oval, broadest above the middle, 18-30mm long; stamens yellow, the anthers sometimes with black basal lobes; style 3-branched, yellow to orange. Open stony habitats, grassy places, maquis, garrigue. Feb-Apr. Italy, Sicily, Rhodes, NW Turkey. Many sub-species are recognised, mostly from mountain habitats, but those from lower elevations include:

2348a subsp. *melantherus,* with blackish-purple anthers (before dehiscence); flowers white striped or speckled with purple or grey on the outside. Maquis and short turf. Oct-Nov. S Greece – C. Peloponnese.

2348b subsp. *weldenii* with white flowers with a flush of blue or violet at the base of the tepals, the throat not yellow and styles bright orange. Stony places, open pine or oak woods. Feb-Mar. NE Italy and W Yugoslavia.

PALM FAMILY Palmae

Shrubs or trees; stems branched or not. Leaves large, pinnately- or palmately-divided. Inflorescences generally large, lateral, occasionally terminal; flowers unisexual or hermaphrodite, small, generally many in spikes or panicles, enveloped by one or more membranous spathes; sepals 3, fused or not; petals 3, fused or not; stamens usually 6. Fruit a berry or drupe. A very large family in tropical and subtropical regions where they are of prime economic importance. Many are grown as pot plants.

2349 *Phoenix theophrasti* **CRETAN PALM.** Tree to 12m with one to several slender main trunks, often branched near the base, crowned by a large fan of leaves. Leaves grey-green, *pinnately-divided* into numerous narrow, tapered leaflets, stiff, those nearest the trunk spine-tipped, yellowish. Flowers in arched panicles, greenish-yellow, among the crown of leaves. Fruit like a small date, 14-16mm long, brownish-yellow, but blackish when ripe, fibrous and inedible. Dry sandy habitats close to the sea. Mar-June. E Crete and SW Turkey. A rare plant, now closely protected, formerly thought to be endemic to Crete. Sometimes cultivated in the Med region.

2350 *Phoenix dactylifera* **DATE PALM.** Similar, but taller, to 30m; fruit (dates) variable, 25-75mm long, orange-brown, sweet and sticky when ripe, edible. Widely cultivated in the Med, especially in SW Spain, N Africa, S Turkey and the E Med. Feb-June. Native of N Africa and SW Asia. Cultivated for many centuries and a very important food crop in many Arab countries.

2351 *Phoenix canariensis* **CANARY PALM.** Like *P. dactylifera,* but not more than 20m tall and with a solitary trunk and green leaves; fruit 15-23mm long, purplish or orange.

Frequently planted for ornament and possibly naturalised in one or two places. (Canary Is.).

2352 *Jubaea chilensis* **JUBAEA PALM**. Like *Phoenix*, to 28m, but with shorter leaves and a *smooth* rather stout grey trunk; leaves leaving diamond-shaped scars when they fall. Planted for ornament. (Chile).

2353 *Trachycarpus fortunei* **CHUSAN PALM**. Tall slender palm; trunk to 15m, solitary, densely covered with dark brown, *matted fibres* of the old leaf-sheaths. Leaves large, bright green, fan-like, divided into numerous narrow, stiff, pointed segments, fused together in the middle of the blade; stalk with spines along the edge. Flowers greenish-white, borne in stout lateral panicles, to 60cm long; male and female on the same tree but in separate panicles. Fruit grape-like, 12-14mm long, bluish-black when ripe. The hardiest palm, much planted. Apr-June. (SE Asia). In China and elsewhere, where it occurs naturally, the densely matted leaf-sheath fibres are used for making cloaks and mats.

2354 *Washingtonia robusta* **WASHINGTONIA**. Similar, but much stouter and with a massive trunk, smooth with diagonal furrows, the upper part densely clothed in the pendent *withered leaves*. Planted in parks and along avenues. (Mexico).

2355 *Washingtonia filifera*. Like *W. robusta*, but trunk even more robust; leaves with *white threads* hanging from the leaf intersections. Planted in parks and along avenues. (S California).

2356 *Livistona australis* **LIVISTONA PALM**. Like *Washingtonia*, but to 25m, with a slender, *ringed* trunk. Occasionally planted in parks, gardens and along streets. (Australia).

2357 *Chamaerops humilis* **DWARF FAN PALM**. *Bushy, suckering palm*, sometimes producing trunks up to 4m, but often dwarf because of grazing; trunk covered in grey or whitish fibres. Leaves green or grey-green, fan-shaped, cut for two thirds into up to 20 pointed, narrow lanceolate segments; stalk long, with a spine-toothed margin. Flowers yellowish, borne in dense lateral panicles, to 35cm long. Fruit globose to oblong, 12-30mm, yellow or brown when ripe. Garrigue, sandy habitats, gullies, stony pastures, generally close to the coast. Apr-June. Iberian Peninsula and N Africa, eastwards to Italy and Malta. Cultivated for ornament in the Med. The young growing tips are eaten as a vegetable in some regions and the tough leaf-fibres used for matting, brooms and rope. Together with *Phoenix theophrasti*, the only native European palms.

ARUM FAMILY Araceae

A large family of primarily tropical or subtropical plants. The temperate members are stemless, with basal leaves. The tiny flowers are borne on a thickened axis or spadix that is elongated into a sterile appendage or appendix; the fertile part is enclosed, or partly enclosed, in a tubular fleshy sheath, the spathe, which often broadens and flattens out into a showy limb; flowers generally without a perianth and usually unisexual, the male carried above the female on the spadix, or on separate plants. Fruit a cluster of berries, sometimes brightly coloured.

2358 *Dracunculus vulgaris* **COMMON DRAGON ARUM**. Tall, tuberous, robust perennial, to 1m, occasionally taller; 'stem' thick strongly blotched, formed from the leaf-stalks and flower-stem. Leaves deep green, often with white streaks, *deeply divided* into 10-15, linear, lanceolate to oblong, more or less equal, segments, the margins often wavy. Spathe rich velvety reddish-purple, greenish outside, broadly lanceolate, 25-40cm long; spadix deep maroon-black, shiny, erect and very stout,

tapered to the tip; inflorescence foul smelling. Berries borne in a large oblong head, orange-red when ripe. Rocky places, scrub, fields, roadsides, hedgerows, dry hillsides, generally at low altitudes. Apr-July. Algeria, Corsica and Sardinia eastwards to Turkey, including Crete, but not Cyprus. One of the most dramatic plants to be seen in the Med region. It is of considerable ornamental value and is much grown in gardens, despite its dreadful smell in bloom. A white-spathed form has been occasionally found in the wild.

2359 *Helicodiceros muscivorus [Dracunculus muscivorus]* **DRAGON'S MOUTH.** Medium, tuberous perennial. Leaves greyish-green, deeply dissected into *very unequal* linear-lanceolate segments. Spathe pale green with purple spots and streaks, very hairy on the inner surface, 15-30cm long, the blade reflexed; spadix protruding, purple, covered by a mass of long hair-like sterile flowers. Rocky and grassy habitats, close to the sea. Mar-June. Balearic Is., Corsica and Sardinia.

2360 *Ambrosinia bassii* **AMBROSINIA.** Low tuberous-rooted, hairless perennial, less than 7cm tall. Leaves elliptical to oblong, 2-7cm long, plain green. Spathe greenish-white spotted with red, 1.5-2cm long, with an inflated tube which has a sharp bend near its base and an upturned pointed tip; spadix small, completely enclosed within the tube of the spathe. Fruit a many-seeded berry. Dry habitats, scrub and grassy places, at low altitudes. Oct-Dec, occasionally later. Corsica, Sardinia, C and S Italy and Sicily.

Arum **ARUMS.** Tuberous perennials with heart- to arrowhead-shaped leaves, long-stalked, untoothed. Flowers unisexual, borne on a swollen axis or spadix which has a long terminal appendage; perianth absent, the male flowers above the female, often separated by hair-like sterile flowers, with further sterile flowers above the male; the whole inflorescence enveloped by a large fleshy spathe, split along one side. Fruit a bright red berry, borne in elongated clusters, generally after the leaves have withered. Most species are foul-smelling in flower and attract a host of flies and small beetles.

2361 *Arum italicum* **LARGE CUCKOO PINT.** A short to medium perennial, with a horizontal tuber, often patch-forming. Leaves appearing in the autumn, triangular-heart-shaped with the basal lobes diverging and with conspicuous *white or cream* veins. Spathe pale yellowish to whitish-green internally, green, occasionally flushed with purple, externally, 15-30cm long, drooping at the pointed apex; appendix of spadix pale yellow, cylindrical. Fruiting spike large, 10-15cm long. Moist, generally shaded habitats, hedgerows, scrub and rocky places. Apr-May. T. Like other arums, this species has poisonous properties.

inflorescence

    2361a Subsp. *neglectum* is distinguished by its plain green leaves, sometimes with dark blotches, with the basal lobes converging, sometimes overlapping. W Med.

    2361b Subsp. *albispathum* has the spathe pure white inside. Turkey eastwards.

    2361c Subsp. *byzantinum* has the stalk of the inflorescence as long as the leaf-stalks (not shorter) and a green spathe edged or flushed with purple. E Balkan Peninsula, Crete.

2362 *Arum maculatum* **LORDS AND LADIES, CUCKOO PINT.** Short perennial with horizontal tubers, often patch-forming. Leaves appearing in the spring, blunt arrow-shaped, shiny bright green, often with small *black blotches*, the basal lobes diverging. Spathe pale yellowish-green, flushed, spotted or streaked with purple, rarely entirely yellowish-green, 10-20cm long; spadix usually purple, cylindrical, about half as long as the spathe. Fruiting spike relatively small, usually 3-4cm long. Woodland, hedgerows, ditches, close to old walls and buildings, sometimes on cultivated land. Apr-May. T – except the extreme E Med.

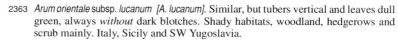

2363 *Arum orientale* subsp. *lucanum* [*A. lucanum*]. Similar, but tubers vertical and leaves dull green, always *without* dark blotches. Shady habitats, woodland, hedgerows and scrub mainly. Italy, Sicily and SW Yugoslavia.

2364 *Arum conophalloides*. Like *A. orientale*, but the inflorescence stalk *much exceeding* the leaves, up to 50cm long; spathe to 50cm long, the spadix pinkish-purple, spindle-shaped, 10-35mm diam. (not 3-6mm). Rocky slopes in hills and mountains. Apr-May. Turkey, Cyprus and Iraq.

2365 *Arum elongatum* [*A. orientale* subsp. *elongatum*]. Like *A. orientale*, but leaves appearing in the autumn and spathe brownish-purple inside; spadix *as long as* the spathe, to 25cm. Similar habitats and flowering time. Greece eastwards to Turkey.

2366 *Arum hygrophilum*. Like *A. orientale*, but spathe smaller, 8-14cm long (not 13-25cm) and spadix dark purple, *very slender*, less than 3mm wide (not 3-6mm). Moist and shaded habitats, roadsides, ditches. Mar-Apr. Cyprus and the extreme E Med.

2367 *Arum dioscoridis*. Short perennial with vertical tubers. Leaves arrowhead-shaped, dark green, unmarked, with strongly diverging basal lobes. Spathe greenish outside, but dark purple in the lower half inside shading to greenish-yellow above, heavily marked with large *purple blotches*, 20-30cm long; spadix dark purple, the appendage club-shaped to cylindrical. Rocky slopes, scrub, margins of fields and cultivated land, stream margins. Mar-May. S Turkey, Iraq and Cyprus. Sometimes grown in gardens.

2368 *Arum creticum* **CRETAN ARUM**. Medium perennial with vertical, globose tubers. Leaves large, plain deep, shiny, green, appearing in the autumn, arrowhead-shaped, long-stalked. Spathe pale yellowish-green to yellow, 8-13cm long, with an inflated tube and a narrow blade that often folds *backwards* leaving the spadix protruding; spadix yellow, cylindrical, somewhat shorter, or longer than the spathe. Rocky habitats, scrub, gullies, in the hills and mountains. Mar-May. Crete and Karpathos. Grown in gardens. The boldest and most handsome European arum.

2369 *Arum idaeum*. Similar, but spathe milky-white, the blade not folded backwards and the *spadix* purple or blackish-purple, not protruding from the spathe. Rocky mountain habitats. Apr-May. Crete – endemic.

2370 *Arum pictum* **AUTUMN ARUM**. Short to medium perennial with vertical, globose tubers. Leaves appearing in the autumn *just before flowering time*, thick and leathery, deep shiny green with creamy veins, heart-shaped to arrowhead-shaped. Spathe deep purple, 15-25cm long; spadix deep purple, shorter than the spathe, cylindrical, narrowed below. Rocky ground and scrub, often beneath pines. Oct-Nov. Balearic Is., Corsica, Sardinia and Italy.

2371 *Arum petteri* [*A. nigrum*] **DALMATIAN ARUM**. Short perennial with vertical, almost globose, tubers. Leaves plain dull green, arrowhead-shaped, appearing in the autumn. Spathe deep *purplish-black*, 15-20cm long, the apex erect; spadix blackish, shorter than the spathe. Scrub and open stony and rocky habitats. Mar-Apr. W Yugoslavia, Albania and N Greece.

Biarum **BIARUMS**. Rather like small arums, but the leaves narrow not lobed or heart-shaped, the blade narrowed or rounded at the base. Inflorescences not stalked, resting on the ground, the male and female flowers separated by a ring of hair-like sterile flowers. Fruit a cluster of white or greenish berries, at or just above ground level. Most of the species are foul-smelling in flower.

2372 *Biarum tenuifolium* **NARROW-LEAVED BIARUM**. Low tuberous perennial, very variable. Leaves narrowly oblong to linear, 10-20mm wide, sometimes with very wavy margins, produced before or after the spathes appear. Spathes pale brownish-green to deep chocolate, 8-30cm long, erect to recurved or hooded; spadix deep blackish-purple, *projecting* well beyond the spathe, with sterile thread-like flowers above and below the male flowers. Rocky places, scrub, garrigue, stony pastures. July-Nov. Iberian Peninsula, N Africa, Italy eastwards to Turkey and parts of the extreme E Med – not Cyprus.

2373 *Biarum bovei* (incl. *B. dispar*). Similar, but leaves broadly oblong. Spathe rather inflated below (the tubular part) and the spadix *without* sterile flowers above the male ones. Oct-Dec. S Spain, Sardinia, N Africa, Turkey and Egypt. *B. carratracense* (2374), from Malaga in S Spain is very like this but slightly smaller; it may well be inseparable.

2375 *Biarum spruneri* **SPRING BIARUM**. Like *B. tenuifolium*, but the spadix *not* projecting beyond the spathe and spadix with sterile flowers above the male flowers. Rocky habitats, olive groves, dry grassy places. Apr-June. S Greece.

2376 *Biarum davisii* **CRETAN BIARUM**. Low tuberous perennial. Leaves appearing after flowering, oval to elliptical, rather leathery, deep green, sometimes with a wavy margin, often flat on the ground, short-stalked. Spathes *creamy*, speckled with brownish-purple often, only 3-5cm long, with a swollen, bladder-like base and a short hood-like tip; spadix maroon, slender, protruding tongue-like from the mouth of the spathe. Dry stony hillslopes, rock crevices, grassy places. Oct-Nov. Crete and SW Turkey. Unlike the other species this one has no appreciable smell.

Arisarum **ARISARUMS**. Small tuberous-rooted, hairless perennials, with heart-shaped leaves. Inflorescences arum-like, but small, the spathe fused below into a tube, not slit all the way down with the edges overlapping.

2377 *Arisarum vulgare* **FRIAR'S COWL**. Short to medium perennial, generally patch-forming. Leaves oval to heart-shaped, plain green or with darker spots or blotches. Inflorescence long-stalked, held among or above the leaves; spathe narrow, 4-5cm long, green to chocolate-brown, often striped in the lower half and speckled, *hooded above*, tubular below; spadix greenish, slightly protruding from the mouth of the spathe. Berries greenish. Shaded or semi-shaded habitats, rocky places, scrub, banks, open woodland. Oct-May. T. A common plant in the Med region; often mistaken for an *Arum*.

2378 *Arisarum simorrhinum*. Similar, but with the inflorescences held beneath the leaves; spathe broader and shorter, finely hairy outside; spadix not protruding, *greatly swollen* at the tip into a rounded blob which almost closes the mouth. Rocky habitats, especially crevices in exposed places. S and E Spain and NW Africa.

2379 *Arisarum proboscideum* **MOUSE PLANT**. Low patch-forming perennial. Leaves pale, rather bright green, heart-shaped. Inflorescences held below the leaves, generally close to the ground; spathe dark chocolate-brown, strongly hooded at the apex with the tip drawn out into a long *mouse-tail-like* appendage to 5-15cm long; spadix whitish, hidden within the spathe. Berries greenish. Shaded habitats, scrub woodland, rock crevices. Mar-May. SW Spain and C and S Italy. This curious little plant has 'flowers' that resemble mice when held in the palm of the hand, hence the common name.

ORCHID FAMILY Orchidaceae

A very large family found in many parts of the world. Many of the tropical species are epiphytic, growing on the trunks and branches of trees. Med species are all terrestrial and the following description applies to them. Tuberous or rhizomatous perennials with alternate (spirally arranged) leaves, often aggregated towards the base of the plant into a loose rosette; the upper leaves may be similar to the lower or sheath- or bract-like; some species may be saprophytic with scale-like leaves without green pigment – chlorophyll.

Flowers solitary or in a spike or raceme, sometimes congested into a distinct head, which often elongates in fruit; sepals 3, green or coloured, often similar to the petals, sometimes larger; petals 3, the lower one modified into a distinctive lip or labellum, often lobed or ridged, sometimes extended behind into a nectar-containing spur; stamens generally two, fused to the stigma into a column, the pollen aggregated into detachable masses or pollinia; ovary inferior, located behind all the other flower parts, stalked or not. Fruit a 3-parted capsule containing many minute seeds. In most orchids the flower twist through 180° at a very early stage so that the flower as seen with the lip at the bottom is actually upside down; this process is called resupination.

Epipactis **HELLEBORINES**. Flowers short-stalked, nodding to horizontal, borne in one-sided racemes; sepals and petals often similar, held closely together or spreading; lip folded or jointed near the middle, the basal part more or less cupped, not spurred, the tip rounded to triangular. A number of species occur in Med countries, but mostly in the higher mountains above 500m. The following three can sometimes be found at lower altitudes.

2380 *Epipactis helleborine [Helleborine latifolia]* **BROAD-LEAVED HELLEBORINE**. Medium to tall rhizomatous perennial, to 1.2m, though generally far less; stems hairy, often purplish, especially in the lower part. Leaves 4-10, green. oval or rounded, *broad*, pointed. Flowers up to 50, variable in colour, but the sepals usually greenish or greenish-yellow and the petals pale pinkish-violet to purplish-red, often with a greenish midvein; lip 9-11mm long, pink with a reddish-brown base, the tip oval to heart-shaped, the tip curved under to give the lip a roundish appearance. Fruit smooth or rough. In woodland, especially Beech, but also mixed or coniferous woods and scrub, occasionally on sand-dunes or in more exposed places. May-July. T – not Balearic Is. or parts of the extreme E Med.

2381 *Epipactis microphylla [Helleborine microphylla]* **SMALL-LEAVED HELLEBORINE**. Short to medium, rhizomatous perennial; stem with basal sheathing scales, hairy in the upper part. Leaves small, only 3-6, lanceolate to linear-lanceolate, usually not more than 30mm long. Flowers up to 15, yellowish-brown like the rest of the plant, but occasionally yellowish or whitish, often purple tinged, with a rather sickly fragrance; lip 6.5-7mm long, generally rather greyish-brown, whitish or pale pink, with a greenish-brown base, the pointed tip not recurved. Dry woodlands, often Beech or Hazel, woodland clearings, sometimes in vineyards. May-early July. T – not N Africa. Primarily a mountain plant in the Med region, but sometimes coastal or lowland.

2382 *Epipactis atrorubens [E. atropurpurea, Helleborine atrorubens]* **DARK RED HELLEBORINE**. Similar, but leaves larger, mostly more than 40mm long, and flowers *deep* blackish- or reddish-purple, the sepals generally with a greenish tinge. Woods and dry pastures, scrub, rocky places and occasionally sand-dunes. June-July. Spain, France, Italy, Balkans and Turkey; rare in the Med region.

Cephalanthera **CEPHALANTHERAS**. Leafy rhizomatous perennials. Flowers borne in lax spikes, often one-sided, not scented, ascending to erect; sepals and petals similar, rarely opening widely, often pointed, generally forming a bell-shape; lip constricted in the middle, forward pointing and with a downcurved tip, with several distinct ridges running along the upper surface, not spurred.

2383 *Cephalanthera longifolia* **NARROW-LEAVED HELLEBORINE**. Tufted, short to medium perennial; stems erect, usually narrowly winged in the upper part, hairless, with 2-3 basal sheaths. Leaves 7-20 *narrow*, lanceolate to linear, long-pointed; bracts, except the lowermost, much shorter than the flowers. Flowers 5-16, pure white with yellowish-orange markings inside the lip; sepals and petals pointed, half-opening; lip 7-10mm long, shorter than the sepals, with 3-5 ridges inside. Woods and scrub, shaded rocky places. Apr-June. T – not Balearic Is., Crete, parts of N Africa or the extreme E Med.

2384 *Cephalanthera damasonium [C. alba]* **WHITE HELLEBORINE**. Similar, but generally not clump-forming and with angled stems with 4-10, oblong to lanceolate leaves. Flowers white or cream, often hardly opening, all but the uppermost *exceeded* by their bracts; lip 12-17mm long. Woods, scrub, grassy places, usually on lime-stone. May-June. T – but generally in the mountains, rarely coastal.

2385 *Cephalanthera rubra* **RED HELLEBORINE**. Rather slender, short to medium perennial; stems erect, ridged, stickily-hairy in the upper part and with several brown basal sheaths. Leaves few, 5-8, dark green, oblong to lanceolate, pointed; bracts generally shorter than the leaves. Flowers *bright pink*, rarely white, rather open, the sepals and petals narrowly pointed; lip 18-23mm long, whitish with a violet-pink apex and 7-9 brownish-yellow or pale yellow ridges. Forest, woodland clearings, scrub, pathsides, generally in rather dry places. May-June. T – not Balearic Is.

2386 *Limodorum abortivum [Ionorchis abortivum]* **VIOLET BIRD'S NEST ORCHID**. Medium to tall, often rather stout, violet-tinged saprophyte; stems erect, with numerous violet-tinged scales – *no green leaves*. Flowers rather large, 38-46mm across, violet; sepals and petals spreading, pointed, the petals slightly smaller; lip 14-17mm long, yellowish stained with violet, unlobed and with a short spur, to 15mm long, at the base. Coniferous woods (especially pine), grassy woodland clearing, scrub, rocky places. Apr-July. T. Considered by some botanists to be parasitic, though most believe it to be a saprophyte thriving on decaying vegetation. During very dry seasons few plants will be seen in flower and the flowers may fail to open properly. Short-spurred plants with a narrow, linear lip from the S Iberian Penin-sula and N Africa are sometimes distinguished as var. *trabutianum* (2386a).

2387 *Neottia nidus-avis* **BIRD'S NEST ORCHID**. Short to medium, *yellowish-brown* plant, saprophytic. Stem erect, without leaves, but with scale-like, semi-membranous sheaths, overlapping one another. Flowers numerous, in a spike-like raceme, sickly-scented, yellowish-brown like the rest of the plant, very occasionally yel-lowish or whitish; sepals and petals similar, not spreading; lip 8-12mm long, greyish-brown, 2-lobed, spurless. Shady woodland on rich humusy soils often devoid of other vegetation. May-July. T – not Balearic Is., Cyprus or parts of the extreme E Med. The species gets its common name from the dense tuft of inter-twined roots which resemble a bird's nest. Plants may sometimes be monocarpic, dying after flowering and seeding.

2388 *Listera ovata* **GREATER** or **COMMON TWAYBLADE**. Short to medium perennial; stem slender, hairy in the upper part and with several brownish sheaths at the base. Leaves *two*, almost opposite, broad-oval, deep green, ribbed. Flowers small, green or greenish-yellow, many borne in a long slender spike; sepals and petals not spreading widely but forming a loose hood; lip 7-15mm long, yellowish-green, vertical, forked above the middle into two lobes, spurless. Woodland, scrub, grassy places, marshy ground. May-July. T – not Balearic Is., Cyprus or much of the extreme E Med. A widespread orchid, but often difficult to spot.

2389 *Spiranthes spiralis* **AUTUMN LADY'S TRESSES.** Low to short, tuberous perennial; stem stickily-hairy. Leaves mostly in a basal rosette, to one side of the flower-spike and often withered by flowering time, oval-elliptical; stem leaves scale-like, overlapping; bracts shorter than the flowers. Flowers white, 6-7mm long, up to 20 borne in a slender *spiralled-spike*; outer 2 sepals spreading, the upper sepal and petals fused to form a tube with the lip; lip with upcurved edges, yellowish-green. Dry grassy places, meadows, heaths, garrigue, pine woodland, generally on calcareous soils. Sept.-Nov. T.

2390 *Gennaria diphylla [Coeloglossum diphyllum]* **GENNARIA.** Short tuberous perennial. Leaves 2, *spaced* along the stem, heart-shaped, the uppermost much smaller than the lower. Flowers yellowish-green, many borne in a long slender spike up to 10cm long; sepals and petals almost equal, oblong, forming a loose hood; lip 4-6mm long, oval 3-lobed, with the side lobes narrower than the larger central lobe; spur short, rounded. Woodland, particularly of pine, shady and grassy places, scrub, rock crevices and screes. Feb.-May. C and S Portugal, SW Spain, Sardinia and NW Africa. A rather insignificant little plant, easily overlooked.

Plantanthera **BUTTERFLY ORCHIDS.** Tuberous-rooted perennials with few leaves and lax spikes of white or greenish flowers; lateral sepals spreading, the upper one and the two petals forming a hood; lip unlobed, spurred.

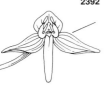

2391 *Platanthera bifolia* **LESSER BUTTERFLY ORCHID.** Short to medium erect perennial. Leaves two, basal, oblong to elliptical, shiny green; stem with several small, spaced, bract-like leaves. Flowers white tinged with green, with a sweet vanilla fragrance; lip 8-15mm long, linear-oblong, *not lobed*, pendent; spur very long, 25-30mm, slender, horizontal to downcurved; anther cells close together and parallel. Meadows and grassy places, open woodland (deciduous and coniferous), scrub, roadsides. May-July. T – not Crete.

2392 *Platanthera chlorantha [Platanthera holmboei]* **GREATER BUTTERFLY ORCHID.** Similar, but a larger plant with greener flowers, scarcely scented, the spur 18-30mm long, distinctly swollen towards the tip; anther cells *diverging* towards the base from one another. Similar habitats and flowering time. T – except for parts of the extreme E Med. Generally starts to flower about two weeks ahead of the previous species. A small form, not more than 30cm tall, with fewer flowers, the lip only 7-10mm long (not 11-15mm) and the spur not dilated towards the end, is distinguished as subsp. *holmboei* (2392a) and is restricted to Cyprus, Turkey, Syria and Israel.

2393 *Neotinea maculata [N. intacta, Orchis intacta]* **DENSE-FLOWERED ORCHID.** Short, tuberous perennial, rarely more than 25cm tall; stem often pinkish-purple, with one or two membranous sheaths at the base. Leaves mostly basal, oblong, ending in a small point; stem leaves smaller and erect, often with small purplish spots arranged in long rows. Flowers small, numerous, borne in a dense, often one-sided, spike, greenish-white or pinkish, with a faint vanilla scent; sepals and petals equal, oval and pointed, *all* forming a hood; lip 4-5mm, long, flat, forward-pointing, 3-lobed, the central lobe larger than the lateral ones; spur short, conical, 1-2mm. Woods, scrub, rough grassy places, maquis, garrigue. Mar-May. T – except parts of the extreme E Med.

Dactylorhiza **MARSH ORCHIDS.** Tuberous perennials; tubers hand-shaped. Leaves decreasing in size up the stem, not sheathing the stem, the uppermost often small and bract-like. Flowers borne in dense cylindrical or conical spikes, often with the bracts poking between the flowers; sepals generally spreading or the upper one coming close to the petals to form a hood; lip prominent, 3-lobed or occasionally unlobed, patterned with various lines or spots.

2394 *Dactylorhiza romana [D. pseudosambucina, D. sulphurea, D. pseudosambucina* subsp. *pseudosambucina]* **ROMAN ORCHID**. A short perennial with a green or purplish stem. Basal leaves up to 10 in a dense rosette, narrow-oblong, unspotted; stem leaves few, smaller, the uppermost bract-like. Flowers pale yellow or purplish with a yellowish centre to the lip, borne in a fairly dense cylindrical spike; lip usually 7-8mm long, 3-lobed, sometimes indistinctly so, *unspotted*; spur 13-20mm long, horizontal to upcurved, distinctly longer than the ovary. Maquis, garrigue, grassy places, scrub, dry rocky slopes. Mar-May. T – not France.

    2394a Subsp. *siciliensis [D. sulphurea* subsp. *siciliensis]*. is distinguished by its conical (not cylindrical) spur which is shorter than, or as long as, the ovary. Sardinia, Italy and Sicily.

    Another form with an orange zone at the base of the lip is sometimes referred to subsp. *bartonii*. The **ELDER-FLOWERED ORCHID**, *Dactylorhiza sambucina* (**2395**), distinguished by having fewer (up to 5) basal leaves and a shorter downward pointing spur, to 15mm long, is found above 500m in the mountains over much of the region.

2396 *Dactylorhiza elata* **ROBUST MARSH ORCHID**. A medium to tall perennial, to 80cm, though often less; stem erect and rather stout. Leaves 6-10. well spaced, erect, bright shiny green, unspotted, broadly elliptical to lanceolate, the uppermost bract-like; bracts at least as long as the flowers. Flowers violet-purple, the lip spotted and lined darker purple, borne in a dense cylindrical spike; lip 9-16mm long, 3-lobed, with the lateral lobes folded back usually; spur slender to conical, as long as the ovary. Wet meadows, marshes, sides of ditches. Apr-June. S Italy, Sicily and N Africa. Widely grown in gardens.

    2396a Subsp. *durandii* is taller, to 110cm, with narrow leaves widest at the base. Iberian Peninsula.

    2396b Subsp. *sesquipedalis* is shorter than the type with elliptical or oval leaves widest in the middle; flowers in a dense spike, the lip scarcely 3-lobed. Iberian Peninsula, S France and Corsica.

2397 *Dactylorhiza maculata* **SPOTTED ORCHID**. Very variable short to medium perennial; stem erect to flexuous. Leaves 6-10 spaced along the stem, oval to oblong, usually with purple-black *spots*, the uppermost leaves bract-like; bracts narrow-lanceolate, the lower shorter than the flowers, the upper longer. Flowers pink, lilac, reddish or purplish, the lip lined and dotted with purple, borne in conical or oblong spikes; lip 7-11mm long, flat, shallowly 3-lobed, the middle lobe short and tooth-like; spur slender, 3-11mm long, downward pointing, about three-quarters the length of the ovary. Meadows, woods, scrub, roadsides, heathland, often on acid soils; mainly in the hills and mountains. May-July. European Med, except for the S Balkans and absent from the islands except for Corsica and Sicily.

2398 *Dactylorhiza saccifera*. Similar, but leaves always unspotted, lower bracts *much longer* than the flowers and spur 7-13mm long, conical-cylindrical. Damp meadows and open woodland, in hills and mountains. May-July. Iberian Peninsula, Italy, Sicily and the Balkan Peninsula.

2399 *Aceras anthropophorum* **MAN ORCHID**. Short to medium, rather slender perennial, rarely more than 40cm tall, often less. Basal leaves oval, blunt, pale shiny green, erect at first; upper leaves smaller and sheathing the stem; bracts membranous, shorter than the flowers. Flowers greenish-yellow, often streaked or edged with red, borne in a long slender, lax spike; sepals and petals forming a close hood above the lip; lip 12-15mm long, pendent, oblong with two slender 'arms' and two shorter spreading 'legs', resembling a *tiny man*; spurless. Grassy habitats, scrub, roadsides, woodland margins, garrigue, often on calcareous soils. Mar-May. T.

Hybridises with species of *Orchis* where they grow in close proximity; especially with *O. militaris*, *O. purpurea* and *O. simia*.

2400 *Comperia comperiana* **KOMPER'S ORCHID**. Short to medium tuberous perennial. Leaves mostly basal, oblong to oval, unspotted; stem leaves 2-3, sheath-like. Flowers brownish-purple with a pale pink lip, borne in a rather dense spike; sepals and petals forming a close hood above the lip; lip large, 30-40mm long, pendent, drawn out into four *thread-like* appendages; spur short, downturned. Open woodland, particularly of conifers. May-June. Aegean Is. of Lesbos and Samos, Turkey, Iraq and the Lebanon. A very local and rather rare species.

Orchis **ORCHIS**. Tuberous-rooted perennials; tubers 2-3 rounded or oval, testicle-like. Leaves often in a basal rosette, those on the stem sometimes forming a distinct sheath. Flowers borne in short to long, generally cone-shaped or cylindrical spikes; sepals and petals often forming a helmet, or the lateral sepals spreading; lower petal forming a lobed or unlobed lip, generally longer than the petals, spurred behind. The genus contains about 35 species in all, mainly native to Europe and W Asia, but extending eastwards to China and southwards to North Africa and the Azores.

2401 *Orchis papilionacea* **PINK BUTTERFLY ORCHID**. Short to medium perennial. Leaves mostly in a basal rosette, lanceolate to linear-lanceolate, pointed; stem leaves sheathing the stem up to the flowers; bracts lanceolate, about as long as the ovary, often flushed with purple or red. Flowers white or pale violet-pink, the lip purplish-violet with darker pink or red dots or streaks, occasionally almost white with pale markings, borne in lax oblong spikes; sepals and petals forming a small pointed helmet, the lateral sepals often with greenish parallel veins; lip 10-16mm long, kidney-shaped to heart-shaped or almost rounded, unlobed or obscurely 3-lobed, with a *finely toothed* margin; spur slightly downcurved, 8-12mm long, conical, shorter than the ovary. Dry grassy and stony habitats, scrub, maquis, garrigue, lowland and in the lower mountains. Mar-Apr. T. A bold and relatively large-flowered orchid often growing in large scattered colonies.

    2401a var. *grandiflora* is distinguished by its larger flowers, the lip 20-25mm long. Spain, N Africa, Crete and perhaps elsewhere.

2402 *Orchis boryi*. Similar, but flowers violet-purple, borne in rounded heads with the *uppermost* (not lowermost) opening first; lateral sepals spreading; lip oblong to rounded, shallowly 3-lobed, smaller, 7-9mm long, violet-purple or whitish. Maquis, garrigue and scrub, generally over limestone. Mar-Apr. S Greece and Crete. This rather rare species is sometimes likened to a large *O. quadripunctata*; both have lips with 2-4 spots. However, it is more closely allied to *O. papilionacea*, differing from both species in that the top flower in the spike opens first and not the lower.

2403 *Orchis morio* **GREEN-WINGED ORCHID**. Low to medium perennial. Leaves mostly in a basal rosette, broadly oval to lanceolate, unspotted; stem leaves sheathing almost up to the flowers; bracts lanceolate, about as long as the ovary. Flowers borne in rather lax oblong spike; sepals and petals purplish-violet, pink, greenish or white, forming a close helmet, the lateral sepals with *prominent* green, occasionally purple veins; lip purple, pink, red or white, often with darker spots in a central pale zone, 8-10mm long, shallowly 3-lobed, rather flat; spur cylindrical, horizontal to upcurved, 8-10mm long, shorter than the lip. Grassy meadows, scrub, banks, maquis, garrigue, open woodland, often on calcareous soils. Often gregarious, sometimes forming substantial colonies. Feb-May. T eastwards to C Yugoslavia – not Greece or Crete.

    2403a Subsp. *picta* is distinguished by its laxer flower-spikes, smaller helmet, 6-8mm long, and spur *as long* as the lip. T. Commoner in the Med region than the type. The form from Cyprus and the extreme E Med is sometimes distinguished as subsp. *libani [O. syriaca]* (2403c).

2403b Subsp. *champagneuxii* is like the type, but the lip is folded along the centre, thus looking narrower from the front, and the spur is distinctly *thickened* at the tip. Iberian Peninsula, S France, N Africa.

2404 *Orchis longicornu* **LONG-SPURRED ORCHID**. Short perennial, not more than 25cm tall. Leaves mostly in a basal rosette, oblong-lanceolate, unspotted; stem with sheathing leaves almost up to the flowers; bracts lanceolate, about as long as the ovary, often flushed with purple or red. Flowers borne in a lax oblong spike; sepals and petals white or pale violet-pink, forming a close helmet 6mm long; lip purplish-violet, 8-10mm long, 3-lobed, folded back from the centre, often with darker spots along the paler central zone; spur upcurved, thickened at the tip, *much longer* than the lip, 13-15mm long. Maquis, garrigue, scrub and dry grassy places. Feb-Apr. Iberian Peninsula and NW Africa eastwards to Italy and Sicily. Very like *O. morio* in some instances, but distinguished by its longer spur.

2405 *Orchis coriophora* **BUG ORCHID**. Low to medium perennial. Leaves mostly in a basal rosette, narrow-lanceolate, unspotted; stem leaves overlapping and sheathing the stem to the top; bracts lanceolate, 1-veined. Flowers small, borne in dense oblong heads, apparently smelling unpleasantly of bed bugs; sepals and petals violet-brown, all forming a close pointed helmet, 5-10mm long; lip 5-8mm long, purplish-green, spotted, with 3 *almost equal* lobes; spur short, downcurved, half as long as the lip. Damp, often poor meadows, banks, hills and roadsides, often on slightly acid soils. Mar-May. T – not Balearic Is., Cyprus or most of the extreme E Med.

2405a Subsp. *fragrans* has darker, *vanilla-fragrant* flowers, the lip longer, 8-11mm, with a larger central lobe; spur at least as long as the lip. Maquis, garrigue, grassy places and scrub, hillslopes. T. This is the common subspecies in the Med region.

2406 *Orchis sancta* **HOLY ORCHID**. Similar, but leaves clasping the base of the stem and lower bracts 3-5-veined. Flowers larger, pale lilac to red, the lip 8-12mm long, with markedly toothed side-lobes; spur *strongly incurved* towards the underside of the lip. Garrigue, dry hillslopes, scrub, on dry sandy or calcareous soils. Apr-May. Aegean Is., Turkey, Cyprus and the E Med.

2407 *Orchis tridentata* **TOOTHED ORCHID**. Short to medium, often rather robust plant, to 45cm. Basal leaves 3-4, oblong and pointed, unspotted; stem leaves small and sheath-like; bracts lanceolate, 1-veined, about as long as the ovary. Flowers borne in a dense cone-shaped spike which soon elongates, fragrant; sepals and petals pale violet-lilac, *sharply pointed*, forming a close helmet, 6-8mm long, often with the tips diverging; lip pale violet-lilac spotted with purple, 3-lobed, the central lobes with two blunt 'legs' with a tiny 'tail' in between; spur downcurved, half as long as the ovary. Grassy habitats, scrub, thickets, woodland, occasionally in maquis or garrigue. Mar-May. Iberian Peninsula eastwards to Turkey and Iraq, but absent from most of the islands, except for Crete.

2408 *Orchis lactea* **MILKY ORCHID**. Similar, but a smaller plant, rarely exceeding 20cm tall. Flowers *pale*, whitish or greenish-pink, often unspotted; spur somewhat longer than the ovary. Dry grassy places, maquis, garrigue, banks. Feb-May. T – not Cyprus nor the SE Med.

2409 *Orchis italica* **ITALIAN MAN ORCHID**. Short to medium. Basal leaves 5-8, oblong-lanceolate, wavy-edged, often flecked or spotted with purplish-brown; stem leaves sheath-like, not reaching the flowers; bracts tiny, oval, 1-veined, much shorter than the ovary. Flowers borne in dense cones or globular clusters, which gradually elongate, the lowermost opening first; sepals and petals pale pink or lilac, purple-veined, forming a helmet 9-11mm long; lip 12-18mm long, tipped and spotted with purple, with *slender pointed* 'arms' and 'legs' and with a similar, but short, 'tail' in between; spur downcurved, half as long as the ovary. Maquis, garrigue, open woodland, scrub, grassy places, hillslopes, often gregarious. Mar-May. T – not France, Corsica or Sardinia. One of the commonest orchids in some parts of the Med.

2410 *Orchis simia* **MONKEY ORCHID**. Short to medium perennial. Basal leaves 3-5, oblong-lanceolate to oval, flat, shiny and unspotted; stem leaves small and sheath-like; bracts tiny, oval-lanceolate, about half as long as the ovary. Flowers borne in oblong spikes, the *uppermost* opening first; sepals and petals pale rose or lilac, rarely white, forming a close helmet 8-10mm long; lip whitish tipped and spotted with pinkish-purple or purple, 3-lobed, the slender 'arms' and 'legs' and small tail all forward curved; spur downcurved, half as long as the ovary. Garrigue, scrub, open woodland, grassy places, roadsides, stony slopes. Late Mar-May. T – not Balearic Is., Corsica or Sardinia.

2411 *Orchis punctulata* **PUNCTATE ORCHID**. A short to medium perennial. Basal leaves 4-7, oblong, unspotted; stem leaves few, sheathing; bracts small, oval, much shorter than the ovary. Flowers many, borne in cylindrical spikes; sepals and petals *yellowish-green*, forming a close helmet 8-15mm long; lip a similar colour, usually purple-spotted, 3-lobed, with short blunt 'arms' and 'legs' and with a small tooth-like 'tail' in between; spur downcurved, about a third the length of the ovary. Garrigue, open forest, particularly of pine, stony slopes, stream margins, occasionally in more open habitats. Feb-Apr. Greece (Thrace) and the E Med, including Rhodes and Cyprus. Colonies sometimes have large and small forms growing side by side.

    2411a Subsp. *sepulchralis* has larger flowers with the spur half as long as the ovary. Greece and Turkey.

2412 *Orchis purpurea* **LADY ORCHID**. Medium to tall, rather robust perennial. Basal leaves 3-6, *shiny deep green*, broadly-oblong, unspotted; stem with one or two sheathing leaves towards the base; bracts oval to lanceolate, shorter than the ovary. Flowers borne in a many-flowered cylindrical spike, fragrant; sepals and petals brownish-purple, forming a close helmet 12-14mm long; lip 10-15mm long, white or pink, finely spotted with deeper purple, 3-lobed, with narrow-oblong 'arms'. The central lobe has short, blunt 'legs' with a small 'tail' in between; spur short, downcurved, about a third the length of the ovary. Woodland, scrub and rough grassy places, generally on calcareous soils. Apr-June. N Spain eastwards to Turkey – absent from most of the islands except for Corsica and Sardinia. A rare and protected British native species. Sometimes found as large colonies in southern Europe, often in association with other species such as *Orchis militaris* and *O. mascula*.

2413 *Orchis collina [O. saccata]* **FAN-LIPPED ORCHID**. Short perennial. Basal leaves 2-4, broad oblong-oval, occasionally with dark spots; stem with sheathing leaves almost up to the flowers, sometimes tinged with purple; bracts oval-lanceolate, mostly 5-7-veined, often purple-tinged, the lower clearly longer than the ovary. Flowers borne in a long rather slender spike; sepals and petals dark olive-green to deep, rather dull purple, the lateral sepals *spreading upwards*, the upper sepal and the petals forming a helmet; lip 9-12mm long, purple to pinkish, not spotted, fan-shaped, unlobed and with a finely toothed margin; spur 5-7mm long, half the length of the ovary. Garrigue, maquis, grassy and rocky places, open woodland and scrub, generally on calcareous soils. Feb-Apr. T. A local species, rather rare in some countries.

2414 *Orchis patens* **GREEN-SPOTTED ORCHID**. Medium to tall perennial, rarely more than 70cm tall. Leaves mostly in a basal rosette, oblong to lanceolate, unspotted; stem with sheathing leaves in the lower part; bracts narrow-lanceolate, pointed, about half the length of the ovary, 5-7-veined. Flowers borne in a lax cylindrical spike; sepals and petals pink or purple with a *central green* zone, often spotted, the lateral sepals spreading and 'wing-like', the upper sepal and petals forming a loose helmet; lip oval, 9-10mm long, purple or pink, usually with darker spots, 3-lobed, the lobes short, somewhat toothed, the central lobe notched; spur small and pouch-like, downwards pointing, about half the length of the ovary. Maquis, garrigue, open woodland, scrub, meadows in the hills and mountains. Mar-May. SE Spain, Balearic Is., N Italy, Sicily, Crete and Algeria. A rather rare and little-known species.

2415 *Orchis spitzelii*. Similar, but not more than 40cm tall and with broader leaves; bracts as long as the ovary. Flowers borne in a *denser*, often globose spike; sepals and petals brownish or greenish, red-spotted; lip with two ridges at the top; spur narrow-conical, one third the length of the ovary. Grassy habitats, mainly in the mountains. E Spain eastwards to Turkey, including Algeria – not Balearic Is., Corsica, Sardinia, Sicily, the Aegean Is. or Cyprus.

2416 *Orchis mascula* subsp. *olbiensis* **EARLY PURPLE ORCHID**. Short to medium perennial; stem often flushed with purple. Basal leaves 3-5, oblong, plain green or rarely with purple spots; stem with several sheathing leaves; bracts lanceolate, 1-3-veined, about as long as the ovary, often purplish. Flowers borne in a lax cylindrical spike, dark purple to pink, occasionally whitish, the lateral sepals *spreading upwards*, the upper sepal and the petals forming a loose helmet; lip 8-14mm long, similarly coloured to the sepals and petals but with a white, dark-spotted, central zone, folded down the middle so appearing narrow from the front, 3-lobed, the middle lobe slightly notched and toothed; spur upcurved, longer than the ovary. Grassy places and scrub, garrigue, open woodland, roadsides. Apr-May. S Spain, Balearic Is., S France, Corsica and NW Africa. The typical plant, subsp. *mascula*, (2416a) is native to much of Europe and W Asia but rarely found close to the Med, except in the mountains.

2417 *Orchis provincialis* **PROVENCE ORCHID**. Short to medium perennial. Basal leaves 2-5 in a lax rosette, lanceolate to oblong, usually brown-spotted; stem with several sheathing leaves in the lower part; bracts lanceolate, 1-3-veined, equalling or longer than the ovary. Flowers borne in rather dense oblong spikes, *yellow*, faintly scented; sepals and petals pale yellow or greenish-yellow, the lateral sepals spreading upwards, the upper sepal and the petals forming a loose helmet; lip 8-12mm long, deeper yellow or orange, brown-spotted in the centre, 3-lobed, the central lobe somewhat longer, notched and toothed; spur upcurved, wider towards the tip, equalling or longer than the ovary. Garrigue, maquis, grassy and rocky habitats, open woodland, often on rather thin poor calcareous soils. Mar-May. Iberian Peninsula eastwards to Balkans, including Crete, but not the Balearic Is.

    2417a Subsp. *pauciflora* [*Orchis pauciflora*] has only 3-7 flowers to a spike, but *larger*, the lip 13-15mm long; leaves unspotted. Similar habitats, but far less common. Corsica eastwards to Greece and the Aegean Is. – not Crete. Considered to be a distinct species by some authorities.

2418 *Orchis anatolica* **ANATOLIAN ORCHID**. A short to medium, rather variable perennial; stem erect or flexuous, often flushed with purple. Basal leaves 2-5, lanceolate to oblong, often spotted or blotched with purple-brown; stem with several sheathing leaves in the lower part; bracts narrow-lanceolate, 1-3-veined, rather shorter than the ovary, greenish to purplish or reddish. Flowers generally rather few (up to 14) in a lax oblong spike, purple or pink, occasionally white, the lateral sepals

spreading, the upper sepal and the petals forming a lax helmet; lip oval, 10-14mm long, usually spotted in the middle, with three rather square lobes, the central one rather longer; spur slender, narrowed towards the apex, horizontal or upcurved, 15-22mm long, *much longer* than the ovary. Maquis, garrigue, grassy and rocky habitats, scrub, hillslopes. Mar-May. Crete and the Aegean Is. eastwards, including Cyprus. Albino forms occur occasionally throughout the range of the species. Often found in association with *O. quadripunctata* and other small orchids.

2418a Subsp. *sitiaca* has greenish-violet flowers, a longer lip and a prominently upcurved spur. Crete – endemic.

2418b Subsp. *troodi* is more robust, to 50cm tall, with the flowers often all facing one direction; lip 13-17mm long; spur up to 25mm long, upcurved. Pine forest, in the mountains. Cyprus – endemic.

2419 *Orchis quadripunctata* **FOUR-SPOTTED ORCHID.** Short plant to 25cm tall, often less; stem often rather flexuous. Basal leaves 2-4, linear to oblong-lanceolate, unspotted, or with purplish-red spots or blotches; stem with several sheathing leaves in the lower part; bracts lanceolate, 1-3-veined, about as long as the ovary, green or purplish. Flowers borne in a lax cylindrical spike, purple, pinkish or occasionally white; sepals *all spreading*, the petals coming together; lip oval, or rounded, 4-5mm long, with three small and rather square lobes, generally with 4 spots in the middle near the top, central lobe notched; spur slender, 10-12mm long, horizontal to downturned, slightly shorter than the ovary. Maquis, garrigue, scrub, stony hillslopes, grassy places. Late Mar-May. Sardinia, Italy and Sicily eastwards, including Crete and Cyprus – not Israel or Egypt.

2420 *Orchis laxiflora* **JERSEY** or **LAX-FLOWERED ORCHID.** Medium to tall, rather slender perennial; stem erect or flexuous. Leaves 3-8, scattered along the stem, *none sheathing*, linear to lanceolate, pointed; bracts lanceolate, 3-5-veined, often flushed with pink or purple. Flowers in long, lax spikes, purple, occasionally white; lateral sepals spreading outwards, the upper sepal and the petals forming a loose helmet; lip almost rounded, 7-10mm long, with a whitish, generally unspotted, central zone, 3-lobed, the middle one shorter than the outer that are folded backwards; spur cylindrical, horizontal to upturned, broadened at the tip to bilobed, 10-12mm long, shorter than the ovary. Marshy ground, damp meadows, streamsides and damp sandy habitats. Mar-May. T. (The only place it occurs in or around Britain is on the island of Jersey.)

2421 *Orchis palustris* **BOG ORCHID.** Very similar, but lip larger, 9-15mm long, with the middle lobe as long as, or longer than, the adjacent lobes, often flecked with violet-purple in the centre; *spur* cylindrical or tapered to the tip. Similar habitats and flowering time. T.

Ophrys **OPHRYS.** Tuberous perennials with bizarre, often insect-like, flowers; stock with 2-3 rounded tubers. Leaves mostly in a basal rosette, but stems generally with one or two sheathing leaves. Flowers borne in short to long, rather lax spikes, occasionally solitary; sepals fairly large, oblong to oval, often spreading, green or variously coloured; petals two, smaller, often hairy, sometimes thread-like; lip large, often with a thick felt of tiny hairs, variously shaped and patterned, unlobed to 3-lobed, generally with a central shiny area, the speculum, spurless. A complex genus with many variations; several species can often be found growing side by side and hybrids are common. The insect-like nature of the lip attracts males of particular insect species, stimulating them into pseudo-copulation during which they pick up pollen.

2422 *Ophrys speculum* *[O. ciliata]* **MIRROR ORCHID, MIRROR OF VENUS.** Short perennial, rarely more than 25cm tall, often less. Basal leaves oblong and blunt, the stem leaves

narrower and more pointed. Spike with 2-10 flowers; sepals green or yellowish, often streaked with purplish-brown, oblong-oval; petals dark purple, lanceolate, hairy, about one third the length of the sepals; lip 10-13mm long, broad, 3-lobed, with a large shiny, *metallic-blue* speculum, surrounded by yellow and fringed with brown or black hairs. Maquis, garrigue, open woodland, grassy places, olive groves. Mar-May. T – not Crete or Cyprus. Often forming large colonies.

2422a Subsp. *lusitanica* is usually taller and with up to 15 flowers to a spike; petals *green*, the lip often narrower and fringed with yellow or rust-coloured hairs. WC Portugal.

2423 *Ophrys lutea* **YELLOW OPHRYS.** Low to short perennial, to 30cm, but sometimes only 5-6cm tall. Basal leaves oval, pointed; stem leaves narrower, often rather short. Spikes with 2-7 flowers generally; sepals green, oblong-oval; petals greenish or yellowish, linear-oblong, about half the length of the sepals; lip 12-18mm long, rounded to oblong, 3-lobed, with a broad flat, *yellow margin* surrounding a central reddish-brown zone which has a narrow 2-lobed, bluish-grey speculum; central lobe of lip rather larger than the lateral lobes and notched at the end. Garrigue, dry rocky and grassy habitats, open scrub, pine woodland, olive groves. Mar-May. C and E Med from S France to Turkey. This widespread Med species is often gregarious and has a wide altitudinal range from the lowland to the mountains.

2423a Subsp. *galilaea* [*Ophrys galilaea*] has a smaller lip, 9-12mm long, with a narrow yellow margin and a broader speculum; central lobe of the lip generally smaller than the outer lobes. T – replaces the typical plant in much of the E Med.

2423b Subsp. *melena*. Like subsp. *galilaea*, but lip blackish-purple, with a very narrow yellow margin covered with blackish-purple hairs. Greece.

2424 *Ophrys fusca* **DULL OPHRYS, SOMBRE BEE ORCHID.** Short to medium perennial to 40cm. Basal leaves oblong-lanceolate, blunt, the stem leaves narrower and pointed. Spikes mostly with 3-10 flowers; sepals green, occasionally pinkish, oblong to oval; petals green, linear, half as long as the sepals, more or less hairless; lip 9-15mm long, horizontal to downcurved, wedge-shaped, 3-lobed, purplish or yellowish-brown, often yellow-edged, with a bluish, greyish or violet-blue W-shaped speculum, appearing like *two eyes*, the lateral lobes short and rounded, the central one notched. Maquis, garrigue, grassy and rocky habitats, open pine woodland, olive groves. Feb-May. T – not E North Africa or Egypt. Often forming large colonies and difficult to spot at first because of its sombre colours. One of the earliest species to flower. Hybridises with *O. lutea*.

2424a Subsp. *omegaifera*. Spikes with 2-6 flowers; lip smaller and *deflexed*, with a pale brown speculum surrounded by a yellowish or whitish band. Italy, Sicily and Crete eastwards to Turkey, not Cyprus.

2424b Subsp. *fleishmannii* [*Ophrys fleishmannii, O. israelitica*]. Like subsp. *omegaifera*, but distinguished by its *finely hairy* petals; lip with a conspicuous white W-shaped border to the speculum. Greece and Crete eastwards, including Cyprus.

2425 *Ophrys iricolor* [*O. fusca* subsp. *iricolor*]. Similar, but spikes with normally only 1-4 flowers, the lip larger, 15-23mm long, with an iridescent *blue*, 2-lobed speculum. Similar habitats and flowering time. T – not Portugal or the Balearic Is. Often to be found growing in close proximity to *O. fusca*,

2425a Subsp. *durieui* [subsp. *atlantica*]. Like the type, but flowers generally only 1-2; lip *larger*, to 30mm long, with proportionately longer lateral lobes. S Spain and NW Africa.

2426 *Ophrys pallida*. Like *O. fusca*, but with white or pale green petals and a smaller lip, only 7-9mm long. Sicily and N Africa.

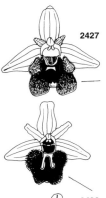

2427 *Ophrys bornmuelleri [O. fuciflora* subsp. *bornmuelleri]* **SHORT-PETALLED OPHRYS, BORN-MUELLER'S ORCHID.** Short to medium perennial, rarely more than 30cm tall. Basal leaves elliptical, often broadest above the middle; stem leaves generally sheath-like, pointed. Spikes mostly with 7-10 flowers; sepals pale- or whitish-green, sometimes flushed with pink; petals yellowish-green to pale pink, oval-triangular, hairy, *very short*, one-sixth the length of the sepals; lip 7-12mm long, oval-triangular to diamond-shaped, brown to purplish-brown with a paler margin, with two small basal, pale brown lumps at the base of the lip, notched at the end; speculum small, mauve to violet-blue, H-shaped, bordered with cream, sometimes with the cross-bar missing, occasionally reduced to two spots. Garrigue, scrub, grassy habitats, open pine woodland. Mar-Apr. S Turkey, Cyprus and the E Med. More robust, but shorter, plants with 3-5 flowers to a spike are sometimes distinguished as subsp. *grandiflora [O. levantina]* (2427a).

2428 *Ophrys sphegodes [O. aranifera]* **EARLY SPIDER ORCHID.** Variable short to medium perennial, rarely more than 45cm tall. Basal leaves oval-lanceolate, blunt, the stem leaves narrower and pointed, sheathing. Spikes with 2-10 flowers; sepals green to yellowish, sometimes flushed with reddish-purple, oblong to lanceolate, blunt; petals green to greenish-purple or brownish or dull red, triangular to lanceolate, at least *half* the length of the sepals; lip 10-12mm long, oval in outline, generally unlobed but with two hairy basal bosses, velvety-brown or dark brown, with an H-shaped violet-blue or purplish speculum, sometimes with the cross-bar of the H missing. Maquis, garrigue, grassy and rocky habitats. Mar-May. T. A widespread and very variable species; hybrids with *O. apifera, O. holoserica* and *O. insectifera* have been recorded.

2428a Subsp. *litigiosa* is a more slender plant with 6-10 smaller flowers to a spike; lip *smaller*, 5-8mm long, pale-brown or blackish-brown, with a small speculum, without basal bosses. Spain, S France, Greece and Crete.

2428b Subsp. *tommasinii [Ophrys tommasinii]* is similar to subsp. *litigiosa*, but with only 3-5 flowers; petals 3-veined (not 1); speculum large, H-shaped, with the cross-bar towards the base. Coastal habitats, garrigue. W Yugoslavia and NW Greece.

2428c Subsp. *atrata [O. atrata]*. Like the type, but petals often with wavy red *edges*; lip blackish-brown or purple, covered with long velvety hairs, often notched at the end and with well developed side lobes; speculum with the crossbar of the H in the middle or towards the base. Spain and Portugal eastwards to Yugoslavia.

2428d Subsp. *mammosa [Ophrys mammosa]*. Like the type, but lip *larger*, 10-15mm long, blackish-brown or purplish with large basal bosses and an H-shaped speculum, often with the cross-bar missing; sepals usually wavy-edged, often stained with dull red. Feb-May. Balkans eastwards to W Turkey and Cyprus.

2428e Subsp. *aesculapii*. Like the type, but the lip wider than long, blackish-brown and with a broad *yellowish* hairless margin; speculum H-shaped; sepals and petals pale olive green. S Greece.

2428f Subsp. *parnassica*. Like subsp. *mammosa*, but the lip usually 3-lobed and with small basal bosses and a yellowish hairless margin. Greece and Crete.

2428g Subsp. *transhyrcana [O. transhyrcana, O. sphegodes* subsp. *sintenisii]*. Like subsp. *mammosa*, but upper sepal often appearing very narrow due to reflexed margins; basal lip *bosses* absent or only poorly developed. Turkey, Cyprus and the E Med.

2428h Subsp. *amanensis*. Like subsp. *transhyrcana*, but sepals and petals deep *pink*; lip with well developed side lobes. Apr-May. S Turkey. (In Britain, the Early Spider Orchid is a rare and protected native species.)

2429 *Ophrys spruneri [O. sphegodes* subsp. *spruneri]* **GRECIAN SPIDER ORCHID.** Short perennial, to 35cm. Basal leaves oblong to lanceolate, pointed; stem leaves partly sheathing.

Spikes with 2-4 flowers; sepals green, purplish-green or deep pink with a green midvein, oblong, the lateral two downward pointing; petal deep pink, more than half the length of the sepals; lip 10-13mm long, rounded or oval, 3-lobed, blackish-brown or purple, velvety, with an H-shaped speculum edged with *white*, occasionally with the cross-bar missing, the side lobes of the lip drooping. Garrigue, grassy and stony habitats, scrub. Feb-Apr. S Greece, Crete and the Aegean Is.

 2429a Subsp. *panormitana* has white, pale pink or purplish sepals and petals; lateral lobes of lip scarcely deflexed. Sicily.

2430 *Ophrys ferrum-equinum* **HORSESHOE ORCHID**. Short perennial. Basal leaves lanceolate, pointed, bluish-green, the stem leaves similar but smaller. Spikes with 2-5 flowers, lax; sepals purple or bright pink, rarely greenish, oblong to almost rounded; petals purple or pink, linear-lanceolate, about half the length of the sepals, hairless; lip 10-12mm long, rounded, obscurely 3-lobed or unlobed with a forward pointing tip, velvety purple or brown, *speculum* deep blue, inverted horseshoe-shaped or consisting of two parallel bars. Maquis, garrigue, grassy and stony habitats, open pine woods. Mar-May. S Greece, Crete and the Aegean Is., W and SW Turkey, including Rhodes.

 2430a Subsp. *gottfriediana* has green, greenish-purple or whitish sepals and a distinctly longer, *3-lobed* lip. Aegean Is.

2431 *Ophrys bertolonii* **BERTOLONI'S BEE ORCHID**. Short to medium perennial, rarely more than 45cm tall. Basal leaves lanceolate, pointed, bluish-green; stem leaves smaller. Spikes with 3-8 flowers; sepals pink or purplish, occasionally whitish, with 3 green veins, oval to oblong; petals pink or purple, hairy-edged, linear-lanceolate, more than half the length of the sepals; lip 10-15mm long, rounded to oblong, unlobed or slightly 3-lobed, depressed in the centre, velvety blackish-purple with a small greenish tip and a conspicuous bluish-violet, *shield-shaped* speculum. Garrigue, dry stony and grassy places, thickets and open woodland. Late Mar-May. Spain eastwards to Yugoslavia, including most of the islands. A rather uncommon orchid, named in honour of A. Bertoloni, a nineteenth century Italian botanist.

2432 *Ophrys lunulata* **CRESCENT OPHRYS**. Short perennial. Basal leaves oblong to lanceolate, forming a rosette; stem leaves smaller and narrower. Spikes lax, with 4-7 flowers; sepals violet-pink, sometimes whitish, oval to oblong, blunt; petals violet-pink, linear-lanceolate, about two thirds the length of, or as long as, the sepals; lip 10-12mm long, oval, markedly 3-lobed, the middle lobe with a notched end, the lateral lobes strongly reflexed, velvety, brown, with a hairless yellowish or greenish *margin* and a whitish or pale violet crescent-shaped speculum. Scrub and grassy or stony slopes. Mar-May. Sardinia and Sicily. Rare.

2433 *Ophrys argolica* **EYED BEE ORCHID**. Short perennial, rarely more than 35cm tall. Basal leaves lanceolate, pointed; stem leaves similar but smaller. Spikes usually with 4-6 flowers; sepals purple or pinkish, rarely whitish or greenish, oblong, the central one upright and often narrower than the lateral two; petals purple or pinkish-violet, velvety, lanceolate to triangular, more than half as long as the sepals; lip 10-12mm long, rounded to oval in outline, unlobed to 3-lobed, redbrown to deep maroon, velvety, the margin often yellowish and hairless, the speculum violet with a *white margin*, spectacle-, horseshoe- or sometimes H-shaped. Garrigue, wooded and grassy habitats, meadows, olive groves, sanddunes. Feb-Apr. S Greece and Crete eastwards to S Turkey and Syria, including Cyprus. Forms with white sepals and a yellowish lip are sometimes assigned to var. *flavescens* (2433a).

2434 *Ophrys reinholdii* **REINHOLD'S BEE ORCHID**. Similar, but the petals recurved, green, brown or pinkish-violet, the lip more distinctly 3-lobed and *blackish-purple*;

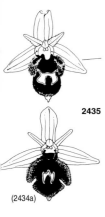

speculum consisting of two white or pale violet lines, commas or spots, linked or separate from one another. Grassy and sandy places, scrub, coniferous woodland. S Greece, Aegean Is., SW Turkey. Eastern forms from S Turkey to Syria and Iraq with larger flowers and less recurved side lobes, as well as paler lip markings, are often called subsp. *straussii* (2434a).

2435 *Ophrys umbilicata [O. carmeli* subsp. *orientalis, O. scolopax* subsp. *orientalis]*. Short perennial, rarely more than 20cm tall. Basal leaves elliptic-lanceolate, pointed; stem leaves similar though smaller, sometimes absent. Spikes with 5-12 flowers; sepals *greenish-white*, occasionally pale pink, oval, the middle one generally strongly incurved; petals green or yellowish, rarely purplish, lanceolate-triangular, velvety, a third to half the length of the sepals; lip small 6-8mm long, oval to oblong, 3-lobed, velvety brown with a narrow hairless margin and a large blue or brownish-violet, shield-shaped, speculum which encloses 3-4 oblong patches, outlined in yellow or whitish; midlobe of lip broadest towards the apex. Maquis, garrigue, grassy and stony places, coniferous plantations, olive groves. Mar-Apr. S Turkey and Cyprus eastwards.

(2434a)

2435a Subsp. *attica [Ophrys arachnites, O. attica, O. carmeli* subsp. *attica, O. flavomarginata, O. scolopax* subsp. *attica]*. Like the type, but a more robust plant to 35cm tall; sepals *pure green*; lip 8-15mm long. S Greece, Ionian Is. and Rhodes, W and S Turkey and Cyprus eastwards.

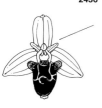

2436 *Ophrys scolopax* **WOODCOCK ORCHID.** Short to medium perennial to 45cm tall. Basal leaves lanceolate, pointed; stems leaves narrower and more pointed. Spikes with 3-12 flowers; sepals pink or purplish-violet, rarely green or whitish, oblong, the middle one erect; petals usually the same colour as the sepals, lanceolate-triangular, hairy, up to half the length of the sepals; lip 8-12mm long, oval to almost rounded, distinctly 3-lobed, brownish or blackish-purple, velvety except for a narrow hairless margin, the tip often 3-toothed, speculum large, violet or blue to purplish-brown, with a yellow or whitish margin, H-shaped, or enclosing several rounded or shield-like patches; basal bosses of lip small, 4-6mm long. Maquis, garrigue, meadows, open woodland. Mar-May. T – eastwards to Cyprus but excluding the extreme E Med.

2436a Subsp. *cornuta [Ophrys cornuta]* is similar, but the lip has a wide hairless margin with long *horn-like* appendage on each side near the base, these often up to 10mm long, and forward pointing. S Italy, Balkans, Crete and SW Turkey, Rhodes.

2436b Subsp. *apiformis*. Like subsp. *cornuta*, but the lip is strongly recurved and with a prominent forward pointing tip; side lobes with a shorter appendage. N Africa.

2436c Subsp. *heldreichii [Ophrys oestrifera* subsp. *heldreichii]* is like the type, but flowers *larger*, the lip 13-15mm long, the basal appendages to 5mm long. Greece, Crete and the Aegean Is.

The form from Cyprus is sometimes distinguished as a species in its own right, *O. lapethica [O. pseudoscolopax]* (2436d), and has rather smaller flowers than usual.

2437 *Ophrys cretica* **CRETAN BEE ORCHID.** Short perennial. Basal leaves oblong-lanceolate, pointed, the stem leaves smaller and narrower. Spike with 3-8 flowers; sepals green, brown or purplish, often bicolored, oblong; petals the same colour as the sepals but only a half their length; lip 11-14mm long, oval, 3-lobed, *blackish-purple* with short, hairy, side lobes, the speculum white or bluish with a white margin, H- or shield-shaped, or consisting of several spots. Garrigue, grassy and stony places, scrub, olive groves. Mar-Apr. S Greece, Crete and Aegean Is. The Aegean and Greek forms of this strikingly distinct species are often assigned to subsp. *naxia* (2437a) and subsp. *karpathensis* (2437b) respectively; however, the differences are very slight and probably not significant.

2438 *Ophrys kotschyi [O. cypria]* **CYPRUS BEE ORCHID.** Similar, but sepals plain green and the lateral lobes of the lip strongly reflexed. Garrigue, sand-dunes, pine and cypress woodland or plantations, scrub. Mar-early Apr. Cyprus – endemic.

2439 *Ophrys kurdica* **KURDISH BEE ORCHID.** Like *O. cretica*, but sepals relatively large, greenish-pink to pink; lip with a whitish, generally H-shaped, speculum. Damp grassy places. Mar-May. SE Turkey – endemic and little known.

2440 *Ophrys fuciflora* **LATE SPIDER ORCHID.** Short to medium perennial, to 55cm tall, occasionally taller. Basal leaves oval to oblong, blunt, the stem leaves narrower, pointed. Spikes with 2-8 flowers, sometimes more; sepals pink, purplish or whitish, oval; petals the same colour as the sepals, velvety, triangular to linear-lanceolate, up to one third the length of the sepals; lip 9-13mm long, oval to rounded, usually unlobed but with a large *forward pointing* tip, velvety dark brown-purple, occasionally with a yellowish margin and a velvety boss on each side of the base; speculum violet to blue with a yellow to green margin, very variable in shape, often with irregular dots or blotches. Maquis, garrigue, grassy places, scrub, banks open woodland. Apr-May. T – not Cyprus, parts of N Africa and the extreme E Med.

2440a Subsp. *candica* is distinguished by having pale purple, pink or whitish sepals and petals and a brown or violet-brown, *shield-shaped* speculum with a distinct white or yellowish margin. Mid Mar-May. SE Italy, Greece, Rhodes and Crete.

2440b Subsp. *exaltata [Ophrys exaltata]*. Often more robust than the type; sepals pink with green veins, occasionally deep mauve-pink; lip 3-lobed with distinct basal bosses, the side lobes small; speculum *reduced*, H-shaped or consisting of spots or lines; petals about one third the length of the sepals. Maquis turf. Mar-Apr. Corsica, Capri, S Italy and Sicily.

2440c Subsp. *oxyrrhynchos* is similar to subsp. *exaltatus*, but sepals and petals are *green*; petals tiny, up to one fifth the length of the sepals; lip variable, maroon-brown to yellowish-green. Apr-May. Sardinia and Sicily.

2441 *Ophrys arachnitiformis* **FALSE SPIDER ORCHID.** Short to medium perennial, to 40cm tall. Basal leaves oval-lanceolate, blunt, the stem leaves reduced, small and bract-like. Spike with 2-9 flowers; sepals usually pink, sometimes purplish, whitish or pale green, oblong to lanceolate, blunt; petals usually pink, slightly more than half the length of the sepals, linear-lanceolate, hairy or hairless; lip 8-10mm long, rectangular to oval, usually unlobed, the tiny tip forward pointing, velvety-brown, flushed with violet-purple; speculum H- or X-shaped, blue or dark purple with a whitish or yellowish margin. Garrigue, maquis, grassy habitats, pastures. Mar-May. Spain, S France, Sardinia, Italy, Sicily, Yugoslavia and Algeria. Uncommon. Very variable and often considered to be a hybrid between *O. holoserica* and *O. sphegodes*.

2442 *Ophrys tenthredinifera* **SAWFLY ORCHID.** Short to medium perennial, to 45cm tall. Basal leaves oval to lanceolate, blunt or pointed, the stem leaves similar though generally narrower. Spikes with 3-8 flowers; sepals pink, purplish or purplish-violet, occasionally whitish, oval; petals purplish or purplish-violet, velvety, triangular, one third the length of the sepals; lip 11-14mm long, generally unlobed, square in outline, purplish-brown with a broad *yellowish margin*; speculum small, brown-spotted, usually 2-lobed. Maquis, garrigue, grassy and stony places, scrub. Iberian Peninsula and N Africa eastwards to Turkey – not Cyprus. A characteristic plant of the Med littoral – the square lip with its broad yellowish margin make it easy to identify.

2443 *Ophrys apifera* **BEE ORCHID.** Short to medium perennial to 50cm tall, very variable. Basal leaves oval to lanceolate, blunt; stem leaves similar though smaller. Spikes with 2-9, occasionally up to 15, flowers; sepals bright pink or purple, rarely

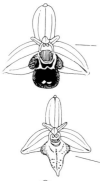

white, always with a green mid-vein, broadly oval-oblong; petals green or purplish, linear-lanceolate to almost triangular, short, less than one third the length of the sepals; lip 10-13mm long, brown or purplish-brown, 3-lobed, the lateral lobes short and hairy, the central lobe with a short tip *bent backwards*; speculum basal, shield-shaped, brown or violet with a yellowish margin. Maquis, garrigue, grassy places, meadows, woodland clearings, open pine forest, occasionally on sand-dunes. Apr-May. T. Like several other species of *Ophrys*, this species may be common some years but apparently rare in others. The flowers are insect-pollinated, but in northern Europe, where it also occurs, self-pollination appears to be more common. Hybridises with *O. holoserica*, *O. sphegodes* and various other orchids when growing in close proximity.

2443a var. *trollii* **WASP ORCHID** is distinguished by its narrow, often pointed lip which is usually yellowish-green and rather mottled. Occurs occasionally almost throughout the range of the species. Forms of the typical plant with white or greenish-white sepals and a yellowish lip are distinguished as var. *chlorantha* (2443b), (France, Rhodes and Cyprus).

2443c Subsp. *jurana [O.a. subsp. botteronii]* is distinguished by its larger petals which are about two thirds the length of the sepals; lip often indistinctly 5-lobed. S France and N Italy.

2444 *Ophrys bombyliflora* **BUMBLE BEE ORCHID.** Low to short perennial, to 25cm tall, though often less. Basal leaves oblong-lanceolate, forming a flattish rosette; stem leaves erect and partly clasping the scape. Spike with 2-5 flowers; sepals green, occasionally whitish, oval, blunt; petals greenish with a purplish base, triangular, about one third the length of the sepals; lip *small*, 7-8mm long, 3-lobed, with the lateral lobes deflexed in the middle and the middle one with a terminal 'tooth', intense velvety-black to deep brown with a central bluish-violet, shield-shaped or 2-parted, speculum. Maquis, garrigue, grassy and stony habitats, scrub, olive groves. Mar-May. T – not Cyprus, but often scarce and rare in some countries.

2445 *Himantoglossum hircinum [Loroglossum hircinum]* **LIZARD ORCHID.** Short to tall, erect, tuberous perennial, rarely more than 90cm tall; stem often with pale purplish markings. Basal leaves 4-6, elliptic-oblong, dull green, unspotted, often partly withered at flowering time; stem leaves smaller and sheathing. Flowers borne in a long, many-flowered cylindrical spike, foul-smelling; sepals and petals small, green, finely spotted or streaked with purple, forming a helmet above the lip; lip 30-50mm, *very long* and tail-like, often somewhat spiralled, green but whitish, dotted with purple or pink in the centre, with two short 'arms' and a long linear central lobe which is notched at the tip; spur short. conical, 3-4mm. Grassy habitats, scrub, streamsides, open marshy woodland, road verges, occasionally on sand-dunes. Apr-June. Spain and N Africa eastwards to Turkey – absent from most of the islands, except Sardinia, and from much of the S Balkans.

2445a Subsp. *calcaratum [Himantoglossum calcaratum]* is distinguished by its longer 'arms', 12-20mm long (not 5-10mm), more deeply cleft middle lobe to the lip and longer spur, 7-12mm. The flowers are often a deeper reddish-violet colour. Grassy places, thickets and scrub, mainly in the hills and mountains. S Yugoslavia, Greece and Turkey; often treated as a distinct species. A fascinating orchid to watch as the long lip unfurls from the buds. In France it is given the common name 'Orchis bouc' or Goat Orchid because of its unpleasant smell. In Britain it is very rare and protected.

2446 *Barlia robertiana [B. longibracteata, Himantoglossum longibracteatum, Loroglossum longibracteatum]* **GIANT ORCHID.** Stout rather sombre, short to medium, tuberous perennial, rarely more than 50cm tall; stem often suffused with purple or reddish-brown. Leaves plain green, the lower large, oval to oblong, blunt, the upper smaller and bract-like; bracts lanceolate, *longer* than the flowers and suffused with violet or reddish-brown. Flowers borne in a dense cylindrical spike, with an iris-like fragrance; sepals reddish-violet, spreading; petals green spotted with pink or purple, or unspotted, forming a helmet; lip 15-20mm, violet-pink or greenish, spotted with purple in the centre, with two short 'arms', the central lobe rather longer and divided into two spreading 'legs'; spur short, 4-6mm long, downturned. Garrigue, maquis, grassy places, scrub, open woodland, banks, roadsides. Feb-Apr. T – not the extreme E Med. One of the earliest Med orchids to come into flower.

2447 *Anacamptis pyramidalis* **PYRAMIDAL ORCHID**. Rather slender short to medium, tuberous perennial. Leaves narrow-oblong to linear-lanceolate, pale green, channelled, decreasing in size up the stem, with the uppermost small and bract-like; bracts linear-lanceoalte, generally purplish, slightly longer than the ovary. Flowers borne in a *cone-shaped* (pyramidal) spike that slowly elongates to a cylindrical spike; sepals and petals bright pink, purplish-pink or rarely blood-red or white, the lateral sepals spreading, the upper sepal and the petals forming a small helmet; lip short, 5-8mm, coloured like the sepals and petals, with three *almost equal* lobes; spur very slender, cylindrical, 12-14mm long, horizontal to downcurved. Maquis, garrigue, grassy places, scrub, roadsides, occasionally in open pine woodland, rarely on sand-dunes. Mar-May. T – except parts of the extreme E Med. Smaller plants from Crete and parts of the E Med, with pale pink flowers are sometimes assigned to var. *brachystachys* (2447a), which generally occurs in the hills and lower mountains. One of the most widespread and common European orchids. In Britain it is almost exclusively confined to chalk grasslands and calcareous soils. The flowers are pollinated by butterflies and moths.

Serapias **TONGUE ORCHIDS**. Like *Ophrys*, more typical of the Med region than anywhere else. Tuberous perennials with unspotted leaves; bracts large and often coloured like the sepals. Flowers borne in dense to lax spikes; sepals and petals forming a close helmet above the lip; lip large and tongue-like, pointing downwards, with two short upturned side-lobes, spurless. The species tend to hybridise with other genera where they grow in close proximity – especially with species of *Dactylorhiza*, *Ophrys* and *Orchis*.

2448 *Serapias cordigera* **HEART-FLOWERED ORCHID**. Short to medium perennial. Leaves narrow-lanceolate, channelled, sharply pointed, the basal sheath-like, purplish with red spots; bracts shorter than the flowers. Flowers borne in a short globose or oblong spike, with up to 10 flowers; sepals and petals pale reddish-purple outside, deeper within; lip 20-35mm long, purplish or reddish, occasionally yellowish, with a broad *heart-shaped* central lobe, twice as long as the sepals overall and with two black lumps or ridges near the base, hairy in the mouth. Damp grassy habitats, scrub, maquis, open marshy woodland, streamsides. Late Mar-May. T – not Balearic Is., Cyprus or parts of the extreme E Med.

2449 *Serapias neglecta* [*S. cordigera* var. *neglecta*] **SCARCE SERAPIAS**. Similar, but generally a smaller plant, not more than 30cm tall, the basal leaf-sheaths green and unspotted, the bracts green tinged with violet, equalling or somewhat longer than the flowers; sepals and petals lilac; lip somewhat longer, red or purplish, with a yellowish or orange *centre*. Maquis, damp meadows and sandy places, generally close to the coast. Late Mar-May. SE France eastwards to Greece – not S Italy or Sicily. A smaller flowered form, generally with red flowers, from the Ionian Is., is sometimes called subsp. *ionica* (2449a). The species is rather rare and local.

2450 *Serapias vomeracea* [*S. longipetala*, *S. pseudocordigera*] **LONG-LIPPED SERAPIAS**. Short to medium perennial. Leaves linear, channelled, grey-green, the basal sheath-leaves green; bracts *much longer* than the flowers, mostly suffused with reddish-violet

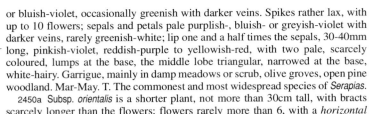

or bluish-violet, occasionally greenish with darker veins. Spikes rather lax, with up to 10 flowers; sepals and petals pale purplish-, bluish- or greyish-violet with darker veins, rarely greenish-white; lip one and a half times the sepals, 30-40mm long, pinkish-violet, reddish-purple to yellowish-red, with two pale, scarcely coloured, lumps at the base, the middle lobe triangular, narrowed at the base, white-hairy. Garrigue, mainly in damp meadows or scrub, olive groves, open pine woodland. Mar-May. T. The commonest and most widespread species of *Serapias*.

    2450a Subsp. *orientalis* is a shorter plant, not more than 30cm tall, with bracts scarcely longer than the flowers; flowers rarely more than 6, with a *horizontal* (not upright) helmet; lip 28-34mm long. Damp meadows and marshes, streamsides. S Italy and Sicily eastwards to Turkey and Cyprus.

    2450b Subsp. *laxiflora* [*Serapias laxiflora*]. Like subsp. *orientalis*, but flowers up to 12 in a laxer spike, smaller, the lip 18-25mm long. Dry habitats, grassy places, hillslopes, garrigue, roadsides. Italy and Sicily eastwards to Turkey, including Crete and Cyprus.

2451 *Serapias lingua* [*S. elongata*] **TONGUE ORCHID**. Short perennial, rarely more than 25cm tall. Leaves narrow-lanceolate, grey-green, the basal sheaths green, sometimes spotted; bracts as long as the flowers, violet-tinted. Flowers up to 9 in a lax spike; sepals and petals violet, purple or pinkish-violet, often speckled with green; lip 24-32mm long, red to violet, occasionally whitish or yellowish, with a *single* black lump at the base, the lateral lobes often purplish, the central lobe oblong-lanceolate, rather narrow. Maquis, garrigue, damp meadows and grassy places, scrub, olive groves, sandy places, sometimes in partial shade, often near the coast. Mar-May. Iberian Peninsula and NW Africa eastwards to Greece – not Balearic Is. Together with *S. vomeracea*, the commonest Tongue Orchid.

2452 *Serapias parviflora* [*S. occulta*] **SMALL-FLOWERED TONGUE ORCHID**. Short perennial, to 35cm tall, though often less. Leaves linear-lanceolate, channelled and often curving upwards, the basal sheaths green, usually speckled with red or purple; bracts generally shorter than the flowers, flushed with pale red or purple. Flowers *small*, borne in a lax spike; sepals and petals brownish-red to violet-red, rarely greenish or whitish; lip 13-18mm long, usually dark red or brownish-red, with two purplish-black lumps at the base, the central lobe narrow triangular-lanceolate. Garrigue, grassy habitats, coastal sands, olive groves, field margins. Mar-May. Iberian Peninsula and NW Africa eastwards to Turkey – absent from most of the islands except for Corsica, Sardinia and Sicily. Hybridises with *S. lingua* in some areas, particularly SE France.

GRASS FAMILY Gramineae

Annual or perennial herbs, often tufted, sometimes rhizomatous or creeping. Leaves alternate, in two ranks, usually linear, sheathing the stem at their base; sheaths very variable, generally with overlapping margins and with a membranous ligule at the junction of sheath and leaf-blade. Inflorescences very variable from a spike or raceme to a panicle. Flowers usually hermaphrodite, with usually 1, 3 or 6 stamens and a pistil enclosed inside two bracts called the lemma and the palea, the whole called a floret; florets arranged alternately into spikelets with two empty bracts (glumes) at the base; styles normally 2. Fruit achene-like (grain), one per fertile flower. A very large family with many species in the Med region; only some of the most common and widespread are included here.

2453 *Lolium temulentum* **DARNEL**. Stiff, short to medium annual, generally tufted and with erect stems. Leaves hairless, green, the blade 3-13mm wide; ligule not more than 2mm long. Flowers borne in erect spikes, somewhat zig-zagged between the spikelets, green; spikelets 8-28mm long with the lower glume usually suppressed but the upper one exceeding the length of the spikelet; lemma with a stiff, rough awn, up to 20mm long, occasionally awnless. Cultivated, waste and fallow land, woodland fringes and olive groves. Apr-May. T.

2454 *Vulpia ciliata* **BEARDED FESCUE**. Low to short tufted annual, with erect stems. Leaves green or sometimes reddish, the blade to 2mm wide, but often inrolled, hairless; ligule very short. Inflorescence a very narrow panicle, erect and one-sided, branched towards the base; spikelets 5-11mm long (excluding the awns), the lower glume *minute*, the upper to 4mm long; lemma covered with long white hairs on the outside, the awn 10-12mm long, rough and stiff. Waste and dry sandy ground, sometimes coastal, often in garrigue. Apr-May. T.

2455 *Desmazenia rigida [Catapodium rigidum]* **FERN-GRASS**. Low to short, hairless, generally tufted annual; stems erect. Leaves pointed, the blade not more than 2mm wide, flat to inrolled; ligules membranous, to 3mm long. Inflorescence a more or less one-sided panicle, with rather distant spikelets; spikelets 4-10mm long, with equal green glumes, to 2.5mm long; lemma elliptical, only 2-2.5mm long, awnless. Dry habitats, cultivated, fallow and waste ground, roadsides, olive groves and coastal sands. Mar-Sept. T.

2456 *Sphenopus divaricatus*. Low to short, hairless, rather slender annual, tufted or not. Leaves linear to filiform. Inflorescence a panicle, often with two branches at each node, the branches generally bare for a half their length; spikelets small, 2-3mm long with the upper glume twice the size of the lower; lemma 1.5-2mm long, smooth and *awnless*. Mainly coastal habitats, sandy and rocky, as well as salt marshes. Mar-July. West and central Med.

2457 *Poa bulbosa* **BULBOUS MEADOW GRASS**. Tufted, short to medium, hairless perennial, with erect stems, *bulbous* at the base. Leaves mostly basal, often greyish, sometimes purplish, the blade thread-like; ligule pale and membranous, 4-6mm long. Inflorescence an oblong panicle, often one-sided; spikelets 4-6mm long, often purplish, the glumes more or less equal, to 3mm long; lemma somewhat shorter, awnless. Dry rocky and stony ground, waste places, field boundaries, roadsides. Mar-June. T. Forms in which the spikelets are flowerless and replaced by tiny plantlets are referred to var. *vivipara* (2457a).

2458 *Cynosurus echinatus* **ROUGH DOG'S-TAIL**. Low to tall, variable, hairless, often tufted annual; stems erect to spreading. Leaves green, the blade flat, to 5mm wide; ligule to 10mm long. Inflorescence a dense, oblong or rounded panicle, *shiny*, green or purplish; spikelets 8-12mm long, with equal glumes; lemma with a long and stiff, rough awn, 9-12mm long. Dry rocky and stony places, generally in the hills, cultivated land. Mar-June. T.

2459 *Lamarckia aurea* **GOLDEN DOG'S-TAIL**. More or less hairless, low to short annual; stems usually tufted, erect, rough below the inflorescence. Leaves linear, the blade only 1mm wide, with rough margins; ligule membranous, to 10mm long, pointed or rounded. Inflorescence dense and one-sided with the outer spikelets *sterile*; fertile inner spikelets with narrow, equal glumes, 3-4mm long; lemma broadly elliptical with a stiff awn 10-12mm long. Cultivated, fallow and waste ground, field boundaries, roadsides, stony hillslopes. Mar-June. T.

2460 *Briza maxima* **LARGE QUAKING GRASS**. Erect, hairless, short to medium annual; stems erect, often solitary, but plants usually growing close together. Leaves flat, the blade 2-4mm wide, slightly rough to touch. Inflorescence a lax panicle with papery spikelets *drooping* on slender stalks; spikelets pale green or purplish, 12-20mm long, the glumes equal, boat-shaped, often stained with blackish-purple; lemma similar but slightly longer, with a short point, but awnless. Cultivated, fallow and waste land, roadsides, hillslopes, garrigue and maquis. Mar-June. T. Often cultivated for ornament.

2461 *Echinaria capitata.* Low to short annual with solitary or tufted stems. Leaves grey or green, the blade 2-3mm wide, *finely hairy* on both surfaces; ligule only 1mm long, membranous. Inflorescence a dense, prickly, rounded to oval panicle, green to pale straw-coloured; spikelets small, with the equal glumes only 2-2.5mm long; lemma slightly longer, with 3-5-awned lobes which eventually become recurved, the awns 3-4mm long; palea 2-awned. Rocky and sandy open habitats, often in the hills. April-June. T.

2462 *Melica ciliata* **HAIRY MELICK.** Low to short, tufted to creeping perennial; stems slender, erect. Leaves rather rigid with rolled blades, 1-4mm wide, without a prominent midrib; ligule very short and membranous. Inflorescence a *hairy panicle* with the spikelets well spaced, with short erect branches; spikelets 4-8mm long, with equal glumes which are deciduous; lemma lanceolate, pointed, with a hairy margin, 7-9-veined. Dry stony and rocky habitats, roadsides. Mar-June. Almost throughout the Med, but not Cyprus. Cultivated as an ornamental species.

2463 *Melica minuta.* Like the last species, but with hairless lemmas and with unequal glumes. Similar habitats and flowering time. T.

2464 *Bromus madritensis* **COMPACT BROME.** Short to medium, generally tufted annual with erect stems. Leaves tapered, not more than 5mm wide, covered in *soft white* hairs. Inflorescence a dense to lax panicle, often wedge-shaped, with short branches; spikelets 3-6cm long, often paired, the glumes not equal, the upper longer; lemma with a long rough awn, 12-16mm long, hairy or hairless. Cultivated, waste and fallow land, roadsides, olive groves, coastal and inland – a common weed. Mar-July. T.

2465 *Bromus squarrosus.* Similar to the last species, but awn *reflexed* at right angles to the lemma; glumes 3-9-veined, not 1-3. Dry slopes and roadsides, waste ground. Mar-June. T.

2466 *Brachypodium retusum* **MEDITERRANEAN FALSE-BROME.** Stiff, rhizomatous, short to medium perennial; rhizomes much-branched. Leaves *tough*, the blade inrolled when dry, 2-4mm wide. Inflorescence stiffly erect, a slender panicle with alternating spikelets; spikelets 20-30mm long, linear, bluish-grey with pointed glumes; lemma 7-8mm long, with a short awn only about 3-4mm long. Dry rocky and sandy habitats. May-Sept. West and central Med.

2467 *Aegilops geniculata.* Low to medium, tufted annual, with erect stems. Leaves with a flat blade, 2-3mm wide, finely hairy on the upper surface usually; ligule very short. Inflorescence condensed, with 1-2 *vestigial* spikelets at the base of the fertile ones; fertile spikelets urn-shaped, usually only 2-4, with equal glumes 7-8mm long; lemma with a long rough awn, 15-30mm long, erect to spreading. Waste and fallow ground, roadsides, hillslopes, margins of cultivation, olive groves, coastal habitats. Mar-June. T.

2468 *Dasypyrum villosum [Secale villosum, Triticum villosum].* Short to tall annual with hairless, erect stems. Leaves with blades 1-5mm wide, smooth to hairy; ligule membranous, truncated at the apex. Inflorescence a slender, *two-sided* spike, up to 12cm long; spikelets 7-22mm long (excluding the awns), with equal glumes; lemma 6-14mm long, with awns variable in length, often very long, 7-60mm. Dry grassy habitats, roadsides. Apr-June. Almost throughout, but not Cyprus.

2469 *Hordeum murinum [including H. leporinum]* **WALL BARLEY.** Short to medium annual, generally tufted, with erect, smooth stems. Leaves with linear blades, 2-4mm wide, hairy on both surfaces, with shiny sheaths; ligule membranous, not more than 1mm long. Inflorescence a dense panicle, spike-like, rather fragile; spikelets with both glumes and lemmas awned, the awns 10-25mm long, rough. Fallow and waste ground, roadsides, garrigue, olive groves; a weed of cultivated land. Mar-July. T.

2470 *Taeniatherum caput-medusae [Elymus caput-medusae]*. Low to medium annual with erect, hairless stems. Leaves with flat or inrolled blades, 2-6mm wide, hairy or not. Inflorescence a *bristly* spike to 15cm long; spikelets with rough awns 15-60mm long; lemma with an awn 50-120mm long. Rocky and stony habitats, mainly on hillslopes and in garrigue, dry fields. Apr-July. T.

2471 *Avena sterilis* **WINTER WILD OAT**. Medium to tall, green or bluish-green annual; stem solitary or grouped. Leaves linear to linear-lanceolate, to 15mm wide, hairless or somewhat hairy on the margin; ligule 4-6mm long, membranous. Inflorescence a lax panicle with spikelets drooping on slender stalks; spikelets gaping, with only the lower two flowers awned, the glumes equal, pointed and as long as the spikelet; lemma with a slender awn, 30-60mm long, *twisted* below a distinct elbow. Cultivated, waste and fallow land, roadsides. Mar-May. T.

2472 *Avena barbata* **BEARDED WILD OAT**. Similar to the last species, but lemmas with two short awns at the apex as well as the usual long one from the dorsal surface. Similar habitats. Feb-June. T.

2473 *Lagurus ovatus* **HARE'S-TAIL**. Low to medium, soft-hairy, grey-green annual; stems erect to decumbent, solitary or fascicled. Leaves linear to lanceolate, flat; ligule hairy and membranous, 2-3mm long. Inflorescence dense, egg-shaped, *white and soft*, 10-40mm long; spikelets equal, bristle-tipped and hairy; lemma semi-transparent, often somewhat hairy, with an awn up to 15mm long. Dry stony, rocky and sandy places, coastal and inland. Mar-July. T. Plants in very poor arid places may be very dwarf, only 3-4cm tall. Widely grown in gardens as an ornamental grass.

2474 *Rotraria cristata [Festuca cristata, Koeleria cristata, K. phleoides, Lophochloa cristata]* **CRESTED HAIR-GRASS**. Slender, generally tufted, short to medium annual. Leaves with flat, rather soft, blades, 3-5mm wide, hairy; ligule, 2mm long, toothed. Inflorescence cylindrical, rather dense, up to 60mm long; spikelets with the lower glume shorter than the upper, and silvery; lemma 4-5mm long, pointed, with a short awn in the notched apex. Fallow and waste ground, stony places. Feb-May. T.

2475 *Ammophila arenaria* **MARRAM GRASS**. Tough rhizomatous grass, patch-forming; stems erect, medium to tall, stout and smooth. Leaves with inrolled blades, 4-5mm wide when opened out, greenish or brownish, minutely hairy on the ribs; *ligules* narrow and pointed, to 25mm long. Inflorescence a slender spike-like panicle with closely packed erect spikelets; spikelets 10-16mm long, gaping when mature, with equal, pointed glumes; lemma 9-12mm long, with a very short, stiff awn in the apical notch, with a circle of hairs at the base. Coastal sands and dunes. May-July. T. Widely planted for dune stabilisation.

2476 *Phalaris aquatica* **BULBOUS CANARY GRASS**. Tufted, tall perennial to 1.5m, with smooth stems. Leaves grey-green, flat, 2-15mm wide, more or less smooth; ligule not toothed, 4-6mm long. Inflorescence a dense oblong panicle, to 12cm in length; spikelets dense, 4-5mm long only, with equal glumes winged on their keels; lemma 3-4.5mm long, hairy, *not* awned. Cultivated, waste and fallow land, roadsides, hillslopes, often in damp places. Feb-July. T.

2477 *Stipa capensis [S. tortilis]* **MEDITERRANEAN NEEDLE-GRASS**. Densely tufted annual generally with erect stems. Leaves linear, flat to inrolled, only 1-1.5mm wide, finely hairy to hairless; ligule very short, with a minutely hairy margin. Inflorescence a dense panicle up to 6cm long; spikelets with unequal, membranous glumes; lemma much shorter, 4-7mm long, hairy, with very long awns to 10cm long, all twisted together. Garrigue, stony places, waste and fallow land. Mar-June. T.

2478 *Stipa pennata* **NEEDLE-GRASS.** Tufted perennial grass, with erect and rather stiff stems to 60cm. Leaves with long sheaths, grey-green, the blades linear, inrolled, and rigid, 1mm wide. Inflorescence a panicle, but with few florets, the lower part enclosed in the upper leaf-sheath; florets with pointed, equal glumes, hairless, 30-60mm long; lemma with a very long flexuous and twisted, feathery awn, up to 30cm long. Rocky, stony and grassy habitats, May-July. Local throughout, except for most of the islands.

2479 *Stipa bromoides.* Similar, but awns short, not more than 1.3cm long; inflorescence clear of the uppermost leaf-sheath. Dry rocky and stony habitats, garigue and open maquis. May-Aug. T.

2480 *Stipa tenacissima* **ESPARTO GRASS.** Tough, tufted, grass, often forming extensive and dominant colonies; stems to 1.5m tall, sometimes more. Leaves inrolled and with the margins overlapping, 1mm diameter, smooth; ligule short and with a hairy margin and *feathered tip.* Inflorescence a dense, spike-like panicle to 35cm long; spikelets 1-flowered, with equal, membranous glumes, to 30mm long; lemma shorter and membranous, with a notched tip and a long awn to 60mm long, the awn twisted and feathered in the lower part. Rocky and grassy habitats, open woodland, coastal, and inland. Apr-July. Iberian Peninsula, Balearic Is. and NW Africa. Used locally for rope and paper making; occasionally planted outside its native region.

2481 *Cynodon dactylon* **BERMUDA GRASS.** Patch-forming, stoloniferous, low to short perennial. Leaves linear, pointed, usually flat, hairless, sometimes rough along the margins; ligule reduced to a row of hairs. Inflorescence consisting of 3-6 *finger-like* spikes arising from the same point on the stem; spikelets 2-3mm long, stalkless, with equal, pointed glumes; lemma as long as the spikelet, hairy along the three veins. Cultivated and waste lands, roadsides, garrigue, saline habitats. Mar-Nov. T; probably originated in tropical Africa, but widespread in many of the warmer regions of the world.

2482 *Lygeum spartum* **ALBARDINE.** Tough, rhizomatous, short to tall perennial. Leaves somewhat inrolled and rush-like, only 1.5mm wide, curled over at the tip, hairless; ligule 6-7mm long. Inflorescence often only 2-flowered, enclosed in a *whitish* bract-like sheath; spikelets without glumes; lemmas fused together below and with long silky hairs, free and hairless above, pointed. Grassy habitats, often on saline soils and near the coast. S Spain, Balearic Is., Sardinia, Italy, Sicily and N Africa.

(2481)

2483 *Aeluropus littoralis [Poa littoralis].* Low to short, rhizomatous perennial with many *prostrate* stems, hairless. Leaves lanceolate, to 2mm wide, strongly veined; ligule a ring of hairs. Inflorescence a branched spike; spikelets with equal glumes, not more than 1.5mm long; lemma longer, keeled, hairless. Sandy habitats and salt marshes, coastal. Apr-July. Scattered throughout – not Portugal.

2484 *Echinochloa crus-galli* **COCKSPUR GRASS.** Robust annual grass to 1m. Leaves with linear, pointed blades, dark green, flat and 8-20mm wide; ligule *absent.* Inflorescence a panicle with one-sided, spike-like branches; spikelets to almost 4mm long, with unequal, rather broad glumes; lemma oval, equalling the inner glume, but with a stiff, rough awn up to 30mm long. Ditches, marshes and other wet places, sometimes on cultivated or waste land. Aug-Nov. T.

2485 *Setaria pumila [S. glauca, S. lutescens]* **YELLOW BRISTLE-GRASS.** Low to medium annual, with a solitary or several erect stems. Leaves with a pointed, flat blade, 4-10mm wide, hairless or somewhat hairy; ligule a ring of hairs. Inflorescence dense and cylindrical, bristly, to 10cm long, erect; spikelets yellowish or reddish, 3mm long, with unequal glumes, awnless (the apparent awns are actually bristles from the base of each spikelet). Cultivated, waste and fallow land, roadsides, olive groves, hillslopes, often in wet places such as ditches. July-Oct. T. A casual in Britain.

2486 *Paspalum dilatatum.* Stout perennial with woody rhizomes; stems erect to 1.5m, hairy only at the lower nodes. Leaves linear, flat, to 15mm wide, with a *thickened* margin, hairless; ligule short and membranous, white-hairy behind. Inflorescence a branched spike, the spikes drooping, 5-10cm long; spikelets one-sided, but borne in 2 or 4 rows on the underside of the rachis, with only a single glume; lemma membranous to shiny-white, often rounded, awnless. Damp habitats, ditches and marshes in particular. June-October. Naturalised locally throughout, especially in the warmer parts of the Med. (South America).

2487 *Imperata cylindrica.* Medium to tall, rhizomatous perennial; stem smooth, densely hairy at the nodes. Leaves linear, channelled with a distinct midrib above, rough on the margins, hairless. Inflorescence a dense silky-white panicle to 20cm long; spikelets paired, with almost equal, hairy glumes; lemma hyaline, short and pointed. Sandy habitats, coastal or inland, occasionally along irrigation ditches or rivers. Apr-July. T.

2488 *Saccharum ravennae.* Tufted, rhizomatous perennial with erect stems to 2m; stems hairless. Leaves linear, to 15mm wide, rough on *both* surfaces, with a prominent midrib, hairy towards the base above and along the sheaths; ligule membranous, fringed with hairs. Inflorescence a dense feathery panicle, often reddish or purplish or whitish, to 60cm long; spikelets paired, 4-6mm long, hairy at base, with almost equal glumes; lemma hyaline, awnless or with a short, 4-6mm long, awn at the apex. Moist habitats, stream and river margins, ditches, coastal sands. June-Oct. Almost throughout – not Portugal or Sardinia.

2489 *Digitaria sanguinalis* **HAIRY FINGER-GRASS.** Low to short annual; stems decumbent at the base and rooting at the nodes. Leaves linear to lanceolate, rather soft, flat, 3-10mm wide, hairy or hairless; ligule 1-2mm, membranous. Inflorescence consisting of 4-16 spike-like fingers arising from the same place; spikelets paired, 2-3mm long, with markedly unequal glumes; lemma awnless, sometimes minutely hairy. Cultivated and fallow land, often if irrigated, and sandy places. Mar-Sept. T.

2490 *Digitaria ischaemum* **SMOOTH FINGER-GRASS.** Like the last, but inflorescence with not more than 6 fingers; spikelets with upper glume *equalling* the spikelet (not half as long). Mainly in sandy habitats Almost throughout – not Sardinia, Albania, Greece, Crete or Cyprus.

2491 *Hyparrhenia hirta [Andropogon hirta].* Tufted, medium to tall perennial; stems smooth. Leaves linear, pointed, 1-3mm wide, hairless except sometimes towards the base; ligule 3-4mm long, toothed, membranous. Inflorescence a panicle of paired racemes, each *enclosed* in leaf-like spathes, hairy at the joints; spikelets with equal glumes, the lower bearded on the back; lemma 3-4.5mm long, with a stout awn, to 20mm long, which is twisted and hairy in the lower part. Dry rocky and stony habitats, hillsides, roadsides, occasionally in open woodland. Feb-Nov. T.

2492 *Parapholis incurva [Lepturus incurvatus, Pholiurus incurvatus]* **CURVED SEA HARD-GRASS.** Tufted, low to short annual, not more than 15cm tall; stems (culms) prostrate to curved. Leaves linear, pointed, 1-2mm wide, rough above and on margins, hair-

less, the sheaths often reddish; ligules membranous, tiny. Inflorescence a cylindrical spike to 10cm long, strongly curved, rigid and jointed; spikelets alternate, pressed close to the main axis, 4-6mm long, with glumes as long as the spikelets; lemma membranous, hidden by the glumes. Salt marshes and moist coastal habitats, occasionally inland. Apr-July. T.

2493 *Sorghum halepense* **JOHNSON GRASS**. Large erect perennial, to 2.5m tall, though often less; stems with silky hairs at the *nodes*. Leaves hairless, with a very rough margin. Inflorescence a large terminal panicle to 30cm long; spikelets 4-5.5mm long, with leathery glumes, keeled; lemma of fertile flowers notched at the apex and with an awn up to 12mm long; awn twisted and brown in the lower part. Cultivated, fallow and waste land, often in moist places. Apr-Nov. Widely naturalised weed throughout. (probably North Africa and SW Asia).

2494 *Arundo donax* **GIANT REED**. Very large and robust rhizomatous, patch-forming, grass; stems *bamboo-like*, to 6m, occasionally more. Leaves rough and tough, grey-green, to 60mm wide. Inflorescence borne on two year old stems, a large panicle to 60cm long, silky and purple-tinged; spikelets 12-18mm long, with pointed, almost equal glumes; lemma notched at the apex and with a short awn, silkily-hairy and giving the whole inflorescence a silvery appearance. Damp places, ditches, river and stream margins, dune depressions. June-Oct. T, often planted. Widely used for shelter belts, for matting, basket making and for shading roofs and shelters. The largest grass in the region.

SEDGE FAMILY Cyperaceae

A large cosmopolitan family. The members are superficially like the grasses but differ in their closed leaf-sheaths and solid, often triangular stems. The flowers are borne on spikelets generally with only one (not two) bracts to each; stamens 2-3. Fruit a small 2-3-faced nut.

2495 *Cyperus papyrus* **PAPYRUS**. A giant grass-like plant with the lower stems and roots immersed in fresh water; rootstock rhizomatous and woody. Stems erect, robust, 2-5m tall, thick and spongy, leafless, sheathed below and terminating in a ruff of 4-10 bracts. Rays of inflorescence *many*, 100 or more, longer than the bracts, green. Spikelets reddish or straw-coloured; glumes 1.5-2mm long. Marshy habitats and lakes. May-Sept. Naturalised in Sicily and the extreme SE Med. (Nile Valley to C Africa). Papyrus has been used for many centuries in Africa and the Nile region for making paper, for shelters and rafts.

2496 *Cyperus capitatus* [*C. mucronatus, Schoenus mucronatus*]. A tough, creeping, bluish- or greyish-green, short to medium, hairless perennial; stems erect and wiry. Leaves often becoming yellowish, narrow with *inrolled* margins. Bracts leaf-like, 3-4, erect and exceeding the inflorescence. Spikelets terminal, without rays, forming a head 1.5-4cm across, each 10-15mm long; glumes with a green keel and a rigid apex. Sandy coastal habitats, dunes. Feb-June. T.

2497 *Cyperus laevigatus*. Low to medium perennial, with mat-forming rhizomes; stems erect, bunched or solitary, rounded or triangular in section. Leaves generally few and very reduced. Inflorescence a head of spikelets, without rays, and exceeded by an erect *bract*; remaining bracts small and glume-like. Spikelets unstalked, 4-20mm long; glumes pale green to blackish, generally with a pale stripe.Marshy habitats, lake and stream margins, irrigation ditches. Nov-June. T.

2498 *Cyperus rotundus*. Short to medium, tufted perennial, rhizomatous, not densely tufted; stems erect triangular in section. Leaves basal and rather crowded, often exceeding the stems, dark green, *flat* and with a rough margin. Bracts leaf-like,

often 3, unequal. Inflorescence with 3-9 spreading rays, the spikelets 7-14mm long; glumes laxly overlapping, dark brown or reddish, keeled, with inconspicuous veins. Weed of moist cultivated and waste land, pool margins and irrigation ditches. July-Nov. T.

2499 *Cyperus glaber*. Similar, but a more densely tufted plant, without long rhizomes. Spikelets forming a dense heads with 2-5 rays; bracts erect to spreading; glumes closely overlapping. Similar habitats. June-Oct. T.

2500 *Cyperus longus [Pycreus longus]* **GALINGALE**. Like *C. rotundus* but a more robust plant to 1.5m, though often less and very variable; rhizomes thick and far-reaching. Leaves 3-10mm not 2-5mm) wide. Bracts 3-6. Inflorescences with 8-12 rays. Similar habitats. May-Sept. T.

2501 *Cyperus esculentus [C. melanorhizus, Pycreus esculentus]* **TIGER NUT**. A tufted, low to medium hairless perennial with long scaly rhizomes and tuberous roots; stems erect. Leaves shorter or longer than the stems, 2-10mm wide. Bracts 2-9. Inflorescence an *umbel* (sometimes compound) with 4-10 spreading rays; glumes pale yellow or brownish, with prominent raised veins. Moist habitats. June-Sept. Scattered T. Locally cultivated in the Med for its edible tubers, known as tiger nuts; the cultivated form is var. *sativus*.

RUSH FAMILY Juncaceae

Perennial herbs, rarely annual, with narrow leaves sheathing at the base. Flowers regular (actinomorphic) borne usually in crowded cymes or heads; perianth segments 6; stamens 6, occasionally 3. Fruit a 1- or 3-parted capsule.

2502 *Juncus maritimus* **SEA RUSH**. A densely tufted, medium to tall perennial, with erect stems to 1m; stems stiff and ridged. Leaves 2-4, almost basal, generally shorter than the stems, *sharply* pointed. Inflorescence an interrupted panicle; bracts sharply pointed, the largest longer than the inflorescence. Flowers greenish or pale yellowish-brown. Capsule 2.5-3.5mm long. Coastal salt marshes. July-Aug. T.

2503 *Juncus rigidus*. Similar, but capsule exceeding (not equalling) the perianth segments. Coastal sands and salt marshes. Sardinia, Italy and Sicily.

2504 *Juncus acutus* **SHARP RUSH**. A robust densely tufted, tall perennial, to 1.8m tall; stems 2-5mm diameter. Leaves basal, 2-5, often longer than the stems, sharply pointed; bracts exceeding the *dense* rounded inflorescence. Flowers brown or reddish-brown. Capsule 5-6mm long. Sandy coastal habitats and salt marshes, occasionally inland. Mar-May. T.

2505 *Juncus littoralis [J. tommasinii]*. Similar, but less robust (to 1m); stems 3mm diameter. Inflorescence *much-branched*, many-flowered and less dense. Capsule 2.5-4mm long. Apr-May. Scattered T.

2506 *Juncus articulatus* **JOINTED RUSH**. Very variable rhizomatous, medium to tall perennial; stems leafy. Leaves linear, *jointed*, smooth or lined. Inflorescence terminal, without exceeding bracts and with erect to spreading branches; flowers dark brown to blackish. Capsule 2.5-3.5mm long. Damp grassy habitats, heaths, marshes, river and pool margins, dune depressions. Apr-Sept. Almost T, but rather rare in N Africa.

2507 *Juncus striatus*. Similar, but leaves clearly grooved and flowers in a more rounded head; perianth segments 3.5-5mm long (not 2.5-3.5mm). Capsule *beaked*. Damp habitats. Scattered localities from the Iberian Peninsula to Turkey.

2508 *Juncus effusus* **SOFT RUSH.** A densely tufted, medium to tall, patch-forming perennial; stems erect, smooth or faintly lined, glossy when young. Leaves soft-tipped, mostly basal, the stem leaves reduced to bladeless sheaths. Inflorescence lax, with erect to spreading branches; lowest *bract* long and with a narrow sheath; flowers pale brown, each with 2 small bracts at the base. Damp habitats; marshes, meadows, pool and river margins, ditches. Apr-Aug. T.

2509 *Juncus bulbosus* **BULBOUS RUSH.** A tufted, *non-rhizomatous*, short to medium perennial, very variable; stems erect to spreading (sometimes floating), usually swollen at the base. Leaves indistinctly jointed, often somewhat grooved. Inflorescence a rather sparse cluster with spreading to almost erect branches; flowers greenish to dark brown. Capsule 2.2-3.5mm long. Wet habitats, often submerged; generally on acid soils. May-Sept. W & C Med, rare elsewhere.

SELAGINELLA FAMILY Selaginellaceae

Non-flowering, spore-bearing plants with erect and creeping stems and tiny scale-like 1-veined leaves. Spores in special tiny organs, sporangia.

2510 *Selaginella denticulata* **MEDITERRANEAN SELAGINELLA.** A small, low, creeping pale green, moss-like plant, with delicate, much-branched flattened stems. Leaves in 4 rows, the outer two larger and spreading, the upper two smaller and pressed close to the stem; all leaves oval, fine-toothed, not more than 2.5mm long and unstalked. Spores borne in tiny unstalked cones, inconspicuous, terminal on lateral branches. Moist shaded habitats, rocks, old walls and banks. Feb-May. T.

QUILLWORT FAMILY Isoetaceae

A family of spore-bearing, evergreen, aquatic or marginal plants with short 2-3-lobed stems and quill-like leaves borne in basal rosettes. Sporangia sunken in the leaf-bases.

2511 *Isoetes histrix* **MEDITERRANEAN QUILLWORT.** Low terrestrial perennial with 3-lobed stems. Leaves linear, flat, to 10cm long, with a membranous margin the lower part; old leaf-bases persistent, shiny black and *horn-like*. Sandy habitats which are winter flooded, in a variety of different situations, including woodland. Scattered localities in the W & E Med.

2512 *Isoetes durieui*. Similar, but leaves to 12cm long and often recurved. Similar habitats. W & C Med, not the Balkans.

HORSETAIL FAMILY Equisetaceae

Perennial herbs with rather brittle, jointed and grooved, stems. Leaves in whorls, coming together in sheath-like bases. Spores borne in cone-like structures.

2513 *Equisetum palustre* **MARSH HORSETAIL.** Short to medium perennial, with green branched or sometimes unbranched stems; branches 6-10 at most nodes, except the lowermost. Stems with 6-10 grooves and loose green sheaths with black-tipped teeth. Cones 10-30mm long, blunt. Damp grassy habitats and marshes, stream margins and ditches. Almost T.

2514 *Equisetum ramosissimum*. Similar, but often taller, to 1m, and branches in whorls of 8-20; cones 6-12mm long, shortly pointed. Similar habitats. T.

2515 *Equisetum arvense* **COMMON HORSETAIL.** Short to tall rhizomatous perennial with both sterile and fruiting stems; sterile stems with branches in whorls of 6-19, with green sheaths; fertile stems unbranched and *brown*, appearing before the sterile stems. Cones large, 1-4cm long. Damp grassy habitats, meadows, roadsides, banks and stream margins. T – not Cyprus apparently.

2516 *Equisetum telmateia.* Similar, but *branches* in whorls of 20-40 and cones larger, 4-8cm long. Wet habitats by streams and rivers, ditches. T.

FERNS Pteridophyta

A large group with many different families in temperate and tropical regions of the world. Most are rhizomatous and the rhizomes and stems are bare or scaly, spreading or short. Leaves (fronds) very variable, divided or not. Spores (asexual) minute, borne in sporangia on the undersurface of the leaf or on special fertile branches. Spores germinate to produce small liverwort-like prothalli which bear the sexual generation which, after fertilisation, develops the asexual (fern) phase of the plant.

Cheilanthes **CHEILANTHES.** Small tufted ferns of dry rocky habitats with persistent leaves (fronds); stalks reddish- or yellowish-brown.

2517 *Cheilanthes pteridioides [C. fragrans, C. odora]* **SCENTED CHEILANTHES.** A small rather tough, tufted fern. Leaves up to 15cm long, though often far less, narrow-traingular in outline, scented of coumarin when bruised, bright green when fresh, 2-pinnate, with the leaflets small, oblong to rounded, blunt-toothed; stalks about as long as the blade, shiny red-brown, with a few scattered scales. Fertile fronds with the sori half-hidden below the recurved margins of the leaflets, hairless. Dry rocky habitats, old walls. T.

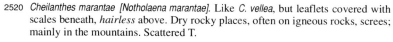

2518 *Cheilanthes vellea [Cheilanthes catanensis, Notholaena vellea, N. lanuginosa]* **SCALY CHEILANTHES.** Similar, but larger, with leaves linear-lanceolate in outline, up to 25cm long and *covered* on both surfaces with yellowish hairs (sometimes absent from the upper surface on old fronds). Dry rocky habitats, generally on calcareous rocks. W & C Med, Cyprus and parts of the eastern Med.

2519 *Cheilanthes persica.* Like *C. vellea*, but leaflets convex (not flat), with inrolled margins which hide the sori. Dry rocky habitats. C & E Med from Crete and Balkans eastwards.

2520 *Cheilanthes marantae [Notholaena marantae].* Like *C. vellea*, but leaflets covered with scales beneath, *hairless* above. Dry rocky places, often on igneous rocks, screes; mainly in the mountains. Scattered T.

2521 *Cheilanthes hispanica.* Like *C. persica*, but leaf-stalk longer than (not equalling) the leaf-blade; leaf-blade (lamina) glandular-hairy. Rocky places and cliffs. Iberian Peninsula.

2522 *Adiantum capillus-veneris* **MAIDENHAIR FERN.** Tufted perennial with short scaly rhizomes. Leaves to 60cm long, rather delicate, 2-4-pinnately-lobed, the leaflets pale to bright green, rhomboidal to fan-shaped or oblong, with slender *hair-like* stalks, generally with 2-3 irregular, shallow, rounded lobes, hairless; stalks slender and wiry, blackish-brown, scaly only at the base. Fertile leaflets (pinnae) with sori on the undersurface partially hidden by the recurved leaflet-margin. Damp, shaded rocks, often on limestone, sometimes by waterfalls or where water drips down cliffs, occasionally along irrigation ditches. T. Often grown as a house plant and widespread in both temperate and subtropical regions of the world.

2523 *Pteris cretica.* Short rhizomatous perennial with tufted leaves; rhizome slender, dark brown and scaly. Leaves up to 70cm long, pinnate or 2-pinnate, the leaflets up to 7 pairs, *linear*, slightly toothed at the apex, the lowest pair of leaflets often forked; stalk slender, pale brown, erect. Fertile leaflets with marginal sori beneath, somewhat narrower than the sterile leaflets. Damp shaded rocks, stream-sides, by old buildings. W and C Med. A widespread species in warm-temperate and subtropical regions of the Old World. Widely cultivated and sometimes becoming naturalised in the region as a whole; many different forms exist in gardens.

2524 *Pteris vittata.* Similar to *P. cretica*, but leaves to 90cm, lanceolate (not oval) in outline and with 10 or more pairs of leaflets; leaflets never forked and usually heart-shaped at the base. Similar habitats. Scattered localities from Spain and the Balearics to Italy, Sicily, Greece, Cyprus and the eastern Med. Also widespread in subtropical and warm-temperate regions of the Old World.

Asplenium **SPLEENWORTS.** Tufted perennials with short, dark-scaly rhizomes, often erect although occasionally creeping. Leaves with dark stalks and hairless blades. Sori borne along the veins on the undersurface of the leaves.

2525 *Asplenium trichomanes* **MAIDENHAIR SPLEENWORT.** Leaves up to 20cm long, narrow-oblong in outline, pinnate, with up to 30 pairs of small leaflets; leaflets leathery, oblong to rounded, slightly toothed in the upper half; stalks dark and shiny, red-dish- or blackish-brown, with a narrow, pale brown *wing*. Sori linear, covering the surface of the fertile fronds. Rocky habitats and old walls, often on igneous rocks. T.

2526 *Asplenium marinum* **SEA SPLEENWORT.** Similar, but with leaves up to 30cm long with reddish-brown, tough (not brittle) stalks. Sori submarginal. Coastal rocks and walls. W & C Med eastwards to Sicily.

2527 *Asplenium petrarchae.* Like *A. trichomanes,* but leaf-stalks *covered* in dense glandular hairs. Rocky habitats, mainly of limestone. Scattered localities in the W & C Med, east as far as Greece but not Crete.

2528 *Asplenium fontanum* **SMOOTH ROCK SPLEENWORT.** Leaves to 25cm long, though often far less, pale green, 2-pinnate, spreading to arched, elliptical to oblong in outline, with the lowermost leaflets *reduced* and often deflexed; leaflets oblong, pinnate-ly-lobed, slightly toothed; stalks pale green or straw-coloured with a reddish-brown base. Sori covering most of the undersurface of the leaflets. Limestone rocks. W & C Med.

2529 *Asplenium obovatum.* Leaves to 30cm long, stiff, bright green, oval to lanceolate in outline, 2-pinnate with a tapered apex, the leaflets rounded, short-stalked; stalk reddish-brown, with a few scattered, narrow scales. Sori oblong, submarginal. Rocky habitats and old walls, often close to the sea. Scattered localities from Portugal to Turkey.

2530 *Asplenium onopteris [A. adiantum-nigrum* subsp. *onopteris]* **ACUTE-LEAVED SPLEENWORT.** Leaves to 40cm long, bright shiny green, 2-4-pinnate, triangular in outline and with a tapered apex, rather leathery, the leaflets curved and tapered to the tip, final segments lanceolate, pointed; stalks dark reddish-brown, shiny often, usually equal in length to the blade, *thickened* at the base. Sori linear, median. Rock crevices, igneous or occasionally limestone, woodland and stream margins, often in the mountains, but also at lower altitudes. T.

2531 *Asplenium ruta-muraria* **WALL RUE.** A small tufted fern with leaves up to 15cm long, though often only 4-7cm, leathery, oval to lancolate in outline, 2-pinnate, with *relatively few* pairs (2-4) of stalked leaflets, the leaflets diamond-shaped to fan-shaped, toothed to notched; stalks green, darker at the base. Sori linear, median. Rocks and old walls. T. Also occurs in Asia and North America.

2532 *Ceterach officinarum [Asplenium ceterach].* A tufted, evergreen fern. Leaves thick and leathery, linear to narrow-oblong in outline, pinnately-lobed, with 9-12 semi-circular leaflets on each side of the midrib, the leaflets untoothed or blunt-toothed, dark green and hairless above but covered beneath with pale rusty-brown scurfy scales. Sori linear, diagonal across leaflets of fertile fronds but partially hidden by the dense scales. Dry rocky habitats and old walls, often in the full sun. T. During hot dry periods the fronds roll in towards the centre of the plant to prevent desiccation, with the scaly undersurfaces pointing outwards.

2533 *Phyllitis scolopendrium [Asplenium scolopendrium]* **HART'S-TONGUE FERN**. A robust fern forming a broad shuttlecock shape, with the leaves sometimes overwintering, or partly so. Leaves to 60cm long, pale green at first but darkening with age, linear-lanceolate, *unlobed*, hairless, becoming leathery, heart-shaped at the base, the margin often wavy; stalks up to half as long as the blade, scaly. Sori linear, paired below on the upper half of fertile fronds. Rocky habitats, woodland, hedgerows and other shady places. Scattered throughout much of the W & C Med and Turkey but generally rather rare in the region as a whole. Widely cultivated in gardens, where many different forms exist.

2534 *Phyllitis sagittata [P. hemionitis].* Similar, but leaves not more than 30cm long, with *ear-like* projections at the base of the blade, these sometimes pointing forwards horizontally. Damp, shaded habitats. W & C Med, including Crete.

2535 *Dryopteris dilatata* **BROAD BUCKLER FERN**. A broad, shuttlecock-shaped fern with erect to spreading leaves and a black or dark brown, scaly, erect rhizome. Leaves to 1.5m long, lancolate to narrow-triangular, 3-pinnate, with 15-25 pairs of primary divisions, dark green, sparsely *glandular* beneath; stalks as long as to half as long as the blade, covered in dark brown or blackish scales. Sori round, median. Shady places, mainly in woodland. Scattered localities from Spain to Italy, not Balearic Is. or Sardinia. Cultivated in gardens.

2536 *Dryopteris borreri [D. paleacea].* Very like the common European Male Fern, *D. felix-mas*. Differs from *D. dilatata* by its leaves being only 1-2-pinnate, each with up to 35 pairs of primary divisions. Scattered mainland localities from the Iberian Peninsula to Yugoslavia.

2537 *Dryopteris villarii [D. rigida].* Like *D. dilatata*, but leaves 2-pinnate, not more than 40cm long; stalks pale greenish-yellow with reddish-brown scales. Sori in two rows. Rocky habitats, often in woodlands, especially of pine, but rarely at sea level. Almost throughout, except for parts of N Africa and the extreme E Med. The Med plant, with rather pale green leaves, is generally referred to subsp. *pallida*.

2538 *Polypodium cambricum [P. australe]* **SOUTHERN POLYPODIUM**. A *spreading*, rhizomatous fern with scattered basal, rather pale green, leaves; rhizomes very scaly. Leaves overwintering, pinnate, with usually 14 or more pairs of narrow-lanceolate, toothed leaflets, tapered to the tips. Sori elliptical, borne in a row on each side of the midrib on fertile fronds. Damp shady rocks and rock crevices (limestone or igneous), on banks or in woodland. Almost T.

2539 *Marsilea quadrifolia* **WATER CLOVER**. A small freshwater aquatic fern with slender creeping rhizomes. Leaves hairless, with *four* triangular leaflets, each 1-2cm across, the outer margin rounded; stalks slender, to 15cm. Sori linear, enclosed by a case of modified fronds. Wet habitats, rice paddies, deltas and places that are seasonally flooded. Local and often rather rare from the Iberian Peninsula to Yugoslavia, except the islands.

BIBLIOGRAPHY

Alpine Garden Society Quarterly Bulletins – many useful articles on the Mediterranean region and mountains of Europe and western Asia.

Atchley, S.C. (1938). *Wild Flowers of Attica.*

Bacon, L. (1979). *Mountain Flower Holidays.* Produced by the Alpine Garden Society. A useful guide.

Baroni, E. (1955). *Guida Botanica d'Italia.*

Blamey, M. & Grey-Wilson, C. (1989). *The Illustrated Flora of Britain and Northern Europe.* In many ways the northern counterpart to this book, covering the plants (except grasses, sedges, rushes etc.) north of the Mediterranean zone.

Boissier, P.E. (1867-88). *Flora Orientalis.* The classic flora of western Asia.

Bonner, A. (1982). *Plants of the Balearic Islands.* An illustrated field guide.

Brangham, A.N. (1962). *The Naturalist's Riviera.*

Caballero, A. (1940). *Flora Analitica de España.*

Coste, H. (1901-06). *Flore Descriptive et Illustrée de la France.* A classic flora.

Coutinho, A.X.P. (1939). *Flora de Portugal.*

Davis, P.H. (1965-88). *Flora of Turkey.* A marvellously detailed, multi-volumed work; some illustrations.

Danesch, E. & O. (1969). *Orchideen Europas.* Splendid photographs.

Feinbrun, & Koppel, R. (1960). *Wild Plants in the land of Israel.*

Fiori, A. (1923-29). *Nuova Flora Analitica d'Italia.*

Fitter, R., Fitter, A. & Farrer, A. (1984). *Collins Guide to Grasses, Sedges, Rushes, Ferns of Britain and Northern Europe.*

Flahault, C. (1937). *Distribution Géographique des Végétaux dans la Région Méditerranéenne Française.*

Franco, J. do A. (1971). *Nova Flora de Portugal.* The most up-to-date flora of Portugal.

Fournier, P. (1961). *Les Quatre Flores de la France, Corse comprise.*

Grey-Wilson, C. (1988). *The Genus Cyclamen.* An illustrated monograph.

Grey-Wilson, C., Mathew, B. & Blamey, M. (1981). *Bulbs. The Bulbous Plants of Europe and their Allies.* The only comprehensive book on these plants, covering all the bulbs of the region.

Halliday, S. & Lushington, L. (1988). *Flowers of Northern Cyprus.*

Halacsy, E. von. (1900-08). *Conspectus Florae Graecae.* A classic work, poorly illustrated.

Hayek, A. (1927-33). *Prodromus Florae Peninsulae Balcanicae.* Another classic work, covering all the Balkans.

Holmboe, J. (1914). *Studies on the Vegetation of Cyprus.* Generally superseded by Meikle's *Flora of Cyprus.*

Huxley, A. et al (1992). *The New Royal Horticultural Society Dictionary of Gardening.*

Huxley, A. & Taylor, W. (1977). *Flowers of Greece.* Perhaps the best popular flora of Greece, illustrated with photographs and drawings.

Jahandiez, E. & Maire, R. (1931-41). *Catalogue des Plantes du Maroc.* A useful list of Moroccan plants.

Lazaro E Ibiza, B. (1920-21). *Compendio de la Flora Española.*

Mabberley, D.J. (1987). *The Plant-book.* A dictionary of plant families and genera – a most useful reference work, though unillustrated.

Maire, R. (19 -). *Flore de l'Afrique du Nord.*

Marret, L. (1926). *Les Fleurs de la Côte d'Azur.*

Masefield. G.B., Wallis, M., Harrison, S.G. & Nicholson, B.E. (1969). *The Oxford Book of Food Plants.* A beautiful and engrossing book.

Mathew, B. (1981) *The Iris.* (1982) *The Crocus.* (1989) *Hellebores.*

Matthews, A. (1968). *Lilies of the Field.*

Meikle, R.D. (1987-85). *Flora of Cyprus.*

Mitchell, A. & Wilkinson, J. (1982). *The Trees of Britain and Northern Europe.*

Morley, B. Illustrated by Everard, B. (1970). *Wild Flowers of the World.*

Nelson, E. (1962). *Monographie und Ikonographie der Gattung Ophrys.*

Phillips, R. & Rix, M. (1989). *Bulbs.* A guide to the world's bulbs; excellent photographs.

Polunin, O. (1969). *Flowers of Europe: a Field Guide.* Very selective but useful.

Polunin, O. (1980). *Flowers of Greece and the Balkans.* A good field guide.

Polunin, O. & Huxley, A. (1965). *Flowers of the Mediterranean.* A very popular guide.

Polunin, O. & Smythies, B.E. (1973). *Flowers of South-west Europe.*

Polunin, O. & Walters, M. (1985). *A Guide to the Vegetation of Britain and Europe.* A most readable book, well illustrated.

Post, G.E. (1932). *Flora of Syria, Palestine and Sinai.*

Quezel, F. & Santa, S. (1962). *Nouvelle Flore de l'Algérie.*

Rechinger, K. H. (1943). *Flora Aegaea.* A well-researched flora.

Rouy, G.C.C. et al (1893-1921). *Flore de France.*

Schönfelder, I. & P. (1984). *Collins Photoguide to the Wild Flowers of the Mediterranean.* Translated in 1990 from *Die Kosmos-Mittelmeerflora.*

Sfikas, G. (1987). *Wild Flowers of Crete.* Light but readable, poor photographs.

Straka, H, Haeupler, H., Garcia, L. L. & Orell, J. (1987). *Guide to the Flora of Majorca.*

Sundermann, H. (1975). *Europäische und Mediterrane Orchideen.* One of the best small guides to European orchids.

Tackholm, V. (1956). *Student's Flora of Egypt.* Easy to use.

Thompson, H.S. (1914). *Flowering Plants of the Riviera.*

Turrill, W.B. (1929). *The Plant Life of the Balkan Peninsula.*

Tutin, T.G. et al., (1968-80). *Flora Europaea.* The leading work of reference, unillustrated.

Vedel, H. (1978). *Trees and Shrubs of the Mediterranean.* A small but useful book.

Willkomm, H. M. & Lange, J. (1861-80). *Prodromus Florae Hispanicae.*

Williams, J.G. & E.W. & Arnott, N. (1978). *A Field Guide to the Orchids of Britain and Europe (with North Africa and the Middle East).*

Zohary, M. (1962). *Plant Life of Palestine.*

INDEX OF ENGLISH NAMES

Figures refer to species numbers used in the book. Those in **bold** type are illustrated in the colour section.

538

542

INDEX OF SCIENTIFIC NAMES

Figures refer to species numbers used in the book. Those in **bold** type are illustrated in the colour section. Names in *italic* type are synonyms.

Lotus palustris 627
Lotus peregrinus 637
Lotus preslii 628
Lotus siliquosus **680**
Lotus tenuifolius 626
Lotus tenuis 626
Lotus tetragonolobus **682**
Lotus tetraphyllus **630**
Lotus uliginosus **629**
Lupinus albus **485**
Lupinus angustifolius **486**
Lupinus hirsutus **484**
Lupinus luteus **483**
Lupinus micranthus **484**
Lupinus varius **487**
Lycium barbarum **1552**
Lycium chinense 1553
Lycium europaeum **1548**
Lycium ferocissimum **1551**
Lycium halimifolium **1552**
Lycium intricatum 1549
Lycium rhombifolium 1553
Lycium schweinfurthii 1550
Lycium vulgare **1552**
Lycopersicon esculentum 1569
Lycopsis arvensis **1413**
Lycopsis variegata **1415**
Lygeum spartum **2482**
Lygia passerina **946**
Lygos monosperma 480
Lygos raetam **479**
Lygos sphaerocarpa **478**
Lyrolepis diae 1922
Lysimachia atropurpurea **1191**
Lysimachia dubia 1192
Lysimachia linum-stellatum **1190**
Lysimachia serpyllifolia **1193**
Lythrum borsythenicum 1050
Lythrum hyssopifolia 1046
Lythrum junceum **1045**
Lythrum portula **1049**
Lythrum thymifolia 1048
Lythrum tribracteatum 1047

Malcolmia chia **318**
Malcolmia confusa **320**
Malcolmia flexuosa 317
Malcolmia lacera 314
Malcolmia littorea **313**
Malcolmia maritima **316**
Malcolmia nana **320**
Malcolmia parviflora **315**
Malcolmia ramosissima **315**
Malope malacoides **891**
Malope trifida **892**
Malva aegyptia **894**
Malva althaeoides **903**
Malva cretica **893**
Malva erecta **898**
Malva mauritiana **898**
Malva moschata **895**
Malva neglecta **899**
Malva nicaeensis 900
Malva parviflora **897**
Malva sherardiana **902**
Malva sylvestris **898**
Malva tournefortiana 896
Malva verticillata **901**
Malvella sherardiana **902**
Mandragora autumnalis **1573**

Mandragora officinarum **1574**
Mantisalca salmantica **1988**
Maresia nana **320**
Marjorana hortensis 1519
Marrubium alysson 1448
Marrubium candidissimum 1447
Marrubium incanum 1447
Marrubium peregrinum 1446
Marrubium vulgare **1445**
Marsdenia erecta **1272**
Marsilea quadrifolia **2539**
Matricaria aurea 1888
Matricaria inodora **1885**
Matricaria perforata 1885
Matricaria recutita **1887**
Matricaria trichophylla 1886
Matricaria chamomilla **1887**
Matthiola fruticulosa 328
Matthiola incana 327
Matthiola longipetala **330**
Matthiola sinuata 326
Matthiola tricuspidata 329
Matthiola tristis **328**
Maytenus senegalensis **873**
Medicago aculeata **609**
Medicago arabica **623**
Medicago arborea **598**
Medicago blancheana 611
Medicago ciliaris **604**
Medicago circinnata **692**
Medicago constricta **614**
Medicago coronata **619**
Medicago denticulata **618**
Medicago disciformis **615**
Medicago echinus 603
Medicago hispida **618**
Medicago intertexta **602**
M. i. var. *ciliaris* **604**
Medicago laciniata **620**
Medicago littoralis **606**
M. l. var. *inermis* 606a
Medicago lupulina **594**
Medicago maculata **623**
Medicago marina **605**
Medicago minima **622**
Medicago murex **613**
Medicago orbicularis **599**
Medicago polycarpa **618**
Medicago polymorpha **618**
Medicago praecox **621**
Medicago rigidula **610**
Medicago rotata **616**
Medicago rugosa **601**
Medicago sativa **596**
M. s. subsp. *falcata* **596a**
Medicago scutellata **600**
Medicago secundiflora 595
Medicago suffruticosa **597**
Medicago tenoreana 617
Medicago tornata 608
Medicago tribuloides **607**
Medicago truncatula **607**
Medicago turbinata **612**
Melandrium album 158
Melia azedarach **843**
Melica ciliata **2462**
Melica minuta 2463
Melilotus albus **570**
Melilotus altissimus **579**
Melilotus arvensis **571**

Melilotus elegans 574
Melilotus indicus 572
Melilotus infestus 575
Melilotus italicus 573
Melilotus messanensis 577
Melilotus neapolitanus 580
Melilotus officinalis **571**
Melilotus segetalis 576
Melilotus sulcatus 578
Melissa altissima **1502**
Melissa officinalis **1502**
Melissa romana **1502**
Mentha aquatica **1525**
Mentha crispa **1521**
Mentha hirsuta **1525**
Mentha incana **1522**
Mentha insularis 1523
Mentha longifolia **1522**
Mentha pulegium **1524**
Mentha rotundifolia 1523
Mentha spicata **1521**
Mentha suaveolens 1523
Mentha sylvestris **1521**
Mentha viridis **1521**
Mentha vulgaris **1524**
Mercurialis annua **820**
Merendera attica **2130**
Merendera filifolia 2132
Merendera sobolifera 2131
Mesembryanthemum
  crystallinum **118**
Mesembryanthemum
  nodiflorum **119**
Micromeria graeca 1506
Micromeria juliana **1504**
Micromeria myrtifolia 1507
Micromeria nervosa **1505**
Micropus bombicinus **1821**
Micropus discolor **1821**
Micropus erectus **1822**
Middendorfia borysthenicum
  1050
Mimosa farcta **444**
Minuartia geniculata 132
Minuartia hybrida 133
Minuartia mediterranea **131**
Misopates orontium **1611**
Moehringia pentandra **127**
Mollugo cerviana 124
Molucella frutescens **1471**
Molucella laevis 1468
Molucella spinosa **1467**
Moricandia arvensis **354**
Morisia monanthos **366**
Morus alba **41**
Muscari armeniacum **2210**
Muscari atlanticum **2206**
Muscari commutatum **2208**
Muscari comosum **2201**
Muscari cycladicum 2203
Muscari gussonei 2202
Muscari inconstrictum **2209**
Muscari neglectum **2206**
Muscari parviflorum **2211**
Muscari pulchellum 2207
Muscari spreitzenhoferi 2205
Muscari weissii 2204
Myagrum aegyptium **372**
Myoporum laetum **1676**
Myrtus communis **1052**

Phlomis lanata **1459**
Phlomis lunariifolia 1457
Phlomis lychnitis **1460**
Phlomis purpurea **1465**
Phlomis samia 1464
Phlomis tuberosa 1463
Phoenix canariensis **2351**
Phoenix dactylifera **2350**
Phoenix theophrasti **2349**
Pholiurus incurvatus 2492
Phormium tenax **2252**
Phyla nodiflora **1420**
Phyllitis hemionitis **2534**
Phyllitis sagittata **2534**
Phyllitis scolopendrium **2533**
Physalis alkekengi **1560**
Physalis peruviana 1561
Physalis somnifera **1558**
Physanthyllis tetraphylla **691**
Phytolacca acinos **112**
Phytolacca americana **112**
Phytolacca arborea **113**
Phytolacca decandra **112**
Phytolacca dioica **113**
Picnomon acarna **1965**
Picridium tingitanum **2061**
Picris altissima 2048
Picris echioides **2046**
Picris hieracioides **2049**
Picris pauciflora 2047
Picris sprengeriana 2048
Pinus brutia **2**
Pinus canariensis **7**
Pinus halepensis **1**
P. halepensis subsp. *brutia* **2**
Pinus maritima **5**
Pinus nigra **4**
P. n. subsp. pallasiana 4a
Pinus pinaster **5**
Pinus pinea **3**
Pinus radiata **6**
Pistachia atlantica 864
Pistachia palaestina 862
Pistachia vera **863**
Pistacia × saportae 866
Pistacia lentiscus **865**
Pistacia lentiscus × *Pistacia terebinthus* **866**
Pistacia terebinthus **861**
Pisum elatius 555a
Pisum sativum **555**
P. s. subsp. elatius 555a
Pittosporum tobira **402**
Pittosporum undulatum 403
Plantago afra **1706**
Plantago albicans **1708**
Plantago amplexicaulis 1709
Plantago arenaria 1705
Plantago bellardii **1703**
Plantago cornuti 1695
Plantago coronopus **1696**
Plantago crassifolia 1699a
Plantago cretica **1704**
Plantago indica 1705
Plantago lagopus **1702**
Plantago lanceolata **1701**
Plantago macrorhiza 1698
Plantago major **1693**
Plantago maritima **1699**
P. m. subsp. crassifolia 1699a

Plantago media 1694
Plantago psyllium 1705
Plantago ramosa 1705
Plantago seraria 1697
Plantago squarrosa 1707
Plantago subulata 1700
Platanthera bifolia **2391**
Platanthera chlorantha **2392**
P. c. subsp. holmboei 2392a
Platanthera holmboei **2392**
Platanus × hybrida 401
Platanus occidentalis × *orientalis* 401
Platanus orientalis **400**
Plumbago auriculata **1213**
Plumbago capensis **1213**
Plumbago europaea **1212**
Plumbago indica 1214
Plumbago rosea 1214
Poa bulbosa **2457**
P. b. var. vivipara 2457a
Poa littoralis **2483**
Podocytisus caramanicus **451**
Podospermum canum 2051
Podospermum lacineatum **2050**
Poinciana pulcherrima **732**
Polycarpon alsinifolium **141**
Polycarpon peploides 142
Polycarpon polycarpoides 142
Polycarpon tetraphyllum **141**
Polygala comosa 851
Polygala exilis 848
Polygala monspeliaca **847**
Polygala myrtifolia **846**
Polygala nicaeensis **849**
Polygala preslii 853
Polygala rupestris **845**
Polygala sardoa 854
Polygala venulosa **852**
Polygala vulgaris 850
Polygonum equisetiforme 71
Polygonum maritimum **70**
Polygonum romanum 72
Polygonum salicifolium 73
Polypodium australe **2538**
Polypodium cambricum **2538**
Posidonia oceanica 2085
Potentilla hirta **412**
Poterium spinosum **411**
Poterium verrucosum **410**
Prasium majus **1444**
Primula palinuri **1188**
Procopiania circinalis 1392
Procopiania cretica **1390**
Procopiania insularis 1391
Prolongoa pectinata **1902**
Prosopis farcta **444**
Prosopis juliflora **445**
Prosopis stephaniana **444**
Prunella alba **1474**
Prunella grandiflora **1472**
Prunella laciniata **1474**
Prunella vulgaris 1473
Prunus armeniaca **422**
Prunus communis **421**
Prunus domestica **426**
P. d. subsp. insititia 426a
Prunus dulcis **421**
P. d. var. dulcis 421a
Prunus lusitanica 427

Prunus persica **423**
P. p. var. nucipersica 423a
Prunus prostrata **425**
Prunus spinosa **424**
Pseudognaphalium luteo-album **1823**
Pseudorlaya maritima **1174**
Pseudorlaya minuscula 1175
Pseudorlaya pumila **1174**
Psoralea americana 509
Psoralea bituminosa **508**
Psoralea dentata 509
Pteranthus dichotomous **140**
Pteris cretica **2523**
Pteris vittata **2524**
Pterocephalus brevis 1740
Pterocephalus involucratus 1740
Pterocephalus multiflorus 1741
Pterocephalus palaestinus **1751**
Pterocephalus parnassi **1742**
Pterocephalus perennis 1742
Pterocephalus plumosus **1739**
Ptilostemon chamaepeuce **1967**
P. c. var. cyprius 1967a
Ptilostemon gnaphaloides 1968
Ptilostemon hispanicus 1970
Ptilostemon stellatus **1969**
Ptychotis ammoides **1138**
Ptychotis heterophylla **1137**
Ptychotis saxifraga **1137**
Pulicaria arabica 1846
Pulicaria dysenterica **1843**
Pulicaria odora 1845
Pulicaria sicula 1844
Punica granatum **1064**
Putoria calabrica **1275**
Pycnocomon rutifolium **1752**
Pycreus esculentus **2501**
Pycreus longus **2500**
Pyracantha coccinea **417**
Pyrostegia venusta **1688**
Pyrus amygdaliformis **416**
Pyrus parviflora **416**

Quercus aegilops **28**
Quercus coccifera **24**
Q. c. subsp. calliprinos 24a
Quercus faginea **30**
Quercus ilex **25**
Quercus infectoria 29
Quercus macrolepis **28**
Quercus pubescens **31**
Quercus rotundifolia 26
Quercus suber **27**

Ranunculus arvensis **244**
Ranunculus asiaticus **257**
R. b. subsp. aleae 240
Ranunculus bullatus **256**
R. b. subsp. sytheraeus 256a
Ranunculus chius 246
Ranunculus cornutus **236**
Ranunculus cupreus **250**
Ranunculus falcatus **224**
Ranunculus ficaria **252**
R. f. subsp. ficariiformis 252a
Ranunculus ficarioides 253
Ranunculus flabellatus **249**
Ranunculus gracilis **247**
Ranunculus isthmicus 248